# *A FIRST COURSE IN INTEGRATION*

EDGAR ASPLUND
UNIVERSITY OF STOCKHOLM

LUTZ BUNGART
UNIVERSITY OF CALIFORNIA, BERKELEY

HOLT, RINEHART AND WINSTON
NEW YORK · CHICAGO · SAN FRANCISCO · TORONTO · LONDON

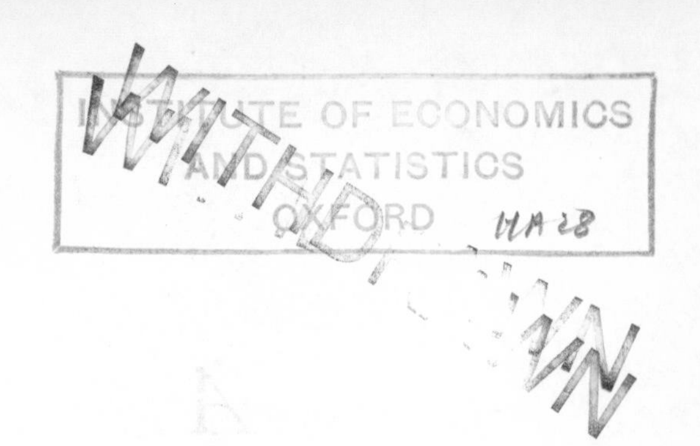




LIBRARY OF CONGRESS CATALOG CARD NUMBER 66–10122

**20550–0116**

PRINTED IN THE UNITED STATES OF AMERICA

# Preface

This undergraduate textbook on the theory of Lebesgue integration is designed for use in a one-semester or two-quarter undergraduate course in the junior or senior year.

Quite soon after the appearance of Lebesgue's famous theory of integration, it was felt that his thesis should be taught in the regular university mathematics courses, preferably to replace the Riemann integration theory, which it superseded at the professional level. The initial difficulties in presenting Lebesgue's material were rapidly smoothed out, but inertia in the educational system worked against carrying out the program. Indeed, one could not expect a majority of the colleges and universities to offer an undergraduate course in integration theory before a well-established need for this theory was felt in important domains of application. This need is now growing, and we hope that this book will help to satisfy it.

By "integration theory" we mean that the technique of integrating functions is developed first and is then used for the measuring of sets, rather than the other way around. The choice of the "integration first" approach was mostly a matter of taste, but also made it possible to arrive at meaningful and interesting theorems on integration as early as possible in the course. This is the approach to Lebesgue integration pioneered by F. Riesz (see Bibliographical Comments on Chapters 1 and 2 at the end of the book), an approach that has been partially forgotten in recent years with the appearance of so many graduate-level books favoring a measure theoretic approach. Because the student at the stage for which this book is intended has had much instruction on functions but little or no instruction on set theory (subsequent developments in high school mathematics may change this, of course), he can get to the core of the matter more rapidly by functional methods than by set theoretic ones. The functions play the role of "prefabricated parts," with which the student is already familiar. For the same kind of unmathematical reasons, which are nevertheless of tangible importance, we have emphasized series more than sequences. Series are the practical tools of the applied scientist and hence have an air of being more concrete than sequences, although the step from the one to the other is trivial. It is also true that the use of series gives some statements a particularly nice appearance (compare Lemma 2.1.10, by J. Mikusiński).

The amount of material included is large enough to make the book a meaningful first textbook for those who plan to go on to graduate studies in mathematics. The only prerequisite is the material usually covered in a two-year calculus sequence, though it may be useful to precede a course in Lebesgue integration with a course that gives a rigorous foundation for calculus. Within this scope we have tried to organize the material so that parts of the book can be used for other purposes. For instance, the following sections can be omitted without causing gaps later on: 2.0, 2.6, 3.4, 3.5, 4.1, 4.4, 5.3, 5.4, 5.5, 5.6, 6.7, 9.3, and 9.4. Of these, several sections are not intended to be covered in class, but to be used as additional reading material for the interested student. These sections are: 2.0, 2.6, 3.4, 5.4, and 6.7.

Special attention has been given to a kind of "minimal course," consisting of Chapters 1 and 2. These two chapters—with the exception, perhaps, of Section 2.6—could even replace the customary Riemann integration theory in the standard analysis courses. Chapters 1 to 4 constitute a course that could be meaningful for certain engineering students and which could be supplemented with parts of Chapter 5 and/or Chapter 8—the last alternative may be especially attractive to students of statistics. The rest of the book, Chapters 6, 7, and 9, comprising what one may call the "differentiation theory," is slightly more difficult than the other chapters, so that its omission would lighten the course more than would appear from the number of pages involved. In Chapter 10, Lebesgue integration, as well as the differentiation theory, are applied to the study of Fourier series. The sections of this chapter are not meant to exhaust the topic of Fourier series, but rather to give some applications of what has been done in the preceding chapters. The sections of Chapter 10 can be fitted in at various places in the book (see the interdependence diagram at the end of this preface).

The book is divided into sections that are grouped in ten chapters. With a few exceptions each section is designed for a one-hour lecture. Each chapter starts with a short introduction in which the material of that chapter is outlined and in which comments on its dependence on sections of other chapters are made. Each section ends with a few exercises, usually of a simple nature, and there is a larger collection of exercises at the end of each chapter. The book contains enough exercises for both class and home work. A summary of the main results completes each chapter. At the speed of approximately one section per lecture, the book will serve as a textbook for a one-term (15-week) course of three lectures a week. The authors have used the material of the book for such a course at the University of California at Berkeley. However, by omitting some of the sections or chapters, the book is also suited to serve as a textbook for a one-quarter or two-quarter course. To facilitate the selection of material for such shorter courses, we have included two interdependence diagrams at the end of this preface.

We have included Section 1.0 to specify our terminology; here a theorem on double series is proved, since it may not be well known to all students. Whenever this unfamiliarity with a theorem of calculus appeared likely, we have included a proof in the body of the text. We have also endeavored to make this book somewhat repetitive in certain places to achieve a maximum independence among chapters. We have not hesitated to repeat similar proofs rather than use devices like general lemmas that would make the presentation more elegant, but also more obscure, to the beginner. We have chosen to develop the theory of integration for the Lebesgue integral, but we have done it in such a way that the proofs are also valid for the Daniell integral. Such possible generalizations are pointed out at appropriate places; they are applied in Chapters 4 and 8 to several variables and Stieltjes integration, respectively.

The best way to learn about a subject is, of course, to read not only one book, but several. In the literature section at the end of this text we have indicated some books that may be used for collateral reading. They are all modern and well written, so that the serious student will certainly not waste the time he may devote to them. Valuable also will be the time spent on some of the first papers of the pioneers in this field.

Thanks and appreciation are extended to David Goheen, who read the manuscript so carefully and made many suggestions for improving the presentation. Among our colleagues, particular thanks are due to Professor John Todd, who suggested adding some material (Chapter 10) and to Professor Michel Loève, who patiently discussed many problems. Finally, our thanks go to Mrs. Ollie Cullers and to Mrs. Jeanne Robinson for their patience and skill in typing the manuscript.

*Stockholm, Sweden*
*Berkeley, California*
*February 1966*

EDGAR ASPLUND
LUTZ BUNGART

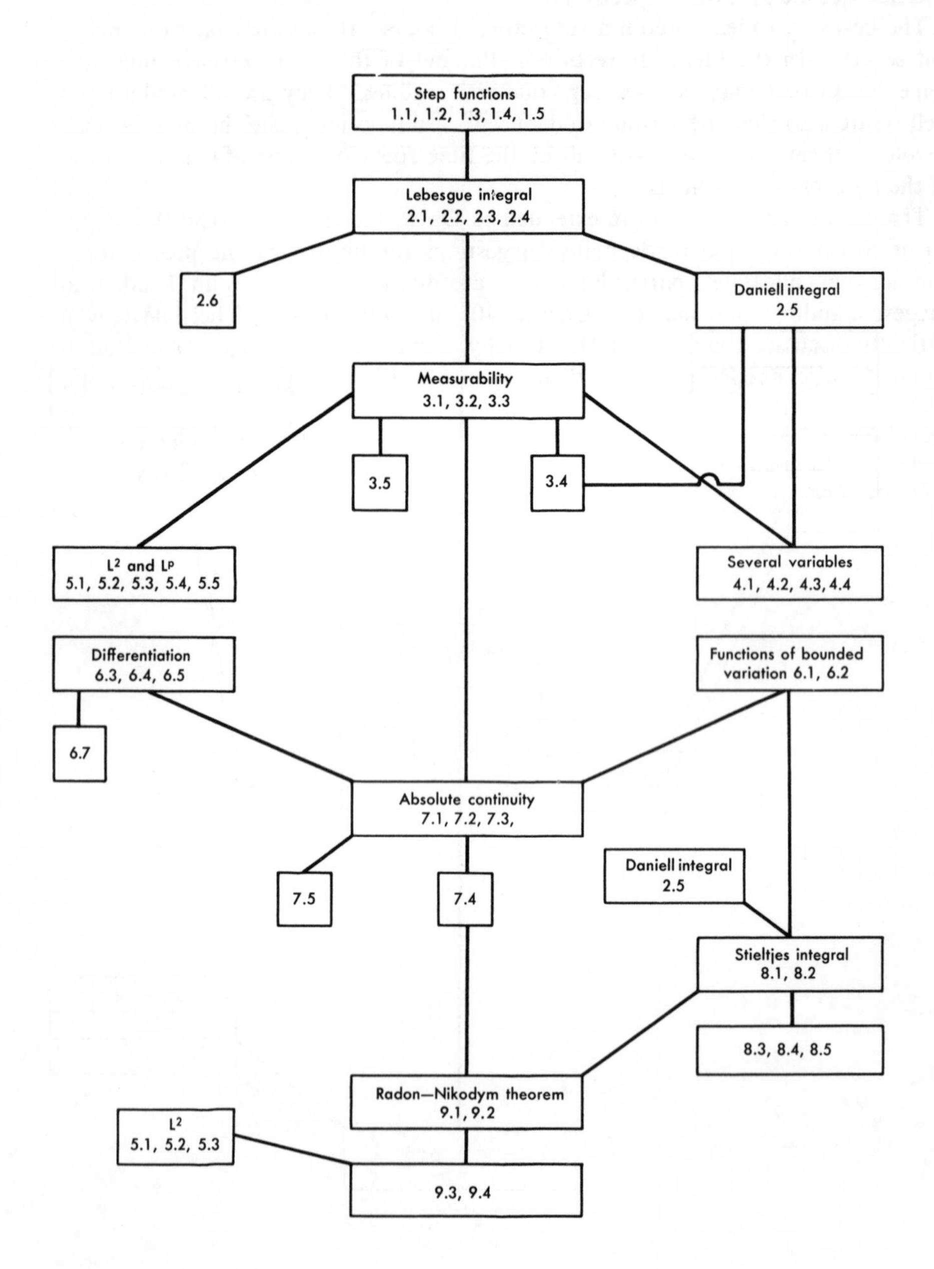

Step functions
1.1, 1.2, 1.3, 1.4, 1.5
Lebesgue integral
2.1, 2.2, 2.3, 2.4
2.6
Daniell integral
2.5
Measurability
3.1, 3.2, 3.3
3.5
3.4
L² and Lᵖ
5.1, 5.2, 5.3, 5.4, 5.5
Several variables
4.1, 4.2, 4.3, 4.4
Differentiation
6.3, 6.4, 6.5
Functions of bounded variation 6.1, 6.2
6.7
Absolute continuity
7.1, 7.2, 7.3,
7.5
7.4
Daniell integral
2.5
Stieltjes integral
8.1, 8.2
8.3, 8.4, 8.5
Radon—Nikodym theorem
9.1, 9.2
L²
5.1, 5.2, 5.3
9.3, 9.4

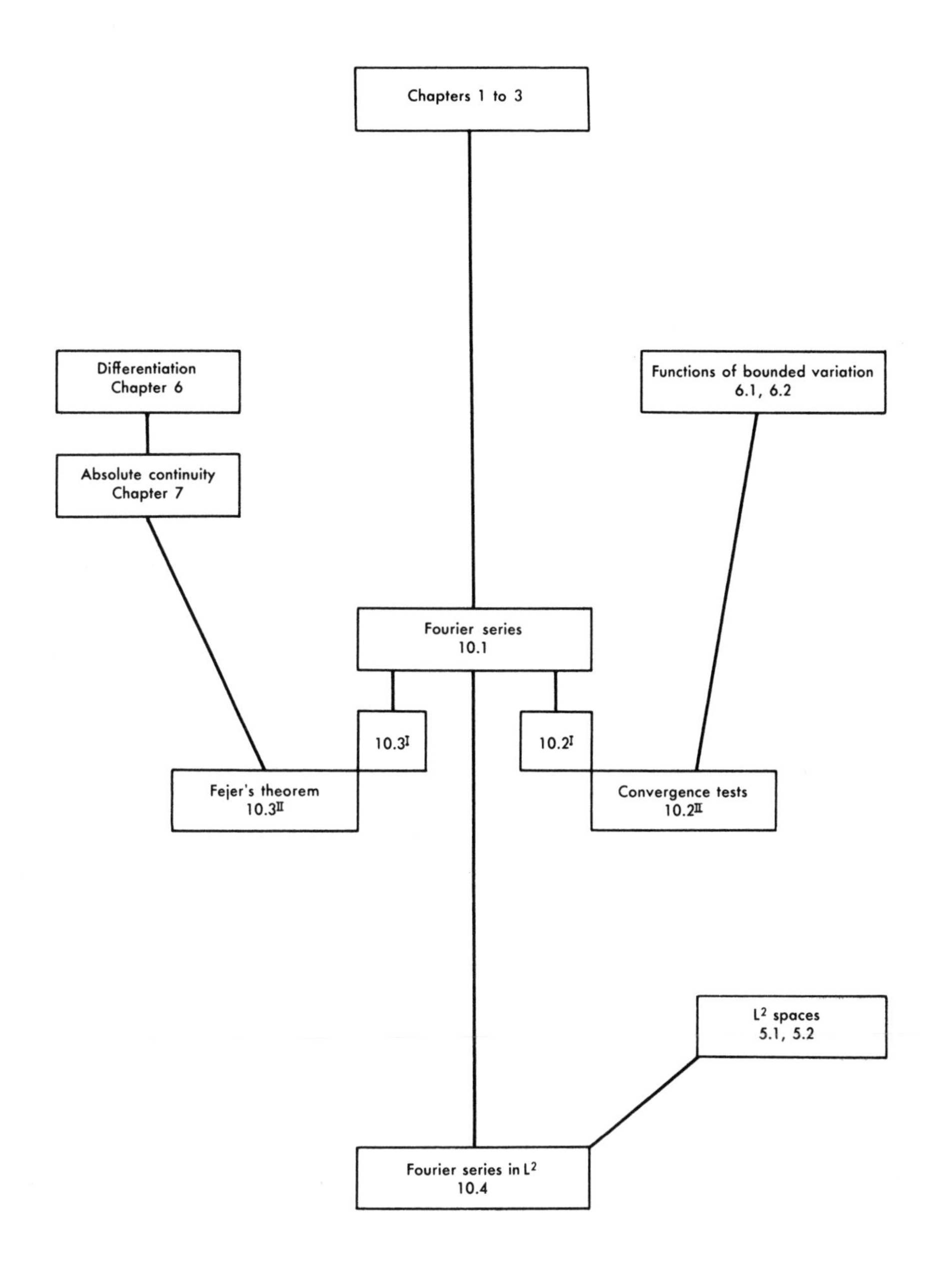

Chapters 1 to 3
Differentiation
Chapter 6
Functions of bounded variation
6.1, 6.2
Absolute continuity
Chapter 7
Fourier series
10.1
10.3I
10.2I
Fejer's theorem
10.3II
Convergence tests
10.2II
L2 spaces
5.1, 5.2
Fourier series in L2
10.4

# Contents

*A FIRST COURSE IN INTEGRATION*

# I

# Step Functions and Null Sets

This chapter begins with a preliminary section (1.0) in which we recall a few definitions and theorems that commonly have their place in a calculus course. We hope to clarify in this way our usage of standard symbols and concepts. The preliminary section also presents a proof of the fundamental theorem on double series which, as it seems, is not part of every calculus course. This theorem should be well understood by the student since it is used very often, usually without reference and in many places inconspicuously.

After these preliminaries we proceed with the definition of the integral for step functions and with a discussion of its fundamental properties. For a nonnegative step function the integral is just the area under its graph. Consideration of the relationship between the convergence of a sequence or series of step functions and the convergence of the corresponding sequence or series of their integrals leads us to the concepts of a null set and of convergence almost everywhere (a.e.). By its very definition, a null set is the unpleasant set on which an increasing sequence of step functions with the pleasant property that the limit of the sequence of their integrals exists, diverges; and it is the desire of the mathematician to forget about such sets.

It will become apparent in the next chapter that the present chapter, though it deals only with the very elementary step functions, already contains all the machinery necessary to handle the proofs of the theorems in the theory of Lebesgue integration. In fact, all the convergence theorems for sequences or series of Lebesgue integrable functions can be found for step functions somewhere in this chapter. For this reason we advise the student to work out the exercises on piecewise linear functions in part D of Section 1.6. This will prepare him for an understanding of the discussion of the Daniell integral in Section 2.5 of the next chapter for which in particular Exercises 1.6.21 through 1.6.24 are important.

## 1.0 THE REAL LINE

Throughout this book, $R$ will denote the real line. The points on $R$ are sometimes also referred to as (real) numbers. In addition to the points on $R$ two additional points $+\infty$ and $-\infty$ are considered. These points are not points on $R$. They are not real numbers. Therefore they cannot be added to or subtracted from any real number. However, an order relation is defined on $+\infty$, $-\infty$, and the real numbers:

$$-\infty < a < +\infty \qquad \text{for all real numbers } a.$$

Instead of $+\infty$, the symbol $\infty$ is sometimes used.

We denote a set of points with a common property $P(x)$ (like "$x \neq 0$") by

$$\{x : P(x)\}.$$

Certain subsets, called *intervals*, on the real line are denoted by special symbols:

$$[a, b] = \{x : a \le x \le b\},$$
$$(a, b) = \{x : a < x < b\},$$
$$[a, b) = \{x : a \le x < b\},$$
$$(a, b] = \{x : a < x \le b\}.$$

The right side is read in each case, the set of all points (on the real line) such that $\cdots$. In $[a, b]$, $a, b$ are points on the real line satisfying $a \le b$. In $(a, b)$, $a, b$ also satisfy $a \le b$ but are not required to be points on the real line; $a = -\infty$ or $b = \infty$ or both are permitted. For instance,

$$(-\infty, \infty) = R.$$

In $(a, b]$, $a = -\infty$, and in $[a, b)$, $b = \infty$ is permitted and in both cases $a \le b$. The phrase "an interval $I$ with end points $a, b$" refers to a set $I$ equal to one of $[a, b]$, $(a, b)$, $[a, b)$, or $(a, b]$. An interval $I$ with end points $a, b$ is called *bounded* if $a$ and $b$ are both real numbers. If $a = b$, the interval is called *degenerate*, and *nondegenerate* if $a < b$. If $a = b$, $[a, b]$ consists of the single point $a$, while $(a, b)$, $[a, b)$, and $(a, b]$ do not contain any points at all. A set that does not contain any points is called *empty* and is denoted by $\varnothing$. Thus, for instance,

$$(a, a) = \varnothing.$$

We assume that the student is familiar with the notion of union and intersection of sets. If $\{E_n\}$ is a sequence of sets on the real line,

$$\bigcup E_n \quad \text{or} \quad \bigcup_{n=1}^{\infty} E_n$$

denotes the *union* of the $E_n$. This is the set that contains all the points that occur in any of the $E_n$.

$$\bigcap E_n \quad \text{or} \quad \bigcap_{n=1}^{\infty} E_n$$

is the *intersection* of the $E_n$, which is the set of those points that belong to each of the $E_n$.

Let us now briefly recall the notion of convergence. A sequence $\{a_n\}$ of real numbers (indexed on the integers $n \ge 1$) *converges* to the real number $a$, or in symbols

$$\lim_{n \to \infty} a_n = a,$$

if for each $\varepsilon > 0$ there is an integer $N > 0$ such that

$$|a_n - a| \le \varepsilon$$

for $n \ge N$. The sequence $\{a_n\}$ is a *Cauchy sequence* if, for each $\varepsilon > 0$, there is an $N > 0$ such that

$$|a_n - a_m| \le \varepsilon$$

for $n, m \geq N$. This is often expressed symbolically as

$$\lim_{n,m\to\infty} |a_n - a_m| = 0.$$

In calculus it is shown that every convergent sequence is a Cauchy sequence and every Cauchy sequence converges to exactly one point on the real line. The latter property is referred to as the completeness of the real line. A sequence that does not converge is sometimes called a divergent sequence.

There are two more properties pertaining to sequences that are of importance in this book. These are the following.

1.0.1 **PROPERTY** *If $\{a_n\}$ is an increasing sequence, $a_n \leq a_{n+1}$, and if there is a real number $b$ such that $a_n \leq b$ for all $n$, then $\{a_n\}$ converges.*

1.0.2 **PROPERTY** *If $\{a_n\}$ is a sequence contained in a bounded interval $[a, b]$, then there is a subsequence $\{a_{n(k)}\}$ of $\{a_n\}$ that converges.*

Property 1.0.2 will be used in some of the exercises. In the text we will mainly make use of Property 1.0.1. Notice that an increasing sequence $\{a_n\}$ that does not converge must have the following property; to every real number $M$ there is an integer $N > 0$ such that

$$a_n \geq M \qquad \text{for } n \geq N.$$

We say in this case that $\{a_n\}$ *diverges to infinity* and we write

$$\lim_{n\to\infty} a_n = \infty.$$

As an application let us consider series, which play an important role in our treatment. A series is just a sequence of numbers; it is usually denoted by

$$\sum a_n \quad \text{or} \quad \sum_n a_n.$$

A series $\sum a_n$ is said to be *convergent* to $s$ if the sequence $\{s_m\}$,

$$s_m = \sum_{n=1}^{m} a_n,$$

converges to $s$, and we write

$$s = \sum_{n=1}^{\infty} a_n.$$

In this case we have

$$\lim_{m\to\infty} (s - s_m) = 0$$

which can also be written as

$$\lim_{m\to\infty} \sum_{n=m+1}^{\infty} a_n = 0.$$

If $\{s_m\}$ diverges the series $\sum a_n$ is also called *divergent*. Property 1.0.1 implies the following, for instance.

**1.0.3 PROPERTY** *A series $\sum a_n$ with nonnegative terms $a_n \geq 0$ either converges or it diverges to $\infty$. It converges if and only if there is a number $M$ such that*

$$\sum_{n=1}^{m} a_n \leq M$$

*for all $m$. In this case one writes briefly*

$$\sum_{n=1}^{\infty} a_n < \infty.$$

A series $\sum a_n$ is called *absolutely* convergent if the series $\sum |a_n|$ converges.

**1.0.4 PROPERTY** *An absolutely convergent series $\sum a_m$ converges.*

*Proof* Let

$$s_m = \sum_{n=1}^{m} a_n, \qquad t_m = \sum_{n=1}^{m} |a_n|$$

and suppose $\{t_m\}$ converges to $t$. The sequence $\{s_m\}$ is a Cauchy sequence because, for $m \leq k$,

$$|s_m - s_k| = \left| \sum_{n=m+1}^{k} a_n \right| \leq \sum_{n=m+1}^{k} |a_n|$$
$$\leq \sum_{n=m+1}^{\infty} |a_n| = t - t_m,$$

whence

$$\lim_{m,k\to\infty} |s_m - s_k| = 0.$$

Thus $\{s_m\}$ converges.

The following theorem on double series will be used at many places, sometimes without reference.

**1.0.5 THEOREM** *For each $n$ let $\sum_k a_{nk}$ be a series. Suppose $\{a_m : m = 1, \cdots\}$ is any enumeration of the doubly indexed sequence $\{a_{nk} : n = 1, \cdots, k = 1, \cdots\}$* (as for instance in Figure 1.1). *The following statements are equivalent:*

(a) *For each $n$, $\sum_{k=1}^{\infty} |a_{nk}| < \infty$ and $\sum_{n=1}^{\infty} (\sum_{k=1}^{\infty} |a_{nk}|) < \infty$.*
(b) *$\sum |a_m|$ converges.*

*If either Statement* (a) *or* (b) *holds, then $\sum_n (\sum_{k=1}^{\infty} a_{nk})$ converges to the same sum as $\sum a_m$,*

$$\sum_{n=1}^{\infty}\left(\sum_{k=1}^{\infty} a_{nk}\right) = \sum_{m=1}^{\infty} a_m.$$

*Proof* Suppose Statement (a) holds. Let $M$ be any integer and choose integers $N$ and $K$ so large that $a_1, \cdots, a_M$ occur among

$$\{a_{nk}: n \le N, k \le K\};$$

then

$$\sum_{m=1}^{M} |a_m| \le \sum_{n=1}^{N}\left(\sum_{k=1}^{K} |a_{nk}|\right) \le \sum_{n=1}^{\infty}\left(\sum_{k=1}^{\infty} |a_{nk}|\right).$$

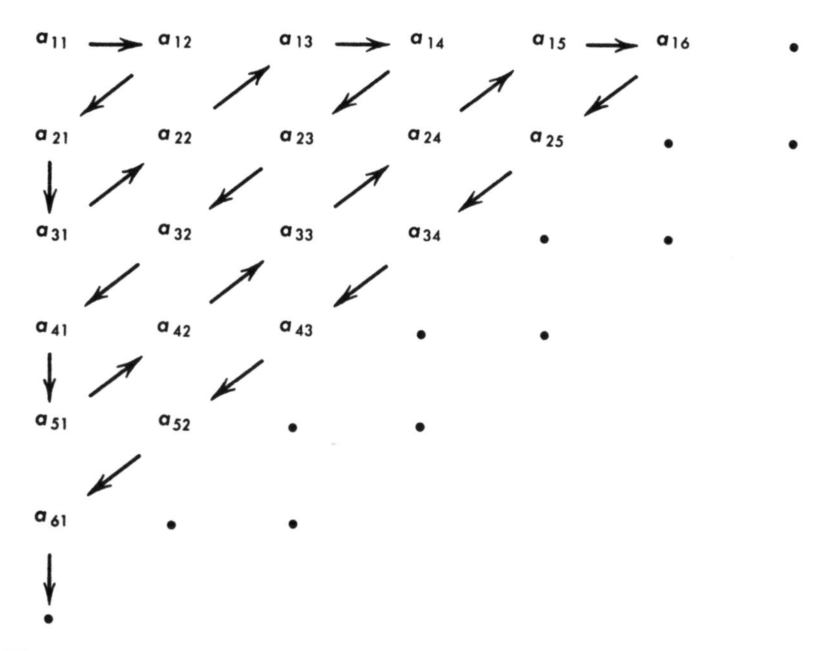


Figure 1.1 The diagram indicates one possible way of enumerating a doubly indexed sequence $\{a_{nk}: n \ge 1, k \ge 1\}$.

This proves that the sequence $\{\sum_{m=1}^{M} |a_m|\}$ is bounded and therefore $\sum |a_m|$ converges. Moreover, by passing to the limit in the last inequality we obtain

$$\sum_{m=1}^{\infty} |a_m| \le \sum_{n=1}^{\infty}\left(\sum_{k=1}^{\infty} |a_{nk}|\right).$$

Now assume that Statement (b) holds. Let $K$ be an integer and, for a fixed $n$, choose the integer $M$ so large that $a_{n1}, \cdots, a_{nK}$ occur among $a_1, \cdots, a_M$; then

$$\sum_{k=1}^{K} |a_{nk}| \le \sum_{m=1}^{M} |a_m| \le \sum_{m=1}^{\infty} |a_m|$$

so that $\sum_k |a_{nk}|$ converges for each $n$. Now let us prove that $\sum_n (\sum_{k=1}^{\infty} |a_{nk}|)$ converges. Pick any integer $N \geq 1$ and choose the integer $K$ so large that

$$\sum_{k=1}^{\infty} |a_{nk}| - \sum_{k=1}^{K} |a_{nk}| \leq \frac{1}{N}$$

for $n = 1, \cdots, N$; finally let $M$ be an integer such that the elements in $\{a_{nk} : n \leq N, k \leq K\}$ occur among $a_1, \cdots, a_M$. Then

$$\begin{aligned}\sum_{n=1}^{N}\left(\sum_{k=1}^{\infty} |a_{nk}|\right) &\leq \sum_{n=1}^{N}\left(\sum_{k=1}^{K} |a_{nk}| + \frac{1}{N}\right) \\ &= \sum_{n=1}^{N}\left(\sum_{k=1}^{K} a_{nk}\right) + 1 \\ &\leq \sum_{m=1}^{M} |a_m| + 1 \\ &\leq \sum_{m=1}^{\infty} |a_m| + 1\end{aligned}$$

which proves that $\sum_n (\sum_{k=1}^{\infty} |a_{nk}|)$ converges. Passing to the limit, we get

$$\sum_{n=1}^{\infty}\left(\sum_{k=1}^{\infty} |a_{nk}|\right) \leq \sum_{m=1}^{\infty} |a_m| + 1.$$

Thus we have proved that the statements in (a) and (b) are equivalent. Suppose that either (a) or (b) holds; then both (a) and (b) hold. We want to prove that under these hypotheses $\sum_n (\sum_{k=1}^{\infty} a_{nk})$ converges to the same sum as $\sum a_m$. We have already shown that

$$\sum_{m=1}^{\infty} |a_m| \leq \sum_{n=1}^{\infty}\left(\sum_{k=1}^{\infty} |a_{nk}|\right) \leq \sum_{m=1}^{\infty} |a_m| + 1.$$

Let $C$ be any positive number and apply the above formula to $Ca_{nk}$ and $Ca_m$, respectively. This yields

$$C\sum_{m=1}^{\infty} |a_m| \leq C\sum_{n=1}^{\infty}\left(\sum_{k=1}^{\infty} |a_{nk}|\right) \leq C\sum_{m=1}^{\infty} |a_m| + 1$$

or, since $C$ is positive,

$$\sum_{m=1}^{\infty} |a_m| \leq \sum_{n=1}^{\infty}\left(\sum_{k=1}^{\infty} |a_{nk}|\right) \leq \sum_{m=1}^{\infty} |a_m| + \frac{1}{C}.$$

But $C$ is arbitrary, so we have, in fact,

$$\sum_{n=1}^{\infty}\left(\sum_{k=1}^{\infty}|a_{nk}|\right) = \sum_{m=1}^{\infty}|a_m|$$

that is, the statement is proved for series with nonnegative terms. For series with general terms we make use of the following decomposition. Let

$$b_{nk} = |a_{nk}| - a_{nk}, \qquad b_m = |a_m| - a_m.$$

The series $\sum b_m$ has nonnegative terms and satisfies Condition (b):

$$\sum_{m=1}^{\infty} b_m \leq \sum_{m=1}^{\infty} |a_m| < \infty.$$

Thus the above conclusion applies to the series $\sum_k b_{nk}$ and $\sum b_m$, and we obtain the desired result,

$$\sum_{n=1}^{\infty}\left(\sum_{k=1}^{\infty} a_{nk}\right) = \sum_{n=1}^{\infty}\left(\sum_{k=1}^{\infty}|a_{nk}|\right) - \sum_{n=1}^{\infty}\left(\sum_{k=1}^{\infty} b_{nk}\right)$$

$$= \sum_{m=1}^{\infty}|a_m| - \sum_{m=1}^{\infty} b_m = \sum_{m=1}^{\infty} a_m;$$

this proves at the same time the convergence of the series $\sum a_m$ and $\sum_n (\sum_{k=1}^{\infty} a_{nk})$.

Finally, let us say a few words about functions. A function $f$ assigns to every point $x$ of its domain of definition a real number $f(x)$; $\infty$ and $-\infty$ can never be "values" of a function. Thus

$$f(x) = \frac{1}{|x|}$$

defines a function on the set $(-\infty, 0) \cup (0, \infty)$, but it does not define a function on the real line. However,

$$g(x) = \begin{cases} \dfrac{1}{|x|} & \text{for } x \neq 0 \\ 0 & \text{for } x = 0 \end{cases}$$

does define a function on the real line (see Figure 1.2).

We shall have occasion to use the notion of continuity for functions. Let $E$ be a subset of the real line $R$. A function $f$ defined on $E$ is *continuous* at a point $x \in E$ if

$$\lim_{n\to\infty} f(x_n) = f(x)$$

for every sequence $\{x_n\}$ of points in $E$ that converges to $x$. An equivalent definition is the following:

$$\lim_{\substack{y\to x \\ y\in E}} f(y) = f(x)$$

meaning that for each $\varepsilon > 0$ there is a $\delta > 0$ such that

$$|f(x) - f(y)| \leq \varepsilon$$

for all $y \in E$ satisfying $|x - y| \leq \delta$.

Suppose $f$ is a continuous function on the closed bounded interval $[a, b]$. There are two important properties of $f$ that will be used later in the text.

1.0.6 **Property** *The function $f$ assumes its maximum on $[a, b]$, that is, there is a point $x_0$ in $[a, b]$ with $f(x_0) \geq f(x)$ for all $x \in [a, b]$.*

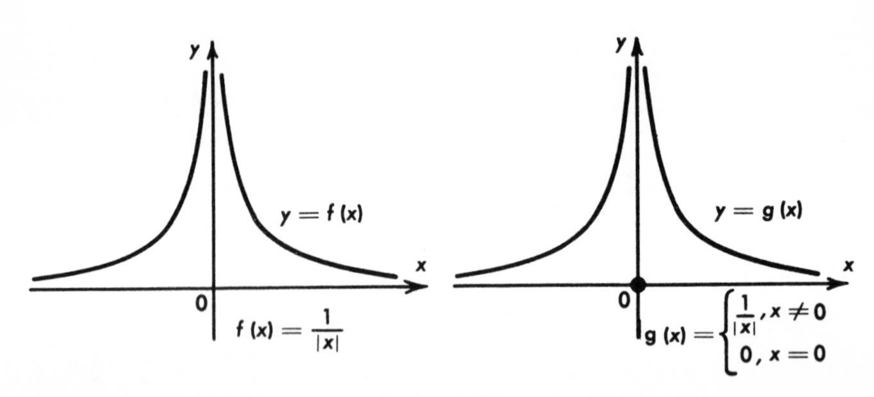


Figure 1.2 The first of the two diagrams pictures the graph of a function that is defined only on $R - \{0\}$, while the second one shows the graph of a function defined on all of $R$.

1.0.7 **Property** *The function $f$ assumes on $[a, b]$ all values in between $f(a)$ and $f(b)$.*

The continuity of a function of $k$ variables is defined similarly as for functions of one variable. If we denote a point $x$ in Euclidean space $R^k$ by

$$x = (x_1, \cdots, x_k),$$

where $x_1, \cdots, x_k$ are the coordinates of $x$, then a function $f$ of $k$ variables is just a function on $R^k$,

$$f(x) = f(x_1, \cdots, x_k).$$

Recall that the distance of two points $x$ and $y$ in $R^k$ is defined as

$$|x - y| = ((x_1 - y_1)^2 + \cdots + (x_k - y_k)^2)^{1/2}.$$

A sequence $\{x^n\}$ of points in $R^k$ converges to $x \in R^k$ if

$$\lim_{n\to\infty} |x^n - x| = 0,$$

which is the same as saying

$$\lim_{n\to\infty} x_j^n = x_j, \qquad j = 1, \cdots, k.$$

With this notion of distance and convergence for $R^k$ the definition of continuity of a function $f$ on a set $E$ in $R^k$ is identical to the one given above for the case $k = 1$.

Similarly as for functions of one variable we have:

**1.0.8 PROPERTY** *Suppose $f$ is a continuous function on the closed rectangle*

$$Q = \{x\colon a_j \leq x_j \leq b_j, 1 \leq j \leq k\}.$$

*Then $f$ assumes its maximum on $Q$, that is, there is an $x_0 \in Q$ with $f(x_0) \geq f(x)$ for all $x \in Q$.*

### *EXERCISES*

*1.0.1* Prove that

$$\sum_{n=1}^{\infty} q^n = \frac{q}{1-q} \qquad \text{for} \quad 0 \leq q < 1.$$

*Hint* Prove first that $\sum_{n=1}^{m} q^n = q(1 - q^m)/(1 - q)$ by subtracting $q \sum_{n=1}^{m} q^n$ from $\sum_{n=1}^{m} q^n$.

*Remark* We will use this formula very often:

$$\sum_{n=1}^{\infty} 2^{-n} = 1.$$

*1.0.2* Deduce from Theorem 1.0.5 that Statement (a) is also equivalent to (c): $\sum_{n=1}^{\infty} |a_{nk}|$ converges for each $k$ and $\sum_{k=1}^{\infty} (\sum_{n=1}^{\infty} |a_{nk}|)$ converges. If either Statement (a) or (c) holds, then

$$\sum_{n=1}^{\infty}\left(\sum_{k=1}^{\infty} a_{nk}\right) = \sum_{k=1}^{\infty}\left(\sum_{n=1}^{\infty} a_{nk}\right).$$

## 1.1 STEP FUNCTIONS AND THEIR INTEGRALS

We will proceed in two steps in our definition of the Lebesgue integral. First we establish the integral for a class of very simple functions; these are the step functions, sometimes also called elementary functions. This step will be discussed in this section. The second step, concerned with the definition of the Lebesgue integral for the wide class of Lebesgue integrable functions, will be performed in the next chapter.

Let us introduce now the concept of a step function in a formal definition.

**1.1.1 DEFINITION** *A function $\varphi$ on the real line with the following properties is called a step function: There are a finite number $a_0, \cdots, a_n$ of points on the* *real line and real numbers* $c_1, \cdots, c_n$ *such that*

(a) $a_0 \leq a_1 \leq \cdots \leq a_n$,
(b) $\varphi(x) = c_k$ *for* $a_{k-1} < x < a_k$, $\quad k = 1, \cdots, n$,
(c) $\varphi(x) = 0$ *for* $x < a_0$ *and* $x > a_n$.

*The sequence of numbers* $(a_0, \cdots, a_n;\ c_1, \cdots, c_n)$ *is called a presentation for the step function* $\varphi$, *and* $n$ *the length of the presentation.*

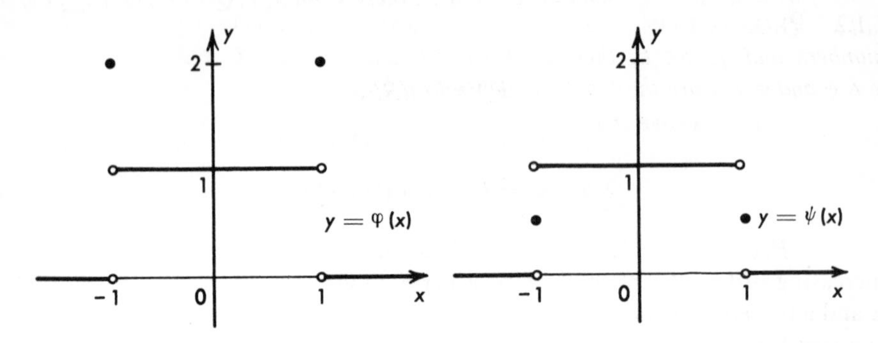


Figure 1.3 The two different step functions $\varphi$ and $\psi$ both have the presentation $(-1, 1;\ 1)$. Here and in the following a dot always belongs to the graph, while a circle does not.

A presentation hence consists of two lists, the first listing subdividing points and the second, values of the step function. In case $a_{k-1}$ and $a_k$ coincide for some $k$, Condition (b) will be void and $c_k$ can be any number.

We will reserve the Greek letters $\varphi$, $\psi$, $\xi$, $\eta$, and $\zeta$ for step functions.

Notice that the definition specifies only that $\varphi$ be constant over the open intervals $(a_{k-1}, a_k)$; there is no requirement concerning the values $d_k = \varphi(a_k)$ of $\varphi$ at the end points of these intervals. Thus it may happen that two different step functions have the same presentation. For instance, let $\varphi$ be the step function defined by

$$\varphi(x) = \begin{cases} 0 & \text{for } |x| > 1 \\ 1 & \text{for } |x| < 1 \\ 2 & \text{for } |x| = 1. \end{cases}$$

Then $(-1, 1;\ 1)$ is a presentation for $\varphi$. But $(-1, 1;\ 1)$ is also a presentation for the step function $\psi$ defined by

$$\psi(x) = \begin{cases} 0 & \text{for } |x| > 1 \\ 1 & \text{for } |x| < 1 \\ \tfrac{1}{2} & \text{for } |x| = 1. \end{cases}$$

See Figure 1.3.

On the other hand, given any step function $\psi$, we can find more than one presentation for it. Take for instance our step function $\psi$ belonging to the presentation $(-1, 1;\ 1)$. The presentation $(-1, 0, 1;\ 1, 1)$ would also be a presentation for $\psi$, the difference being that $(-1, 1;\ 1)$ lists only the points of discontinuity of $\psi$ while $(-1, 0, 1;\ 1, 1)$ also lists other points. The specific presentation $(a_0, \cdots, a_n;\ c_1, \cdots, c_n)$ for a step function $\varphi$ that lists only the points of discontinuity $a_0 < \cdots < a_n$ of $\varphi$ is the presentation of shortest length for $\varphi$.

Let $L$ be the set of step functions on the real line. Then

**1.1.2 PROPOSITION** *$L$ has the following property (1): If $a$ and $b$ are real numbers and $\varphi, \psi \in L$, then $a\varphi + b\psi \in L$ and $\varphi \wedge \psi \in L$ and $\varphi \vee \psi \in L$ where $\varphi \wedge \psi$ and $\varphi \vee \psi$ are the functions defined by*

$$\varphi \wedge \psi(x) = \min\ (\varphi(x), \psi(x)),$$

$$\varphi \vee \psi(x) = \max\ (\varphi(x), \psi(x)).$$

*Proof* Let $a_0, \cdots, a_n$ be the points of discontinuity of $\varphi$ and $\psi$ in increasing order. Then we can find a presentation $(a_0, \cdots, a_n;\ c_1, \cdots, c_n)$ for $\varphi$ and a presentation $(a_0, \cdots, a_n;\ d_1, \cdots, d_n)$ for $\psi$. Now it is clear that $a\varphi + b\psi$ is a step function with presentation

$$(a_0, \cdots, a_n;\ ac_1 + bd_1, \cdots, ac_n + bd_n).$$

Furthermore, $\varphi \wedge \psi$ is a step function with presentation

$$(a_0, \cdots, a_n;\ c_1 \wedge d_1, \cdots, c_n \wedge d_n),$$

and $\varphi \vee \psi$ has presentation

$$(a_0, \cdots, a_n;\ c_1 \vee d_1, \cdots, c_n \vee d_n).$$

The set $L$ is thus a (real) vector space or linear space. Property (1), and some further properties listed below, are fundamental for this course. Therefore we enumerate them separately.

Among the step functions, the characteristic functions of bounded intervals play an important role. If $I$ is a bounded interval, then the characteristic function $\chi_I$ of $I$ is defined by

$$\chi_I(x) = \begin{cases} 0 & \text{for } x \notin I \\ 1 & \text{for } x \in I. \end{cases}$$

For any set $I$, $\chi_I$ will always denote the characteristic function of $I$, defined by the same formula as above.

**1.1.3 LEMMA** *Every step function is a linear combination of a finite number of characteristic functions of mutually disjoint bounded intervals each of which is either closed or open.*

*Proof* In fact, if $(a_0, \cdots, a_n; c_1, \cdots, c_n)$ is the shortest presentation for the step function $\varphi$, then

$$\varphi = \sum_{k=1}^{n} c_k \chi_{(a_{k-1}, a_k)} + \sum_{k=0}^{n} \varphi(a_k) \chi_{[a_k, a_k]}.$$

**1.1.4 COROLLARY** *Every step function is a linear combination of characteristic functions of bounded closed intervals.*

*Proof* According to the lemma we need to prove this only for a characteristic function $\chi_{(a,b)}$ of a bounded open interval, and we have in fact

$$\chi_{(a,b)} = \chi_{[a,b]} - \chi_{[a,a]} - \chi_{[b,b]}.$$

The last corollary can be of help in proving theorems that are linear in their assertions, that is, which have the property that if the assertion holds for two step functions $\varphi$ and $\psi$, then it is true also for any linear combination $a\varphi + b\psi$. For in this case the assertion has to be proved only for a characteristic function of a bounded closed interval, which is usually much easier. As an example we refer to Exercise 1.1.3.

Sometimes, however, a theorem is more easily established for a characteristic function of a bounded open interval. We leave it to the exercises (Exercise 1.1.3) to establish for the characteristic functions of such intervals a proposition corresponding to Corollary 1.1.4.

We close this section with the definition of the integral for step functions. The next section will be devoted to exploring some of the basic properties of this integral.

**1.1.5 DEFINITION** *Let $\varphi$ be a step function and $(a_0, \cdots, a_n;\ c_1, \cdots, c_n)$ its presentation of shortest length. We define*

$$\int \varphi \, dx = \sum_{k=1}^{n} c_k (a_k - a_{k-1})$$

*and call this number the integral of $\varphi$.*

For a nonnegative step function $\varphi$, this is just the area under the graph of $\varphi$ (see Figure 1.4). With the convention

$$\varphi(x + 0) = \lim_{\substack{h \to 0 \\ h > 0}} \varphi(x + h), \qquad \varphi(x - 0) = \lim_{\substack{h \to 0 \\ h > 0}} \varphi(x - h)$$

one can also write the definition of the integral in the following way:

$$\int \varphi \, dx = \sum_{k=1}^{n} (\varphi(a_k - 0) \cdot a_k - \varphi(a_{k-1} + 0) \cdot a_{k-1})$$

$$= \sum_{k=0}^{n} (\varphi(a_k - 0) - \varphi(a_k + 0)) \cdot a_k,$$

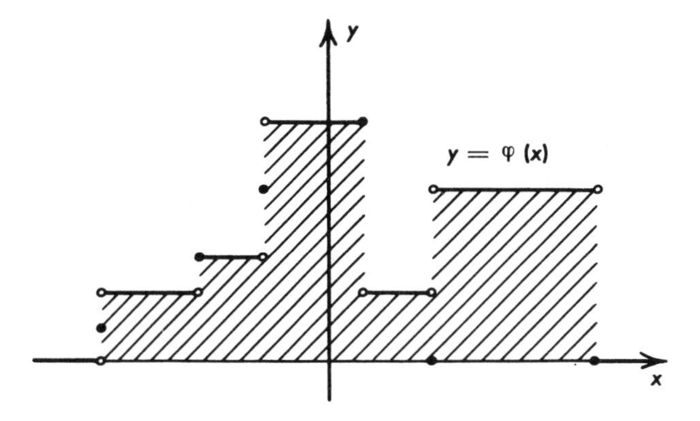


Figure 1.4 For a nonnegative step function $\varphi$ the integral $\int \varphi\, dx$ is just the area under the graph of $\varphi$.

the latter since $\varphi(a_0 - 0) = \varphi(a_n + 0) = 0$. Thus, if $(b_0, \cdots, b_m;\ d_1, \cdots, d_m)$ is any other presentation of $\varphi$,

$$\int \varphi\, dx = \sum_{k=0}^{m} (\varphi(b_k - 0) - \varphi(b_k + 0)) \cdot b_k$$

since $\varphi$ is continuous at those $b_k$'s that are not in the set $\{a_0, \cdots, a_n\}$, and therefore

$$\varphi(b_k - 0) - \varphi(b_k + 0) = 0.$$

*This shows in particular that we could have chosen any presentation for $\varphi$ in the definition of $\int \varphi\, dx$.*

## *EXERCISES*

*1.1.1* Use only Property (1) and no other special property of step functions to establish that $|\varphi|$ is a step function if $\varphi$ is.

*Hint* Express $|\varphi|$ in terms of

$$\varphi^+ = \varphi \vee 0, \qquad \varphi^- = -(\varphi \wedge 0) = (-\varphi) \vee 0.$$

For any function $f$, $f^+ = f \vee 0$ is called the positive part of $f$ and $f^- = -(f \wedge 0)$ the negative part of $f$ (see Figure 1.5).

*1.1.2* The integer part $[f]$ of a function $f$ is defined by

$$[f](x) = n \qquad \text{if } n \leq f(x) < n + 1, \qquad n = 0, \pm 1, \cdots;$$

$[f](x)$ is the largest integer smaller than, or equal to, $f(x)$. Prove that $[\varphi] \in L$ if $\varphi \in L$.

*Hint* Use presentations.

*1.1.3* Prove that every step function is a linear combination of characteristic functions of bounded open intervals.

*1.1.4* Let $(a_0, \cdots, a_n;\ c_1, \cdots, c_n)$ be a presentation for $\varphi$. Find a presentation for $|\varphi|$ and prove

$$\left|\int \varphi\, dx\right| \leq \int |\varphi|\, dx.$$

*1.1.5* Let $a, b, c$ be any numbers; that number among $a, b, c$ which is in between the two others is denoted by mid $(a, b, c)$. Using only Property (1) prove that if $\varphi, \psi, \eta \in L$, then mid $(\varphi, \psi, \eta) \in L$ also.

*Hint* Prove

$$\begin{aligned} \text{mid}\,(\varphi, \psi, \eta) &= (\varphi \wedge \psi) \vee (\psi \wedge \eta) \vee (\eta \wedge \varphi) \\ &= (\varphi \vee \psi) \wedge (\psi \vee \eta) \wedge (\eta \vee \varphi). \end{aligned}$$

## 1.2 BASIC PROPERTIES OF THE INTEGRAL

In the previous section we have seen that the integral for a step function $\varphi$ is given by the formula

$$\int \varphi\, dx = \sum_{k=1}^{n} c_k(a_k - a_{k-1}) \tag{1.2.1}$$

where $(a_0, \cdots, a_n;\ c_1, \cdots, c_n)$ is any presentation for $\varphi$. We are now going to establish some of the working tools for this integral. One of these working tools is the linearity of the integral:

**1.2.2 PROPOSITION** *The integral $\int \varphi\, dx$ on the vector space $L$ has the following linearity property* (2)*: If $\varphi, \psi \in L$ and $a, b$ are any real numbers, then*

$$\int (a\varphi + b\psi)\, dx = a\int \varphi\, dx + b\int \psi\, dx.$$

*Proof* If $\varphi, \psi \in L$, then we can find presentations $(a_0, \cdots, a_n;\ c_1, \cdots, c_n)$ for $\varphi$ and $(a_0, \cdots, a_n;\ d_1, \cdots, d_n)$ for $\psi$ that have the same list of subdividing points. The step function $a\varphi + b\psi$ will have the presentation

$$(a_0, \cdots, a_n;\ ac_1 + bd_1, \cdots, ac_n + bd_n)$$

and thus

$$\begin{aligned}\int (a\varphi + b\psi)\,dx &= \sum_{k=1}^{n} (ac_k + bd_k)(a_k - a_{k-1}) \\ &= a \sum_{k=}^{n} c_k(a_k - a_{k-1}) + b \sum_{k=1}^{n} d_k(a_k - a_{k-1}) \\ &= a \int \varphi\,dx + b \int \psi\,dx.\end{aligned}$$

Another useful property is the positivity of the integral. The right-hand side of (1.2.1) is certainly nonnegative whenever all the $c_k$ are nonnegative. Thus we have proved the following proposition.

**1.2.3 PROPOSITION** *The integral is positive, that is, it has Property* (3)*: If $\varphi \in L$ and $\varphi \geq 0$, then $\int \varphi\,dx \geq 0$.*

This proposition has some important consequences that are used over and over again. It implies for instance the monotonicity of the integral and a certain continuity property. The monotonicity says the following; if $\varphi \geq \psi$, then $\int \varphi\,dx \geq \int \psi\,dx$. In fact, $\varphi - \psi \geq 0$, and thus by the last two propositions

$$\int \varphi\,dx - \int \psi\,dx = \int (\varphi - \psi)\,dx \geq 0$$

and hence

$$\int \varphi\,dx \geq \int \psi\,dx.$$

The monotonicity in turn implies that

$$\pm \int \varphi\,dx \leq \int |\varphi|\,dx$$

for every step function $\varphi$ because $\pm\varphi \leq |\varphi|$; therefore we have

$$\left| \int \varphi\,dx \right| \leq \int |\varphi|\,dx.$$

Furthermore, if $\varphi^+$ denotes the positive and $\varphi^-$ the negative part of the step function $\varphi$ (see Figure 1.5),

$$\varphi^+(x) = [\varphi \vee 0](x) = \begin{cases} \varphi(x) & \text{if } \varphi(x) \geq 0 \\ 0 & \text{if } \varphi(x) \leq 0, \end{cases}$$

$$\varphi^-(x) = -[\varphi \wedge 0](x) = \begin{cases} 0 & \text{if } \varphi(x) \geq 0 \\ -\varphi(x) & \text{if } \varphi(x) \leq 0, \end{cases}$$

then $\varphi^+$ and $\varphi^-$ are nonnegative step functions and

$$\varphi = \varphi^+ - \varphi^-, \qquad |\varphi| = \varphi^+ + \varphi^-.$$

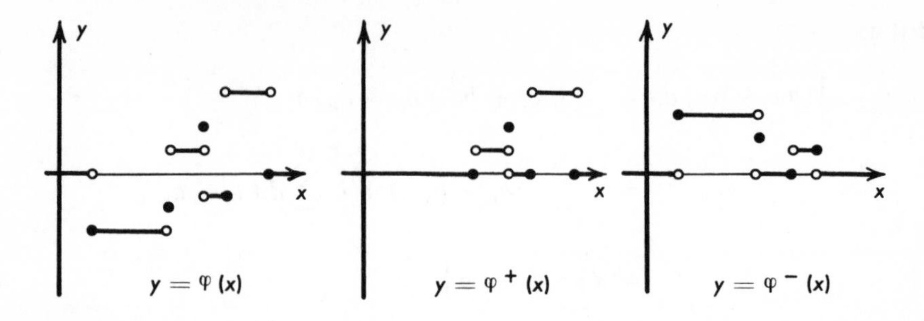


Figure 1.5 The diagrams show the graphs of a step function $\varphi$ and its positive and negative parts $\varphi^+$ and $\varphi^-$.

The last of the two equations implies $\varphi^+ \leq |\varphi|$ and $\varphi^- \leq |\varphi|$, whence

$$\int \varphi^+ \, dx \leq \int |\varphi| \, dx, \qquad \int \varphi^- \, dx \leq \int |\varphi| \, dx.$$

We collect these results in a corollary.

1.2.4 COROLLARY

(a) *If* $\varphi, \psi \in L$ *and* $\varphi \geq \psi$, *then*

$$\int \varphi \, dx \geq \int \psi \, dx.$$

(b) *For any* $\varphi \in L$,

$$\left| \int \varphi \, dx \right| \leq \int |\varphi| \, dx.$$

$$\int \varphi^+ \, dx \leq \int |\varphi| \, dx, \qquad \int \varphi- \, dx \leq \int |\varphi| \, dx.$$

Finally, we have the following continuity property.

1.2.5 PROPOSITION *Suppose* $\{\varphi_n\}$ *is a sequence of step functions all vanishing outside the same interval* $[a, b]$. *Let* $M_n$ *be the maximum value of* $\varphi_n$ *and suppose that* $\{M_n\}$ *tends to zero as n tends to infinity. Then*

$$\lim_{n \to \infty} \int \varphi_n \, dx = 0.$$

*Proof* We have

$$|\varphi_n| \leq M_n \chi_{[a,b]}$$

and thus

$$\left| \int \varphi_n \, dx \right| \leq \int |\varphi_n| \, dx \leq \int M_n \chi_{[a,b]} \, dx = M_n(b - a).$$

Taking limits on both sides, we obtain the desired result.

The last proposition is the basic tool in the theory of Riemann integration for continuous functions. However, if one wants to define the integral for a more general class of functions this proposition proves less useful. The hypothesis that

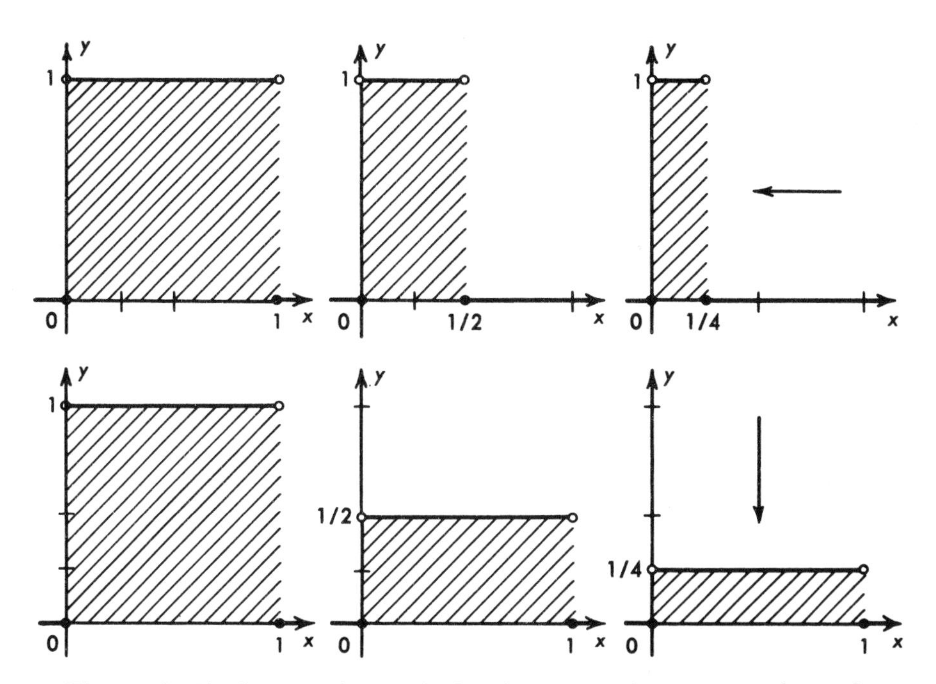


Figure 1.6 The first row pictures the first three terms of the sequence $\{\chi_{(0,2^{-n})}\}$, while the second row shows the first three terms of the sequence $\{2^{-n}\chi_{(0,1)}\}$. These two examples characterize the two different ways in which the sequence of integrals corresponding to a sequence of step functions decreasing to zero, can converge to zero.

the maxima $M_n$ of the $|\varphi_n|$ tend to zero, which is also expressed by saying that $\{\varphi_n\}$ tends uniformly to zero, is too strong. Consider for instance the following example. The sequence $\{\varphi_n\}$,

$$\varphi_n = \chi_{(0,2^{-n})}, \tag{1.2.6}$$

of step functions vanishing off (0, 1] tends to zero everywhere (see Figure 1.6), that is,

$$\lim_{n\to\infty} \varphi_n(x) = 0$$

for all $x$. However, the maximum $M_n$ of $\varphi_n$ is always equal to 1 so that Proposition 1.2.5 does not apply. Nevertheless, we have

$$\lim_{n\to\infty} \int \varphi_n \, dx = \lim_{n\to\infty} 2^{-n} = 0.$$

Now, one cannot expect to prove the assertion of Proposition 1.2.5 using only the hypothesis that

$$\lim_{n\to\infty} \varphi_n(x) = 0 \qquad \text{for all } x,$$

as is shown by Exercises 1.2.2 and 1.2.3. Some additional assumption is needed. For instance, the assumption

$$\varphi_n \geq \varphi_{n+1} \geq 0 \qquad \text{for all } n \tag{1.2.7}$$

will prove sufficient though it may be replaced by other criteria (see Exercise 1.2.5). Condition (1.2.7) is certainly satisfied by our example (1.2.6). Now we assert:

**1.2.8 THEOREM** *The integral has the following continuity property* (4): *Suppose* $\{\varphi_n\}$ *is a sequence of step functions such that* $\varphi_n \geq \varphi_{n+1} \geq 0$ *for all* $n$ *and* $\lim_{n\to\infty} \varphi_n(x) = 0$ *for all* $x$; *then*

$$\lim_{n\to\infty} \int \varphi_n \, dx = 0.$$

*Proof* Let $M$ be any number greater than the maximum value of $\varphi_1$ so that $M^{-1}\varphi_n \leq 1$ for all $n$. If we prove

$$\lim_{n\to\infty} \int M^{-1}\varphi_n \, dx = 0,$$

then we will also have

$$\lim_{n\to\infty} \int \varphi_n \, dx = 0.$$

Thus we may as well assume that $\varphi_n \leq 1$ for all $n$.

Let $[a, b]$, $a < b$ be an interval outside of which $\varphi_1$ vanishes. Then $\varphi_n$ vanishes off $[a, b]$ for all $n$, since $0 \leq \varphi_n \leq \varphi_1$. Now we want to show that, for each $\varepsilon > 0$, there is an integer $N$ such that

$$\int \varphi_n \, dx < \varepsilon$$

for all $n \geq N$. This would certainly be accomplished if we could find an $N$ with

$$\varphi_N \leq \frac{\varepsilon}{2(b-a)} \chi_{[a,b]}$$

since then

$$\int \varphi_n \, dx \leq \int \varphi_N \, dx \leq \frac{\varepsilon}{2(b-a)} \int \chi_{[a,b]} \, dx = \frac{\varepsilon}{2} < \varepsilon$$

for all $n \geq N$. However, the example (1.2.6) shows that we cannot expect

$$\varphi_N \leq \frac{\varepsilon}{2(b-a)} \chi_{[a,b]}$$

to hold everywhere for any $N$, since $\chi_{(0,2^{-n})}$ has the value 1 at points close to the point of discontinuity 0 for all $n$. Thus we suspect that we might be able to prove for some $N$ that

$$\varphi_N(x) \leq \frac{\varepsilon}{2(b-a)} \chi_{[a,b]}(x)$$

for all $x$ that are not close to the points of discontinuity of $\varphi_N$. This can be accomplished in the following way.

Let $\{a_k\}$ be a sequence that lists all the points of discontinuity of all the $\varphi_n$. Define $\psi_n$ to be the step function

$$\psi_n = \frac{\varepsilon}{2(b-a)} \chi_{[a,b]} + \sum_{k=1}^{n} \chi_k$$

where $\chi_k$ is the characteristic function of the open interval $(a_k - \varepsilon 2^{-k-2}, a_k + \varepsilon 2^{-k-2})$. Then $\psi_n$ will be greater or equal to 1 in a whole open interval around each of the points $a_1, \cdots, a_n$, while the integral of $\psi_n$ is smaller than $\varepsilon$; in fact,

$$\int \psi_n \, dx = \frac{\varepsilon}{2(b-a)} \int \chi_{[a,b]} \, dx + \sum_{k=1}^{n} \int \chi_k \, dx$$

$$= \frac{\varepsilon}{2} + \frac{\varepsilon}{2} \sum_{k=1}^{n} 2^{-k} < \frac{\varepsilon}{2} + \frac{\varepsilon}{2} = \varepsilon.$$

Therefore it suffices to prove that $\varphi_N \leq \psi_N$ for some integer $N$, since we would then have

$$\int \varphi_n \, dx \leq \int \varphi_N \, dx \leq \int \psi_N \, dx < \varepsilon$$

for all $n \geq N$ and this would complete the proof.

Consider therefore the sets

$$E_n = \{x : \varphi_n(x) > \psi_n(x)\} = \{x : \varphi_n(x) - \psi_n(x) > 0\}.$$

Each $E_n$ is a system of disjoint intervals. Since $\psi_n \leq \psi_{n+1}$ and $\varphi_n \geq \varphi_{n+1}$, we have

$$\varphi_n - \psi_n \geq \varphi_{n+1} - \psi_{n+1}$$

and thus

$$E_{n+1} \subset E_n \subset [a, b].$$

To prove $\varphi_N \leq \psi_N$ for some $N$, we need only show that $E_N$ is empty for some $N$. Suppose this would not be the case. Let $x_n$ be the left-most end point of the system of intervals $E_n$. Since $E_{n+1} \subset E_n \subset [a, b]$, we have

$$x_n \leq x_{n+1} \leq b.$$

Thus $\{x_n\}$ is an increasing bounded sequence. It converges therefore to a point $x$. But $x$ cannot be equal to any of the points $a_k$, since in the open interval $(a_k - \varepsilon 2^{-k-2}, a_k + \varepsilon 2^{-k-2})$ around $a_k$, $\varphi_n \leq 1 \leq \psi_n$ for $n \geq k$; therefore $x_n$ cannot belong to it for any $n \geq k$. Thus $x$ is a point of continuity for all $\varphi_n$.

Since $x_n$ is an end point of $E_n$, we can find a point $y_n \in E_n$ very close to $x_n$, say for instance,

$$x_n \leq y_n \leq x + 2^{-n}.$$

Then $\lim_{n\to\infty} y_n = x$ also, and

$$\varphi_k(y_n) \geq \frac{\varepsilon}{2(b-a)} \qquad \text{for} \quad n \geq k$$

since

$$\varphi_k(y_n) \geq \varphi_n(y_n) > \psi_n(y_n) \geq \frac{\varepsilon}{2(b-a)}.$$

Thus, $\varphi_k$ being continuous at $x$, we find that

$$\varphi_k(x) = \lim_{n\to\infty} \varphi_k(y_n) \geq \frac{\varepsilon}{2(b-a)}$$

for all $k$, which contradicts the hypothesis $\lim_{k\to\infty} \varphi_k(x) = 0$ for all $x$.

Here ends the proof of Theorem 1.2.8.

*An Alternate Proof of Theorem 1.2.8* We now give another proof of Theorem 1.2.8, which may shed some more light on it. However, we have to use the concept of upper semicontinuity, which seems to be a little artificial in the present context.

A step function $\varphi$ is said to be upper semicontinuous if the value of $\varphi$ at any point $x$ is greater or equal to the value of $\varphi$ at nearby points, or formally

$$\varphi(x) \geq \max(\varphi(x+0), \varphi(x-0)).$$

For the discussion of upper semcontinuity for general functions we refer the reader to Section 6.3. An upper semicontinuous step function $\varphi$ has the important property that the set

$$\{x : \varphi(x) \geq \delta\}$$

is a finite union of disjoint *closed* intervals for any $\delta$; in fact, if $a$ is a left end point of one of the nondegenerate intervals making up the set $\{x : \varphi(x) \geq \delta\}$, then

$$\varphi(a) \geq \max(\varphi(a+0), \varphi(a-0)) \geq \varphi(a+0) \geq \delta$$

and thus $a$ belongs to the set. A similar argument holds for a right end point.

We are now ready to prove a special case of Theorem 1.2.8.

1.2.9 LEMMA *Let $\{\varphi_n\}$ be a sequence of upper semicontinuous step functions such that $\varphi_n \geq \varphi_{n+1} \geq 0$ for all $n$ and $\lim_{n\to\infty} \varphi_n(x) = 0$ for all $x$. Then*

$$\lim_{n\to\infty} \int \varphi_n \, dx = 0.$$

*Proof* Let $[a, b]$, $a < b$ be an interval outside of which $\varphi_1$ vanishes. All $\varphi_n$ will then vanish off $[a, b]$, since $0 \leq \varphi_n \leq \varphi_1$. Let $\varepsilon > 0$; we have to produce an $N$ such that

$$\int \varphi_n \, dx < \varepsilon \qquad \text{for} \quad n \geq N.$$

For this it suffices to prove that there is an $N$ with

$$\varphi_N < \delta \chi_{[a,b]}$$

where $\delta = \varepsilon/(b - a)$, since then for $n \geq N$

$$\int \varphi_n \, dx \leq \int \varphi_N \, dx < \delta \int \chi_{[a,b]} \, dx = \varepsilon.$$

Suppose we could not find such an $N$; then

$$E_n = \{x : \varphi_n(x) \geq \delta\}$$

is not empty for any $n$. Let $x_n$ be the leftmost end point of the closed intervals that make up $E_n$ so that $x_n \in E_n$. Because $\varphi_n \geq \varphi_{n+1}$, we have $E_n \supset E_{n+1}$ and thus $x_n \leq x_{n+1}$. Also, $x_n \leq b$ so that $\{x_n\}$ is a bounded increasing sequence. Therefore $\{x_n\}$ converges to a point $x$; $x_n$ belongs to $E_k$ for $n \geq k$, since $E_n \subset E_k$ for $n \geq k$. Therefore $\varphi_k(x_n) \geq \delta$ for $n \geq k$, from which we can derive

$$\varphi_k(x) \geq \varphi_k(x - 0) = \lim_{n\to\infty} \varphi_k(x_n) \geq \delta > 0.$$

This holds for all $k$, which contradicts the hypothesis that $\lim_{k\to\infty} \varphi_k(x) = 0$ for all $x$. This completes the proof of Lemma 1.2.9.

Let $\varphi$ be any nonnegative step function. We claim that for any $\varepsilon > 0$ we can find an upper semicontinuous step function $\psi$ such that

$$0 \leq \psi \leq \varphi \qquad \text{and} \qquad \int \varphi \, dx - \int \psi \, dx \leq \varepsilon.$$

In fact, let $(a_0, \cdots, a_n;\ c_1, \cdots, c_n)$ be the presentation of shortest length for $\varphi$; we have $c_k \geq 0$ for $1 \leq k \leq n$. The step function

$$\psi = \sum_{k=1}^{n} c_k \chi_k,$$

where $\chi_k$ is the characteristic function of the closed interval $[a_{k-1} + \delta,\ a_k - \delta]$, is well defined for

$$2\delta \leq \min \{a_k - a_{k-1}\colon\ 1 \leq k \leq n\}.$$

Furthermore $\psi$ is upper semicontinuous and satisfies $0 \leq \psi \leq \varphi$, as well as

$$\int \varphi \, dx - \int \psi \, dx = \sum_{k=1}^{n} c_k(a_k - a_{k-1}) - \sum_{k=1}^{n} c_k(a_k - a_{k-1} - 2\delta) = 2\delta \sum_{k=1}^{n} c_k \leq \varepsilon$$

if we choose $\delta$ small enough.

Now let $\{\varphi_n\}$ be any sequence of step functions satisfying $\varphi_n \geq \varphi_{n+1} \geq 0$ for all $n$ and

$$\lim_{n\to\infty} \varphi_n(x) = 0$$

for all $x$. Let $\varepsilon > 0$ and choose for each $n$ an upper semicontinuous step function $\psi_n$ with $0 \leq \psi_n \leq \varphi_n$ and

$$\int \varphi_n \, dx - \int \psi_n \, dx < \varepsilon \cdot 2^{-n}.$$

It is easily verified that

$$\eta_k = \psi_1 \wedge \cdots \wedge \psi_k$$

is again upper semicontinuous. Since $\eta_k \geq \eta_{k+1}$ and

$$\lim_{k\to\infty} \eta_k(x) = 0$$

because of $\eta_k \leq \psi_k \leq \varphi_k$, we can apply Lemma 1.2.9, yielding

$$\lim_{k\to\infty} \int \eta_k \, dx = 0.$$

Furthermore, we have

$$\begin{aligned}
\int (\varphi_k - \eta_k) \, dx &= \int (\varphi_k - \psi_1) \vee \cdots \vee (\varphi_k - \psi_k) \, dx \\
&\leq \int (\varphi_1 - \psi_1) \vee \cdots \vee (\varphi_k - \psi_k) \, dx \\
&\leq \int [(\varphi_1 - \psi_1) + \cdots + (\varphi_k - \psi_k)] \, dx \\
&\leq \varepsilon \sum_{j=1}^{k} 2^{-j} \leq \varepsilon.
\end{aligned}$$

Taking the integer $N$ so large that $\int \eta_k \, dx \leq \varepsilon$, for $k \geq N$, we finally get

$$\int \varphi_k \, dx \leq 2\varepsilon \qquad \text{for} \quad k \geq N.$$

This completes the second proof of Theorem 1.2.8.

## *EXERCISES*

*1.2.1* Prove that $-\int \varphi^- \, dx \leq \int \varphi \, dx \leq \int \varphi^+ \, dx$ for $\varphi \in L$.

*1.2.2* Let $[a, b]$ be any interval with $a < b$. Show that there is a sequence $\{\varphi_n\}$ of step functions vanishing off $[a, b]$ that satisfies

$$\lim_{n\to\infty} \varphi_n(x) = 0 \qquad \text{for all } x,$$

but for which

$$\lim_{n\to\infty} \int \varphi_n \, dx = 0$$

fails to be true. (In fact, one can choose $\varphi_n \geq 0$ with $\int \varphi_n \, dx = 1$.)

*1.2.3* Show that there is a sequence $\{\varphi_n\}$ of nonnegative step functions such that $\varphi_n \leq 1$ and

$$\lim_{n\to\infty} \varphi_n(x) = 0 \qquad \text{for all } x,$$

but $\lim_{n\to\infty} \int \varphi_n \, dx = 0$ fails to be true.

*1.2.4* Let $\varphi_n, \varphi \in L$ be such that

$$\varphi_n \leq \varphi_{n+1} \leq \varphi \qquad \text{for all } n \geq 1,$$
$$\lim_{n\to\infty} \varphi_n(x) = \varphi(x) \qquad \text{for all } x.$$

Prove that

$$\lim_{n\to\infty} \int \varphi_n \, dx = \int \varphi \, dx.$$

*1.2.5* Let $\{\varphi_n\}$ be a sequence of nonnegative step functions all vanishing off the interval $[a, b]$ and satisfying $\varphi_n \leq 1$. Suppose that

$$\lim_{n\to\infty} \varphi_n(x) = 0 \qquad \text{for all } x.$$

Prove that

$$\lim_{n\to\infty} \int \varphi_n \, dx = 0.$$

*Hint* Show first that if the sequence $\{\varphi_n\}$ is "almost decreasing" in the sense that

$$\int (\varphi_n - \varphi_{n-1})^+ \, dx < \varepsilon 2^{-n} \qquad \text{for} \quad n = 2, 3, \cdots,$$

then the proof of Theorem 1.2.8 works if one puts

$$\psi_n = \frac{\varepsilon}{2(b-a)} \chi_{[a,b]} + \sum_{k=1}^{n} \chi_k + \sum_{k=2}^{n} (\varphi_k - \varphi_{k-1})^+, \qquad n = 2, 3, \cdots$$

(in fact, one can show that $\psi_n - \varphi_n$ is nondecreasing by proving that $\psi_n - \varphi_n - (\psi_{n-1} - \varphi_{n-1}) \geq (\varphi_n - \varphi_{n-1})^-$ for $n \geq 3$) and proves that there exists an $N$ such that

$$\int \varphi_n \, dx < \frac{3}{2} \varepsilon \qquad \text{if} \qquad n \geq N.$$

If $\{\varphi_n\}$ is not "almost decreasing," construct the sequence $\{\vartheta_n\}$ by putting

$$\vartheta_1 = \varphi_1 \vee \varphi_2 \vee \cdots \vee \varphi_{n(1)},$$
$$\vartheta_2 = \varphi_{n(1)+1} \vee \varphi_{n(1)+2} \vee \cdots \vee \varphi_{n(2)},$$
$$\vdots$$
$$\vartheta_k = \varphi_{n(k-1)+1} \vee \varphi_{n(k-1)+2} \vee \cdots \vee \varphi_{n(k)},$$

choosing the increasing sequence $n(0) = 0, n(1), \cdots, n(k), \cdots$ inductively, so that

$$\int \vartheta_k \, dx > \lim_{n\to\infty} \int \varphi_{n(k-1)+1} \vee \varphi_{n(k-1)+2} \vee \cdots \vee \varphi_n \, dx - \varepsilon 2^{-k-1}, \qquad k = 1, 2, \cdots$$

Show that $\vartheta_k$ is "almost decreasing" and that

$$\int \vartheta_k \, dx < \frac{3}{2}\varepsilon \qquad \text{if} \quad k \geq K$$

implies that

$$\int \varphi_n \, dx < \frac{3}{2}\varepsilon \qquad \text{if} \quad n \geq n(K).$$

## 1.3 NULL SETS

The continuity property (4) that we have proved in the preceding section (Theorem 1.2.8) has the following consequence. Suppose $\{\varphi_n\}$ is an increasing sequence of step functions that converges everywhere to a step function $\varphi$; then

$$\lim_{n\to\infty} \int \varphi_n \, dx = \int \varphi \, dx.$$

In fact, the sequence $\{\psi_n\}$, $\psi_n = \varphi - \varphi_n$, of step functions satisfies $\psi_n \geq \psi_{n+1} \geq 0$ for all $n$ and

$$\lim_{n\to\infty} \psi_n(x) = 0 \qquad \text{for all } x$$

so that we can apply (4), yielding

$$\lim_{n\to\infty} \int \psi_n \, dx = \int \varphi \, dx - \lim_{n\to\infty} \int \varphi_n \, dx = 0.$$

Suppose now $\{\varphi_n\}$ is an increasing sequence of step functions, $\varphi_{n+1} \geq \varphi_n$, and $f$ a function on the real line such that

$$f(x) = \lim_{n\to\infty} \varphi_n(x)$$

for all $x$. Furthermore, assume that the increasing sequence $\{\int \varphi_n \, dx\}$ converges. In this case it would be only natural to extend the definition of the integral to $f$ by setting

$$\int f \, dx = \lim_{n\to\infty} \int \varphi_n \, dx.$$

We will do so in Chapter 2. But in order to get a satisfactory theory we have to look more closely into the matter of convergence.

Let us try to go one step further in our consideration of the increasing sequence of step functions $\{\varphi_n\}$. Let us not assume that $\{\varphi_n\}$ converges but only that the sequence of integrals $\{\int \varphi_n \, dx\}$ converges. Since $\varphi_{n+1} \geq \varphi_n$, $\{\varphi_n(x)\}$ either converges or it diverges to infinity for a given $x$. The latter case is not impossible; the increasing sequence $\{n\chi_{[0,0]}\}$, for instance, diverges for $x = 0$ while $\int n\chi_{[0,0]}\,dx = 0$ for all $n$. However, the set of points $x$ for which $\{\varphi_n(x)\}$ diverges cannot be too large; it cannot be a whole interval $(a, b)$ with $a < b$. Namely, suppose $\{\varphi_n(x)\}$ diverges for each $x \in (a, b)$; then

$$\psi_n = (M\chi_{(a,b)} - \varphi_n)^+$$

with $M > 0$ satisfies $\psi_n \geq \psi_{n+1} \geq 0$ for all $n$ and

$$\lim_{n\to\infty} \psi_n(x) = 0 \qquad \text{for all } x.$$

Thus by Property (4),

$$\lim_{n\to\infty} \int \psi_n\,dx = 0.$$

If we take the limit on the left-hand side of the inequality

$$\int (\varphi_n + \psi_n)\,dx \geq \int [\varphi_n + (M\chi_{(a,b)} - \varphi_n)]\,dx = \int M\chi_{(a,b)}\,dx,$$

we obtain

$$\lim_{n\to\infty} \int \varphi_n\,dx \geq M(b - a),$$

which cannot hold for all $M$ unless $\{\int \varphi_n\,dx\}$ diverges.

Suppose now $\{\varphi_n\}$ is an increasing sequence of step functions such that the corresponding sequence $\{\int \varphi_n\,dx\}$ of integrals converges. Experience will show us later that the set of points $x$ for which $\{\varphi_n(x)\}$ diverges is negligible as far as the theory of integration is concerned. See especially Theorem 1.5.3 in this regard.

1.3.1 DEFINITION *A set $E$ is said to be negligible or to be a null set if there is an increasing sequence of step functions $\{\varphi_n\}$, $\varphi_n \leq \varphi_{n+1}$, such that $\{\varphi_n(x)\}$ diverges for each $x \in E$ while $\{\int \varphi_n\,dx\}$ converges.*

It is inherent in this definition that a subset of a null set is again a null set. Also, *we may assume that the $\varphi_n$ in the definition are nonnegative*; for if not, then $\{\varphi_n - \varphi_1\}$ is a sequence of nonnegative step functions with the same properties as $\{\varphi_n\}$.

There is another formulation of this definition that turns out to be more flexible in many instances.

1.3.2 PROPOSITION *$E$ is a null set if and only if there is a series $\sum \varphi_n$ of step functions such that $\sum \varphi_n(x)$ diverges for each $x \in E$ while $\sum_{n=1}^{\infty} \int |\varphi_n|\,dx < \infty$.*

*Proof* Suppose $E$ is a null set and $\{\varphi_n\}$ an increasing sequence of step functions such that $\{\varphi_n(x)\}$ diverges for $x \in E$ and $\{\int \varphi_n\,dx\}$ converges. Let $\psi_n = \varphi_{n+1} - \varphi_n$, then

$$\sum_{n=1}^{m} \psi_n = \varphi_{m+1} - \varphi_1.$$

Thus $\sum \psi_n(x)$ diverges for $x \in E$ while $\sum \int |\psi_n|$ converges:

$$\sum_{n=1}^{\infty} \int |\psi_n|\, dx = \sum_{n=1}^{\infty}\left(\int \varphi_{n+1}\, dx - \int \varphi_n\, dx\right)$$

$$= \lim_{m\to\infty} \int \varphi_{m+1}\, dx - \int \varphi_1\, dx.$$

Conversely, suppose $E$ is a set and $\sum \varphi_n$ a series of step functions satisfying

$$\sum_{n=1}^{\infty} \int |\varphi_n|\, dx < \infty$$

that diverges at every point $x \in E$. Then $\sum |\varphi_n(x)|$ diverges for $x \in E$.

$$\psi_k = \sum_{n=1}^{k} |\varphi_n|$$

defines therefore an increasing sequence of step functions having the property that $\{\psi_k(x)\}$ diverges for $x \in E$ while $\{\int \psi_k\, dx\}$ converges. Thus $E$ is a null set.

It is easily verified that *one may require the $\varphi_n$ to be nonnegative in the above proposition* (Exercise 1.3.1).

Proposition 1.3.2 allows us now to give a simple proof of the fact that the union $E = \bigcup_{n\geq 1} E_n$ of a sequence $\{E_n\}$ of null sets is again a null set. Let, for each $n$, $\sum_k \varphi_{nk}$ be a series of step functions such that $\sum \varphi_{nk}(x)$ diverges for $x \in E_n$ and $\sum_{k=1}^{\infty} \int |\varphi_{nk}|\, dx < \infty$. We may assume that

$$\sum_{k=1}^{\infty} \int |\varphi_{nk}|\, dx \leq 2^{-n},$$

for, if this is not the case, we replace each $\varphi_{nk}$ by $2^{-n}M^{-1}\varphi_{nk}$ where

$$M > \sum_{k=1}^{\infty} \int |\varphi_{nk}|\, dx.$$

The set $\{\varphi_{nk}: n = 1, \cdots, k = 1, \cdots\}$ is countable, so we can enumerate it in a sequence $\{\varphi_j\}$. Then $\sum |\varphi_j(x)|$ diverges for $x \in E$ and

$$\sum_{j=1}^{\infty} \int |\varphi_j|\, dx = \sum_{n=1}^{\infty}\sum_{k=1}^{\infty} \int |\varphi_{nk}|\, dx \leq \sum_{n=1}^{\infty} 2^{-n} < \infty$$

which proves that $E$ is a null set. Thus we have shown:

**1.3.3 PROPOSITION** *Let $\{E_n\}$ be a sequence of null sets. Then $E = \bigcup_{n\geq 1} E_n$ is again a null set.*

There is another way of introducing null sets on the real line which is less suitable for our purposes but which demonstrates the smallness of null sets more clearly. To do this we need the notion of total length of a countable (finite or denumerably infinite) system $\{I_k\}$ of intervals with end points $a_k \leq b_k$. The *total length* of the system $\{I_k\}$ is equal to

$$\sum_{k=1}^{\infty} (b_k - a_k)$$

if this sum converges, and infinite otherwise.

1.3.4 DEFINITION *A set E on the real line is said to be of measure zero if for every $\varepsilon > 0$ there is a system $\{I_k\}$ of open intervals of total length less than or equal to $\varepsilon$ that covers E, that is,*

$$E \subset \bigcup_{k\geq 1} I_k.$$

For instance, every denumerable set $\{a_1, a_2, \cdots\}$ is of measure zero. Namely, if $\varepsilon > 0$, then

$$I_k = (a_k - 2^{-k-1}\varepsilon, a_k + 2^{-k-1}\varepsilon)$$

defines a system of open intervals of total length

$$\sum_k (a_k + \varepsilon 2^{-k-1} - a_k + \varepsilon 2^{-k-1}) = \sum_k \varepsilon 2^{-k} \leq \varepsilon.$$

Thus *we may drop the hypothesis that the $I_k$ be open* in Definition 1.3.4. Namely, if $\{I_k\}$ is a system of intervals with end points $a_k \leq b_k$ that covers $E$ and has a total length less than or equal to $\varepsilon$, and $\{J_\ell\}$ is a system of open intervals of total length less than or equal to $\varepsilon$ that covers $\{a_k, b_k\colon\ k = 1, \cdots\}$, then

$$\{(a_k, b_k), J_\ell\colon\ k \geq 1, \ell \geq 1\}$$

is a system of open intervals of total length less than or equal to $2\varepsilon$ that covers $E$.

The relationship to null sets is made clear by the following proposition.

1.3.5 PROPOSITION *Let E be a set of points on the real line. The following statements are equivalent.*

(a) *E is a null set.*
(b) *E is of measure zero.*
(c) *E is contained in the union of a countable system of open intervals of finite total length, each $x \in E$ belonging to infinitely many intervals of the system.*

*Proof* We show that statement (a) implies (b), (b) implies (c), and (c) implies (a).

Suppose that $E$ is a null set. Let $\{\varphi_n\}$ be an increasing sequence of non-negative step functions such that $\{\varphi_n(x)\}$ diverges for $x \in E$, while

$$\lim_{n\to\infty} \int \varphi_n\, dx = M$$

exists. We may assume that

$$\lim_{n\to\infty} \int \varphi_n \, dx \leq \varepsilon,$$

where $\varepsilon > 0$ is a preassigned number; for if this is not already the case, we replace $\varphi_n$ by $(\varepsilon/M)\varphi_n$. Now let $\psi_n = [\varphi_n]$, the integer part of $\varphi_n$; by definition,

$$\psi_n(x) = m \qquad \text{if} \quad m \leq \varphi_n(x) < m + 1,$$

where $m$ is a nonnegative integer. Again $\{\psi_n\}$ is an increasing sequence of non-negative step functions such that $\{\psi_n(x)\}$ diverges for $x \in E$, while

$$\lim_{n\to\infty} \int \psi_n \, dx \leq \varepsilon,$$

since $\psi_n \leq \varphi_n$ for each $n \geq 1$. For convenience we let $\psi_0 = 0$. The set where $\psi_n - \psi_{n-1}$ is positive, that is, greater than or equal to 1, is a finite system of intervals of total length less than or equal to $\int (\psi_n - \psi_{n-1}) \, dx$. Each $x \in E$ must be contained in one of these intervals for a suitable $n$, because $\psi_n(x) = \psi_{n-1}(x)$ for all $n$ would imply $\psi_n(x) = \psi_0(x) = 0$. Let $\{I_k\}$ be the collection of all these intervals; the system $\{I_k\}$ has a total length less than or equal to

$$\sum_{n=1}^{\infty} \int (\psi_n - \psi_{n-1}) \, dx = \lim_{k\to\infty} \int \psi_k \, dx \leq \varepsilon$$

and $E \subset \bigcup_{k\geq 1} I_k$. This proves that $E$ is of measure zero.

Now suppose that $E$ is of measure zero. For each $n$ let $\{I_{nk}\}$ be a system of open intervals of total length less than or equal to $2^{-n}$ covering $E$. Reorder $I_{nk}$ into a sequence $\{I_l\}$. Then $\{I_l\}$ is a system of open intervals of total length at most $\sum_{n=1}^{\infty} 2^{-n} = 1$ and each $x \in E$ is contained in infinitely many of the $I_l$.

Finally assume $\{I_k\}$ is a system of open intervals of finite total length such that each $x \in E$ is contained in infinitely many of the $I_k$. If $\chi_k$ denotes the characteristic function of $I_k$, then $\sum \chi_k$ is a series of step functions that diverges on $E$, while

$$\sum_{k=1}^{\infty} \int \chi_k \, dx$$

is equal to the total length of the system $\{I_k\}$ and thus is finite.

## *EXERCISES*

*1.3.1* $E$ is a null set if and only if there is a series $\sum \varphi_n$ of nonnegative step functions such that $\sum \varphi_n(x)$ diverges for $x \in E$ and $\sum \int \varphi_n \, dx$ converges.

*1.3.2* Show that if $\sum \varphi_n$ is a series of step functions such that

$$\sum_{n=1}^{\infty} \int |\varphi_n| \, dx < \infty,$$

then the series $\sum \int \varphi_n \, dx$ is absolutely convergent and the series $\sum \varphi_n(x)$ converges absolutely for all $x$ outside some null set $E$.

*1.3.3* For $n \geq 1$, let

$$\varphi_n = \sum_{k=1}^{2^n} \chi_{kn}$$

where $\chi_{kn}$ is the characteristic function of $[k2^{-n}, k2^{-n} + 2^{-2n}]$; prove that $\sum \varphi_n$ diverges at most on a null set.

*1.3.4* Prove that the series $\sum \varphi_n$ of the previous exercise diverges on a set that is everywhere dense in [0, 1], that is, every point $x$ in [0, 1] is the limit of a sequence $\{x_k\}$ in [0, 1] such that $\sum \varphi_n(x_k)$ diverges for all $k$.

*1.3.5* Let $\sum \varphi_n$ be any series of step functions such that $\sum \int |\varphi_n| \, dx$ converges. Show that there is a null set $E$ such that $\lim_{n\to\infty} \varphi_n(x) = 0$ for $x \notin E$.

## 1.4 EXAMPLES

In the following we will discuss four examples of sets, two of which are null sets and two of which are not. They should give some intuitive idea of these concepts.

1.4.1 EXAMPLE *Every countable set $\{a_n : n = 1, \cdots\}$ of points on the real line is a null set.*

In fact, we have already seen in the previous section that, for each $\varepsilon > 0$, $\{a_n : n = 1, \cdots\}$ can be covered by the system

$$(a_n - 2^{-n}\varepsilon, \ a_n + 2^{-n}\varepsilon)$$

of open intervals of total length less than or equal to $2\varepsilon$.

1.4.2 EXAMPLE *No interval $I$ with end points $a < b$ is a null set.*

We have proved this in the beginning of the preceding section just before Definition 1.3.1, where it was shown that an increasing sequence $\{\varphi_n\}$ of step functions, for which $\{\int \varphi_n \, dx\}$ converges, cannot diverge at every point of $(a, b)$.

It seems imperative that an interval $I$ with end points $a < b$ must not be a null set, since, after all, we know that such sets are of consequence even as we define the integral of a step function. Nevertheless, there exist null sets that are non-denumerable and have as many points as an interval. The Cantor set discussed in the following example is such a set.

1.4.3 EXAMPLE: THE CANTOR SET The Cantor set may be defined using ternary expansions. A *ternary expansion* is formally written

$$0 \cdot a_1 a_2 \cdots a_k \cdots$$

where $a_k = 0$, 1, or 2. Such a ternary expansion represents the number to which the series

$$a = \sum_{k=1}^{\infty} a_k 3^{-k}$$

converges. This is a number in the unit interval [0, 1], since

$$0 \leq \sum_{k=1}^{\infty} a_k 3^{-k} \leq \sum_{k=1}^{\infty} 2 \cdot 3^{-k} = 2 \cdot \frac{3^{-1}}{1 - 3^{-1}} = 1.$$

Conversely, every number in [0, 1] admits at least one ternary expansion. For instance, 1 has the expansion

$$1 = 0 \cdot 222 \cdots .$$

If $a$ is any number in [0, 1] different from 1, we can construct the ternary expansion of $a$ in a way similar to the decimal expansion of $a$. The numbers $a_k$ are defined by induction in the following way: $a_1$ is the largest integer smaller than or equal to $3 \cdot a$; if $a_1, \cdots, a_k$ have been defined, let

$$a^k = \sum_{n=1}^{k} a_n \cdot 3^{-n};$$

$a_{k+1}$ is then the largest integer smaller than or equal to

$$3^{k+1}(a - a^k).$$

It is easily checked that the $a_k$ can only be integers 0, 1, or 2, and that the ternary expansion $0 \cdot a_1 a_2 \cdots$ represents $a$ (Exercise 1.4.2). One number can have two different ternary expansions; for instance,

$$0 \cdot 0222 \cdots \qquad \text{and} \qquad 0 \cdot 1000 \cdots$$

represent the same number $3^{-1}$. But this is the only type of ambiguity (Exercise 1.4.3).

Similarly, each number in [0, 1] has a binary expansion

$$0 \cdot b_1 b_2 \cdots b_k \cdots$$

where $b_k$ is either 0 or 1. This expansion represents the number

$$\sum_{k=1}^{\infty} b_k 2^{-k}.$$

The Cantor set is the set of real numbers in [0, 1] that admit ternary expansions $0 \cdot a_1 a_2 \cdots a_k \cdots$ where $a_k$ is either 0 or 2. A real number can have only one such expansion, since if a number has two ternary expansions, one of them contains a 1.

Now we define a mapping $f$ from the Cantor set onto the interval [0, 1] to show that the Cantor set contains at least as many elements as [0, 1]. We let

$$f(0 \cdot a_1 a_2 \cdots a_k \cdots) = 0 \cdot b_1 b_2 \cdots b_k \cdots$$

where the right-hand side is a binary expansion with

$$b_k = 0 \text{ if } a_k = 0, \qquad b_k = 1 \text{ if } a_k = 2.$$

To prove that the Cantor set is a null set we use Proposition 1.3.5. For each $n$, the union of the $2^n$ disjoint intervals

$$[0 \cdot a_1 a_2 \cdots a_n 000 \cdots, 0 \cdot a_1 a_2 \cdots a_n 222 \cdots]$$

$$a_1, a_2, \cdots, a_n = 0 \quad \text{or} \quad 2$$

cover the Cantor set (see Figure 1.7). The length of each of these intervals is $3^{-n}$, so the total length is $2^n \cdot 3^{-n} = (2/3)^{-n}$. Since $n$ was arbitrary, we can find

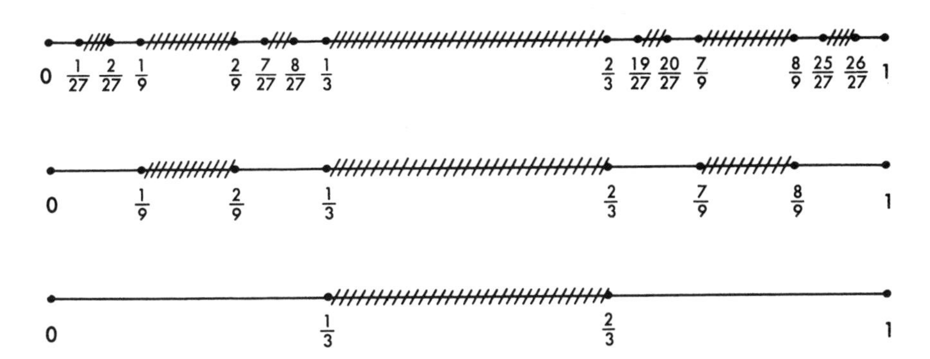


Figure 1.7 The numbers in the interval $(1/3, 2/3)$ do not belong to the Cantor set $C$, since their ternary expansions begin at 0.1; this is indicated by shading in the diagram. The numbers in $(1/9, 2/9)$ and $(7/9, 8/9)$ do not belong to $C$ either because their ternary expansions begin at $0.a_1 1$, and so forth. Thus, if we shade in each step the middle thirds of the unshaded intervals, we obtain the Cantor set as the set of points that do not lie in any shaded portion of $[0, 1]$.

coverings of arbitrarily small total length. This proves that the Cantor set is a null set.

1.4.4 EXAMPLE *The following set will be referred to again later on. It is not only too large to be a null set but has other unpleasant properties that make it wholly unfit for the theory of integration.*

Call two real numbers $a$ and $b$ equivalent if $a - b$ is a rational number. Then the set

$$K_a = \{x : a - x \text{ is rational}\}$$

consists of all numbers equivalent to $a$. Every real number $x$ belongs to some set $K_a$, namely, $x \in K_x$. For any real numbers $a$ and $b$, $K_a$ is either the same as $K_b$ or $K_a$ and $K_b$ are disjoint sets. Suppose that $K_a$ and $K_b$ are not disjoint; then there is an $x \in K_a \cap K_b$. If $y \in K_a$, there exist rational numbers $r_1, r_2, r_3$ such that

$$a - x = r_1, \qquad b - x = r_2, \qquad a - y = r_3.$$

But then

$$b - y = r_3 - r_1 + r_2$$

which is a rational number, whence $y \in K_b$. This shows $K_a \subset K_b$, and similarly we find $K_b \subset K_a$. Thus indeed

$$K_a = K_b \qquad \text{or} \qquad K_a \cap K_b = \varnothing .$$

Now pick out of each of the different sets $K_a$ one representative and call the set thus obtained $K$. For this construction of $K$ we have just employed the so-called *axiom of choice* which permits us to form a set ($K$ in this case) by picking one element out of each set of a family of sets. For a discussion of the axiom of choice see the Bibliographical Comment on Chapter 3 at the end of the book. We claim now that $K$ cannot be a null set. To prove this, let

$$r_1, r_2, \cdots$$

be an enumeration of the rational numbers. Then the union of the sets

$$r_k + K = \{y : y = r_k + x \text{ for some } x \in K\}$$

is the real line, because each real number $y$ belongs to one $K_a$ and $K$ contains an element $x \in K_a$ and thus $y = r_k + x$ for some rational number $r_k$. If $K$ were a null set, each of the sets $r_k + K$ would also be a null set. Namely, if $\{(a_j, b_j)\}$ is a system of open intervals of total length less than or equal to $\varepsilon$ that covers $K$, then

$$\{(r_k + a_j, r_k + b_j)\}$$

is a system of intervals covering $r_k + K$ and having total length at most $\varepsilon$. Thus if $K$ were a null set,

$$\bigcup_{k=1}^{\infty} (r_k + K)$$

which is the whole real line, would be a null set, too, by Proposition 1.3.3. This is certainly impossible, and $K$ is therefore not a null set.

## *EXERCISES*

*1.4.1* Which of the following sets is a null set and which is not?
(a) The rational numbers in [0, 1];
(b) the irrational numbers in [0, 1].

*1.4.2* Let $a$ be any number in [0, 1] different from 1. Define a sequence of numbers $\{a_k\}$ by induction on $k$ in the following way: $a_1$ is the largest integer smaller than or equal to $3a$; if $a_1, \cdots, a_k$ have been defined, let

$$a^k = \sum_{n=1}^{k} a_n \cdot 3^{-n}.$$

Then $a_{k+1}$ is the largest integer smaller than or equal to $3^{k+1}(a - a^k)$. Prove by induction on $k$

$$a_k < 3 \qquad \text{and} \qquad 3^k(a - a^k) < 1,$$

and derive from this that $\{a^k\}$ converges to $a$.

*1.4.3* Let $a$ be any number in $[0, 1]$ different from 1 and $0 \cdot a_1 a_2 \cdots a_k \cdots$ be its ternary expansion constructed in the previous exercise. Suppose $a$ has another ternary expansion $0 \cdot c_1 c_2 \cdots c_k \cdots$. Prove that there is a $k$ such that

$$c_1 = a_1, \cdots, c_{k-1} = a_{k-1}, \qquad a_k - c_k = 1$$
$$c_j = 2, \qquad a_j = 0 \qquad \text{for} \qquad j > k.$$

*Hint* Let $k$ be the smallest integer such that $a_k \neq c_k$. Then $a_k > c_k$ by the construction of $a_k$ and thus

$$a_k + \sum_{j=1}^{\infty} a_{k+j} 3^{-j} = c_k + \sum_{j=1}^{\infty} c_{k+j} 3^{-j},$$

or

$$a_k - c_k + \sum_{j=1}^{\infty} a_{k+j} 3^{-j} = \sum_{j=1}^{\infty} c_{k+j} 3^{-j}.$$

The left-hand side is at least 1, while the right-hand side is at most 1.

*1.4.4* Prove that the set of numbers in $[0, 1]$ that admit a decimal expansion $0 \cdot d_1 d_2 \cdots d_k \cdots$ with $d_k \neq 5$ for all $k$ is a null set.

*1.4.5* Show that one can construct the set $K$ in Example 1.4.4 as a subset of $[0, 1)$.

## 1.5 CONVERGENCE ALMOST EVERYWHERE

We adapt ourselves now to disregard null sets and what happens when using them, since null sets will be irrelevant for most considerations. Nevertheless, to make all statements precise, we introduce the following nomenclature.

**1.5.1 DEFINITION** *If some property holds for all real numbers $x$ outside some null set, this property is said to hold almost everywhere (abbreviated a.e.), or it is said to hold for almost all $x$ (abbreviated a.a.$x$).*

For instance, if $\{\varphi_n\}$ is an increasing sequence of step functions such that $\{\int \varphi_n \, dx\}$ converges, then

$$\{\varphi_n\} \qquad \text{converges a.e.}$$

or

$$\{\varphi_n(x)\} \qquad \text{converges for a.a.}x,$$

by the very definition of a null set (Definition 1.3.1).

**1.5.2 DEFINITION** *If a function on the real line vanishes almost everywhere, then this function is called a null function. Two functions on the real line that differ by a null function are called equivalent.*

As an application of these concepts and in preparation of the next chapter, we now generalize the continuity property (4) (Theorem 1.2.8) and derive some consequences of it.

**1.5.3 THEOREM** *Suppose $\{\varphi_n\}$ is a decreasing sequence of nonnegative step functions, $\varphi_n \geq \varphi_{n+1} \geq 0$, such that*

$$\lim_{n\to\infty} \varphi_n(x) = 0$$

*for almost all $x$. Then*

$$\lim_{n\to\infty} \int \varphi_n \, dx = 0.$$

*Proof* Let $E$ be a null set such that

$$\lim_{n\to\infty} \varphi_n(x) = 0 \qquad \text{for } x \notin E.$$

We can find an increasing sequence $\{\psi_n\}$ of nonnegative step functions that diverges to infinity on $E$, while

$$M = \lim_{n\to\infty} \int \psi_n \, dx$$

exists. The sequence $\{\eta_n\}$ of step functions defined by

$$\eta_n = (\varphi_n - \varepsilon\psi_n)^+$$

is decreasing for any $\varepsilon > 0$ and satisfies

$$\lim_{n\to\infty} \eta_n(x) = 0$$

for all $x$. Therefore we can apply Theorem 1.2.8, yielding

$$\lim_{n\to\infty} \int \eta_n \, dx = 0.$$

We have the inequality

$$\varphi_n = (\varphi_n - \varepsilon\psi_n) + \varepsilon\psi_n \leq \eta_n + \varepsilon\psi_n$$

and therefore

$$\lim_{n\to\infty} \int \varphi_n \, dx \leq \lim_{n\to\infty} \int \eta_n \, dx + \lim_{n\to\infty} \int \varepsilon\psi_n \, dx$$

$$\leq \varepsilon \lim_{n\to\infty} \int \psi_n \, dx = \varepsilon M.$$

Since $\varepsilon$ was arbitrary, we obtain $\lim_{n\to\infty} \int \varphi_n \, dx = 0.$

**1.5.4 COROLLARY** *Let $\psi \in L$ be a step function and suppose $\sum \varphi_n$ is a series of nonnegative step functions such that*

$$\sum_{n=1}^{\infty} \varphi_n \geq \psi \quad \text{a.e.}$$

*Then*

$$\sum_{n=1}^{\infty} \int \varphi_n \, dx \geq \int \psi \, dx.$$

Here we make the convention that the sum of a divergent series of nonnegative numbers is $\infty$, and $\infty > a$ for all real numbers $a$. The statement of the corollary is trivial if $\sum \int \varphi_n \, dx$ diverges. Thus we may assume in the proof that $\sum \int \varphi_n \, dx$ converges.

*Proof* The sequence $\{\eta_n\}$ of step functions

$$\eta_n = \left(\psi - \sum_{k=1}^{n} \varphi_k\right)^+$$

is decreasing and satisfies

$$\lim_{n \to \infty} \eta_n(x) = 0$$

for almost all $x$. Thus by the previous theorem

$$\lim_{n \to \infty} \int \eta_n \, dx = 0.$$

We have the inequality

$$\psi = \left(\psi - \sum_{k=1}^{n} \varphi_k\right) + \sum_{k=1}^{n} \varphi_k \leq \eta_n + \sum_{k=1}^{n} \varphi_k$$

and thus

$$\begin{aligned} \int \psi \, dx &\leq \int \eta_n \, dx + \sum_{k=1}^{n} \int \varphi_k \, dx \\ &\leq \int \eta_n \, dx + \sum_{k=1}^{\infty} \int \varphi_k \, dx. \end{aligned}$$

Letting $n$ tend to infinity, we obtain the desired result:

$$\int \psi \, dx \leq \sum_{k=1}^{\infty} \int \varphi_k \, dx.$$

1.5.5 COROLLARY *Let $\sum \varphi_n$ be a series of step functions such that $\sum_{n=1}^{\infty} \varphi_n = 0$ almost everywhere. Suppose that $\sum \int |\varphi_n| \, dx$ converges, then*

$$\sum_{n=1}^{\infty} \int \varphi_n \, dx = 0.$$

*Proof* The series $\sum |\varphi_n|$ converges almost everywhere. Since $\varphi_n^+ \leq |\varphi_n|$ and $\varphi_n^- \leq |\varphi_n|$, $\sum \varphi_n^+$ and $\sum \varphi_n^-$ also converge absolutely almost everywhere. Furthermore,

$$0 = \sum_{n=1}^{\infty} \varphi_n = \sum_{n=1}^{\infty} (\varphi_n^+ - \varphi_n^-) = \sum_{n=1}^{\infty} \varphi_n^+ - \sum_{n=1}^{\infty} \varphi_n^- \quad \text{a.e.}$$

Thus for each $m$,

$$\sum_{n=1}^{\infty} \varphi_n^+ \geq \sum_{n=1}^{m} \varphi_n^- \qquad \text{a.e.}$$

Now we can apply Corollary 1.5.4, which yields

$$\sum_{n=1}^{\infty} \int \varphi_n^+ \, dx \geq \sum_{n=1}^{m} \int \varphi_n^- \, dx. \tag{1.5.6}$$

The series $\sum \int \varphi_n^+ \, dx$ and $\sum \int \varphi_n^- \, dx$ both converge; namely, $\varphi_n^+ \leq |\varphi_n|$, $\varphi_n^- \leq |\varphi_n|$, and therefore

$$\sum_{n=1}^{\infty} \int \varphi_n^+ \, dx \leq \sum_{n=1}^{\infty} \int |\varphi_n| \, dx < \infty,$$

$$\sum_{n=1}^{\infty} \int \varphi_n^- \, dx \leq \sum_{n=1}^{\infty} \int |\varphi_n| \, dx < \infty.$$

Hence we can pass to the limit in (1.5.6) and we obtain

$$\sum_{n=1}^{\infty} \int \varphi_n^+ \, dx \geq \sum_{n=1}^{\infty} \int \varphi_n^- \, dx.$$

Interchanging the roles of $\varphi_n^+$ and $\varphi_n^-$ we obtain the opposite inequality, so we have in fact

$$\sum_{n=1}^{\infty} \int \varphi_n^+ \, dx = \sum_{n=1}^{\infty} \int \varphi_n^- \, dx.$$

This implies finally,

$$0 = \sum_{n=1}^{\infty} \int \varphi_n^+ \, dx - \sum_{n=1}^{\infty} \int \varphi_n^- \, dx = \sum_{n=1}^{\infty} \int \varphi_n \, dx.$$

The preceding theorem and its corollaries dealt with convergent sequences and series of integrals. There is one important lesson that can be learned from them. In each theorem there is given a sequence or series of functions and a relation that holds almost everywhere, and the conclusion is that a similar relation will hold for the integrals provided one additional hypothesis is satisfied; in Theorem 1.5.3, for instance, this additional hypothesis is the requirement that the sequence $\{\varphi_n\}$ be decreasing. Such an additional assumption is absolutely vital to insure the desired result, but the type of additional assumption may vary much and it will be the task to find one that will place as weak a restriction on the sequence or series as possible. This will be done in the next chapter after we have extended the definition of the integral to a more general class of functions.

## *EXERCISES*

*1.5.1* Show that the set $N$ of null functions is a vector space, that is, if $f$ and $g$ belong to $N$ and $a$, $b$ are real numbers, then $af + bg \in N$. Prove also that $f \wedge g$ and $f \vee g$ belong to $N$ if both $f$ and $g$ do.

*1.5.2* Prove that the vector space $N$ is in fact an ideal in the ring of all functions; that is, if $f \in N$ and $g$ is any function, then $fg \in N$.

*1.5.3* Let $\{f_n\}$ be a sequence of null functions. Prove that $\sum f_n$ converges almost everywhere to 0.

*1.5.4* Let $\{\varphi_n\}$ be an increasing sequence of step functions and $\psi$ any step function such that $\lim_{n\to\infty} \varphi_n(x) \geq \psi(x)$ for almost all $x$. Prove that $\lim_{n\to\infty} \int \varphi_n \, dx \geq \int \psi \, dx$.

*1.5.5* Let $\{\varphi_n\}$ be an increasing sequence of step functions such that $\lim_{n\to\infty} \varphi_n(x) \geq 1$ for almost all $x$. Prove that the sequence $\{\int \varphi_n \, dx\}$ diverges to infinity.

# 1.6 EXERCISES

## A. Step Functions and Their Integral

1.6.1 Let $I$ and $J$ be intervals. Express the characteristic functions of

$$\text{(a) } I \cup J, \quad \text{(b) } I \cap J, \quad \text{(c) } I - J, \quad \text{(d) } I \triangle J$$

in terms of $\chi_I$ and $\chi_J$. ($I - J$ is the set of points in $I$ that do not belong to $J$;

$$I \triangle J = (I \cup J) - (I \cap J)$$

is called the symmetric difference of $I$ and $J$.)

1.6.2 Prove that the product of two step functions is again a step function.

1.6.3 For any step function $\varphi$ and real number $h$ define the functions $\varphi_h$ and $\check{\varphi}$ by

$$\varphi_h(x) = \varphi(x + h), \qquad \check{\varphi}(x) = \varphi(-x).$$

Prove that $\varphi_h$ and $\check{\varphi}$ are again step functions.

1.6.4 For any step function $\varphi$ and real number $k \neq 0$ define the function ${}_k\varphi$ by

$${}_k\varphi(x) = \varphi(kx).$$

Prove that ${}_k\varphi$ is again a step function.

1.6.5 Let

$$\varphi_n(x) = \begin{cases} 0 & \text{if } x \notin [0, 1] \\ 1 & \text{if } x \in [0, 1] \text{ and } [2^n x] \text{ is even} \\ -1 & \text{if } x \in [0, 1] \text{ and } [2^n x] \text{ is odd.} \end{cases}$$

Prove that the $\varphi_n$ are step functions and that

$$\int \varphi_n \varphi_k \, dx = \begin{cases} 0 & \text{if } n \neq k \\ 1 & \text{if } n = k. \end{cases}$$

1.6.6 Prove $\int \varphi_h \, dx = \int \varphi \, dx$ and $\int \check{\varphi} \, dx = \int \varphi \, dx$ for $\varphi \in L$ (see 1.6.3).

*Hint* Prove this first for characteristic functions of closed intervals.

1.6.7 Prove $|k| \cdot \int {}_k\varphi \, dx = \int \varphi \, dx$ for $\varphi \in L$ and $k \neq 0$ (see 1.6.4).

*Hint* Prove this first for characteristic functions of closed intervals.

1.6.8 Prove $\lim_{h \to 0} \int |\varphi_h - \varphi| \, dx = 0$ (see 1.6.3).

*Hint* Prove this first for characteristic functions of open intervals.

1.6.9 Prove $\lim_{k \to 1} \int |{}_k\varphi - \varphi| \, dx = 0$ (see 1.6.4 and 1.6.7).

*Hint* Prove this first for characteristic functions of open intervals.

## B. Null Sets

1.6.10 Let $E$ be a null set. Why is $R - E$ not a null set?

1.6.11 Let $E$ be a null set; prove that

$$\{x : x - y \text{ is rational for some } y \in E\}$$

is again a null set.

1.6.12 Let $E$ be a null set. Prove that $h + E$ and $kE$ are again null sets for any real numbers $h$ and $k$ (see Exercises 1.6.6 and 1.6.7).

1.6.13 Let $E$ be a null set. Prove that $E^2 = \{x^2 : x \in E\}$ is a null set.

*Hint* Suppose first that $E$ is contained in the bounded interval $[0, c]$ and observe that $|b^2 - a^2| \leq 2c\,|b - a|$ for $a, b \in [0, c]$. Use Proposition 1.3.5.

1.6.14

(a) Let $E$ be a null set and $f$ a differentiable function with bounded derivative, that is, there is a constant $C \geq 0$ such that $|f'(x)| \leq C$ for all $x$. Prove that the set

$$f(E) = \{y : y = f(x) \text{ for some } x \in E\}$$

is a null set.

*Hint* Use the mean value theorem to prove $M - m \leq C(b - a)$ if $M$ is the maximum and $m$ the minimum of the continuous function $f$ on the closed bounded interval $[a, b]$. Then use Proposition 1.3.5.

(b) Let $E$ be a null set and $f$ a continuously differentiable function. Prove that $f(E)$ is a null set.

*Hint* $f'$ is bounded on every interval, so the hint for (a) is useful.

## C. Convergence

**1.6.15** Let $\varphi$, $\varphi_n$, $\psi$ be step functions and suppose $\{\varphi_n\}$ is an increasing sequence such that $\lim_{n\to\infty} \varphi_n(x) = \varphi(x)$ for all $x$. Prove that

$$\lim_{n\to\infty} \int \psi\varphi_n \, dx = \int \psi\varphi \, dx.$$

**1.6.16** Suppose $\{\varphi_n\}$ is a decreasing sequence of nonnegative step functions such that $\lim_{n\to\infty} \int \varphi_n \, dx = 0$. Prove that $\{\varphi_n\}$ tends to zero almost everywhere.

*Hint* Choose a subsequence $\{\varphi_{n(k)}\}$ with

$$\int \varphi_{n(k)} \, dx \leq 2^{-k}$$

and then consider $\sum_k \varphi_{n(k)}$. This series diverges at $x$ if $\{\varphi_n(x)\}$ does not converge to zero.

**1.6.17** Let $\{\varphi_n\}$ be an increasing sequence of step functions such that

$$\left\{x\colon \lim_{n\to\infty} \varphi_n(x) > 0\right\}$$

is not a null set. Prove that

$$\lim_{n\to\infty} \int \varphi_n \, dx > 0$$

if $\lim_{n\to\infty} \varphi_n(x) \geq 0$ for all $x$.

**1.6.18** Let $\sum \varphi_n$ be a series of nonnegative step functions. Suppose there is a step function $\varphi$ such that

$$\left\{x\colon \sum_{n=1}^{\infty} \varphi_n(x) > \varphi(x)\right\}$$

is not a null set. Prove that

$$\sum_{n=1}^{\infty} \int \varphi_n \, dx > \int \varphi \, dx$$

if $\sum_{n=1}^{\infty} \varphi_n(x) \geq \varphi(x)$ for all $x$.

**1.6.19** Let $\sum \varphi_n$ be a series of step functions such that $\sum \int |\varphi_n|\, dx$ converges. Suppose $\sum_{n=1}^{\infty} \varphi_n \geq 0$ almost everywhere. Prove that $\sum_{n=1}^{\infty} \int \varphi_n\, dx \geq 0$.

*Hint* Prove first

$$-\sum_{n=m}^{\infty} \int |\varphi_n|\, dx \leq \sum_{n=1}^{m-1} \int \varphi_n\, dx,$$

using Corollary 1.5.4.

**1.6.20** Let $\{\varphi_n\}$ be the sequence of step functions defined in Exercise 1.6.5. Prove that

$$\left\{\frac{1}{n^2} \sum_{k=1}^{n^2} \varphi_k\right\}$$

tends to zero almost everywhere.

*Hint* Prove first that

$$\int \left(\frac{1}{n^2} \sum_{k=1}^{n^2} \varphi_k\right)^2 dx = \frac{1}{n^2},$$

using Exercise 1.6.5, and then show that

$$\sum_n \left(\frac{1}{n^2} \sum_{k=1}^{n^2} \varphi_k\right)^2$$

diverges at most on a null set (see Exercise 1.3.5).

*Remark* It follows from the above exercise that in fact

$$\left\{\frac{1}{m} \sum_{k=1}^{m} \varphi_k\right\}$$

tends to zero almost everywhere because we have for $n^2 < m \leq (n+1)^2$,

$$\begin{aligned}
\left|\frac{1}{m} \sum_{k=1}^{m} \varphi_k - \frac{1}{n^2} \sum_{k=1}^{n^2} \varphi_k\right| &\leq \left|\frac{1}{m} \sum_{k=1}^{m} \varphi_k - \frac{1}{m} \sum_{k=1}^{n^2} \varphi_k\right| + \left|\frac{1}{m} \sum_{k=1}^{n^2} \varphi_k - \frac{1}{n^2} \sum_{k=1}^{n^2} \varphi_k\right| \\
&\leq \frac{1}{m}(m - n^2) + \left|\frac{1}{m} - \frac{1}{n^2}\right| n^2 \\
&\leq \frac{1}{n^2}((n+1)^2 - n^2) + \left(\frac{1}{n^2} - \frac{1}{(n+1)^2}\right) n^2 \\
&= \frac{2n+1}{n^2} + \frac{2n+1}{(n+1)^2}
\end{aligned}$$

which tends to zero as $n$ tends to infinity. Let

$$x_k = \tfrac{1}{2}(1 - \varphi_k(x));$$

it is easily checked that $0 \cdot x_1 x_2 \cdots x_k \cdots$ is a binary expansion of $x$ for each $x$ in $[0, 1)$. We have

$$\frac{1}{m}\sum_{k=1}^{m} \varphi_k(x) = \frac{1}{m}\sum_{k=1}^{m}(1 - 2x_k)$$
$$= 1 - \frac{2}{m}\sum_{k=1}^{m} x_k.$$

Thus

$$\lim_{m \to \infty} \frac{1}{m}\sum_{k=1}^{m} x_k = \frac{1}{2}$$

for almost all $x$. Expressed in words this means that *for a.a.* $x \in [0, 1)$ *the frequency of occurrence of the figure* 1 *in a binary expansion of* $x$ *is* ½ *or equal to the frequency of occurrence of the figure* 0. *Thus the set of points in* $[0, 1)$ *with a binary expansion in which the occurrences of* 1 *and* 0 *is disproportionate, is a null set.*

## D. Piecewise Linear Functions

In the following exercises we let $\varphi$ and $\psi$ denote piecewise linear functions instead of step functions, suspending our earlier convention for the moment. A *piecewise linear function* $\varphi$ has the following property: there is a finite sequence of points $a_0 \leq a_1 \leq \cdots \leq a_n$ and numbers $c_1, \cdots, c_{n-1}$ such that with $c_0 = c_n = 0$,

$$\varphi(x) = \begin{cases} 0 & \text{for } x \leq a_0 \text{ and } x \geq a_n \\ c_k & \text{for } x = a_k,\ 1 \leq k \leq n-1 \\ \dfrac{(a_k - x)c_{-1} + (x - a_{k-1})c_k}{a_k - a_{k-1}} & \text{for } a_{k-1} < x < a_k,\ 1 \leq k \leq n. \end{cases}$$

A piecewise linear function is thus a continuous function. It is linear on the intervals $[a_{k-1}, a_k]$. The sequence $(a_0, \cdots, a_n;\ c_1, \cdots, c_{n-1})$ may be called a presentation for $\varphi$ as a piecewise linear function (see Figure 1.8).

1.6.21 Show that the definition

$$\int \varphi\, dx = \sum_{k=1}^{n} \frac{(c + c_{k-1})(a_k - a_{k-1})}{2}$$

of the integral of the piecewise linear function $\varphi$ is independent of the presentation $(a_0, \cdots, a_n;\ c_1, \cdots, c_{n-1})$ for $\varphi$.

1.6.22 Show that the set of all piecewise linear functions is a vector space and that $\varphi \vee \psi$ and $\varphi \wedge \psi$ are piecewise linear functions if $\varphi$ and $\psi$ are.

1.6.23 Show that

$$\int (a\varphi + b\psi)\, dx = a\int \varphi\, dx + b\int \psi\, dx$$

if $\varphi$ and $\psi$ are piecewise linear functions and $a, b$ are real numbers; also show that $\int \varphi \, dx \geq 0$ if $\varphi \geq 0$.

**1.6.24** Show that if $\{\varphi_n\}$ is a decreasing sequence of nonnegative piecewise linear functions such that

$$\lim_{n\to\infty} \varphi_n(x) = 0$$

for all $x$, then

$$\lim_{n\to\infty} \int \varphi_n \, dx = 0.$$

*Hint* Let $M_n$ be the maximum value of $\varphi_n$; prove that $\lim_{n\to\infty} M_n = 0$ (see the proof of Lemma 1.2.9).

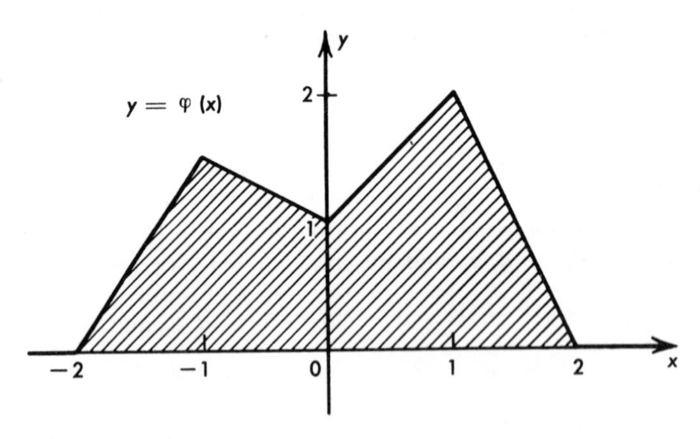


Figure 1.8 This is the graph of the piecewise linear function $\varphi$ with presentation $(-2, -1, 0, 1, 2;\ 3/2, 1, 2)$. Since $\varphi$ is nonnegative, $\int \varphi \, dx$ is just the area under the graph.

**1.6.25** Show that a subset $E$ of the real line is a null set (in the sense of Definition 1.3.1, using step functions) if and only if there is an increasing sequence $\{\varphi_n\}$ of piecewise linear functions such that $\{\varphi_n(x)\}$ diverges for each $x \in E$ and $\{\int |\varphi_n| \, dx\}$ converges.

*Hint* Let $E$ be any set. Show first that the following two statements are equivalent:

(a) There is an increasing sequence $\{\varphi_n\}$ of piecewise linear functions such that $\{\varphi_n(x)\}$ diverges for $x \in E$ and $\{\int \varphi_n \, dx\}$ converges.

(b) There is a series $\sum \varphi_n$ of nonnegative piecewise linear functions such that $\sum \varphi_n(x)$ diverges for $x \in E$ and $\sum \int \varphi_n \, dx$ converges.

Actually, you have only to copy the proof of Proposition 1.3.8. Now show that (b) holds if and only if $E$ is a null set, that is, if and only if there is a series $\sum \psi_n$ of nonnegative step functions such that $\sum \psi_n(x)$ diverges for $x \in E$ and $\sum \int \psi_n\, dx$ converges. This is best done with the help of figures (Figure 1.9). If the step functions $\psi_n$ are given and $M_n$ is the maximum value of $\psi_n$, then construct a piecewise linear function $\varphi_n \geq \psi_n$ as indicated by the dotted line in the first of the figures. If the spikes are narrow, you can assure that

$$\varepsilon_n = \int \varphi_n\, dx - \int \psi_n\, dx$$

is small. How small do you have to make $\varepsilon_n$? The second of the figures shows you how to construct a step function $\psi_n$ from a piecewise linear function $\varphi_n$ with the

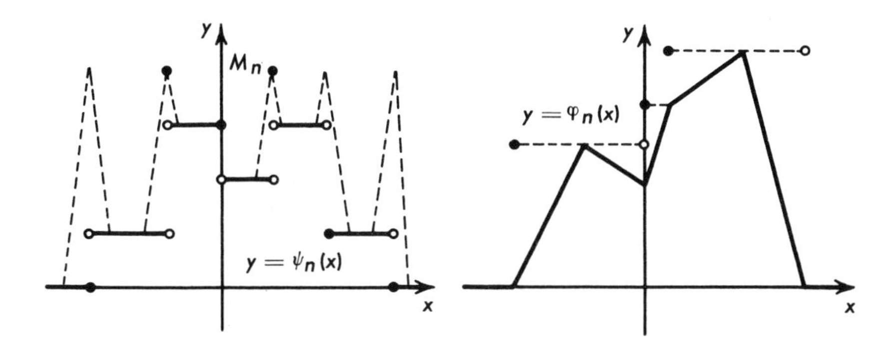


Figure 1.9 The dotted lines in the first diagram indicate how to find a piecewise linear function $\varphi_n \geq \psi_n$ for which $\int \varphi_n\, dx - \int \psi_n\, dx$ is small. The second diagram shows how to find a step function $\psi_n \geq \varphi_n$ such that $\int \psi_n\, dx \leq 2 \int \varphi_n\, dx$.

properties $\varphi_n \leq \psi_n$ and

$$\int \psi_n\, dx \leq 2 \int \varphi_n\, dx.$$

1.6.26 Prove Theorem 1.5.3 and Corollaries 1.5.4 and 1.5.5 for piecewise linear functions. Compare the unhindered transcription of their proofs from the corresponding proofs for step functions ("soft" or "abstract" results) with the not so complete similarity in Exercises 1.6.22 through 1.6.24 ("hard" or "concrete" results).

1.6.27 Let $\eta$ and $\zeta$ be step functions; define a new function $\eta * \zeta$ by

$$\eta * \zeta(a) = \int \check{\eta}_{-a} \zeta\, dx$$

where $\check{\eta}_{-a}(x) = \eta(a - x)$ (see Exercises 1.6.3 and 1.6.2). Prove that $\eta * \zeta$ is a piecewise linear function and that $\eta * \zeta = \zeta * \eta$.

*Hint* Prove this first for characteristic functions of open intervals.

1.6.28 Let $\eta$ and $\zeta$ be step functions and define $\eta * \zeta$ as in the preceding exercise. Prove that $\int \eta * \zeta \, dx = \int \eta \, dx \cdot \int \zeta \, dx$.

## SUMMARY

For every step function $\varphi$ on the real line, there is a set of numbers

$$(a_0, \cdots, a_n; \; c_1, \cdots, c_n), \; a_{k-1} \leq a_k,$$

called a presentation for $\varphi$, with this property (Definition 1.1.1):

$$\varphi(x) = \begin{cases} 0 & \text{for } x \notin [a_0, a_n] \\ c_k & \text{for } x \in (a_{k-1}, a_k). \end{cases}$$

A step function is a linear combination of characteristic functions of closed bounded intervals (Corollary 1.1.4); it is also a linear combination of characteristic functions of bounded open intervals (Exercise 1.1.3).

The set of step functions is denoted by $L$.

For a step function $\varphi$ with presentation $(a_0, \cdots, a_n; \; c_1, \cdots, c_n)$, the integral is defined as

$$\int \varphi \, dx = \sum_{k=1}^{n} c_k(a_k - a_{k-1})$$

(Definition 1.1.5). For a nonnegative step function $\varphi$, $\int \varphi \, dx$ is just the area bounded by the graph of $\varphi$ and the $x$-axis.

Basic properties of step functions and their integrals are the following:

(1) If $\varphi, \psi \in L$, then $a\varphi + b\psi$, $\varphi \vee \psi$, $\varphi \wedge \psi$ all belong to $L$ where $a$, $b$ are real numbers (Proposition 1.1.2).

(2) If $\varphi, \psi \in L$, then, for any real numbers $a$, $b$,

$$\int (a\varphi + b\psi) \, dx = a \int \varphi \, dx + b \int \psi \, dx$$

(Proposition 1.2.2).

(3) If $\varphi \in L$ and $\varphi \geq 0$, then $\int \varphi \, dx \geq 0$ (Proposition 1.2.3).

(4) If $\{\varphi_n\}$ is a decreasing sequence of nonnegative $\varphi_n \in L$ and $\lim_{n \to \infty} \varphi_n(x) = 0$ for all $x$, then

$$\lim_{n \to \infty} \int \varphi_n \, dx = 0$$

(Theorem 1.2.8).

Other useful properties of step functions are the following (Corollary 1.2.4):

$$\int \varphi \, dx \le \int \psi \, dx \qquad \text{if } \varphi \le \psi,$$

$$\left| \int \varphi \, dx \right| \le \int |\varphi| \, dx,$$

$$\int \varphi^+ \, dx \le \int |\varphi| \, dx,$$

$$\int \varphi^- \, dx \le \int |\varphi| \, dx.$$

A subset $E$ of the real line is a null set or a negligible set if there is an increasing sequence $\{\varphi_n\}$ of step functions such that $\{\varphi_n(x)\}$ diverges for $x \in E$ and $\{\int \varphi_n \, dx\}$ converges (Definition 1.3.1). The following are equivalent definitions:

(a) There is a series $\sum \varphi_n$ of (nonnegative) step functions such that $\sum \varphi_n(x)$ diverges, while $\sum \int |\varphi_n| \, dx$ converges (Proposition 1.3.2).
(b) For each $\varepsilon > 0$ there is a countable system of (open) intervals of total length less than or equal to $\varepsilon$ that covers $E$ (Proposition 1.3.5).

Every subset of a null set is a null set. The union of a countable number of null sets is again a null set (Proposition 1.3.3). In particular, every countable set is a null set (Example 1.4.1).

A property for points on the real line is said to hold almost everywhere if it holds for all points outside some null set; it is then also said to hold for almost all $x$ (Definition 1.5.1). For instance, Property (4) of the integral for step functions is also valid if one requires the sequence $\{\varphi_n\}$ only to converge to zero almost everywhere (Theorem 1.5.3).

If $\sum \varphi_n$ is a series of step functions such that

$$\sum_{n=1}^{\infty} \varphi_n = 0 \qquad \text{a.e.},$$

$$\sum_{n=1}^{\infty} \int |\varphi_n| \, dx < \infty,$$

then $\sum_{n=1}^{\infty} \int \varphi_n \, dx = 0$ (Corollary 1.5.5).

# 2

# The Lebesgue Integral

Again we begin a chapter with a preliminary section; in this one we recall briefly the procedure that is usually followed in defining the Riemann integral of a continuous function on a closed bounded interval. Actually, this section is included only for comparison. We use a method independent of it when we prove in Section 2.1 that a continuous function on a closed bounded interval is Lebesgue integrable.

The Lebesgue integrable functions are by definition those functions that equal almost everywhere the sum $\sum_{n=1}^{\infty} \varphi_n$ of a series $\sum \varphi_n$ of step functions for which $\sum \int |\varphi_n| \, dx$ converges. This is Beppo Levi's theorem for step functions so that, as so often in mathematics, part of the main theorem is put into a definition. The case in which the $\varphi_n$ are arbitrary Lebesgue integrable functions of course requires some further consideration. Beppo Levi's theorem has as its consequence several theorems on the interchangeability of the integral sign and limit operations.

In Section 2.5 we finally realize that, with the exception of some applications, our theorems and propositions have been proved solely with the help of the basic properties (1) to (4). Thus they apply to any setting where we have a linear space $L$ of "elementary" functions (on some set) for which an integral with the properties (1) to (4) is defined. Such an abstract integral is called a Daniell integral. In addition to the examples in Section 2.5 we shall learn more about the usefulness of this abstract notion in Chapters 4 and 8 where iterated integration and Stieltjes integration are considered.

Section 2.6 on Riemann integration is somewhat out of line with the rest of the chapter. The material in it is not actually needed anywhere; it is included only so the student who has learned about the now-historical concept of Riemann integrable functions can find out about its relation to the concept of Lebesgue integrable functions.

## 2.0 THE RIEMANN INTEGRAL FOR CONTINUOUS FUNCTIONS

Recall that a function $f$ on a closed bounded interval $[a, b]$ is *continuous* if for each $x \in [a, b]$ and $\varepsilon > 0$ there is a $\delta > 0$ such that

$$|f(x) - f(y)| \le \varepsilon \quad \text{if} \quad y \in [a, b] \quad \text{and} \quad |x - y| \le \delta.$$

In this definition $\delta$ may depend on $x$ and $\varepsilon$. However, since the function $f$ is continuous on the closed bounded interval $[a, b]$, it is in fact *uniformly continuous*, meaning that for each $\varepsilon > 0$ there is a $\delta > 0$ (depending only on $\varepsilon$) such that

$$\text{(2.0.1)} \qquad |f(x) - f(y)| \le \varepsilon \quad \text{if} \quad x, y \in [a, b] \quad \text{and} \quad |x - y| \le \delta.$$

This theorem is usually proved in calculus.

The uniform continuity of $f$ on $[a, b]$ is used to give the construction of the Riemann integral $\int_a^b f\,dx$ of $f$ on $[a, b]$. Let us recall the procedure.

To any subdivision $\Delta$ of $[a, b]$,

(2.0.2) $$\Delta:\ a = a_0 < a_1 < \cdots < a_m = b,$$

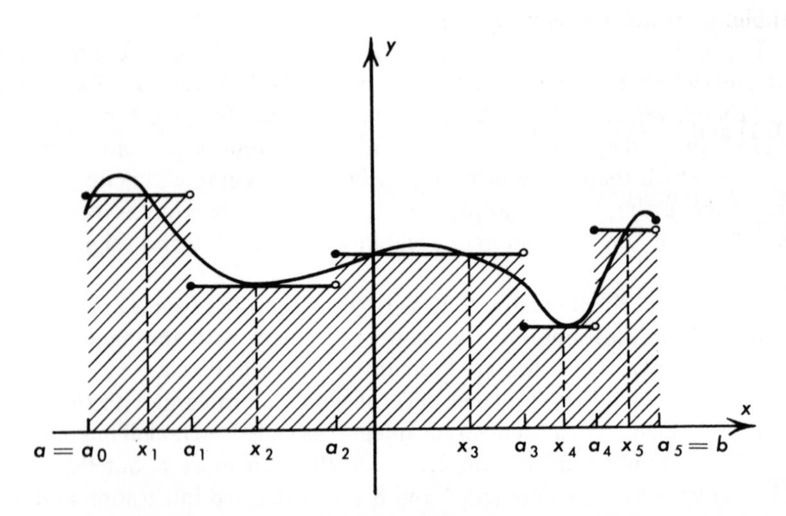


Figure 2.1 The nonnegative continuous function $f$ on $[a, b]$ is approximated by a nonnegative step function $\varphi$ associated with a subdivision of $[a, b]$. The area under the graph of $\varphi$ constitutes a good approximation to $\int_a^b f\,dx$ if the subdivision is chosen fine enough.

one associates a step function $\varphi$ (Figure 2.1) by choosing $x_i \in [a_{i-1}, a_i]$, $1 \leq i \leq m$, arbitrarily and letting

(2.0.3) $$\varphi(x) = \begin{cases} f(x_i) & \text{for } a_{i-1} \leq x < a_i,\ 1 \leq i \leq m \\ f(b) & \text{for } x = b \\ 0 & \text{for } x \notin [a, b]. \end{cases}$$

Denote by $\ell(\Delta)$ the maximum length of the intervals $[a_{i-1}, a_i]$,

$$\ell(\Delta) = \max\{(a_i - a_{i-1}):\ 1 \leq i \leq m\}.$$

2.0.4 PROPOSITION *For each integer $n \geq 1$, let $\Delta_n$ be a subdivision of* $[a, b]$ *and $\varphi_n$ a step function associated with $\Delta_n$. If*

$$\lim_{n\to\infty} \ell(\Delta_n) = 0,$$

*then* $\{\varphi_n\}$ *tends to* $f$ *uniformly on* $[a, b]$, *that is, for each* $\varepsilon > 0$ *there is an integer* $N$ *such that*

$$|f(x) - \varphi_n(x)| \leq \varepsilon \qquad \text{for} \qquad n \geq N \qquad \text{and all} \qquad x \in [a, b].$$

*Proof* First choose $\delta > 0$ such that (2.0.1) holds. Then let $N$ be an integer such that $\ell(\Delta_n) \leq \delta$ for $n \geq N$. If now $n \geq N$ and $\Delta_n$ is the subdivision (2.0.2) and $\varphi_n$ is defined as in (2.0.3), then for $x \in [a_{i-1}, a_i)$,

$$|f(x) - \varphi_n(x)| = |f(x) - f(x_i)| \leq \varepsilon$$

by (2.0.1) and $|f(x) - \varphi_n(x)| = 0 \leq \varepsilon$ if $x = b$. This proves the proposition.

Since $\{\varphi_n\}$ tends uniformly to $f$ on $[a, b]$, $\{\varphi_n\}$ is a uniform Cauchy sequence on $[a, b]$, that is, if $\varepsilon > 0$, there is an integer $N$ such that

$$\text{(2.0.5)} \qquad |\varphi_n(x) - \varphi_m(x)| \leq \varepsilon \qquad \text{for } n, m \geq N \text{ and } x \in [a, b].$$

This follows from the inequality

$$|\varphi_n(x) - \varphi_m(x)| \leq |\varphi_n(x) - f(x)| + |f(x) - \varphi_m(x)|$$

and the fact that $\{\varphi_n\}$ tends uniformly to $f$. The inequality (2.0.5) can also be written

$$|\varphi_n - \varphi_m| \leq \varepsilon\chi_{[a,b]}$$

from which we get

$$\left| \int \varphi_n \, dx - \int \varphi_m \, dx \right| \leq \int |\varphi_n - \varphi_m| \, dx \leq \varepsilon \, (b - a)$$

for $n, m \geq N$. This means that $\{\int \varphi_n \, dx\}$ is a Cauchy sequence, and the limit of $\{\int \varphi_n \, dx\}$ is called the *Riemann integral* of $f$ on $[a, b]$,

$$\int_a^b f \, dx = \lim_{n \to \infty} \int \varphi_n \, dx.$$

It is shown in calculus that this definition of $\int_a^b f \, dx$ does not depend on the particular choice of the sequence $\{\varphi_n\}$ (Exercise 2.0.1).

## *EXERCISES*

*2.0.1* Suppose $\{\psi_n\}$ and $\{\varphi_n\}$ are sequences of step functions that vanish off $[a, b]$. Prove that if $\{\psi_n\}$ and $\{\varphi_n\}$ tend uniformly to $f$ on $[a, b]$, then

$$\lim_{n \to \infty} \int \varphi_n \, dx = \lim_{n \to \infty} \int \psi_n \, dx.$$

*Hint* Prove that $\{\varphi_n - \psi_n\}$ tends uniformly to zero.

## 2.1 LEBESGUE INTEGRABLE FUNCTIONS

In Section 1.3 we have seen that a series $\sum \varphi_n$ of step functions that satisfies

$$\sum_{n=1}^{\infty} \int |\varphi_n| \, dx < \infty \tag{2.1.1}$$

converges almost everywhere, that is, there is a null set $E$ such that

$$\sum \varphi_n(x)$$

converges absolutely for $x \notin E$. For instance, we can take for $E$ the set of all points $x$ such that $\sum |\varphi_n(x)|$ diverges to infinity; $E$ is then a null set by Proposition 1.3.2. From (2.1.1) we conclude that the series of integrals $\sum \int \varphi_n \, dx$ converges absolutely; namely,

$$\sum_{n=1}^{\infty} \left| \int \varphi_n \, dx \right| \leq \sum_{n=1}^{\infty} \int |\varphi_n| \, dx < \infty.$$

Now consider any function $f$ such that

$$f(x) = \sum_{n=1}^{\infty} \varphi_n(x)$$

for almost all $x$. For instance,

$$f(x) = \begin{cases} \displaystyle\sum_{n=1}^{\infty} \varphi_n(x) & \text{for } x \notin E \\ 0 & \text{for } x \in E \end{cases}$$

is such a function. Then one would like to define the integral of $f$ by the equation

$$\int f \, dx = \sum_{n=1}^{\infty} \int \varphi_n \, dx.$$

This, however, poses some problem since there may be another series $\sum \psi_n$ of step functions converging to $f$ almost everywhere and satisfying

$$\sum_{n=1}^{\infty} \int |\psi_n| \, dx < \infty.$$

So we have to show that

$$\sum_{n=1}^{\infty} \int \psi_n \, dx = \sum_{n=1}^{\infty} \int \varphi_n \, dx. \tag{2.1.2}$$

Corollary 1.5.5 can help us out here. We apply it to the series of step functions $\sum (\varphi_n - \psi_n)$, which converges to zero almost everywhere and satisfies

$$\sum_{n=1}^{\infty} \int |\varphi_n - \psi_n| \, dx \leq \sum_{n=1}^{\infty} \left( \int |\varphi_n| \, dx + \int |\psi_n| \, dx \right)$$

$$= \sum_{n=1}^{\infty} \int |\varphi_n| \, dx + \sum_{n=1}^{\infty} \int |\psi_n| \, dx < \infty.$$

Thus we may conclude that

$$0 = \sum_{n=1}^{\infty} \int (\varphi_n - \psi_n) \, dx = \sum_{n=1}^{\infty} \int \varphi_n \, dx - \sum_{n=1}^{\infty} \int \psi_n \, dx,$$

from which (2.1.2) follows immediately. The following definition is therefore meaningful.

**2.1.3 DEFINITION** *A function $f$ on the real line is said to be (Lebesgue) integrable if there is a series $\sum \varphi_n$ of step functions such that*

(a) $\sum_{n=1}^{\infty} \varphi_n(x) = f(x)$ *for a.a.* $x$,
(b) $\sum_{n=1}^{\infty} \int |\varphi_n| \, dx < \infty$.

*The integral of $f$ is then defined by*

$$\int f \, dx = \sum_{n=1}^{\infty} \int \varphi_n \, dx.$$

Of course, every step function $\varphi$ is integrable, since it is equal everywhere to the series $\sum \varphi_n$ where

$$\varphi_1 = \varphi, \qquad \varphi_n = 0 \qquad \text{for } n \geq 2.$$

We have

$$\sum_{n=1}^{\infty} \int \varphi_n \, dx = \int \varphi \, dx$$

so that Definition 2.1.3 coincides with our earlier definition of the integral for a step function.

Instead of using the characterization of null sets by series of step functions in our definition of an integrable function, we might try to use their characterization by increasing sequences of step functions. In fact, we have the following lemma which will be proved again later on in more generality.

**2.1.4 LEMMA** *Suppose $\{\varphi_n\}$ is an increasing sequence of step functions, $\varphi_{n+1} \geq \varphi_n$, such that*

$$\lim_{n \to \infty} \int \varphi_n \, dx = I$$

*exists. Then $\{\varphi_n\}$ converges almost everywhere and, if $f$ is a function with*

$$f = \lim_{n \to \infty} \varphi_n \quad \text{a.e.,}$$

*then $f$ is integrable and*

$$\int f\,dx = \lim_{n\to\infty} \int \varphi_n\,dx = I.$$

*Proof* We know that $\{\varphi_n\}$ converges outside some null set $E$. Let $f$ be any function that equals the limit of $\{\varphi_n\}$ almost everywhere; for instance

$$f(x) = \begin{cases} \lim \varphi_n(x) & \text{for } x \notin E \\ 0 & \text{for } x \in E. \end{cases}$$

We can now define a series $\sum \psi_n$ that converges to $f$ almost everywhere by

$$\psi_1 = \varphi_1, \qquad \psi_n = \varphi_n - \varphi_{n-1} \qquad \text{for } n \geq 2.$$

We have, in fact,

$$\sum_{n=1}^{m} \psi_n = \varphi_m.$$

On the other hand

$$\begin{aligned} \sum_{n=1}^{m} \int |\psi_n|\,dx &= \int |\varphi_1|\,dx + \sum_{n=2}^{m} \int (\varphi_n - \varphi_{n-1})\,dx \\ &= \int |\varphi_1|\,dx + \int \varphi_m\,dx - \int \varphi_1\,dx \\ &\leq \int |\varphi_1|\,dx + I - \int \varphi_1\,dx \end{aligned}$$

where we make use of the hypothesis $\varphi_{n+1} - \varphi_n \geq 0$. This shows that

$$\sum \int |\psi_n|\,dx$$

converges. Hence $f$ is integrable and

$$\int f\,dx = \sum_{n=1}^{\infty} \int \psi_n\,dx = \lim_{m\to\infty} \int \varphi_m\,dx = I.$$

Lemma 2.1.4, however, cannot be used as a definition of integrable functions. Not even every nonnegative integrable function is a limit almost everywhere of an increasing sequence of step functions (Exercise 2.1.3). But one can show that every integrable function can be written as the difference of two nonnegative integrable functions each of which is the limit almost everywhere of an increasing sequence of nonnegative step functions (Exercise 2.1.4). This fact is used by some authors as the basis for an alternate definition of integrable functions.

The last lemma can be employed to prove that a continuous function on a closed bounded interval is Lebesgue integrable, or more precisely as follows.

2.1.5 PROPOSITION *Let $f$ be a function that is continuous on the closed bounded interval $[a, b]$ and which vanishes outside $[a, b]$, then $f$ is Lebesgue integrable and $\int f\,dx$ coincides with the Riemann integral $\int_a^b f\,dx$ of $f$ on $[a, b]$.*

*Proof* Let $\{\psi_n\}$ be the sequence of step functions defined by

$$\psi_n(x) = \begin{cases} f(x_k^n) & \text{for } a + \dfrac{k-1}{2^n}(b-a) \le x < a + \dfrac{k}{2^n}(b-a), \\ & \qquad\qquad k = 1, \cdots, 2^n \\ f(b) & \text{for } x = b \\ 0 & \text{for } x \notin [a, b] \end{cases}$$

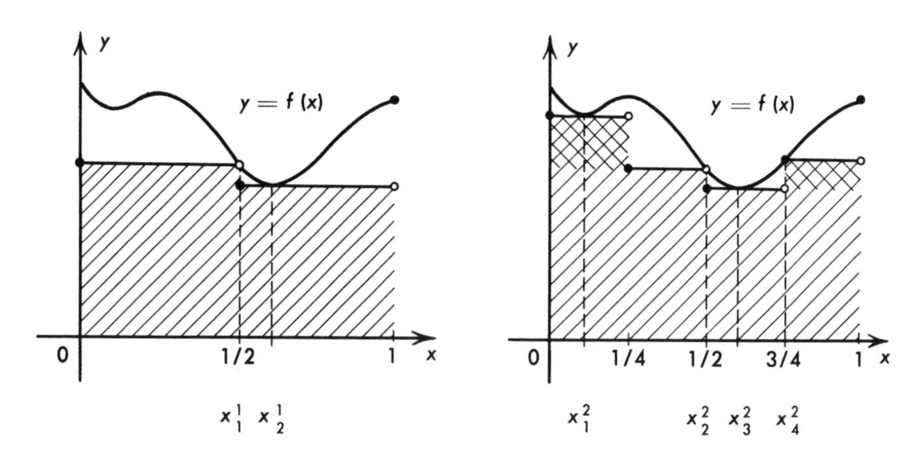


Figure 2.2 The diagrams illustrate the first two terms of the sequence $\{\psi_n\}$ of step functions, which tends increasingly to the continuous function $f$ on $[a, b]$. The area under the graph of $\psi_n$ tends increasingly to $\int f\,dx$.

where $x_k^n$ is any point in the closed interval

(2.1.6) $$[a + (k-1)2^{-n}(b-a), a + k2^{-n}(b-a)]$$

at which $f$ attains its minimum value on that interval (see Figure 2.2). Then $\{\psi_n\}$ is an increasing sequence, since the subdivision

$$a \le a + 2^{-(n+1)}(b-a) \le \cdots \le a + k2^{-(n+1)}(b-a) \le \cdots \le b$$

is obtained from the preceding one by dividing each interval (2.1.6) into two equal parts, and the minimum of $f$ on each of the parts cannot be smaller than the minimum $f(x_k^n)$ on the whole interval. Thus $\{\psi_n\}$ is increasing and it tends to $f$ everywhere,

(2.1.7) $$f(x) = \lim_{n\to\infty} \psi_n(x)$$

for all $x$. One could, of course, cite Proposition 2.0.4 to justify this assertion. Let us, however, present here an alternate proof that does not resort to the concept of uniform continuity.

Certainly, Equation (2.1.7) holds for $x \notin [a, b)$ by the very definition of the $\psi_n$. Now let $x \in [a, b)$ and suppose $\varepsilon > 0$ is given. Since $f$ is continuous on $[a, b]$, we can find a $\delta > 0$ such that

$$|f(x) - f(x')| \leq \varepsilon$$

if $x' \in [a, b]$ and $|x - x'| \leq \delta$. Choose an integer $N$ with

$$2^{-N}(b - a) < \delta.$$

For $n \geq N$, the intervals (2.1.6) have a length less than $\delta$. If say,

$$x \in [a + (k - 1)2^{-n}(b - a), a + k2^{-n}(b - a)),$$

then $\varphi_n(x) = f(x_k^n)$ where $x_k^n$ belongs to the interval (2.1.6). Thus $|x - x_k^n| \leq \delta$ and therefore

$$|f(x) - \varphi_n(x)| = |f(x) - f(x_k^n)| \leq \varepsilon$$

for $n \geq N$. This proves (2.1.7).

The step functions $\psi_n$ are all bounded by $M\chi_{[a,b]}$ where $M$ is the maximum of $f$ on $[a, b]$. Consequently

$$\int \psi_n \, dx \leq M(b - a)$$

and $\{\int \psi_n \, dx\}$ converges. Therefore $f$ is integrable by Lemma 2.1.4 and

$$\int f \, dx = \lim_{n \to \infty} \int \psi_n \, dx.$$

But this is also the definition of the Riemann integral $\int_a^b f \, dx$ of $f$ on $[a, b]$.

We may thus apply everything that one learns in calculus about integration of continuous functions. For instance, let $f$ be the function defined by

$$f(x) = \begin{cases} \dfrac{1}{x} & \text{for } 1 \leq x \leq 2 \\ 0 & \text{for } x \notin [1, 2] \end{cases}$$

Since $f$ is a function as described in Proposition 2.1.5, it is (Lebesgue) integrable and

$$\int f \, dx = \int_1^2 f \, dx = \int_1^2 \frac{1}{x} \, dx$$

$$= \log 2 - \log 1 = \log 2.$$

Next, we present a characterization of integrable functions, using sequences that will prove helpful in a few instances when the employment of series is undesirable.

**2.1.8 PROPOSITION** *A function $f$ on the real line is integrable if and only if there is a sequence $\{\psi_n\}$ of step functions such that*

$$\lim_{n\to\infty} \psi_n(x) = f(x) \qquad \text{for a.a. } x,$$

$$\lim_{n,m\to\infty} \int |\psi_n - \psi_m|\, dx = 0,$$

*and in this case*

$$\int f\, dx = \lim_{n\to\infty} \int \psi_n\, dx.$$

*Proof* Suppose first that $f$ is integrable. Then we can find a series $\sum \varphi_n$ of step functions that converges to $f$ almost everywhere and has the property that $\sum_{n=1}^{\infty} \int |\varphi_n|\, dx < \infty$. Define

$$\psi_n = \sum_{k=1}^{n} \varphi_k;$$

then

$$f(x) = \sum_{k=1}^{\infty} \varphi_k(x) = \lim_{n\to\infty} \psi_n(x)$$

for almost all $x$, and for $n \leq m$,

$$\int |\psi_n - \psi_m|\, dx = \int \left| \sum_{k=n+1}^{m} \varphi_k \right| dx$$

$$\leq \sum_{k=n+1}^{m} \int |\varphi_k|\, dx$$

$$\leq \sum_{k=n+1}^{\infty} \int |\varphi_k|\, dx$$

where we use the convention that the first two sums are zero if $n = m$. The latter sum converges to zero as $n$ tends to infinity, since $\sum \int |\varphi_n|\, dx$ converges. Thus

$$\lim_{n,m\to\infty} \int |\psi_n - \psi_m|\, dx = 0.$$

Conversely, suppose there is a sequence $\{\psi_n\}$ of step functions that converges to $f$ almost everywhere and satisfies

$$\lim_{n,m\to\infty} \int |\psi_n - \psi_m|\, dx = 0.$$

We claim that there is a subsequence $\{\psi_{n(k)}\}$ such that

$$\int |\psi_{n(k)} - \psi_m|\, dx \leq 2^{-k}$$

for $m \geq n(k)$. We can choose $\psi_{n(k)}$ by induction on $k$. First we pick $n(1)$ so large that

$$\int |\psi_{n(1)} - \psi_m| \leq 2^{-1}$$

for all $m \geq n(1)$. If $\psi_{n(k)}$ has been found, we choose $n(k+1) > n(k)$ so large that

$$\int |\psi_{n(k+1)} - \psi_m| \, dx \leq 2^{-(k+1)}$$

for $m \geq n(k+1)$. The sequence $\{\psi_{n(k)}\}$ has then the property

$$\int |\psi_{n(k)} - \psi_{n(k+1)}| \, dx \leq 2^{-k}.$$

Now we will construct a series $\sum \varphi_k$ that converges to $f$ almost everywhere. We let

$$\varphi_1 = \psi_{n(1)},$$
$$\varphi_k = \psi_{n(k)} - \psi_{n(k-1)} \qquad \text{for } k \geq 2.$$

Then we have

$$\sum_{k=1}^{m} \varphi_k = \psi_{n(1)} + \sum_{k=2}^{m} (\psi_{n(k)} - \psi_{n(k-1)}) = \psi_{n(m)} \tag{2.1.9}$$

which proves that $\sum \varphi_k$ converges to $f$ almost everywhere. Furthermore,

$$\begin{aligned} \sum_{k=1}^{m} \int |\varphi_k| \, dx &= \int |\psi_{n(1)}| \, dx + \sum_{k=2}^{m} \int |\psi_{n(k)} - \psi_{n(k-1)}| \, dx \\ &\leq \int |\psi_{n(1)}| \, dx + \sum_{k=2}^{m} 2^{-(k-1)} \\ &\leq \int |\psi_{n(1)}| \, dx + 1. \end{aligned}$$

Thus $\sum \int |\varphi_k| \, dx$ converges. This proves that $f$ is integrable. We also have from (2.1.9)

$$\int f \, dx = \sum_{k=1} \int \varphi_k \, dx = \lim_{m \to \infty} \int \psi_{n(m)} \, dx.$$

The sequence $\{\int \psi_n \, dx\}$ is a Cauchy sequence because

$$\begin{aligned} \left| \int \psi_n \, dx - \int \psi_m \, dx \right| &= \left| \int (\psi_n - \psi_m) \, dx \right| \\ &\leq \int |\psi_n - \psi_m| \, dx \end{aligned}$$

so it converges, and it must then converge to the same limit as the subsequence $\{\int \psi_{n(m)} \, dx\}$, that is,

$$\lim_{n \to \infty} \int \psi_n \, dx = \int f \, dx.$$

This completes the proof.

Finally, we want to derive an equivalent definition of integrable functions which is conveniently used in many applications.

**2.1.10 LEMMA (MIKUSIŃSKI)** *A function $f$ on the real line is integrable if and only if there exists a series $\sum \psi_n$ of step functions satisfying $\sum_{n=1}^{\infty} \int |\psi_n| \, dx < \infty$ and*

$$f(x) = \sum_{n=1}^{\infty} \psi_n(x)$$

*for all $x$ for which $\sum_{n=1}^{\infty} |\psi_n(x)| < \infty$.*

*Proof* The condition implies that $f$ is integrable, because the series $\sum |\psi_n|$ converges almost everywhere and thus $f = \sum_{n=1}^{\infty} \psi_n$ almost everywhere.

Conversely, suppose that $f$ is integrable. Then there is a series $\sum \varphi_n$ of step functions that converges to $f$ almost everywhere and satisfies $\sum_{n=1}^{\infty} \int |\varphi_n| \, dx < \infty$. Let $E$ be a null set such that

$$\sum_{n=1}^{\infty} |\varphi_n(x)| < \infty,$$

$$f(x) = \sum_{n=1}^{\infty} \varphi_n(x) \qquad \text{for all } x \notin E.$$

There is a series $\sum \eta_n$ of nonnegative step functions that diverges on $E$ and satisfies $\sum_{n=1}^{\infty} \int \eta_n \, dx < \infty$. Now define a new series $\sum \psi_n$ of step functions by

$$\psi_{3n-2} = \varphi_n, \; \psi_{3n-1} = \eta_n, \; \psi_{3n} = -\eta_n$$

for $n \geq 1$. Then

$$\sum_{n=1}^{\infty} \int |\psi_n| \, dx = \sum_{n=1}^{\infty} \int |\varphi_n| \, dx + 2 \sum_{n=1}^{\infty} \int \eta_n \, dx < \infty.$$

If $\sum |\psi_n(x)|$ converges, then so does $\sum \eta_n(x)$; whence $x \notin E$ and therefore

$$\sum_{n=1}^{\infty} \psi_n(x) = \sum_{n=1}^{\infty} \varphi_n(x) = f(x).$$

The usefulness of Mikusiński's lemma lies in the fact that it does not mention null sets. We will later have occasion to compare several kinds of integration theories for which the concept of a null set may be different. It is then that Mikusiński's lemma will be of great help. (See, for instance, Section 2.5.)

## *EXERCISES*

*2.1.1* Suppose that $f$ is an integrable function and $g$ is equivalent to $f$ (which means that $f - g$ is a null function). Prove that $g$ is also integrable and $\int f \, dx = \int g \, dx$.

*2.1.2* Suppose that $f$ is an integrable function and $\varphi$ is a step function. Prove that $f\varphi$ is integrable.

*2.1.3* Give an example of a nonnegative integrable function $f$ for which there is no increasing sequence $\{\varphi_n\}$ of step functions with

$$f = \lim_{n\to\infty} \varphi_n \text{ a.e.}$$

*Hint* Let $\{I_k\}$ be a system of open intervals of a total length of at the most ½, which covers the null set of rational numbers in (0, 1). One may assume $I_k \subset (0, 1)$. Define

$$f(x) = \begin{cases} 1 & \text{if } x \notin I_k \text{ for all } k \geq 1 \\ 0 & \text{if } x \in I_k \text{ for some } k \geq 1 \end{cases}$$

and show that $f$ is integrable. Notice that

$$\chi_{[0,1]} - f = \lim_{n\to\infty} (\chi_1 \vee \cdots \vee \chi_n)$$

where $\chi_k$ is the characteristic function of $I_k$. Thus $\chi_{[0,1]} - f$ is the limit of an increasing sequence of step functions, but $f$ is not. (The integral of $f$ is positive, but $f$ is not positive on any nondegenerate interval.)

*2.1.4* Prove that an integrable function $f$ can be written as the difference $f = f_1 - f_2$ of two nonnegative integrable functions $f_1$ and $f_2$, each of which is the limit almost everywhere of an increasing sequence of nonnegative step functions.

*Hint* Let $f = \sum_{n=1}^{\infty} \varphi_n$ a.e. where $\sum_{n=1}^{\infty} \int |\varphi_n|\, dx < \infty$. Show that you can choose $f_1$ and $f_2$ such that

$$f_1 = \sum_{n=1}^{\infty} \varphi_n^+ \text{ a.e.,} \qquad f_2 = \sum_{n=1}^{\infty} \varphi_n^- \text{ a.e.}$$

*2.1.5* In part D of Section 1.6, we have defined piecewise linear functions and their integrals. Why is a piecewise linear function Lebesgue integrable and why does the integral for a piecewise linear function as defined in Exercise 1.6.21 coincide with its Lebesgue integral?

## 2.2 BASIC PROPERTIES OF THE LEBESGUE INTEGRAL

Let us denote the set of all Lebesgue integrable functions by $L^1$. We have to ask ourselves now whether the basic properties (1) to (4) that we established for the step functions in Sections 1.1 and 1.2 will also hold for the elements $f \in L^1$ and their integrals $\int f\, dx$. This is indeed the case; Properties (1) through (3) are easily derived, while the proof of Property (4) will take some more effort.

2.2.1 PROPOSITION *The Lebesgue integrable functions have the following properties.*

(1) *If* $f \in L^1$ *and* $g \in L^1$ *and* $a, b$ *are real numbers, then* $af + bg \in L^1$, $f \vee g \in L^1$ *and* $f \wedge g \in L^1$.

(2) *If* $f \in L^1$ *and* $g \in L^1$ *and* $a, b$ *are real numbers, then*

$$\int (af + bg)\, dx = a \int f\, dx + b \int g\, dx.$$

(3) *If* $f \in L^1$ *is a nonnegative function, then* $\int f\, dx \geq 0$.

*Proof* The proofs of the first assertion in Property (1) and of the assertion in (2) are so simple that we take the liberty of leaving them to the reader (Exercise 2.2.1). In order to prove the last two assertions in (1) we show first that, if $f$ is integrable, then so is $|f|$. By Proposition 2.1.8 there is a sequence $\{\psi_n\}$ of step functions that converges to $f$ almost everywhere and in addition has the property that

$$\lim_{n,m\to\infty} \int |\psi_n - \psi_m|\, dx = 0.$$

Hence $\{|\psi_n|\}$ is a sequence of step functions that converges to $|f|$ almost everywhere, and since

$$\big|\, |\psi_n| - |\psi_m| \,\big| \leq |\psi_n - \psi_m|,$$

we have also

$$\lim_{n,m\to\infty} \int \big|\, |\psi_n| - |\psi_m| \,\big|\, dx = 0.$$

Thus Proposition 2.1.8 tells us that $|f|$ is integrable and

$$\int |f|\, dx = \lim_{n\to\infty} \int |\psi_n|\, dx \geq 0.$$

Now suppose $f$ and $g$ are integrable; then $f \vee g$ and $f \wedge g$ are also integrable, since we have the equations

$$\begin{aligned} f \vee g &= \tfrac{1}{2}(f + g) + \tfrac{1}{2}|f - g| \\ f \wedge g &= \tfrac{1}{2}(f + g) - \tfrac{1}{2}|f - g| \end{aligned} \tag{2.2.2}$$

which are easy to verify (Exercise 2.2.2).

The statement in Property (3) follows immediately from Exercise 1.6.19, but let us give a proof here anyway. We have just seen in the proof of (1) that $\int |f|\, dx \geq 0$ for any integrable function $f$. Thus if $f \geq 0$

$$\int f\, dx = \int |f|\, dx \geq 0.$$

As in the case of step functions, the preceding proposition has the following corollary (see Exercise 2.2.3).

**2.2.3 COROLLARY** *Suppose that $f$ and $g$ are integrable and $f \le g$; then $f^+ = f \vee 0$ and $f^- = -(f \wedge 0)$ and $|f|$ are integrable, and*

$$\int f\,dx \le \int g\,dx,$$

$$\left|\int f\,dx\right| \le \int |f|\,dx,$$

$$\int f^+\,dx \le \int |f|\,dx, \qquad \int f^-\,dx \le \int |f|\,dx.$$

We postpone the statement and proof of Property (4) until the next section, since it will be an immediate consequence of a more general theorem which we are going to attack now. Through Definition 2.1.3 we have been able to enlarge the class of integrable functions from the much-restricted class of step functions to the wider class of Lebesgue integrable functions in a single step. A natural question to ask is whether this step could be repeated and lead to a still wider class of integrable functions. The answer is no—this fact is the key to the usefulness of Lebesgue integration. We will formulate it as a theorem.

**2.2.4 THEOREM** *If $\sum f_n$ is a series of integrable functions such that*

$$\sum_{n=1}^{\infty} \int |f_n|\,dx < \infty,$$

*then $\sum f_n(x)$ converges for almost all $x$, and if $f$ is a function that equals $\sum_{n=1}^{\infty} f_n$ almost everywhere, then $f$ is integrable and*

$$\int f\,dx = \sum_{n=1}^{\infty} \int f_n\,dx.$$

A corollary of this theorem will be the so-called Beppo Levi theorem. However, since Theorem 2.2.4 will be quoted very often we would like to give it a name, too, and since it is so closely connected to its Corollary 2.3.1, the Beppo Levi theorem, *we shall refer to Theorem 2.2.4 also as the Beppo Levi theorem.* Before we go into its proof we deduce a simple lemma which says vaguely that an integrable function is equal to a step function plus a small integrable function.

**2.2.5 LEMMA** *Suppose $f$ is an integrable function and $\varepsilon > 0$. There is a series $\sum \varphi_n$ of step functions converging to $f$ almost everywhere and satisfying*

$$\sum_{n=2}^{\infty} \int |\varphi_n|\,dx \le \varepsilon,$$

*and in this case*

$$\int |f - \varphi_1|\,dx \le \varepsilon,$$

$$\sum_{n=1}^{\infty} \int |\varphi_n|\,dx \le \int |f|\,dx + 2\varepsilon.$$

*Proof* Let $\sum \psi_n$ be any series of step functions that converges to $f$ almost everywhere and satisfies $\sum_{k=1}^{\infty} \int |\psi_k| \, dx < \infty$. Since the series $\sum \int |\psi_k| \, dx$ converges, we can find an integer $m$ such that

$$\sum_{k=m+2}^{\infty} \int |\psi_k| \, dx \leq \varepsilon.$$

Now define

$$\varphi_1 = \sum_{k=1}^{m+1} \psi_k,$$

$$\varphi_n = \psi_{m+n} \qquad \text{for } n \geq 2,$$

then $\sum \varphi_n$ converges to $f$ almost everywhere and we have

$$\sum_{n=2}^{\infty} \int |\varphi_n| \, dx = \sum_{k=m+2}^{\infty} \int |\psi_k| \, dx \leq \varepsilon.$$

Furthermore, $\sum_{n=2}^{\infty} |\varphi_n|$ equals an integrable function $h$ almost everywhere and

$$\int h \, dx = \sum_{n=2}^{\infty} \int |\varphi_n| \, dx \leq \varepsilon.$$

Since $|f - \varphi_1| \leq h$ almost everywhere and $|f| \leq h + |\varphi_1|$ almost everywhere, we get

$$\int |f - \varphi_1| \, dx \leq \int h \, dx \leq \varepsilon$$

and thus

$$\begin{aligned}
\sum_{n=1}^{\infty} \int |\varphi_n| \, dx &= \int |\varphi_1| \, dx + \sum_{n=2}^{\infty} \int |\varphi_n| \, dx \\
&= \int |f - (f - \varphi_1)| \, dx + \sum_{k=m+2}^{\infty} \int |\psi_k| \, dx \\
&\leq \int |f| \, dx + \int |f - \varphi_1| \, dx + \varepsilon \\
&\leq \int |f| \, dx + 2\varepsilon.
\end{aligned}$$

*Proof of Theorem 2.2.4* For each $f_n$ we pick a series $\sum_k \varphi_{nk}$ of step functions such that

$$f_n = \sum_{k=1}^{\infty} \varphi_{nk} \text{ a.e.},$$

$$\sum_{k=1}^{\infty} \int |\varphi_{nk}| \, dx \leq \int |f_n| \, dx + 2^{-n},$$

which is possible by Lemma 2.2.5.

Since

$$\sum_{n=1}^{\infty}\sum_{k=1}^{\infty}\int|\varphi_{nk}|\,dx \le \sum_{n=1}^{\infty}\left(\int|f_n|\,dx + 2^{-n}\right)$$

$$\le \sum_{n=1}^{\infty}\int|f_n|\,dx + 1,$$

the double series $\sum_n \sum_{k=1}^{\infty} \int |\varphi_{nk}|\,dx$ is convergent. Let $\{\varphi_n\}$ be an enumeration of the countable set $\{\varphi_{nk}\}$. Then $\sum \int |\varphi_n|\,dx$ converges (to the same sum as the above double series; see Theorem 1.0.5). Thus $\sum \varphi_n(x)$ converges absolutely for almost all $x$. Let $E$ be the set of points $x$ for which $\sum \varphi_n(x)$ does not converge absolutely, and for each $n$ let $E_n$ be the set of points for which $\sum_k \varphi_{nk}(x)$ does not converge absolutely to $f_n(x)$. Then $F = E \cup \bigcup E_n$ is a null set and, for $x \notin F$,

$$\sum_{n=1}^{\infty} f_n(x) = \sum_{n=1}^{\infty}\sum_{k=1}^{\infty}\varphi_{nk}(x) = \sum_{n=1}^{\infty}\varphi_n(x)$$

(by Theorem 1.0.5). This proves that $\sum f_n$ converges almost everywhere. Also, $\sum \int \varphi_n\,dx$ converges absolutely, since $\sum \int |\varphi_n|\,dx$ converges so that (again by Theorem 1.0.5)

$$\sum_{n=1}^{\infty}\int \varphi_n\,dx = \sum_{n=1}^{\infty}\sum_{k=1}^{\infty}\int \varphi_{nk}\,dx = \sum_{n=1}^{\infty}\int f_n\,dx.$$

Now suppose $f = \sum_{n=1}^{\infty} f_n$ almost everywhere; for instance,

$$f(x) = \begin{cases} \displaystyle\sum_{n=1}^{\infty} f_n(x) & \text{for } x \notin F \\ 0 & \text{for } x \in F. \end{cases}$$

Then by the definition of the integral

$$\int f\,dx = \sum_{n=1}^{\infty}\int \varphi_n\,dx = \sum_{n=1}^{\infty}\int f_n\,dx.$$

This proves the theorem.

2.2.6 COROLLARY *If $f$ is integrable and $\int |f|\,dx = 0$, then $f$ vanishes almost everywhere.*

*Proof* Let $f_n = f$ for all $n$. The series $\sum f_n$ is a series of integrable functions that satisfies

$$\sum_{n=1}^{\infty}\int |f_n|\,dx = 0 < \infty.$$

Thus $\sum f_n(x)$ converges for almost all $x$; but $\sum f_n(x)$ diverges whenever $f(x) \ne 0$, which proves that $f = 0$ almost everywhere.

### *EXERCISES*

*2.2.1* Verify the first assertion in (1) of Proposition 2.2.1 and the assertion in (2) of that proposition.

*2.2.2* Verify Equation (2.2.2).

*2.2.3* Verify Corollary 2.2.3.

*2.2.4* Prove that the function $f$, defined by

$$f(x) = \begin{cases} \dfrac{1}{\sqrt{x}} & \text{for } 0 < x \leq 1 \\ 0 & \text{for } x \leq 0 \text{ and } x > 1 \end{cases}$$

is Lebesgue integrable.

*Hint* Let

$$f_n = f \cdot \chi_{[1/(n+1),1/n]}$$

and consider $\sum f_n$.

*2.2.5* Prove that the function $g$ defined by

$$g(x) = \begin{cases} \dfrac{1}{x^2} \sin x & \text{for } x \geq \pi \\ 0 & \text{for } x < \pi \end{cases}$$

is Lebesgue integrable.

*Hint* Let

$$g_n = g \cdot \chi_{[n\pi,(n+1)\pi]}$$

and consider $\sum g_n$.

## 2.3 CONVERGENCE THEOREMS

We are going to deduce now from Theorem 2.2.4, which we refer to as the Beppo Levi theorem, a corollary that is sometimes called the Beppo Levi theorem and sometimes the *monotone convergence theorem* and which we will always refer to by its latter name.

2.3.1 THEOREM (BEPPO LEVI) (*monotone convergence theorem*). *Let* $\{f_n\}$ *be an increasing sequence of integrable functions and suppose that there is a constant* $M$ *such that*

$$\int f_n \, dx \leq M$$

*for all* $n$. *Then* $\{f_n\}$ *converges almost everywhere, and if* $f$ *is any function such that*

$$f(x) = \lim_{n\to\infty} f_n(x)$$

*for almost all x, then f is integrable and*

$$\int f\,dx = \lim_{n\to\infty} \int f_n\,dx.$$

*(A similar theorem holds for decreasing sequences.)*

*Proof* Let $g_n = f_{n+1} - f_n$; then

$$\sum_{n=1}^{m-1} g_n = f_m - f_1$$

and therefore

$$\sum_{n=1}^{\infty} g_n(x) = \lim_{m\to\infty} f_m(x) - f_1(x),$$

whenever the limit on either side of the equality exists. $\sum g_n$ is a series of non-negative integrable functions and

$$\begin{aligned}\sum_{n=1}^{m-1} \int |g_n|\,dx &= \sum_{n=1}^{m-1} \int g_n\,dx \\ &= \int f_m\,dx - \int f_1\,dx \le M + \left| \int f_1\,dx \right|.\end{aligned}$$

This proves that $\sum \int |g_n|\,dx$ converges, and thus by Theorem 2.2.4, $\sum g_n(x)$ converges for almost all $x$. Consequently,

$$\lim_{m\to\infty} f_m(x) = \sum_{n=1}^{\infty} g_n(x) + f_1(x)$$

exists for almost all $x$. Now let

$$f = \lim_{m\to\infty} f_m \text{ a.e.};$$

for instance

$$f(x) = \begin{cases} \lim_{m\to\infty} f_m(x) & \text{if the limit exists} \\ 0 & \text{otherwise.} \end{cases}$$

Then $\sum_{n=1}^{\infty} g_n = f - f_1$ almost everywhere and therefore $f - f_1$, and hence $f$, is integrable by Theorem 2.2.4, and we have

$$\begin{aligned}\int f\,dx &= \int (f - f_1)\,dx + \int f_1\,dx \\ &= \sum_{n=1}^{\infty} \int g_n\,dx + \int f_1\,dx \\ &= \lim_{m\to\infty} \int f_m\,dx.\end{aligned}$$

An immediate consequence of this theorem is the continuity property (4):

**2.3.2 COROLLARY** *The Lebesgue integral has the following continuity property (4): Suppose $\{f_n\}$ is a decreasing sequence of nonnegative integrable functions, $f_n \geq f_{n+1} \geq 0$, such that*

$$\lim_{n\to\infty} f_n(x) = 0$$

*for (almost) all $x$, then*

$$\lim_{n\to\infty} \int f_n \, dx = 0.$$

The two Beppo Levi theorems have a great similarity to our definition of null sets. Recall that a null set $E$ can be characterized by either one of the following two statements:

(a) *There is a series $\sum \varphi_n$ of step functions such that $\sum \varphi_n(x)$ diverges for $x \in E$ and $\sum \int |\varphi_n| \, dx$ converges.*
(b) *There is an increasing sequence $\{\varphi_n\}$ of step functions such that $\{\varphi_n(x)\}$ diverges for $x \in E$ and $\{\int \varphi_n \, dx\}$ is a bounded sequence (which means that it converges).*

The Beppo Levi Theorem 2.2.4 says in part that we may replace the $\varphi_n$ in (a) by integrable functions, and the monotone convergence theorem implies the same for (b). Thus, in a sense, we have built these two theorems into our definitions at a very elementary stage.

The requirement in the monotone convergence theorem that the sequence $\{f_n\}$ be increasing is sometimes very inconvenient. We would like to drop that condition and just require that $\{f_n(x)\}$ converge for almost all $x$. However, as we have noted already for step functions in Section 1.2 before we proved Property (4), some additional condition is needed to ensure any worthwhile conclusion. Such a condition was discovered by Lebesgue:

**2.3.3 THEOREM (LEBESGUE)** *(dominated convergence theorem). Let $\{f_n\}$ be a sequence of integrable functions such that $\{f_n(x)\}$ converges for almost all $x$. Suppose in addition that there is an integrable function $g$ such that*

$$|f_n| \leq g \text{ a.e.}$$

*for all $n$. If $f$ is a function that equals $\lim_{n\to\infty} f_n$ a.e., then $f$ is integrable and*

$$\int f \, dx = \lim_{n\to\infty} \int f_n \, dx.$$

Before we prove this theorem, we shall establish one half of it in the form of a lemma. This lemma is known in the literature as *Fatou's lemma.* It is often useful when Lebesgue's dominated convergence theorem does not apply. In this lemma we need the concept of the lim inf. Let $\{a_n\}$ be any sequence of numbers and define

$$b_n = \inf \{a_k : k \geq n\}$$

if the infimum exists. Then $\{b_n\}$ is an increasing sequence of numbers. The lim inf of the sequence $\{a_n\}$ is now defined as

$$\liminf a_n = \lim_{n\to\infty} b_n.$$

There are two ways in which the lim inf can fail to exist. First, the numbers $b_n$ might not exist; this is exactly the case when the sequence $\{a_n\}$ is not bounded below. Second, $\{b_n\}$ might diverge to $\infty$.

The concept lim sup is defined similarly; if

$$c_n = \sup \{a_k : k \geq n\},$$

then $\{c_n\}$ is a decreasing sequence if the supremum exists and

$$\limsup a_n = \lim_{n\to\infty} c_n$$

provided that the sequence $\{c_n\}$ converges. Since $b_n \leq c_n$ for all $n$, we have always

$$\liminf a_n \leq \limsup a_n$$

if the lim inf and the lim sup exist. It is easily checked that *a sequence* $\{a_n\}$ *converges if and only if* $\limsup a_n$ *and* $\liminf a_n$ *both exist and are equal, and in this case*

$$\lim_{n\to\infty} a_n = \limsup a_n = \liminf a_n.$$

Namely, suppose that $\{a_n\}$ converges to $a$; then given $\varepsilon > 0$ we can find an integer $N$ such that

$$a - \varepsilon \leq a_k \leq a + \varepsilon$$

for all $k \geq N$, and hence

$$\begin{aligned} a - \varepsilon \leq \inf \{a_k : k \geq n\} &= b_n \leq a_n \\ \leq c_n &= \sup \{a_k : k \geq n\} \leq a + \varepsilon \end{aligned}$$

for $n \geq N$. This proves that

$$a = \liminf a_n = \limsup a_n.$$

Conversely, if $\liminf a_n = \limsup a_n$, then $\{a_n\}$ tends to the same limit, since

$$b_n \leq a_n \leq c_n.$$

2.3.4 LEMMA (FATOU) *Let* $\{f_n\}$ *be a sequence of integrable functions and suppose that* $f_n \geq 0$ *a.e. for all* $n$. *If* $\liminf \int f_n\,dx$ *exists, then* $\liminf f_n(x)$ *exists for almost all* $x$, *and if* $f$ *is any function that equals* $\liminf f_n$ *a.e. then* $f$ *is integrable and*

$$\int f\,dx \leq \liminf \int f_n\,dx.$$

*Proof* We may assume that $f_n \geq 0$ everywhere for all $n$, for the set of points $x$ for which $f_n(x) \geq 0$ fails for any $n$ is a null set, and therefore we may modify each $f_n$ on this set without affecting the conclusion.

Now let $g_n$ be the function defined by

$$g_n(x) = \inf \{f_j(x) : j \geq n\}.$$

The infimum exists, since $f_j(x) \geq 0$ for all $j$. We claim that $g_n$ is integrable. In fact, $g_n$ is the limit of the decreasing sequence of integrable functions $\{h_k\}$,

$$h_k = f_n \wedge \cdots \wedge f_{n+k-1},$$

which satisfy $\int h_k \, dx \geq 0$. Thus $g_n$ is integrable by the monotone convergence theorem. Furthermore,

$$0 \leq \int h_k \, dx \leq \int f_j, \qquad n \leq j < n + k$$

so that

$$0 \leq \int g_n \, dx = \lim_{k \to \infty} \int h_k \, dx \leq \int f_j \, dx, \qquad j \geq n.$$

The sequence $\{g_n\}$ is an increasing sequence of integrable functions satisfying

$$\int g_n \, dx \leq \liminf \int f_j \, dx.$$

Thus, again by the monotone convergence theorem,

$$\lim_{n \to \infty} g_n(x) = \liminf f_n(x)$$

exists for almost all $x$, and if

$$f = \liminf f_n = \lim_{n \to \infty} g_n \text{ a.e.}$$

then $f$ is integrable and

$$\int f \, dx = \lim_{n \to \infty} \int g_n \, dx \leq \liminf \int f_j \, dx.$$

This completes the proof of Fatou's lemma.

*Proof of Theorem 2.3.3* $\{g - f_n\}$ is a sequence of integrable functions satisfying $0 \leq g - f_n \leq 2g$ a.e.; hence

$$\int (g - f_n) \, dx \leq 2 \int g \, dx$$

so that $\liminf \int (g - f_n) \, dx$ exists. Also

$$\lim_{n \to \infty} (g(x) - f_n(x)) = g(x) - f(x) = \liminf (g(x) - f_n(x))$$

for almost all $x$. Thus we may conclude by Fatou's lemma that $g - f$ is integrable and

$$\begin{aligned} \int g \, dx - \int f \, dx = \int (g - f) \, dx &\leq \liminf \left( \int g \, dx - \int f_n \, dx \right) \\ &= \int g \, dx - \limsup \int f_n \, dx \end{aligned}$$

or

$$\int f\,dx \geq \limsup \int f_n\,dx.$$

Similarly, we may apply Fatou's lemma to the sequence $\{g + f_n\}$ which converges almost everywhere to $g + f$. Thus

$$\int g\,dx + \int f\,dx = \int (g + f)\,dx \leq \liminf \left( \int g\,dx + \int f_n\,dx \right)$$
$$= \int g\,dx + \liminf \int f_n\,dx$$

or

$$\int f\,dx \leq \liminf \int f_n\,dx.$$

Together with the previous result, this gives us

$$\liminf \int f_n\,dx \leq \limsup \int f_n\,dx$$
$$\leq \int f\,dx \leq \liminf \int f_n\,dx$$

and hence

$$\int f\,dx = \liminf \int f_n\,dx = \limsup \int f_n\,dx = \lim_{n \to \infty} \int f_n\,dx.$$

As an illustration of Lebesgue's dominated convergence theorem, consider for instance the sequence $\{\psi_n\}$ of piecewise linear functions $\psi_n$ described by Figure 1.3 where $\{\psi_n\}$ tends to zero everywhere and is dominated by $\chi_{(0,1)}$. Thus

$$\lim_{n \to \infty} \int \psi_n\,dx = 0.$$

This can also be verified of course by direct computation.

## EXERCISES

*2.3.1* Do Exercises 2.2.4 and 2.2.5 using the monotone convergence theorem.

*2.3.2* Let $\{f_n\}$ be a decreasing sequence of nonnegative integrable functions, $f_n \geq f_{n+1} \geq 0$, such that

$$\lim_{n \to \infty} \int f_n\,dx = 0.$$

Prove that $\lim_{n \to \infty} f_n = 0$ almost everywhere.

*Hint* This is a generalization of Exercise 1.6.16, but it is now simpler to apply the monotone convergence theorem and Corollary 2.2.6.

*2.3.3* Give an example for which Fatou's lemma applies with a strict inequality.

*2.3.4* Let $\{f_n\}$ be a sequence of integrable functions. Suppose that there is a constant $M$ and an integrable function $g$ such that $|\int f_n\,dx| \leq M$ and $f_n \leq g$ for all $n$. Prove that $\limsup f_n$ exists almost everywhere. Furthermore, if

$$f = \limsup f_n \text{ a.e.}$$

then $f$ is integrable and

$$\int f\,dx \geq \limsup \int f_n\,dx.$$

*Hint* Compare this situation with the one in the proof of Lebesgue's dominated convergence theorem.

*2.3.5* Give an example of a bounded sequence of integrable functions $\{f_n\}$ that converges almost everywhere to a function $f$ that is not integrable. If you assume that all the $\{f_n\}$ vanish off some bounded interval $[a, b]$, then $f$ is integrable and $\int f\,dx = \lim_{n\to\infty} \int f_n\,dx$. Why?

## 2.4 APPLICATIONS

In the present section we want to illustrate the use of the convergence theorems with some applications. The first one is a theorem somewhat similar to the dominated convergence theorem; it will usually be employed in the context of measurable functions which are discussed in the next chapter.

2.4.1 THEOREM *Suppose $\{f_n\}$ is a sequence of integrable functions that converges almost everywhere to a function $f$. If there is an integrable function $g$ with $|f| \leq g$, then $f$ is integrable.*

*Proof* If $a$, $b$, $c$ are any three numbers,

$$\text{mid}(a, b, c)$$

denotes the unique number among $a$, $b$, $c$ that is in between the two others. It is not hard to verify that

$$\begin{aligned}\text{mid}(a, b, c) &= \max\{\min(a, b), \min(b, c), \min(c, a)\}\\ &= \min\{\max(a, b), \max(b, c), \max(c, a)\}\end{aligned}$$

(see Exercise 1.1.5). Thus

$$\begin{aligned}g_n = \text{mid}(-g, f_n, g) &= (-g \wedge f_n) \vee (f_n \wedge g) \vee (g \wedge -g)\\ &= (-g \vee f_n) \wedge (f_n \vee g) \wedge (g \vee -g)\end{aligned} \tag{2.4.2}$$

defines a sequence $\{g_n\}$ of integrable functions, and $\{g_n(x)\}$ tends to $f(x)$ whenever $\{f_n(x)\}$ does, that is, $\{g_n\}$ tends to $f$ almost everywhere. Furthermore, from (2.4.2) we see easily that

$$-g = (-g) \wedge g \leq g_n \leq (-g) \vee g = g$$

or $|g_n| \leq g$. Thus Lebesgue's dominated convergence theorem tell us that $f$ is integrable.

Next we discuss improper Riemann integrable functions. We restrict ourselves here to continuous functions. A brief discussion of more general Riemann integrable functions can be found in Section 2.6.

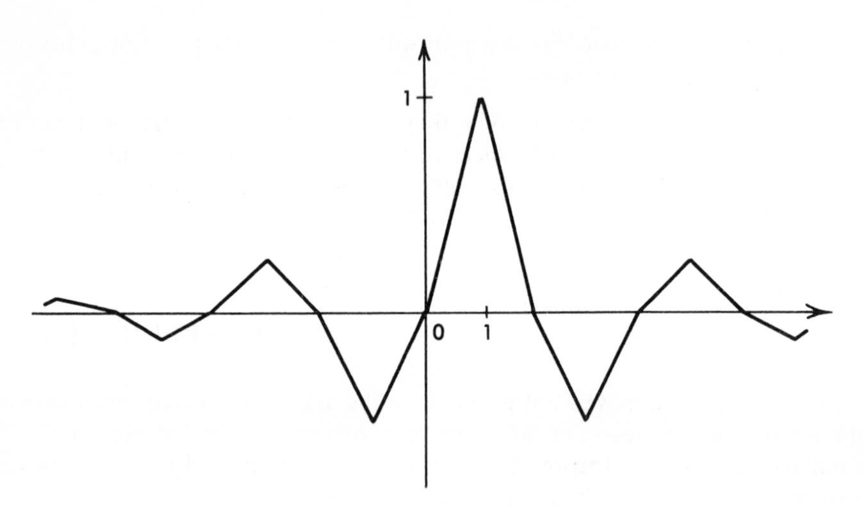


Figure 2.3 An example of an improper Riemann integrable function that is not Lebesgue integrable.

A continuous function on the real line is said to be *improper Riemann integrable* if the limit

$$\lim_{s,t\to\infty} \int_{-s}^{t} f\,dx$$

exists. *Not every improper Riemann integrable function is Lebesgue integrable.* We prove this assertion by an example.

Let $f$ be the function that takes on the value 0 at the even integers, the value $(-1)^n/(|n| + 1)$ at the odd integers $2n + 1$, and is linear in between (see Figure 2.3). Formally, $f$ would be defined by

$$f(x) = \begin{cases} \dfrac{(-1)^n}{|n| + 1}(x - 2n) & \text{if } 2n \leq x \leq 2n + 1 \\[2ex] \dfrac{(-1)^n}{|n| + 1}(2n + 2 - x) & \text{if } 2n + 1 \leq x \leq 2(n + 1) \end{cases}$$

If $2n \leq t \leq 2(n+1)$, $n > 0$, then

$$1 + \int_{-t+2}^{0} f\,dx = \int_{0}^{t} f\,dx = \sum_{m=1}^{n} \frac{(-1)^{m-1}}{m} + \int_{2n}^{t} f\,dx.$$

The last integral tends to zero as $t$, and hence $n$, tends to infinity; in fact

$$\left| \int_{2n}^{t} f\,dx \right| \leq \int_{2n}^{2(n+1)} f\,dx = \frac{1}{n+1}.$$

Thus $\lim_{t \to \infty} \int_0^t f\,dx$ exists, since the series

$$\sum_{m=1}^{\infty} \frac{(-1)^{m-1}}{m}$$

is known to converge, and similarly

$$\lim_{s \to \infty} \int_{-s}^{0} f\,dx$$

exists. We have, moreover,

$$\begin{aligned} \lim_{s,t \to \infty} \int_{-s}^{t} f\,dx &= \lim_{s,t \to \infty} \left( \int_{-s}^{0} f\,dx + \int_{0}^{t} f\,dx \right) \\ &= 2 \sum_{n=1}^{\infty} \frac{(-1)^{m-1}}{m} - 1. \end{aligned}$$

Similarly, we find the equality

$$\int \chi_{[-2n,2n]} |f|\,dx = \int_{-2n}^{2n} |f|\,dx = 2 \sum_{m=1}^{n} \frac{1}{m} - 1 + \frac{1}{n+1}.$$

Consequently,

$$\lim_{n \to \infty} \int \chi_{[-2n,2n]} |f|\,dx$$

does not exist, the series $\sum(1/m)$ being divergent. But if $f$ were Lebesgue integrable, then $|f|$ would be Lebesgue integrable, and since

$$\chi_{[-2n,2n]} |f| \leq |f|$$

we should have by Lebesgue's dominated convergence theorem

$$\lim_{n \to \infty} \int \chi_{[-2n,2n]} |f|\,dx = \int |f|\,dx,$$

a contradiction.

However, the situation is not entirely hopeless. There is a relation between improper Riemann integrable functions and Lebesgue integrable functions if we strengthen our assumption.

2.4.3 PROPOSITION *Suppose $f$ is a continuous function such that $|f|$ is improper Riemann integrable. Then $f$ is improper Riemann integrable and Lebesgue integrable* *and*

$$\lim_{s,t\to\infty} \int_{-s}^{t} f\,dx = \int f\,dx.$$

*Proof* The argument used in the above counterexample actually suggests the proof. The sequence $\{\chi_{[-n,n]}|f|\}$ is an increasing sequence of integrable functions tending to $|f|$ everywhere, and

$$\int \chi_{[-n,n]}|f|\,dx \leq \lim_{n\to\infty} \int_{-n}^{n} |f|\,dx < \infty$$

since $|f|$ is improper Riemann integrable. Thus $|f|$ is Lebesgue integrable by the monotone convergence theorem. Let $\{a_n\}$, $\{b_n\}$ be any two sequences of non-negative numbers tending to infinity. If $\chi_n$ denotes the characteristic function of $[-b_n, a_n]$ then $\{\chi_n f\}$ tends to $f$ everywhere and we have

$$|\chi_n f| \leq |f|$$

so that $f$ is integrable by Lebesgue's dominated convergence theorem, and

$$\int f\,dx = \lim_{n\to\infty} \int \chi_n f\,dx = \lim_{n\to\infty} \int_{-b_n}^{a_n} f\,dx.$$

Since $\{a_n\}$, $\{b_n\}$ may be any sequences tending to infinity, we have

$$\int f\,dx = \lim_{s,t\to\infty} \int_{-s}^{t} f\,dx.$$

It would help the reader to understand the next section if he would first try the following exercises.

## *EXERCISES*

In the following, $\varphi$, $\psi$, and so forth, will denote piecewise linear functions as defined in part D of Section 1.6. We assume also that the student has solved Exercises 1.6.21 through 1.6.24. To prevent confusion, we will denote the integral of a piecewise linear function as defined in Exercise 1.6.21 by $\int \varphi\,d\bar{x}$.

*2.4.1* Prove that every piecewise linear function $\varphi$ is Lebesgue integrable and that

$$\int \varphi\,d\bar{x} = \int \varphi\,dx$$

(the latter being the Lebesgue integral).

*Hint* Use Proposition 2.1.5.

*2.4.2* Call a subset $E$ of the real line a pl-null set if there is a series $\sum \varphi_n$ of piecewise linear functions that diverges on $E$ and satisfies $\sum_{n=1}^{\infty} \int |\varphi_n|\,d\bar{x} < \infty$. (Notice that it follows from Exercise 1.6.22 that $|\varphi_n| = \varphi_n^+ + \varphi_n^-$ is a piecewise linear function.) Now define a function $f$ to be pl-integrable if there is a series $\sum \varphi_n$ of piecewise linear functions that converges to $f$ off some pl-null set and satisfies $\sum_{n=1}^{\infty} \int |\varphi_n| \, d\bar{x} < \infty$. In this case define

$$\int f \, d\bar{x} = \sum_{n=1}^{\infty} \int \varphi_n \, d\bar{x}.$$

Prove that the definition of $\int f \, d\bar{x}$ is meaningful, that is, that it does not depend on the particular choice of the series $\sum \varphi_n$.

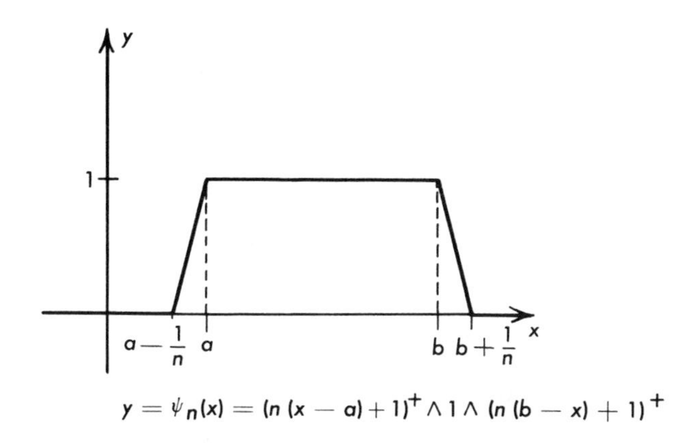


Figure 2.4 The characteristic function of a closed bounded interval $[a, b]$ is the limit of a decreasing sequence of piecewise linear functions $\{\psi_n\}$.

*Hint* Notice that Theorem 1.5.3 and Corollaries 1.5.4 and 1.5.5 are also true for piecewise linear functions (with the obvious notion of piecewise linear-almost everywhere instead of almost everywhere), since their proofs rely only on Properties (1) to (4) which hold for piecewise linear functions.

*2.4.3* Prove that every step function $\psi$ is pl-integrable and that

$$\int \psi \, dx = \int \psi \, d\bar{x}.$$

*Hint* Prove this first for characteristic functions of closed intervals and notice that you may use the monotone convergence theorem for pl-integrable functions, since this theorem was proved using only Properties (1) to (4) and the definition of the integral (see Figure 2.4).

*2.4.4* Use Exercises 2.4.1 and 2.4.3 and the Beppo-Levi theorem for Lebesgue integrable functions and pl-integrable functions to prove that $E$ is a null set (in the sense of Lebesgue) if and only if it is a pl-null set.

*2.4.5* Prove that $f$ is Lebesgue integrable if and only if it is pl-integrable and that in either case

$$\int f\,dx = \int f\,d\bar{x}.$$

## 2.5 THE DANIELL INTEGRAL

If we look over the material discussed so far, we find we have made use mainly of Properties (1) through (4) and no other properties of functions on the real line, an exception being the examples and applications that we have dealt with every now and then. This observation leads us to the following abstraction.

Consider an abstract set $S$ and on $S$ a set $L$ of real-valued functions $\varphi$ with the following property:

(1) If $\varphi$, $\psi \in L$ and $a$,$b$ are real numbers, then

$$a\varphi + b\psi \in L, \varphi \vee \psi \in L \quad \text{and} \quad \varphi \wedge \psi \in L.$$

Then

$$\varphi^+ = \varphi \vee 0, \quad \varphi^- = -(\varphi \wedge 0),$$
$$|\varphi| = \varphi^+ + \varphi^-$$

belong also to $L$. We call the functions $\varphi \in L$ "elementary functions." We assume furthermore that to each elementary function $\varphi \in L$ there is attached a real number, called the (elementary) integral of $\varphi$. We denote this integral of $\varphi$ by

$$\int \varphi\,d\mu;$$

the significance of this notation will become apparent in the next chapter where we deal with measures. We assume that the integral has the following properties:

(2) If $\varphi$, $\psi \in L$ and $a$,$b$ are real numbers, then

$$\int (a\varphi + b\psi)\,d\mu = a\int \varphi\,d\mu + b\int \psi\,d\mu.$$

(3) If $\varphi \in L$ and $\varphi \geq 0$, then $\int \varphi\,d\mu \geq 0$.
(4) If $\{\varphi_n\}$ is a decreasing sequence of nonnegative elementary functions, $\varphi_n \geq \varphi_{n+1} \geq 0$, and $\lim_{n\to\infty} \varphi_n(x) = 0$ for all $x$, then

$$\lim_{n\to\infty} \int \varphi_n\,d\mu = 0.$$

As we did before, we easily deduce from Property (3) that for $\varphi$, $\psi \in L$,

$$\int \varphi\,d\mu \geq \int \psi\,d\mu$$

if $\varphi \geq \psi$, and

$$\left| \int \varphi \, d\mu \right| \leq \int |\varphi| \, d\mu,$$

$$\int \varphi^+ \, d\mu \leq \int |\varphi| \, d\mu, \qquad \int \varphi^- \, d\mu \leq \int |\varphi| \, d\mu.$$

An integral on a set of elementary functions $L$ with Properties (1) to (4) is called a *Daniell integral.* Before we go somewhat deeper into the consequences of Properties (1) to (4) we shall give some examples of Daniell integrals.

2.5.1 EXAMPLE The first example is the one that we have been dealing with all the time. Namely, $S$ is the real line and $L$ is a set of all step functions, and the integral is given by the elementary Lebesgue integral. Properties (1) to (4) were established in Chapter 1.

2.5.2 EXAMPLE This time we let $S$ again be the real line and $L$ the set of all continuous functions on the real line, each of which vanishes off some bounded interval. Property (1) is certainly satisfied. For $\varphi \in L$,

$$\int \varphi \, d\mu = \int \varphi \, dx$$

is the Riemann integral of $\varphi$.

Since the Riemann integral of $\varphi$ coincides with the Lebesgue integral by Proposition 2.1.5, it is clear that Properties (2) to (4) are also going to hold. Property (4), for instance, is a special case of the monotone convergence theorem. However, one can prove Property (4) also without the use of Lebesgue integration (see Exercise 2.5.1).

2.5.3 EXAMPLE $S$ is again the real line, and $L$ the set of piecewise linear functions that have been introduced in part D of Exercise Section 1.6. For $\varphi \in L$,

$$\int \varphi \, d\mu = \int \varphi \, dx$$

denotes the integral of $\varphi$ as defined in Exercise 1.6.21. Properties (1) to (4) have been established in Exercises 1.6.22 to 1.6.24.

2.5.4 EXAMPLE As in Example 2.5.2 we let $S$ be the real line and $L$ the set of continuous functions on $S$, each of which vanishes off some bounded interval. We define the integral of $\varphi \in L$ by

$$\int \varphi \, d\delta = \varphi(0).$$

Properties (1) to (4) are easily verified.

2.5.5 EXAMPLE This time we let $S$ be the set of positive integers $n > 0$ and $L$ the set of all functions on $S$ that vanish off a finite set; that is, if $\varphi \in L$, then there is an integer $N$ such that

$$\varphi(n) = 0 \qquad \text{for} \qquad n \geq N + 1.$$

$L$ is the set of finite sequences. For $\varphi \in L$ define

$$\int \varphi \, d\mu = \sum_{n=1}^{N} \varphi(n)$$

if $\varphi(n) = 0$ for $n \geq N + 1$.

It is not difficult to prove that Properties (1) to (4) are verified. Let us check, for instance, Property (4). Suppose $\{\varphi_n\}$ is a decreasing sequence of nonnegative elementary functions $\varphi_k \in L$ such that

$$\lim_{k\to\infty} \varphi_k(n) = 0$$

for all $n$. Let $N$ be an integer such that $\varphi_1(n) = 0$ for $n \geq N + 1$, then $\varphi_k(n) = 0$ for $n \geq N + 1$ and all $k$. Thus

$$\lim_{k\to\infty} \int \varphi_k \, d\mu = \lim_{k\to\infty} \left( \sum_{n=1}^{N} \varphi_k(n) \right)$$

$$= \sum_{n=1}^{N} \lim_{k\to\infty} \varphi_k(n) = 0.$$

Now we suppose that $L$ is any set of elementary functions on a set $S$ and $\int \varphi \, d\mu$, $\varphi \in L$, an integral such that Properties (1) to (4) are fulfilled. As we did before, we can introduce the concept of a null set. We also call a null set a $d\mu$-null set if we want to stress that the integral $\int \varphi \, d\mu$ was used in its definition. Thus, a $d\mu$-null set $E$ is characterized by either one of the following statements:

(a) There is an increasing sequence, $\{\varphi_n\}$ of elementary functions such that $\{\varphi_n(x)\}$ diverges for $x \in E$ and $\{\int \varphi_n \, d\mu\}$ converges.
(b) There is a series $\sum \varphi_n$ of elementary functions such that $\sum \varphi_n(x)$ diverges for $x \in E$ and $\sum \int |\varphi_n| \, d\mu$ converges.

In (a) as well as in (b) we may also assume that the $\varphi_n$ are nonnegative (see Section 1.3 and in particular Proposition 1.3.2). Also, a countable union of $d\mu$-null sets is again a $d\mu$-null set, the proof being identical to the one given for Proposition 1.3.3.

We can go one step further. The results of Section 1.5 will hold for elementary functions in $L$ instead of step functions if we make the convention that almost everywhere or $d\mu$-almost everywhere means "everywhere except on some $d\mu$-null set." The results of Section 1.5 were used to justify the definition of integrable functions.

2.5.6 DEFINITION *A function $f$ on $S$ is said to be integrable (with respect to $d\mu$), or $d\mu$-integrable, if there is a series $\sum \varphi_n$ of elementary functions that converges* *to $f\,d\mu$ a.e. and satisfies*

$$\sum_{n=1}^{\infty} \int |\varphi_n|\, d\mu < \infty,$$

*and the ($d\mu$-)integral of $f$ is then defined by*

$$\int f\, d\mu = \sum_{n=1}^{\infty} \int \varphi_n\, d\mu.$$

Properties (1) to (4) will again hold for the set $L^1$ of $d\mu$-integrable functions $f$ and their integrals $\int f\, d\mu$ (Section 2.2). Moreover, all the convergence theorems

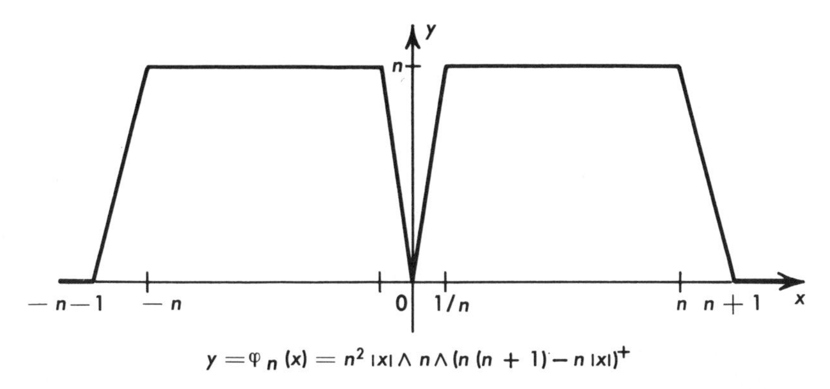


Figure 2.5 The sequence $\{\varphi_n(x)\}$ diverges for every $x \neq 0$, while $\int \varphi_n\, d\delta = \varphi_n(0) = 0$.

proved in Sections 2.2 and 2.3 and Theorem 2.4.1 are valid for $d\mu$-integrable functions, since in their proofs we have made use only of Properties (1) to (4) and their consequences.

Now let us investigate what the null sets and integrable functions in our examples are. For instance,

$$R - \{0\} = (-\infty, 0) \cup (0, \infty)$$

is a $d\delta$-null set in Example 2.5.4. Namely, the sequence $\{\varphi_n\}$ of (piecewise linear) functions in $L$ pictured in Figure 2.5,

$$\varphi_n(x) = \begin{cases} n^2\,|x| & \text{for } 0 \le |x| \le \dfrac{1}{n} \\ n & \text{for } \dfrac{1}{n} \le |x| \le n \\ n(n + 1 - |x|) & \text{for } n \le |x| \le n + 1 \\ 0 & \text{for } n + 1 \le |x| \end{cases}$$

is increasing, tends to infinity at all $x \neq 0$, and satisfies

$$\int \varphi_n \, d\delta = \varphi_n(0) = 0.$$

From this we can deduce that every function $f$ on the real line is $d\delta$ a.e. equal to an elementary function in $L$. In fact, let $\varphi \in L$ be defined by

$$\varphi(x) = \begin{cases} 1 - |x| & \text{for } |x| \leq 1 \\ 0 & \text{for } |x| \geq 1 \end{cases}$$

then $f$ equals the function $f(0)\varphi$ at zero, since $\varphi(0) = 1$, that is,

$$f = f(0)\varphi \qquad d\delta \text{ a.e.}$$

This proves that every function on the real line is integrable with respect to $d\delta$ and

$$\int f \, d\delta = \int f(0)\varphi \, d\delta = f(0)\varphi(0) = f(0).$$

One can prove for Example 2.5.5 that the empty set is the only null set, and that a function $f$ on the positive integers is $d\mu$-integrable if and only if the series $\sum f(n)$ converges absolutely. If $f$ is integrable, then

$$\int f \, d\mu = \sum_{n=1}^{\infty} f(n).$$

We leave the proof to the exercises (Exercise 2.5.3).

In Examples 2.5.1 to 2.5.3, one would perhaps expect that in each case the integrable functions would be the Lebesgue integrable functions and that the integral for an integrable function would be the same in all three cases. This will follow from the following general theorem.

### 2.5.7 THEOREM

COMPARISON THEOREM *Let $L_1$ and $L_2$ be sets of elementary functions on the same set $S$ with integrals*

$$\int \varphi \, d\mu_1 \qquad \text{for } \varphi \in L_1, \qquad \int \psi \, d\mu_2 \qquad \text{for } \psi \in L_2$$

*such that Properties* (1) *to* (4) *hold for $L_1$ with the integral $\int \varphi \, d\mu_1$ and for $L_2$ with the integral $\int \psi \, d\mu_2$. Let $L_i^1$ be the space of $d\mu_i$-integrable functions, $i = 1, 2$. If $L_1 \subset L_2^1$ and*

$$\int \varphi \, d\mu_1 = \int \varphi \, d\mu_2 \qquad \text{for } \varphi \in L_1,$$

*then $L_1^1 \subset L_2^1$ and*

$$\int f \, d\mu_1 = \int f \, d\mu_2 \qquad \text{for } f \in L_1^1.$$

*Proof* Suppose $f$ is $d\mu_1$-integrable. By Mikusiński's lemma there is a series $\sum \varphi_n$ of elementary functions in $L_1 \subset L_2^1$ such that $\sum_{n=1}^{\infty} \int |\varphi_n| \, d\mu_1 < \infty$ and

$$f(x) = \sum_{n=1}^{\infty} \varphi_n(x)$$

for all those $x$ for which the last series converges absolutely. Thus $\sum \varphi_n$ is a series of functions in $L_2^1$ satisfying

$$\sum_{n=1}^{\infty} \int |\varphi_n| \, d\mu_2 = \sum_{n=1}^{\infty} \int |\varphi_n| \, d\mu_1 < \infty.$$

The Beppo-Levi theorem implies therefore that $\sum \varphi_n$ converges absolutely $d\mu_2$ a.e., whence $f = \sum_{n=1}^{\infty} \varphi_n \, d\mu_2$ a.e. Hence $f$ is $d\mu_2$-integrable and

$$\int f \, d\mu_2 = \sum_{n=1}^{\infty} \int \varphi_n \, d\mu_2 = \sum_{n=1}^{\infty} \int \varphi_n \, d\mu_1 = \int f \, d\mu_1.$$

2.5.8 COROLLARY *If we add to the hypotheses of the last theorem that* $L_2 \subset L_1^1$ *and*

$$\int \psi \, d\mu_2 = \int \psi \, d\mu_1 \qquad \text{for } \psi \in L_2$$

*then* $L_1^1 = L_2^1$ *and*

$$\int f \, d\mu_1 = \int f \, d\mu_2 \qquad \text{for } f \in L_1^1 = L_2^1.$$

Let us now apply the last theorem to Examples 2.5.1 to 2.5.3. Let $L_1$ be the space of step functions with

$$\int \varphi \, d\mu_1, \qquad \varphi \in L_1,$$

the elementary Lebesgue integral. Then $L_2$ denotes the set of continuous functions each of which vanishes off some bounded interval, with

$$\int f \, d\mu_2, \qquad f \in L_2,$$

the Riemann integral. Finally, $L_3$ is the set of piecewise linear functions with their integral

$$\int \psi \, d\mu_3, \qquad \psi \in L_3,$$

as defined in Exercise 1.6.21. We have the inclusion

$$L_3 \subset L_2 \subset L_1^1,$$

the latter by Proposition 2.1.5. Furthermore,

$$\int \psi \, d\mu_3 = \int \psi \, d\mu_2 = \int \psi \, d\mu_1 \qquad \text{for } \psi \in L_3;$$

the first equality is proved in calculus, the second one has been established in Proposition 2.1.5 where we have shown that

$$\int f\,d\mu_2 = \int f\,d\mu_1 \qquad \text{for } f \in L_2.$$

Therefore we may conclude, according to Theorem 2.5.7,

$$L_3^1 \subset L_2^1 \subset L_1^1,$$

$$\int f\,d\mu_3 = \int f\,d\mu_2 = \int f\,d\mu_1 \qquad \text{for } f \in L_3^1,$$

$$\int f\,d\mu_2 = \int f\,d\mu_1 \qquad \text{for } f \in L_2^1.$$

To prove that the spaces $L_3^1$, $L_2^1$, and $L_1^1$ are actually equal, we have to show that $L_1^1 \subset L_3^1$. Again we use Theorem 2.5.7. If $\chi$ is the characteristic function of a closed bounded interval $[a, b]$, then

$$\psi_n(x) = \begin{cases} 0 & \text{for } x \leq a - \frac{1}{n} \\ nx - na + 1 & \text{for } a - \frac{1}{n} \leq x \leq a \\ 1 & \text{for } a \leq x \leq b \\ nb + 1 - nx & \text{for } b \leq x \leq b + \frac{1}{n} \\ 0 & \text{for } x \geq b + \frac{1}{n} \end{cases} \tag{2.5.9}$$

defines a sequence $\{\psi_n\}$ of piecewise-linear functions $\psi_n \in L_3$ that decreases to $\chi$ and satisfies $\int \psi_n\,d\mu_3 \geq 0$ (see Figure 2.4). Thus by the monotone convergence theorem, $\chi$ is $d\mu_3$-integrable and

$$\int \chi\,d\mu_3 = \lim_{n\to\infty} \int \psi_n\,d\mu_3 = \lim_{n\to\infty} \int \psi_n\,d\mu_1 = \int \chi\,d\mu_1.$$

Since every step function is a linear combination of characteristic functions of closed bounded intervals, we finally obtain $L_1 \subset L_3^1$ and

$$\int \varphi\,d\mu_1 = \int \varphi\,d\mu_3 \qquad \text{for } \varphi \in L_1.$$

Consequently $L_1^1 = L_3^1$ by Theorem 2.5.7. This proves

$$L_1^1 = L_2^1 = L_3^1$$

and

$$\int f\,d\mu_1 = \int f\,d\mu_2 = \int f\,d\mu_3 \qquad \text{for } f \in L_1^1.$$

This result shows that *either one of the Examples* 2.5.1 *to* 2.5.3 *can serve as the basis for the theory of Lebesgue integration;* Example 2.5.1 is of course the most elementary one.

## *EXERCISES*

*2.5.1* Prove that Property (4) may be replaced by the following: (4′) If $\sum \psi_n$ is a series of nonnegative elementary functions and $\psi \in L$ such that $\sum_{n=1}^{\infty} \psi_n(x) \geq \psi(x)$ for all $x$, then $\sum_{n=1}^{\infty} \int \psi_n\, dx \geq \int \psi\, dx$. (In this condition the sums are to be interpreted as $\infty$ if they diverge.)

*Hint* To prove that (4) implies (4′), apply (4) to $\varphi_n = (\psi - \sum_{k=1}^{n} \psi_n)^+$; to prove that (4′) implies (4) apply (4′) to $\sum_{n=1}^{\infty} (\varphi_n - \varphi_{n+1}) \geq \varphi_1$.

*2.5.2* Let $\{f_n\}$ be a decreasing sequence of nonnegative continuous functions each of which vanishes off some bounded interval. Prove that $\lim_{n\to\infty} \int f_n\, dx = 0$ without reference to Lebesgue integration.

*Hint* If $f_1$ vanishes off $[a, b]$, then all $f_n$ vanish off $[a, b]$. Let $M_n$ be the maximum of $f_n$ on $[a, b]$. Prove that $\lim_{n\to\infty} M_n = 0$.

*2.5.3* Prove that in Example 2.5.5 the empty set is the only null set, and a function $f$ on the positive integers is $d\mu$-integrable if and only if $\sum f(n)$ converges absolutely.

*2.5.4* Generalize Example 2.5.5 in the following way. Let $S$ be any (nonempty) set. Let $L$ be the set of functions $\varphi$ on $S$ with the following property. For each $\varphi$ there is a finite set $\{a_1, \cdots, a_n\}$ in $S$ such that

$$\varphi(x) = 0 \qquad \text{for } x \notin \{a_1, \cdots, a_n\}.$$

Then define the integral of $\varphi$ by

$$\int \varphi\, d\mu = \sum_{x \in S} \varphi(x) = \sum_{k=1}^{n} \varphi(a_k)$$

if $\varphi$ vanishes off $\{a_1, \cdots, a_n\}$. Prove that Properties (1) to (4) hold.

*2.5.5* What are the null sets and what are the integrable functions in Exercise 2.5.4?

# 2.6 RIEMANN INTEGRABLE FUNCTIONS

In this section we want to touch briefly on the relationship between bounded Riemann integrable functions and Lebesgue integrable functions. Since no topic in our book will depend on this discussion, the present section may well be omitted in a first reading of the book. It is included only for the enlightenment of those students that have learned about the concept of Riemann integrability in an advanced calculus course.

We begin by recalling the definition of Riemann integrability. Let $f$ be a bounded function on the bounded closed interval $[a, b]$, say

$$|f(x)| \leq M \qquad \text{for } x \in [a, b].$$

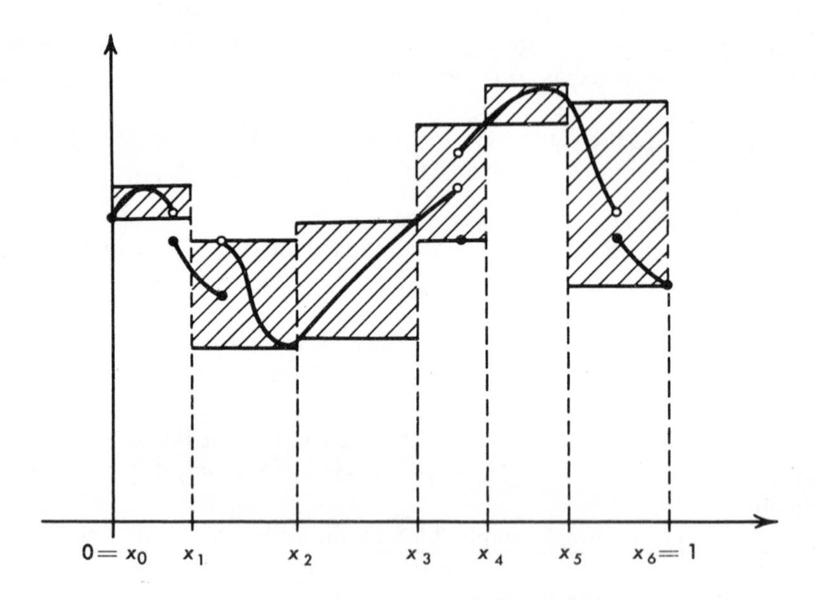


Figure 2.6 The shaded area represents the difference between the upper and lower Darboux sums associated with the subdivision

$$0 = x_0 < x_1 < \cdots < x_6 = 1.$$

We consider subdivisions

$$a = x_0 \leq x_1 \leq \cdots \leq x_m = b$$

of the interval $[a, b]$. Let us denote such a subdivision by the symbol $\Delta$. The subdivision $\Delta$ is said to be of magnitude at most $\delta$ if

$$x_k - x_{k-1} \leq \delta \qquad \text{for } k = 1, \cdots, m.$$

To each subdivision $\Delta$ of $[a, b]$ we associate the upper and lower *Darboux sums,*

$$S(\Delta) = \sum_{k=1}^{m} M_k(x_k - x_{k-1}),$$

$$s(\Delta) = \sum_{k=1}^{m} m_k(x_k - x_{k-1})$$

where $M_k$ denotes the supremum and $m_k$ the infimum of $f$ on $[x_{k-1}, x_k]$. These numbers

$$M_k = \sup \{f(x): x_{k-1} \leq x \leq x_k\},$$
$$m_k = \inf \{f(x): x_{k-1} \leq x \leq x_k\}$$

exist and are in modulus at most $M$, since $|f|$ is bounded by $M$ on $[a, b]$. Notice that $M_k \geq m_k$ and thus

$$S(\Delta) \geq s(\Delta)$$

for all $\Delta$. Now we can formulate the definition of Riemann integrable functions.

2.6.1 DEFINITION *A bounded function $f$ on a closed bounded interval $[a, b]$ is Riemann integrable if and only if for each $\varepsilon > 0$ there is $\delta > 0$ with the property that*

$$S(\Delta) - s(\Delta) \leq \varepsilon$$

*for all subdivisions $\Delta$ of $[a, b]$ of magnitude at most $\delta$* (Figure 2.6).

The Riemann integral of $f$ over $[a, b]$ is the number that is squeezed in by the upper and lower Darboux sums. The existence of this number follows easily from the definition; in fact, we have:

2.6.2 THEOREM *Suppose $f$ is a bounded Riemann integrable function on $[a, b]$. Then there exists exactly one number $A$ with*

$$S(\Delta_1) \geq A \geq s(\Delta_2)$$

*for all subdivisions $\Delta_1$ and $\Delta_2$ of $[a, b]$. If $\{\Delta_n\}$ is any sequence of subdivisions of $[a, b]$, the magnitudes of which tend to zero as $n$ tends to infinity, then*

$$\lim_{n\to\infty} S(\Delta_n) = A = \lim_{n\to\infty} s(\Delta_n).$$

2.6.3 DEFINITION *Let $f$ be a bounded Riemann integrable function. The number $A$, the existence of which is asserted in the theorem, is called the Riemann integral of $f$ and denoted by*

$$R\int_a^b f\,dx = A.$$

*Proof of Theorem 2.6.2* Let $\Delta$ be any subdivision

$$a = x_0 \leq \cdots \leq x_m = b$$

of $[a, b]$. A subdivision $\Delta'$

$$a = y_0 \leq \cdots \leq y_n = b$$

of $[a, b]$ is called a refinement of $\Delta$ if all the points $\{x_k: k = 0, \cdots, m\}$ occur among $\{y_j: j = 0, \cdots, n\}$. We claim that

$$S(\Delta) \geq S(\Delta')$$

if $\Delta'$ is a refinement of $\Delta$. Namely, for any interval $[x_{k-1}, x_k]$ let

$$x_{k-1} = y_j \leq \cdots \leq y_{j+p} = x_k$$

be the points of $\Delta'$ in that interval. Then the supremum $M'_{j+}$ of $f$ on the interval $[y_{j+\ell-1}, y_{j+\ell}]$, $\ell = 1, \cdots, p$, is less than or equal to the supremum $M_k$ of $f$ on $[x_{k-1}, x_k]$, and thus

$$M_k(x_k - x_{k-1}) \geq \sum_{\ell=1}^{p} M'_{j+\ell}(y_{j+\ell} - y_{j+\ell-1}),$$

from which $S(\Delta) \geq S(\Delta')$ follows immediately. Similarly we have

$$s(\Delta) \leq s(\Delta')$$

if $\Delta'$ is a refinement of $\Delta$.

If $\Delta_1$ and $\Delta_2$ are any two subdivisions of $[a, b]$, then

$$S(\Delta_1) \geq s(\Delta_2). \tag{2.6.4}$$

Namely, let $\Delta'$ be the subdivision of $[a, b]$ that contains all the points of $\Delta_1$ and $\Delta_2$. Then $\Delta'$ is a refinement of $\Delta_1$ and $\Delta_2$ and consequently

$$S(\Delta_1) \geq S(\Delta') \geq s(\Delta') \geq s(\Delta_2)$$

as asserted. Let

$$A_1 = \inf \{S(\Delta_1) : \Delta_1 \text{ is a subdivision of } [a, b]\},$$
$$A_2 = \sup \{s(\Delta_2) : \Delta_2 \text{ is a subdivision of } [a, b]\}.$$

From (2.6.4) we have $A_1 \geq A_2$. We have in fact $A_1 = A_2$, since

$$0 \leq A_1 - A_2 \leq \inf \{S(\Delta) - s(\Delta) : \Delta \text{ is a subdivision of } [a, b]\}$$

where the right-hand side is equal to zero by Definition 2.6.1. If we let $A = A_1 = A_2$, then $A$ has the property

$$S(\Delta_1) \geq A \geq s(\Delta_2)$$

for all subdivisions $\Delta_1$ and $\Delta_2$ of $[a, b]$, and $A$ is certainly the only such number.

If $\{\Delta_n\}$ is a sequence of subdivisions of $[a, b]$, the magnitudes of which tend to zero as $n$ tends to infinity, then $A = \lim_{n\to\infty} s(\Delta_n)$ since

$$0 \leq A - s(\Delta_n) \leq S(\Delta_n) - s(\Delta_n)$$

where the limit of the right-hand side vanishes by Definition 2.6.1. $A = \lim_{n\to\infty} S(\Delta_n)$ is proved similarly.

The last theorem has a converse that is frequently used as the basis of an alternate definition of Riemann integrability.

**2.6.5 LEMMA** *A bounded function $f$ on a closed bounded interval $[a, b]$ is Riemann integrable if and only if there is a number $A$ such that*

$$\lim_{n\to\infty} S(\Delta_n) = A = \lim_{n\to\infty} s(\Delta_n) \tag{2.6.6}$$

*for every sequence* $\{\Delta_n\}$ *of subdivisions of* $[a, b]$, *the magnitudes of which tend to zero as n tends to infinity. If such an A exists, then*

$$A = R\int_a^b f\,dx.$$

***Proof*** We have proved already that a Riemann integrable function has these properties. Conversely, suppose $f$ is not Riemann integrable; then, according to Definition 2.6.1, we can find an $\varepsilon > 0$ such that for each $n$ there is a subdivision $\Delta_n$ of $[a, b]$ of magnitude at most $1/n$ and

$$S(\Delta_n) - s(\Delta_n) > \varepsilon.$$

Therefore there cannot be a number $A$ such that (2.6.6) holds, and the function $f$ thus does not satisfy the condition of the lemma.

Let us make here the convention that a function $f$ on an interval $[a, b]$ is called Lebesgue integrable on $[a, b]$ if the function $g$ that equals $f$ on $[a, b]$ and vanishes off $[a, b]$, is Lebesgue integrable; we define in this case

$$L\int_a^b f\,dx = \int g\,dx.$$

The question arises of course whether a bounded Riemann integrable function on a bounded closed interval $[a, b]$ is also Lebesgue integrable on $[a, b]$. The answer is affirmative. To prove it we associate to each subdivision $\Delta$ of $[a, b]$,

$$\Delta : a = x_0 \leq \cdots \leq x_m = b,$$

the following two step functions:

$$\phi(x) = \begin{cases} 0 & \text{for } x \notin [a, b] \\ M_k & \text{for } x \in [x_{k-1}, x_k),\ k = 1, \cdots, m \\ f(b) & \text{for } x = b \end{cases}$$

$$\varphi(x) = \begin{cases} 0 & \text{for } x \notin [a, b] \\ m_k & \text{for } x \in [x_{k-1}, x_k),\ k = 1, \cdots, m \\ f(b) & \text{for } x = b \end{cases}$$

where $M_k$ and $m_k$ are the supremum and infimum of $f$ on $[x_{k-1}, x_k]$, respectively (see Figure 2.6). We have

$$\varphi \leq f \leq \phi \text{ on } [a, b],$$

$$S(\Delta) = \int \phi\,dx, \qquad s(\Delta) = \int \varphi\,dx.$$

Suppose now that $\{\Delta_n\}$ is a sequence of subdivisions of $[a, b]$, the magnitudes of which tend to zero as $n$ tends to infinity. Let $\phi_n$ and $\varphi_n$ be the step functions corresponding to the subdivision $\Delta_n$. If we choose the sequence $\{\Delta_n\}$ such that $\Delta_{n+1}$ is a refinement of $\Delta_n$ for all $n$, then

$$\phi_n \geq \phi_{n+1} \geq \varphi_{n+1} \geq \varphi_n.$$

Thus $\{\varphi_n\}$ is an increasing sequence bounded above by $\phi_1$ and $\{\phi_n\}$ is a decreasing sequence bounded below by $\varphi_1$. Hence

$$G = \lim_{n\to\infty} \phi_n, \qquad g = \lim_{n\to\infty} \varphi_n$$

are Lebesgue integrable.

2.6.7 LEMMA *We have*

$$G = f = g \quad \text{a.e. on } [a, b],$$

*which implies that the bounded Riemann integrable function* $f$ *on* $[a, b]$ *is also Lebesgue integrable on* $[a, b]$. *Furthermore,*

$$L\int_a^b f\,dx = R\int_a^b f\,dx.$$

*Proof* We have

$$\int G\,dx = \lim_{n\to\infty} \int \phi_n\,dx = \lim_{n\to\infty} S(\Delta_n) = R\int_a^b f\,dx,$$

$$\int g\,dx = \lim_{n\to\infty} \int \varphi_n\,dx = \lim_{n\to\infty} s(\Delta_n) = R\int_a^b f\,dx,$$

by the monotone convergence theorem. Consequently,

$$\int (G - g)\,dx \doteq 0.$$

But the relation $\phi_n \geq \varphi_n$ implies $G - g \geq 0$, whence $G - g = 0$ a.e. Since also $G \geq f \geq g$ on $[a, b]$, we see that in fact $G = f = g$ a.e. on $[a, b]$. In particular,

$$R\int_a^b f\,dx = \int G\,dx = L\int_a^b f\,dx = \int g\,dx = R\int_a^b f\,dx.$$

We can get much more from the proof of the last lemma than just the Lebesgue integrability of $f$. We have seen that $G = g$ a.e., or

$$\lim_{n\to\infty} \phi_n(x) = \lim_{n\to\infty} \varphi_n(x) \qquad \text{for a.a.}x.$$

The following lemma will tell us that $f$ must therefore be continuous almost everywhere.

**2.6.8 LEMMA** *Let $f$ be any bounded function on the bounded closed interval $[a, b]$ and $\{\Delta_n\}$ any sequence of subdivisions of $[a, b]$, the magnitudes of which tend to zero as $n$ tends to infinity. Further, $\phi_n$ and $\varphi_n$ denote the step functions associated with $\Delta_n$. If $c$ is a point in $(a, b)$ that is not a division point in any of the subdivisions $\Delta_n$ (of which there are only countably many), then $f$ is continuous at $c$ if and only if $\lim_{n\to\infty} \phi_n(c)$ and $\lim_{n\to\infty} \varphi_n(c)$ exist and*

$$\lim_{n\to\infty} \phi_n(c) = \lim_{n\to\infty} \varphi_n(c).$$

*Proof* Suppose first that $f$ is continuous at $c$. We claim

$$f(c) = \lim_{n\to\infty} \phi_n(c) = \lim_{n\to\infty} \varphi_n(c).$$

Let $\varepsilon > 0$; since $f$ is continuous at $c$, we can find $\delta > 0$ such that $[c - \delta, c + \delta] \subset [a, b]$ and

$$f(c) - \varepsilon \leq f(x) \leq f(c) + \varepsilon \qquad \text{for } x \in [c - \delta, c + \delta].$$

There is an integer $N$ such that $\Delta_n$ is of magnitude at most $\delta$ for $n \geq N$. If

$$\Delta_n : a = x_0 \leq \cdots \leq x_m = b$$

is of magnitude at most $\delta$ and say $c \in (x_{k-1}, x_k)$ (by hypothesis $c$ is different from $x_0, \cdots, x_m$), then $[x_{k-1}, x_k] \subset [c - \delta, c + \delta]$ and hence

$$f(c) - \varepsilon \leq f(x) \leq f(c) + \varepsilon \qquad \text{for } x \in [x_{k-1}, x_k].$$

Since $\phi_n(c)$ is the supremum and $\varphi_n(c)$ the infimum of $f$ on $[x_{k-1}, x_k]$, we have therefore

$$f(c) - \varepsilon \leq \varphi_n(c) \leq \phi_n(c) \leq f(c) + \varepsilon$$

whenever $n \geq N$, which proves our assertion.

Conversely, suppose $\lim_{n\to\infty} \phi_n(c)$ and $\lim_{n\to\infty} \varphi_n(c)$ exist and

$$\lim_{n\to\infty} \phi_n(c) = \lim_{n\to\infty} \varphi_n(c).$$

Let $\varepsilon > 0$ and pick an integer $n$ with

$$0 \leq \phi_n(c) - \varphi_n(c) \leq \varepsilon.$$

If the subdivision $\Delta_n$ is given by the points

$$a = x_0 \leq \cdots \leq x_m = b$$

and say $c \in (x_{k-1}, x_k)$, then we can find $\delta > 0$ with

$$[c - \delta, c + \delta] \subset [x_{k-1}, x_k].$$

Since $\phi_n(c)$ is the supremum and $\varphi_n(c)$ the infimum of $f$ on $[x_{k-1}, x_k]$, we have for $x \in [c - \delta, c + \delta]$,

$$\varphi_n(c) \leq f(x) \leq \phi_n(c)$$

whence

$$|f(c) - f(x)| \leq \phi_n(c) - \varphi_n(c) \leq \varepsilon$$

for $|x - c| \leq \delta$. This proves that $f$ is continuous at $c$.

**2.6.9 COROLLARY** *A bounded Riemann integrable function on a bounded closed interval is continuous almost everywhere.*

The last lemma permits us also to prove that, among the bounded Lebesgue integrable functions, the bounded Riemann integrable functions are actually characterized by Corollary 2.6.9. This is achieved in the following theorem which, in addition, collects the main results of this section.

**2.6.10 THEOREM** *Let $[a, b]$ be a bounded closed interval. A bounded function $f$ on $[a, b]$ is Riemann integrable if and only if it is continuous almost everywhere, and then it is Lebesgue integrable with*

$$R\int_a^b f\,dx = L\int_a^b f\,dx.$$

*Proof* We have seen already in Lemma 2.6.7 that a Riemann integrable function $f$ is Lebesgue integrable on $[a, b]$, and that the Riemann and Lebesgue integrals of $f$ on $[a, b]$ coincide. In Corollary 2.6.9 we saw that a Riemann integrable function is continuous almost everywhere on $[a, b]$.

As for the converse, assume $f$ is continuous almost everywhere on $[a, b]$. Let $\{\Delta_n\}$ be any sequence of subdivisions of $[a, b]$, the magnitudes of which tend to zero as $n$ tends to infinity. $\phi_n$ and $\varphi_n$ denote the corresponding step functions,

$$\varphi_n \le f \le \phi_n \qquad \text{on } [a, b].$$

By Lemma 2.6.8, $\lim_{n\to\infty} \varphi_n(x)$ and $\lim_{n\to\infty} \phi_n(x)$ exist and

$$\lim_{n\to\infty} \varphi_n(x) = \lim_{n\to\infty} \phi_n(x)$$

for almost all $x$. Let $g$, $G$ be functions such that

$$g = \lim_{n\to\infty} \varphi_n \text{ a.e.} \qquad \text{and} \qquad G = \lim_{n\to\infty} \phi_n \text{ a.e.}$$

We have $g = f = G$ a.e. on $[a, b]$, since $\varphi_n \le f \le \phi_n$ on $[a, b]$. Furthermore,

$$|\varphi_n| \le M\chi_{[a,b]}, \; |\phi_n| \le M\chi_{[a,b]} \text{ a.e.}$$

if $M$ is a bound for $|f|$ on $[a, b]$. Thus by Lebesgue's dominated convergence theorem, $G$ and $g$ are Lebesgue integrable and

$$\int G\,dx = \lim_{n\to\infty} \int \phi_n\,dx,$$

$$\int g\,dx = \lim_{n\to\infty} \int \varphi_n\,dx.$$

But $G = g$ a.e. and $g = f = G$ a.e. on $[a, b]$, whence $f$ is Lebesgue integrable and

$$\begin{aligned}\lim_{n\to\infty} S(\Delta_n) &= \lim_{n\to\infty} \int \phi_n\,dx = L\int_a^b f\,dx \\ &= \lim_{n\to\infty} \int \varphi_n\,dx = s(\Delta_n),\end{aligned}$$

$S(\Delta_n)$ and $s(\Delta_n)$ being the upper and lower Darboux sums, respectively. Lemma 2.6.5 now tells us that $f$ is Riemann integrable.

### *EXERCISES*

*2.6.1* Show that a bounded monotone nondecreasing function is Riemann integrable over any bounded interval.

*Hint* Show that a monotone nondecreasing function has only countably many discontinuities (see Proposition 6.2.3).

*2.6.2* Show that the characteristic function of the Cantor set $C$ of Example 1.4.3 (which equals one on $C$ and zero off $C$) is Riemann integrable.

Call a function $f$ on an interval $[a, b]$ essentially Riemann integrable if it can be decomposed into a sum $f = f_R + f_N$ where $f_R$ is a bounded Riemann integrable function on $[a, b]$ and $f_N$ is a null function (that is, $f$ is equivalent to a bounded Riemann integrable function).

*2.6.3* Show that $R\int_a^b f_R\,dx$ is the same for all such decompositions of an essentially Riemann integrable function $f$ on $[a, b]$.

*2.6.4* Show that, if the function $f$ on the interval $[a, b]$ is nonnegative and essentially Riemann integrable, then there exists an increasing sequence $\{\varphi_n\}$ of step functions with

$$f = \lim_{n\to\infty} \varphi_n \text{ a.e. on } [a, b].$$

*2.6.5* Give an example of a bounded integrable function $f$ on $[0, 1]$ which is not essentially Riemann integrable (see Exercise 2.1.3).

## 2.7 EXERCISES

### A. Basic Properties of Lebesgue Integrable Functions

2.7.1 For any function $f$ on the real line and any number $k$, let $f_k$ be defined by $f_k(x) = f(x + k)$. Prove the following:

(a) If $f$ is integrable, then $f_k$ is also integrable and

$$\int f\,dx = \int f_k\,dx.$$

(b)
$$\lim_{k\to 0} \int |f - f_k|\,dx = 0.$$

*Hint* Use the corresponding results for step functions (Exercises 1.6.6 and 1.6.8) and Proposition 2.1.8.

2.7.2 Prove that the characteristic function $\chi_K$ of the set $K$ in Example 1.4.4 is not integrable, even though you have chosen $K$ as a subset of $[0, 1)$. (See Exercise 1.4.5.)

2.7.3 For any function $f$ on the real line and any number $k \neq 0$ let ${}_kf$ be defined by ${}_kf(x) = f(kx)$. Prove the following:

(a) If $f$ is integrable, then so is ${}_kf$ and $\int f\,dx = \frac{1}{|k|}\int {}_kf\,dx$.

(b)
$$\lim_{k\to 1}\int |f - {}_kf|\,dx = 0.$$

*Hint* Use the corresponding results for step functions (Exercises 1.6.7 and 1.6.9) and Proposition 2.1.8.

2.7.4 Let $f$ be an integrable function and suppose there are real numbers $\alpha$, $\beta$ with

$$\alpha \leq f(x) \leq \beta$$

for all $x$. We have seen in Exercise 2.1.2 that $f\chi_{[a,b]}$ is integrable for all real numbers $a \leq b$. Prove that for each pair $a \leq b$ there is a real number $\gamma \in [\alpha, \beta]$ such that

$$\int f\chi_{[a,b]}\,dx = \gamma(b - a)$$

(this is the mean value theorem for integrals).

*Hint*

$$\alpha\int \chi_{[a,b]}\,dx \leq \int f\chi_{[a,b]}\,dx \leq \beta\int \chi_{[a,b]}\,dx.$$

## B. Problems on Limits (Abstract)

2.7.5 Suppose $\{f_n\}$ is a sequence of integrable functions and $\sum_{n=1}^{\infty}\int |f_n|\,dx < \infty$. Prove that $\{f_n\}$ converges to zero almost everywhere.

2.7.6 Suppose $f$ is integrable. We have seen in Exercise 2.1.2 that $f\chi_{[-n,n]}$ is also integrable. Prove

(a)
$$\lim_{n\to\infty}\int |f| \wedge n\,dx = \int |f|\,dx,$$

(b)
$$\lim_{n\to\infty}\int_{-n}^{n} f\,dx = \int f\,dx,$$

where

$$\int_{-n}^{n} f\,dx = \int f\chi_{[-n,n]}\,dx.$$

**2.7.7** Give an example of a sequence $\{f_n\}$ of integrable functions vanishing off [0, 1] that converges to zero almost everywhere and satisfies

$$\lim_{n\to\infty} \int f_n \, dx = 0,$$

but which is not dominated by an integrable function.

*Hint* Consider $f_n = (2^n/n)\chi_n$ where $\chi_n$ is the characteristic function of $(1 - 2^{-n+1}, 1 - 2^{-n})$.

**2.7.8** Let $f$ be an integrable function; prove that
(a) $f\chi_{(-\infty,t)}$ is integrable for all real numbers $t$;
(b) $F(t) = \int f\chi_{(-\infty,t)} \, dx = \int_{-\infty}^{t} f \, dx$ is continuous in $t$.

**2.7.9** Prove the following:

(a) Suppose $\{f_n\}$ is a sequence of nonnegative integrable functions that is bounded by a nonnegative integrable function $g$, $0 \leq f_n \leq g$. Prove that lim sup $f_n$ exists almost everywhere, and if $f$ is a function such that

$$f = \limsup f_n \text{ a.e.},$$

then $f$ is integrable and

$$\int f \, dx \geq \limsup \int f_n \, dx.$$

(b) Suppose $\{f_n\}$ is a sequence of integrable functions bounded in modulus by a nonnegative integrable function $g$, $0 \leq |f_n| \leq g$. Prove that lim sup $f_n$ and lim inf $f_n$ exist a.e., and if $f^1$ and $f^2$ are functions satisfying

$$f^1 = \limsup f_n \text{ a.e.}, \qquad f^2 = \liminf f_n \text{ a.e.},$$

then $f^1$ and $f^2$ are integrable and

$$\int f^1 \, dx \geq \limsup \int f_n \, dx \geq \liminf \int f_n \, dx \geq \int f^2 \, dx.$$

*Hint* Compare with the similar situation in the proof of Theorem 2.3.3.

**2.7.10** Suppose $\{f_n\}$ is a sequence of nonnegative integrable functions that converges to zero almost everywhere. If there is a constant $M$ such that $\int f_1 \vee \cdots \vee f_n \, dx \leq M$ for all $n$, then $\lim_{n\to\infty} \int f_n \, dx = 0$.

**2.7.11** Suppose $f$ is an integrable function. Prove the following:
(a) For every $t$,

$$g_t(x) = f(x) \sin tx$$

defines an integrable function (and similarly, $f(x) \cos tx$ is integrable).

*Hint* Let $\{\varphi_n\}$ be a sequence of step functions that converges to $f$ a.e. Apply Theorem 2.4.1 to the sequence $\{\varphi_n(x) \sin tx\}$.

(b) Let

$$\hat{f}(t) = \int g_t \, dx;$$

prove that $\hat{f}$ is continuous.

(c) Suppose that $xf$ is also integrable. Prove that $\hat{f}$ is differentiable and

$$\frac{d}{dt} \hat{f}(t) = \int x f(x) \cos tx \, dx.$$

*Hint* Use the mean value theorem to prove

$$\left| \frac{\sin (t + h)x - \sin tx}{hx} \right| \leq 1 \qquad \text{for } h, x \neq 0.$$

2.7.12 Let $f(x, t)$ be a function of two variables that is integrable as a function of $x$ for each value of $t$ and differentiable as a function of $t$ for each value of $x$. Suppose there is an integrable function $g$ such that

$$\left| \frac{\partial}{\partial t} f(x, t) \right| \leq g(x)$$

for all $x$ and $t$. Prove that

(a) $\dfrac{\partial}{\partial t} f(x, t)$ is integrable as a function of $x$ for each value of $t$.

*Hint* Use the mean value theorem to prove that

$$\left| \frac{1}{h} (f(x, t + h) - f(x, t)) \right| \leq g(x).$$

(b)
$$\frac{d}{dt} \int f(x, t) \, dx = \int \frac{\partial}{\partial t} f(x, t) \, dx.$$

## C. Problems on Limits (Concrete)

In the following, a function $f$ which is defined on an interval $(a, b)$ is called integrable if the function $F$ defined by

$$F(x) = \begin{cases} f(x) & \text{if } x \in (a, b) \\ 0 & \text{if } x \notin (a, b) \end{cases}$$

is integrable, and we let

$$\int_a^b f \, dx = \int F \, dx.$$

2.7.13 Prove that

(a) $e^{-|x|}$ is integrable;

(b) $e^{-nx^2+x}$ is integrable (notice: $-nx^2 + x \leq -|x|$ for $|x| \geq 2$);

(c) $\lim\limits_{n \to \infty} \displaystyle\int e^{-nx^2+x} \, dx = 0.$

2.7.14 Prove that
(a) $e^{-x}x^{\alpha-1}$ is integrable on $(0, \infty)$ if $\alpha > 0$;
(b) $(1 - x/n)^n x^{\alpha-1}$ is integrable on $(0, n)$ if $\alpha > 0$;
(c) $\lim_{n\to\infty} \int_0^n (1 - x/n)^n x^{\alpha-1}\, dx = \int_0^\infty e^{-x}x^{\alpha-1}\, dx$ if $\alpha > 0$.

*Hint* Use the inequality $\log(1 - x/n) \leq -x/n$ for $0 \leq x \leq n$, to dominate the function in (b); also recall $\lim_{n\to\infty}(1 + t/n)^n = e^t$. The function

$$\Gamma(\alpha) = \int_0^\infty e^{-x}x^{\alpha-1}\, dx$$

is known as the gamma function.

2.7.15 Prove that

$$\frac{e^{-x}}{1 - e^{-x}}\, x^{\alpha-1}$$

is integrable on $(0, \infty)$ for $\alpha > 1$ and

$$\int_0^\infty \frac{e^{-x}}{1 - e^{-x}}\, x^{\alpha-1}\, dx = \Gamma(\alpha) \sum_{n=1}^\infty \frac{1}{n^\alpha}.$$

*Hint* $\sum_{n=1}^\infty e^{-nx} = (e^{-x})/(1 - e^{-x})$.

2.7.16 In calculus one establishes the equality

$$\int_a^b x^\alpha \log x\, dx = \frac{x^{\alpha+1}}{\alpha + 1}\left(\log x - \frac{1}{\alpha + 1}\right)\Bigg]_a^b$$

for $b \geq a > 0$ and $\alpha \neq -1$. Use this equation to prove that
(a) $x^{-n-1} \log x$ is integrable on $(1, \infty)$ for $n \geq 1$;
(b) $\int_1^\infty x^{-n-1} \log x\, dx = 1/n^2$ for $n \geq 1$;
(c) $x^{-1}(x - 1)^{-1} \log x$ is integrable on $(0, 1)$;
(d) $\int_1^\infty x^{-1}(x - 1)^{-1} \log x\, dx = \sum_{n=1}^\infty 1/n^2$.

*Hint* $1/(x - 1) = \sum_{n=1}^\infty x^{-n}$ for $x > 1$.

## D. Product of Functions

2.7.17 Prove the following exercises:
(a) Suppose $g$ is an integrable function and $|g|$ is bounded. Prove that there is a constant $M$ and a sequence $\{\varphi_n\}$ of step functions which converges to $g$ a.e. and satisfies $|\varphi_n| \leq M$ for all $n$.

(b) Suppose $f$ is an integrable function and $g$ is a function with the property that there is a constant $M$ and a sequence $\{\varphi_n\}$ of step functions such that $|\varphi_n| \leq M$ for all $n$ and $\lim_{n\to\infty} \varphi_n = g$ a.e. Prove that $fg$ is integrable. (See Exercise 2.1.2.)

2.7.18 Give an example of an integrable function $f$ such that $f^2$ is not integrable. Why must such a function be unbounded? (See Exercise 2.7.17.)

2.7.19 Suppose $f$ and $g$ are integrable functions, $|g|$ is bounded, and

$$\lim_{x\to\infty} g(x) = 0 = \lim_{x\to-\infty} g(x).$$

Then $g(x)f(x/n)$ is an integrable function by Exercise 2.7.17. Prove that

$$\lim_{n\to\infty} \frac{1}{n} \int g(x) f\left(\frac{x}{n}\right) dx = 0.$$

(See Exercise 2.7.3.)

2.7.20 Suppose the integrable function $f$ vanishes outside $[0, 1]$; then $x^n f$ is integrable for $n \geq 1$ by Exercise 2.7.17. Prove that $\lim_{n\to\infty} \int f x^n \, dx = 0$.

2.7.21 If $f$ is integrable and $|f| < 1$, then $f^n$ is integrable for all $n \geq 1$ by Exercise 2.7.17. Prove that $\lim_{n\to\infty} \int f^n \, dx = 0$.

2.7.22 Show that, if $f, g \geq 0$ are integrable, then so is $\sqrt{fg}$.

*Hint* Notice that the function

$$xa + \frac{1}{x} b,$$

$a, b \geq 0$, on $(0, \infty)$ has an absolute minimum at $x_0 = \sqrt{b/a}$, and its value at $x_0$ is $2\sqrt{ab}$. Use this to prove that for all $a, b \geq 0$,

$$2\sqrt{ab} = \lim_{n\to\infty} \min \left\{ r_k a + \frac{1}{r_k} b : 1 \leq k \leq n \right\}$$

where $r_k$ is an enumeration of the positive rational numbers, $r_k > 0$. Then let $a = f(x)$, $b = g(x)$.

2.7.23 Suppose $g$ is an integrable function and $f$ is any function such that $f|g|$ is integrable. If

$$\alpha \leq f(x) \leq \beta$$

for all $x$, then there is $\gamma \in [\alpha, \beta]$ with

$$\int f \, |g| \, dx = \gamma \int |g| \, dx.$$

(See Exercise 2.7.4.)

## E. Improper Riemann Integration

**2.7.24** The function $x^{-1}\sin x$ (which is to be interpreted as one for $x = 0$) is improper Riemann integrable, but not Lebesgue integrable.

**2.7.25** State and prove a proposition similar to Proposition 2.4.3 that would apply to Exercise 2.2.4.

## F. $L^1$ as a Pseudo-metric Space

On $L^1$ we define a distance between elements $f, g \in L^1$ by $\|f - g\| = \int |f - g|\, dx$. For $\|f - 0\|$ we also write $\|f\|$.

**2.7.26** Prove that $\|f - g\|$ is a pseudometric for $L^1$, that is,

$$\|f - f\| = 0, \ \|f - h\| \le \|f - g\| + \|g - h\|.$$

Actually, $\|f\|$ is a pseudonorm for $L^1$, that is,

$$\|af\| = |a|\, \|f\|,$$
$$\|f + g\| \le \|f\| + \|g\|.$$

What can you say about $f$ if $\|f\| = 0$?

**2.7.27** Suppose $\{f_n\}$ is a sequence of elements in $L^1$ with

$$\lim_{n, m \to \infty} \|f_n - f_m\| = 0$$

(that is, $\{f_n\}$ is a Cauchy sequence). Prove that
(a) there is a subsequence $\{f_{n(k)}\}$ of $\{f_n\}$ and a function $f \in L^1$ such that

$$f = \lim_{k \to \infty} f_{n(k)} \text{ a.e.},$$

$$\int f\, dx = \lim_{k \to \infty} \int f_{n(k)}\, dx,$$

$$\lim_{k \to \infty} \|f - f_{n(k)}\| = 0.$$

*Hint* Choose a subsequence $\{f_{n(k)}\}$ with

$$\|f_{n(k)} - f_{n(k-1)}\| \le 2^{-k}$$

and consider

$$f_{n(1)} + \sum_{k=2}^{\infty} (f_{n(k)} - f_{n(k-1)}).$$

(b)
$$\lim_{n \to \infty} \|f - f_n\| = 0 \qquad \text{if } f \text{ is as in (a).}$$

*Hint* $\|f - f_n\| \le \|f - f_{n(k)}\| + \|f_{n(k)} - f\|.$

**2.7.28** Construct a sequence $\{f_n\}, f_n \in L^1$, with

$$\lim_{n\to\infty} \|f_n\| = 0,$$

while $\{f_n\}$ does not converge to zero almost everywhere. (But a subsequence of $\{f_n\}$ must converge to zero by Exercise 2.7.27a).

**2.7.29** Let $f \in L^1$ and $\varepsilon > 0$. Prove that there is a step function (continuous function, pl-function) $\varphi$ with $\|f - \varphi\| \leq \varepsilon$.

*Hint* See Proposition 2.1.8.

Exercise 2.7.27 tells us that $L^1$ is a complete space, and Exercise 2.7.29 means that the space $L$ of step functions is dense in $L^1$.

## G. The Daniell Integral

**2.7.30**

(a) Prove that $x^2\varphi$ is integrable for every step function $\varphi$.

(b) Define an integral $\int \varphi\, d\mu$ for step functions by

$$\int \varphi\, d\mu = \int x^2 \varphi\, dx.$$

Prove that Properties (1) to (4) of Section 2.5 are satisfied.

(c) Prove that for $\varphi \in L$, the function $\phi$ defined by

$$\phi(x) = \varphi(\sqrt[3]{x})$$

is again a step function and

$$3\int \varphi\, d\mu = \int \phi\, dx.$$

*Hint* Prove this first for a characteristic function of a closed interval.

(d) Show that a set $E$ is a $d\mu$-null set if and only if

$$\sqrt[3]{E} = \{y : y = \sqrt[3]{x} \text{ for some } x \in E\}$$

is a null set for Lebesgue integration.

(e) Prove that a function $f$ on the real line is $d\mu$-integrable if and only if the function $F$ defined by

$$F(x) = f(\sqrt[3]{x})$$

is Lebesgue integrable and that, if $f$ is $d\mu$-integrable, then

$$3\int f\, d\mu = \int F\, dx.$$

# SUMMARY

A function $f$ on the real line is (Lebesgue) integrable if there is a series $\sum \varphi_n$ of step functions such that

(a) $$f = \sum_{n=1}^{\infty} \varphi_n \text{ a.e.}$$

(b) $$\sum_{n=1}^{\infty} \int |\varphi_n| \, dx < \infty$$

and in this case the (Lebesgue) integral of $f$ is given by

$$\int f \, dx = \sum_{n=1}^{\infty} \int \varphi_n \, dx$$

(Definition 2.1.3). An equivalent condition for integrability of $f$ is that there is a series $\sum \varphi_n$ of step functions such that $\sum_{n=1}^{\infty} \int |\varphi_n| \, dx < \infty$ and

$$f(x) = \sum_{n=1}^{\infty} \varphi_n(x)$$

for all $x$ for which the last series converges absolutely (Mikusiński's lemma 2.1.10).

An integrable function $f$ is also characterized by the fact that there is a sequence $\{\psi_n\}$ of step functions with the properties

(a) $$f = \lim_{n \to \infty} \psi_n \text{ a.e.}$$

(b) $$\lim_{n \to \infty} \int |\psi_n - \psi_m| \, dx = 0$$

and then

$$\int f \, dx = \lim_{n \to \infty} \int \psi_n \, dx$$

(Proposition 2.1.8).

Every step function is Lebesgue integrable and its Lebesgue integral is just the one defined in Chapter 1. Also, a function $f$, which is continuous on a closed bounded interval $[a, b]$ and vanishes outside $[a, b]$, is Lebesgue integrable and its Lebesgue integral coincides with its Riemann integral on $[a, b]$ (Proposition 2.1.5).

The set of integrable functions is denoted by $L^1$.

Basic properties of integrable functions and their integrals are the following:

(1) If $f, g \in L^1$, then $af + bg, f \vee g$, and $f \wedge g$ all belong to $L^1$ where $a, b$ are real numbers (Proposition 2.2.1).

(2) If $f, g \in L^1$, then for any real numbers $a, b$,

$$\int (af + bg) \, dx = a \int f \, dx + b \int g \, dx$$

(Proposition 2.2.1).

(3) If $f \in L^1$ and $f \geq 0$, then $\int f \, dx \geq 0$ (Proposition 2.2.1).

(4) If $\{f_n\}$ is a decreasing sequence of nonnegative $f_n \in L^1$ and $\lim_{n\to\infty} f_n(x) = 0$ for all $x$, then

$$\lim_{n\to\infty} \int f_n \, dx = 0$$

(Corollary 2.3.2).

Other useful properties of integrable functions are the following (Corollary 2.2.3):

$$\int f \, dx \leq \int g \, dx \qquad \text{if } f \leq g,$$

$$\left| \int f \, dx \right| \leq \int |f| \, dx,$$

$$\int f^+ \, dx \leq \int |f| \, dx, \qquad \int f^- \, dx \leq \int |f| \, dx.$$

The theorems on interchangeability of the integral sign and limit operations, which follow, are always referred to by their names.

## Beppo Levi's Theorem

THEOREM 2.2.4 If $\sum f_n$ is a series of integrable functions such that

$$\sum \int |f_n| \, dx$$

converges, then $\sum f_n$ converges almost everywhere, and if $f$ is any function that equals $\sum_{n=1}^{\infty} f_n$ a.e., then

$$\int f \, dx = \sum_{n=1}^{\infty} \int f_n \, dx.$$

## Monotone Convergence Theorem

THEOREM 2.3.1 If $\{f_n\}$ is an increasing (or a decreasing) sequence of integrable functions such that $\{\int f_n \, dx\}$ is bounded, then $\{f_n\}$ converges almost everywhere; and if $f$ is any function that equals $\lim_{n\to\infty} f_n$ a.e., then

$$\int f \, dx = \lim_{n\to\infty} \int f_n \, dx.$$

## Lebesgue's Dominated Convergence Theorem

THEOREM 2.3.3 If $\{f_n\}$ is a sequence of integrable functions that converges almost everywhere at a function $f$ and if there is an integrable function $g$ such that $|f_n| \leq g$ for all $n$, then $f$ is integrable and

$$\int f \, dx = \lim_{n\to\infty} \int f_n \, dx.$$

## Fatou's Lemma

LEMMA 2.3.4 If $\{f_n\}$ is a sequence of nonnegative integrable functions such that $\liminf \int f_n\,dx$ is finite, then $\liminf f_n(x)$ exists for almost all $x$, and if $f$ is any function with

$$f = \liminf f_n \quad \text{a.e.},$$

then $f$ is integrable and

$$\int f\,dx \leq \liminf \int f_n\,dx.$$

If $\{f_n\}$ is a sequence of integrable functions that converges almost everywhere to a function $f$, and if there is an integrable function $g$ with $|f| \leq g$, then $f$ is integrable (Theorem 2.4.1), but we cannot compute the integral of $f$ in terms of the integrals of $f_n$ as in Lebesgue's dominated convergence theorem.

All these theorems carry over to the setting of the Daniell integral where we have a set $L$ of "elementary" functions defined on an abstract set $S$, and an integral $\int \varphi\,d\mu$ for the functions $\varphi \in L$ subject to the following conditions (Section 2.5):

(1) If $\varphi$, $\psi \in L$, then $a\varphi + b\psi$, $\varphi \vee \psi$, $\varphi \wedge \psi$ all belong to $L$ where $a, b$ are any real numbers.
(2) If $\varphi$, $\psi \in L$, then for all real numbers $a$, $b$,

$$\int (a\varphi + b\psi)\,d\mu = a\int \varphi\,d\mu + b\int \psi\,d\mu.$$

(3) If $\varphi \in L$ and $\varphi \geq 0$, then $\int \varphi\,d\mu \geq 0$.
(4) If $\{\varphi_n\}$ is a decreasing sequence of nonnegative elementary functions, $\varphi_n \geq \varphi_{n+1} \geq 0$, and $\lim_{n\to\infty} \varphi_n(x) = 0$ for all $x$, then

$$\lim_{n\to\infty} \int \varphi_n\,dx = 0.$$

## Comparison Theorem

THEOREM 2.5.7 Suppose $L_1$ and $L_2$ are linear spaces of elementary functions on the same set $S$ with integrals $\int \varphi\,d\mu_1$ for $\varphi \in L_1$ and $\int \psi\,d\mu_2$ for $\psi \in L_2$. Let $L_i^1$ be the set of $d\mu_i$-integrable functions, $i = 1, 2$. If $L_1 \subset L_2^1$ and

$$\int \varphi\,d\mu_1 = \int \varphi\,d\mu_2 \qquad \text{for } \varphi \in L_1$$

then $L_1^1 \subset L_2^1$ and

$$\int f\,d\mu_1 = \int f\,d\mu_2 \qquad \text{for } f \in L_1^1.$$

If also $L_2 \subset L_1^1$ and

$$\int \psi\,d\mu_2 = \int \psi\,d\mu_1 \qquad \text{for } \psi \in L_2$$

then $L_1^1 = L_2^1$ and

$$\int f\,d\mu_1 = \int f\,d\mu_2 \qquad \text{for } f \in L_1^1 = L_2^1$$

(Corollary 2.5.8).

# 3

# Measurability

The set of integrable functions, though endowed with many nice properties, is certainly not perfect in all respects in that we have to impose some extra condition on almost every operation if we do not want it to lead us out of the set. In their quest for perfection mathematicians have of course devised another concept, the measurable function. Any conceivable operation applied to measurable functions leads back to a measurable function. Nevertheless, these measurable functions are closely related to integrable functions. Such a measurable function $f$ might not possess an integral because it can have large values, but if we cut off the function, say by a nonnegative step function $\varphi$, then we obtain an integrable function $\text{mid}(-\varphi, f, \varphi)$ (see Figure 3.1), and this is just the definition of a measurable function. Basic properties are discussed in Sections 3.1 and 3.2, and Section 3.3 considers the related measurable sets, those sets whose characteristic functions are measurable.

The remainder of the chapter, Sections 3.4 and 3.5, is dispensable for the study of this book. However, when another text is read which presents a different (measure theoretic) approach to the theory of integration, these sections will serve to clarify the relationship to our methods. Each of the sections can be studied independently of the other. Section 3.4 shows how a theory of integration can be obtained by knowing only the measure of certain elementary sets, as for instance intervals in the case of Lebesgue integration. Section 3.5 defines an outer measure for every set whether measurable or not and discusses some of its basic properties. This concept of outer measure is especially useful when not very much is known about the nature of the sets that one is dealing with.

## 3.1 MEASURABLE FUNCTIONS

The class of integrable functions that we have just introduced cannot be extended to a larger class with the same type of integral in the way that we extended the class of step functions to the class of integrable functions. Still, it is sometimes desirable to have a larger class in which we can perform certain operations, like taking the product of two functions, without getting outside the class. For instance, in the class of integrable functions it may happen that the product of two integrable functions is not integrable. Namely, let

$$f(x) = \begin{cases} x^{1/2} & \text{if } x \in (0, 1) \\ 0 & \text{if } x \notin (0, 1). \end{cases}$$

Then $f$ is integrable, but $f^2$ is not. However, we do not want our proposed larger class to include pathologic functions of the kind possessed by the characteristic function of the set defined in Example 1.4.4. Loosely speaking, we want a class of functions having the same kind of regularity as the integrable functions, but not necessarily possessing a finite integral.

We will now work again with ordinary Lebesgue integrable functions on the real line, but we will keep in mind the possibility of generalizing our work to the Daniell integral setting of Section 2.5. We can formalize one more property of

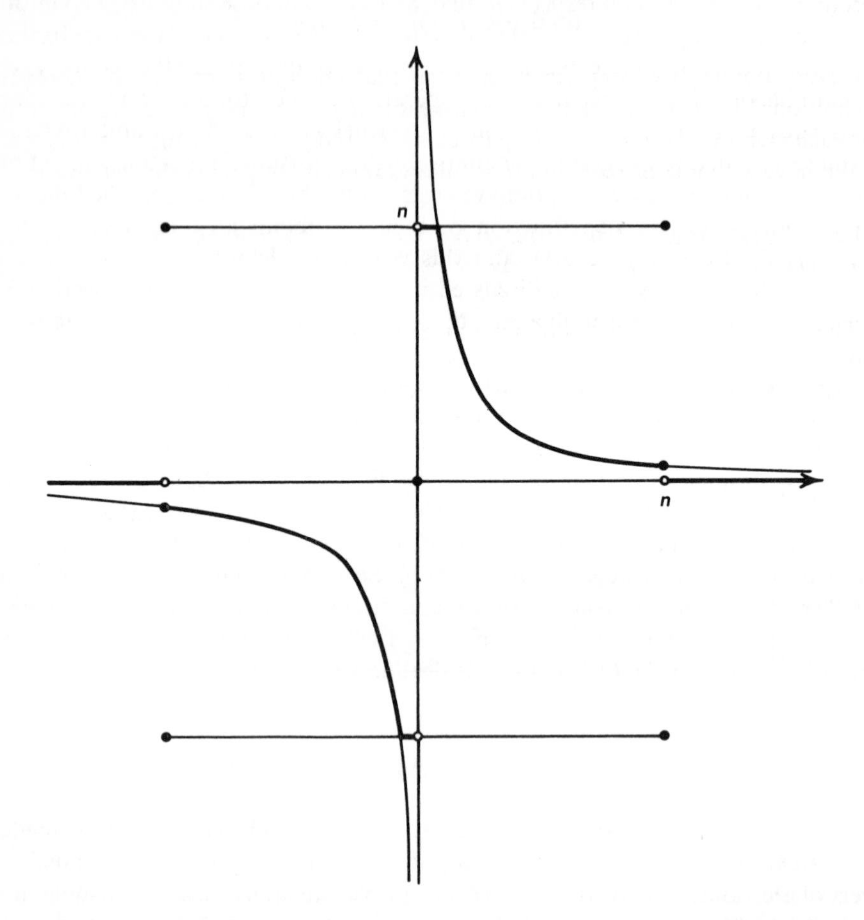


Figure 3.1 The graph of mid$(-\varphi, f, \varphi)$ is traced in heavy lines, where $f$ is the function defined by $f(x) = 1/x$ for $x \neq 0$ and $f(0) = 0$, and $\varphi$ is the characteristic function of $[-n, n]$.

the step functions on the real line in a postulate named Stone's axiom after M. H. Stone:

(5) *If* $\varphi \in L$, *then* $1 \wedge \varphi \in L$.

We will always announce when we make use of properties of step functions that are more special than those covered by Properties (1) to (5). (Properties (1) to (4) are listed in Section 2.5.)

3.1.1 DEFINITION *A function $f$ is called measurable if* mid$(-\varphi, f, \varphi)$ *is integrable for every step function* $\varphi \geq 0$. (See Figure 3.1.)

For the notation mid($a$, $b$, $c$) and its equivalents, see the proof of Theorem 2.4.1. Note also that

$$(\text{mid}(-\varphi, f, \varphi))^+ = f^+ \wedge \varphi,$$
$$(\text{mid}(-\varphi, f, \varphi))^- = f^- \wedge \varphi$$

for every nonnegative step function $\varphi$, so that an equivalent way of expressing Definition 3.1.1 is to say that $f$ is measurable if $f^+ \wedge \varphi$ and $f^- \wedge \varphi$ are integrable for each step function $\varphi \geq 0$. In particular, $f^+$ and $f^-$ are measurable if $f$ is.

We have a simple proposition that follows immediately from the definition.

**3.1.2 PROPOSITION** *All integrable functions are measurable. All constant functions are measurable.*

The second statement follows from Stone's axiom in case the constant is different from zero. We can now prove that the class of measurable functions is closed under linear and order operations (compare Proposition 1.1.2 and Proposition 2.2.1, Property (1)).

**3.1.3 PROPOSITION** *If $f$ and $g$ are measurable functions and $a$, $b$ are real numbers, then*

$$af + bg,\ |f|,\ f \vee g, \text{ and } f \wedge g$$

*are measurable functions.*

*Proof* Let $\varphi$ be any nonnegative step function. Then

$$h_n = \text{mid}(-\varphi, a\ \text{mid}(-n\varphi, f, n\varphi) + b\ \text{mid}(-n\varphi, g, n\varphi), \varphi)$$

defines a sequence of integrable functions satisfying $|h_n| \leq \varphi$ and

$$\lim_{n\to\infty} h_n = \text{mid}(-\varphi, af + bg, \varphi)$$

everywhere, as one can see by considering the cases $\varphi(x) = 0$ and $\varphi(x) > 0$ separately. Hence Lebesgue's dominated convergence theorem proves that mid($-\varphi$, $af + bg$, $\varphi$) is integrable, so that $af + bg$ is indeed measurable. The other three statements now follow from this and the remark after Definition 3.1.1, according to which $f^+, f^-$ and hence $|f| = f^+ + f^-$ are measurable if $f$ is measurable, and thus also

$$f \vee g = \tfrac{1}{2}(f + g) + \tfrac{1}{2}|f - g|,$$
$$f \wedge g = \tfrac{1}{2}(f + g) - \tfrac{1}{2}|f - g|.$$

One can also prove directly that $f \vee g$ and $f \wedge g$ are measurable (Exercise 3.1.1).

The class of measurable functions is also closed under the process of taking pointwise almost everywhere limits of sequences.

**3.1.4 PROPOSITION** *If $\{f_n\}$ is a sequence of measurable functions and $f$ is a function such that*

$$f = \lim_{n \to \infty} f_n \text{ a.e.,}$$

*then $f$ is a measurable function.*

*Proof* If $\varphi$ is a fixed nonnegative step function, then

$$\text{mid}(-\varphi, f, \varphi) = \lim_{n \to \infty} \text{mid}(-\varphi, f_n, \varphi) \text{ a.e.,}$$

and

$$|\text{mid}(-\varphi, f_n, \varphi)| \leq \varphi \qquad \text{for all } n.$$

Hence Lebesgue's dominated convergence theorem proves the integrability of $\text{mid}(-\varphi, f, \varphi)$, so that $f$ is measurable.

In particular, if $\{f_n\}$ is a sequence of integrable functions and

$$f = \lim f_n \text{ a.e.,}$$

then $f$ is measurable. Conversely, if we want to make use of a special property of the ordinary Lebesgue integrable functions on $R$, then we can prove that every measurable function is the limit almost everywhere of a sequence of integrable functions. Namely, there exist sequences of nonnegative step functions that tend to infinity at all points of $R$, for example, the sequence $\{\varphi_n\}$ defined by

$$\varphi_n(x) = \begin{cases} n & \text{if } |x| \leq n \\ 0 & \text{if } |x| > n; \end{cases}$$

$(-n, n; n)$ is a presentation for $\varphi_n$. Now

$$f = \lim_{n \to \infty} \text{mid}(-\varphi_n, f, \varphi_n)$$

is the pointwise limit of a sequence of integrable functions. One can even prove that

$$f = \lim_{n \to \infty} \psi_n \text{ a.e.}$$

for some sequence $\{\psi_n\}$ of step functions if $f$ is measurable (Exercise 3.1.6). In the next section we will prove a weaker statement using only Properties (1) through (5), namely that any measurable function is the limit of a sequence of "generalized step functions."

**3.1.5 COROLLARY** *If the function $f$ is continuous, then it is also measurable.*

*Proof* $f$ is the limit of the sequence $f\chi_{[-n\ n]} = f_n$, and each function $f_n$ is Lebesgue integrable by Proposition 2.1.5.

Actually, our definition of measurable functions depends seemingly on the set of elementary functions that we start with to build up integration theory. That this is really not the case will follow from the following proposition which tells us that we could have used integrable functions in Definition 3.1.1 instead of step functions.

**3.1.6 PROPOSITION** *A function $f$ is measurable if and only if* $\text{mid}(-g, f, g)$ *is integrable for every integrable function* $g \geq 0$.

*Proof* If $\text{mid}(-g, f, g)$ is integrable for every integrable function $g \geq 0$, then, in particular, $\text{mid}(-\varphi, f, \varphi)$ is integrable for every step function $\varphi \geq 0$.

Now suppose $f$ is measurable and $g \geq 0$ is integrable. Let $\sum \varphi_n$ be a series of step functions that converges to $g$ a.e. and satisfies $\sum_{n=1}^{\infty} \int |\varphi_n| \, dx < \infty$. Let $h$ be an integrable function that equals $\sum_{n=1}^{\infty} |\varphi_n|$ a.e.

$$g_n = \text{mid}\left(-\sum_{k=1}^{n} \varphi_k, f, \sum_{k=1}^{n} \varphi_k\right)$$

is integrable and $\{g_n\}$ tends to $\text{mid}(-g, f, g)$ a.e. Furthermore,

$$|g_n| \leq \left|\sum_{k=1}^{n} \varphi_k\right| \leq h \text{ a.e.}$$

so that $\text{mid}(-g, f, g)$ is indeed integrable by Lebesgue's dominated convergence theorem.

**3.1.7 COROLLARY** *If different classes of elementary functions yield the same class of integrable functions, then the corresponding classes of measurable functions are also identical.*

For instance, it does not matter whether we use step functions or piecewise linear functions to define the Lebesgue integral; both methods will yield the same class of measurable functions.

There is another consequence of Proposition 3.1.5 which is so important that we formulate it as a theorem. This theorem is used over and over again, and often without reference to it.

**3.1.8 THEOREM** *If $f$ is a measurable function and* $|f| \leq g$ a.e. *for some integrable function $g \geq 0$, then $f$ is integrable.*

*Proof* Indeed, we have $\text{mid}(-g, f, g) = f$ a.e. in this case.

## *EXERCISES*

*3.1.1* Show that if $f$ and $g$ are measurable functions, then $f \vee g$ and $f \wedge g$ are also measurable, using the formula

$$\begin{aligned} \text{mid}(a, b, c) &= (a \vee b) \wedge (b \vee c) \wedge (c \vee a) \\ &= (a \wedge b) \vee (b \wedge c) \vee (c \wedge a). \end{aligned}$$

*3.1.2* Show that a function $f$ is measurable if and only if mid$(-n\chi_{[-n,n]}, f, n\chi_{[-n,n]})$ is integrable for all $n$.

*3.1.3* Suppose $f$ is measurable. Show that the functions $f_h$ and $\check{f}$ defined by

$$f_h(x) = f(x+h),\ \check{f}(x) = f(-x)$$

are measurable.

*3.1.4* Show that if $f$ is measurable, and $g$ and $h$ are integrable (but not necessarily nonnegative), then mid$(f, g, h)$ is an integrable function.

*Hint* Show that mid $(f, g\ h)$ is measurable and that $|\text{mid}\ (f, g, h)| \leq |g| \vee |h|$.

*3.1.5* Let $f$ and $g$ be two nonnegative measurable functions. Show that the function $h$ defined by

$$h(x) = \begin{cases} \dfrac{f(x)g(x)}{f(x)+g(x)} & \text{if } f(x)+g(x) \neq 0 \\ 0 & \text{if } f(x) = g(x) = 0 \end{cases}$$

is a measurable function.

*Hint* Show that if $a, b \geq 0$, then the minimum of $(t+1)^2 a + (t-1)^2 b$ as $t$ varies over all real numbers is 0 if $a + b = 0$ and $4ab(a+b)^{-1}$ otherwise. Hence, if $\{r_n\}$ is a sequence that enumerates all rational numbers,

$$\lim_{n\to\infty} \tfrac{1}{4} \bigwedge_{k=1}^{n} [(r_k+1)^2 f(x) + (r_k-1)^2 g(x)] = \begin{cases} \dfrac{f(x)g(x)}{f(x)+g(x)} & \text{if } f(x)+g(x) \neq 0 \\ 0 & \text{if } f(x) = g(x) = 0 \end{cases}$$

*3.1.6* Show that if $f$ is a measurable function, then $f = \lim_{n\to\infty} \varphi_n$ a.e. for some sequence of step functions.

*Hint* Define the function $g$ by

$$g(x) = 2^{-k} \qquad \text{for } k-1 \leq |x| < k,\ k = 1, 2, \cdots.$$

To show the property

$$= \lim_{n\to\infty} \varphi_n \text{ a.e.}$$

for a nonnegative measurable function $f$, prove that the function

$$h = \frac{fg}{f+g}$$

is integrable; then write $h$ as the limit almost everywhere of step functions and use the relation

$$f = \frac{gh}{g - h}.$$

Note that this approximation property is very special for the concrete setting of the ordinary Lebesgue integral on the real line.

## 3.2 GENERALIZED STEP FUNCTIONS

In the previous section we used only the original properties (1) to (4) of the class of step functions (elementary functions), except for the proof that all constant functions are measurable which used Property (5) (Stone's axiom) and in Exercise 3.1.6 where we used the special properties of the ordinary step functions on the real line. We come now to statements where we have to use Property (5), because they deal with constructions of measurable functions having only finitely many values, and in particular with such functions taking on only the values 0 and 1.

3.2.1 DEFINITION *A measurable function that takes on only a finite number of different values is called a generalized step function (or simple function).*

In our next proposition we need the following representation of the square of a real number $a$. If $\{r_k\}$ is an enumeration of the rational numbers, then

$$a^2 = \lim_{n\to\infty} \max \{2r_k a - r_k^2 : 1 \leq k \leq n\}.$$

To prove this, note first that the parabola

$$f(x) = 2xa - x^2 = -(a - x)^2 + a^2$$

has its maximum at $a$ where it assumes the value $a^2$. Thus

$$a^2 = \sup \{2xa - x^2 : x \text{ real}\} = f(a)$$

and since we can find rational numbers arbitrarily close to $a$,

$$\begin{aligned} a^2 &= \sup \{2r_k a - r_k^2 : k \geq 1\} \\ &= \lim_{n\to\infty} \max \{2r_k a - r_k^2 : 1 \leq k \leq n\}. \end{aligned}$$

3.2.2 PROPOSITION *If $f_1, \cdots, f_k$ are measurable functions and $P(x_1, \cdots, x_k)$ is a polynomial in $k$ variables, then $P(f_1, \cdots, f_k)$ is measurable.*

*Proof* Let $f$ be a measurable function and $\{r_k\}$ a sequence that enumerates all rational numbers. Since

$$f^2 = \lim_{n\to\infty} \bigvee_{k=1}^{n} (2r_k f - r_k^2),$$

it follows from Proposition 3.1.4 that $f^2$ is a measurable function. Hence if $f$ and $g$ are measurable functions, then

$$fg = \tfrac{1}{4}[(f+g)^2 - (f-g)^2]$$

is also measurable, so that if $P(x_1, \cdots, x_k)$ is a polynomial in $k$ variables with real coefficients and $f_1, \cdots, f_k$ are measurable functions, then $P(f_1, \cdots, f_k)$ is a measurable function.

As an application we obtain this characterization of generalized step functions.

3.2.3 PROPOSITION *A function $f$ is a generalized step function if and only if it is a finite linear combination of measurable characteristic functions of pairwise disjoint sets.*

*Proof* If $f$ is a generalized step function and $\{C_1, C_2, \cdots, C_n\}$ is the entire set of values of $f$, then the functions

$$\chi_k = \frac{\prod_{h\neq k}(f - C_h)}{\prod_{h\neq k}(C_k - C_h)}$$

are measurable characteristic functions, that is, functions that take at each point either the value zero or the value one, in fact

$$\chi_k(x) = \begin{cases} 1 & \text{if } f(x) = C_k \\ 0 & \text{if } f(x) = C_h,\ h \neq k. \end{cases}$$

Then, of course,

$$f = \sum_{k=1}^{n} C_k \chi_k,$$

which is the desired construction.

An intuitively promising way to obtain a generalized step function is to take an ordinary step function $\varphi$ on the real line and compose it with a measurable function $f$. Obviously the function $\varphi \circ f$ has only finitely many values, but we have to prove that it is measurable.

3.2.4 PROPOSITION *A function $f$ is measurable if and only if $\varphi \circ f$ is a generalized step function for every step function $\varphi$. If $f$ is a measurable function, then*

$$f = \lim_{n\to\infty} f_n$$

*for some sequence $\{f_n\}$ of generalized step functions.*

*Proof* Suppose $f$ is measurable. If $\chi$ is the characteristic function of a closed bounded interval $[a, b]$, then

$$\chi(x) = \lim_{n\to\infty} [(nx - na + 1)^+ \wedge 1 \wedge (nb + 1 - nx)^+]$$

and thus

$$\chi \circ f = \lim_{n\to\infty} [(nf - na + 1)^+ \wedge 1 \wedge (nb + 1 - nf)^+];$$

(the function $(nx - na + 1)^+ \wedge 1 \wedge (nb + 1 - nx)^+$ is the function $\psi_n$ in Equation (2.5.9) and Figure 2.4). Hence $\chi \circ f$ is measurable. According to Lemma 1.1.3

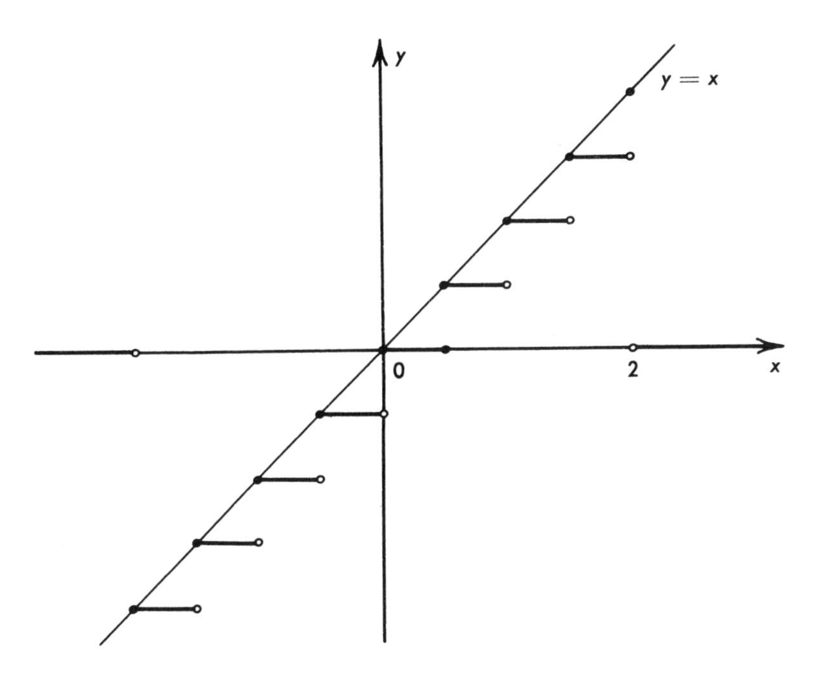


Figure 3.2 The function $x$ is the limit of the sequence $\{\varphi_n\}$ of step functions defined by $\varphi_n(x) = [nx]/n$ for $|x| \leq n$ and $\varphi_n(x) = 0$ for $|x| > n$.

each step function $\varphi$ is a linear combination of characteristic functions of closed bounded intervals; consequently $\varphi \circ f$ is measurable.

Conversely, suppose $\varphi \circ f$ were measurable for each step function. Then we can represent the function $x$ as the limit of a sequence of step functions, for example, the sequence $\{\varphi_n\}$ in Figure 3.2 defined by

$$\varphi_n(x) = \begin{cases} \dfrac{1}{n}[nx] & \text{if } |x| \leq n \\ 0 & \text{if } |x| > n \end{cases}$$

where $[nx]$ denotes the largest integer smaller than or equal to $nx$. Since $0 \leq x - \varphi_n(x) \leq 1/n$ for $|x| \leq n$, we have indeed

$$\lim_{n\to\infty} \varphi_n(x) = x.$$

Thus

$$f = \lim_{n\to\infty} \varphi_n \circ f,$$

proving by Proposition 3.1.4 that $f$ is measurable. This proves also the second assertion of the proposition.

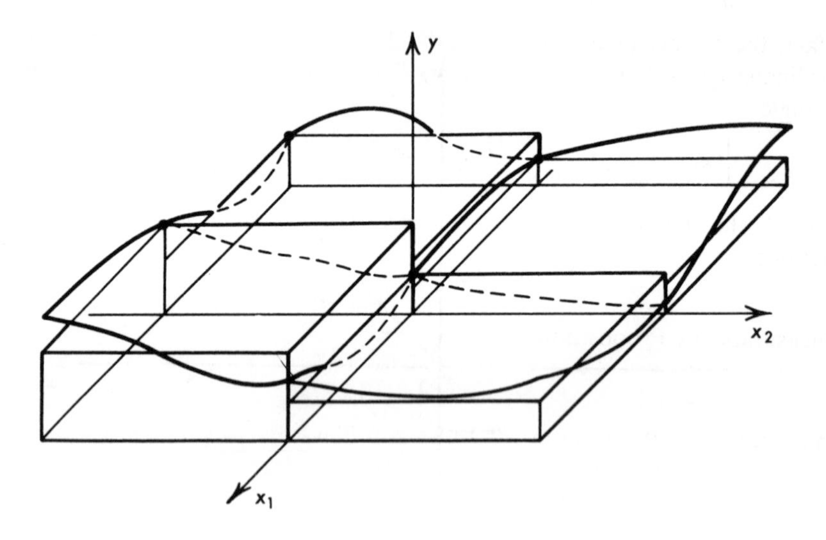


Figure 3.3 Approximation of a continuous function of two variables by step functions.

So far we have found that two classes of functions, polynomials and step functions "operate" on the class of measurable functions in the sense that if $g$ is any such function and $f$ is a measurable function, then $g \circ f$ is measurable. We shall now see how one more passage to the limit proves that continuous functions also operate on the class of measurable functions.

3.2.5 THEOREM *If $f_1, \cdots, f_k$ are measurable functions and $F$ is a continuous function of $k$ variables, then $F(f_1, \cdots, f_k)$ is a measurable function.*

*Proof* We define the sequence $\{\psi_n\}$ by

$$\psi_n(x_1, \cdots, x_k) = \begin{cases} F\left(\frac{1}{n}[nx_1], \cdots, \frac{1}{n}[nx_k]\right) & \text{if } -n \leq x_1, \cdots, x_k < n; \\ 0 & \text{otherwise} \end{cases}$$

(see Figure 3.3). It is a consequence of the continuity of $F$ that

$$F = \lim_{n\to\infty} \psi_n$$

everywhere. Moreover, $\psi_n$ is a linear combination of $(2n^2)^k$ functions of the form

$$\chi_{p_1}(x_1)\chi_{p_2}(x_2)\cdots\chi_{p_k}(x_k) \tag{3.2.6}$$

where $\chi_{p_1}, \cdots, \chi_{p_k}$ is any $k$-tuple of characteristic functions $\chi_p$ of the $2n^2$ intervals

$$\frac{p-1}{n} \le x < \frac{p}{n}, \qquad p = -n^2+1, -n^2+2, \cdots, n^2-1, n^2.$$

In fact, the coefficient of such a term (3.2.6) is the value of $F$ at the point with coordinates $(p_1 - 1)/n, \cdots, (p_k - 1)/n$. This is one corner of the $k$-dimensional rectangle

$$\left\{(x_1, \cdots, x_k): \frac{(p_1-1)}{n} \le x_1 < \frac{p_1}{n}, \cdots, \frac{(p_k-1)}{n} \le x_k < \frac{p_k}{n}\right\}$$

of which the function (3.2.6) is the characteristic function. Since each of the functions

$$\chi_{p_j} \circ f_j, j = 1, \cdots, k,$$

is measurable by Proposition 3.2.4,

$$(\chi_{p_1} \circ f_1)\cdots(\chi_{p_k} \circ f_k)$$

is measurable by Proposition 3.2.2. So it follows that $\psi_n(f_1, \cdots, f_k)$, which is a linear combination of these functions, is also measurable. Finally, since

$$F(f_1, \cdots, f_k) = \lim_{n\to\infty} \psi_n(f_1, \cdots, f_k)$$

it follows that $F(f_1, \cdots, f_k)$ is measurable, as claimed.

As an example let us prove that for any measurable function $f$, the function $g$ defined by

$$g(x) = \begin{cases} \dfrac{1}{f(x)} & \text{if } f(x) \neq 0 \\ 0 & \text{if } f(x) = 0 \end{cases}$$

is also measurable. Indeed, for each integer $n \ge 1$, $nx/(nx^2 + 1)$ is a continuous function of one variable. Thus

$$f_n = \frac{nf}{nf^2 + 1}$$

is measurable by Theorem 3.2.6. Since

$$g(x) = \lim_{n\to\infty} f_n(x)$$

for all $x$, $g$ is measurable also.

As an application of the theory of generalized step functions we shall now show that the set of those generalized step functions that are at the same time integrable functions satisfies Properties (1) to (5) and that the set of integrable functions which is generated by its completion coincides with the original set of integrable functions.

3.2.7 PROPOSITION *The set $L_1$ of all integrable generalized step functions or, in other words, the set of all integrable functions that take on only a finite number of values, is a class of elementary functions satisfying Properties* (1) *to* (5). *The set $L_1^1$ of integrable functions defined by this class of elementary functions coincides with the original set $L^1$ of integrable functions, and the integrals on them are the same.*

*Proof* The verification of Properties (1) and (5) for $L_1$ is left to the reader as an exercise (Exercise 3.2.1). Properties (2), (3), and (4) are evident, since we are dealing with a set of integrable functions. If we now think of $L_2$ as the original class of elementary functions (step functions), then Theorem 2.5.7 shows that $L_1^1 \subset L_2^1$, $L_2^1$ being the original class $L^1$ of integrable functions, and that the integrals coincide on $L_1^1$. But if $f$ is a nonnegative function in $L_2^1$, then $\{\varphi_n \circ f\}$ is a sequence of measurable functions that converges increasingly to $f$ if we define $\varphi_n$ by

$$\varphi_n(x) = \begin{cases} \dfrac{1}{n}\,[nx] & \text{if } |x| \leq n \\ 0 & \text{if } |x| > n \end{cases}$$

(see Figure 3.2). By Theorem 3.1.8, $\varphi_n \circ f$ is in fact integrable because $\varphi_n \circ f \leq f$, and it belongs therefore to $L_1$. Thus, by the monotone convergence theorem, $f \in L_1^1$ and its integral as a function in $L_1^1$ coincides with the integral it has as a function in $L_2^1$, whence $L_1^1 = L_2^1$ and the integrals coincide, as claimed.

## EXERCISES

*3.2.1* Show that if $f$ and $g$ are integrable generalized step functions, then so are $af + bg$ for all real numbers $a$ and $b$, $f \vee g$, $f \wedge g$, and $f \wedge 1$.

*3.2.2* If $f$ is a generalized step function, call

$$f = \sum_{k=1}^{n} c_k \chi_k,$$

where the $\chi_k$ are measurable characteristic functions, a presentation of $f$; and call the number $n$ the length of the presentation. Show that there exists a unique presentation of shortest length for each generalized step function.

*Hint* This is the presentation constructed in the proof of Proposition 3.2.3.

*3.2.3* Show that if

$$f = \sum_{k=1}^{n} C_k \chi_k$$

is the presentation of shortest length of an integrable generalized step function $f$ as defined in Exercise 3.2.2, then $\chi_k$, $k = 1, \cdots, n$ are integrable.

*Hint* $\chi_k \leq |C_k^{-1} f|$.

*3.2.4* Show that if $F(x_1, \cdots, x_k)$ is a continuous function of $k$ real variables and $f_1, \cdots, f_k$ are generalized step functions, then $F(f_1, \cdots, f_k)$ is a generalized step function.

*3.2.5* Show that if $P(x_1, \cdots, x_k)$ is a polynomial and $f_1, \cdots, f_k$ are integrable generalized step functions, then $P(f_1, \cdots, f_k)$ is the sum of an integrable generalized step function and a constant.

*Hint* Use Exercise 3.2.3 to show that for an integrable generalized step function $f_j$ the characteristic function $\chi_j$ of the set

$$E_j = \{x : f_j(x) \neq 0\}$$

is integrable. If $c$ denotes the value of $P(x_1, \cdots \ x_k)$ at the origin, show that there is a constant $M$ with

$$|P(f_1, \cdots, f_k) - c| \leq M(\chi_1 \vee \cdots \vee \chi_k).$$

## 3.3 MEASURABLE SETS

In general, a function that takes on only the values 0 and 1, and no others, is called a characteristic function. Such functions are in a one-to-one correspondence with the subsets of the real line (or the subsets of the abstract set $S$, as the case may be). In symbols, the characteristic function $\chi_A$ and the set $A$ correspond if and only if

$$\chi_A(x) = \begin{cases} 1 & \text{if } x \in A \\ 0 & \text{if } x \notin A \end{cases}$$

$$A = \{x : \chi_A(x) = 1\}.$$

Since we have already dealt with measurable and integrable characteristic functions, what we mean by measurable and integrable sets is clear.

**3.3.1 DEFINITION** *A set $A$ is called measurable if $\chi_A$ is measurable and integrable if $\chi_A$ is integrable.*

Hence the integrable sets form a subfamily of the family of measurable sets.

**3.3.2 Definition** *If $A$ is an integrable set, put*

$$\sigma(A) = \int \chi_A \, dx.$$

*If $A$ is measurable but not integrable, put $\sigma(A) = \infty$. Then $\sigma(A)$ is called the measure of $A$.*

Subject to the general principle that in this book we treat chiefly the case of the ordinary Lebesgue integral on the real line (although in a readily generalizable manner), we have here introduced the special notation $\sigma$ for the measure in this case. In general, if the integral of the elementary functions $\varphi$ on $S$ is denoted $\int \varphi \, d\mu$, the corresponding measure of sets will be denoted $\mu(A)$. Hence for Lebesgue integration we have a notational exception, since we write $\sigma(A)$ and not $x(A)$ for the measure.

The following proposition lists the main properties of the family of measurable sets.

**3.3.3 Proposition**

(a) *If $A$ and $B$ are measurable sets, then the sets*

$$A \cup B,\ A \cap B,\ A - B,$$
$$A \,\Delta\, B = (A - B) \cup (B - A) = A \cup B - A \cap B$$

*are measurable and we have*

(1) *$\sigma(A) = 0$ if and only if $A$ is a null set,*
(2) *$\sigma(A \cup B) \leq \sigma(A) + \sigma(B)$ with equality if $A \cap B = \varnothing$,*
(3) *$\sigma(A) \leq \sigma(B)$ if $A \subset B$.*

(b) *If $\{A_n\}$ is an increasing sequence of measurable sets, then $A = \bigcup_{n=1}^{\infty} A_n$ is measurable and*

$$\sigma(A) = \lim_{n\to\infty} \sigma(A_n).$$

(c) *If $\{A_n\}$ is a decreasing sequence of measurable sets, then $A = \bigcap_{n=1}^{\infty} A_n$ is measurable, and if in addition $\sigma(A_n)$ is finite for some $n$, then*

$$\sigma(A) = \lim_{n\to\infty} \sigma(A_n).$$

(d) *If $\{A_n\}$ is any sequence of measurable sets, then $A = \bigcup_{n=1}^{\infty} A_n$ is measurable and*

$$\sigma(A) \leq \sum_{n=1}^{\infty} \sigma(A_n)$$

*with equality holding if the $A_n$ are pairwise disjoint.*

*Proof* We leave the proof of part (a) of this proposition to the reader as Exercise 3.3.1.

To prove the rest of the proposition let in each case $\chi_n$ be the characteristic function of $A_n$. In (b) and (c) we have

$$\chi_A = \lim_{n\to\infty} \chi_n$$

and in (d)

$$\chi_A = \lim_{n\to\infty} (\chi_1 \vee \cdots \vee \chi_n)$$

so that in each case $A$ is measurable. If the limit in (b) exists, then $\chi_A$ is integrable by the monotone convergence theorem and

$$\sigma(A) = \int \chi_A \, dx = \lim_{n\to\infty} \int \chi_n \, dx = \lim_{n\to\infty} \sigma(A_n).$$

If $\sigma(A_n)$ diverges to infinity, then $\sigma(A) = \infty$ because we have $\sigma(A_n) \leq \sigma(A)$. Thus part (b) holds also in this case. If, say, $\sigma(A_1)$ is finite in (c), then $\sigma(A_n)$ is finite for all $n$ since $A_n \subset A_1$. Therefore (c) follows also from the monotone convergence theorem. The inequality in (d) is trivial if $\sum \sigma(A_n)$ diverges. If this sum converges then $\sum \chi_n$ converges almost everywhere, and if $h$ is a function such that

$$h = \sum_{n=1}^{\infty} \chi_n \text{ a.e.}$$

then $h$ is integrable by Beppo Levi's theorem. Since $\chi_A \leq h$ a.e., we conclude

$$\sigma(A) \leq \int h \, dx = \sum_{n=1}^{\infty} \int \chi_n \, dx = \sum_{n=1}^{\infty} \sigma(A_n),$$

and if the $A_n$ are pairwise disjoint, we have in fact $\chi_A = h$ a.e. so that equality holds in the last inequality.

Notice that in (c), $\sigma(A)$ may be different from the limit of the sequence $\{\sigma(A_n)\}$ if none of the $\sigma(A_n)$ is finite (Exercise 3.3.1).

The following theorem is only slightly more than a reformulation of Proposition 3.2.4.

3.3.4 THEOREM *A function $f$ is measurable if and only if one of the following equivalent statements holds:*

(a) *$\{x : f(x) \geq c\}$ is measurable for all real numbers $c$.*
(b) *$\{x : f(x) > c\}$ is measurable for all real numbers $c$.*
(c) *$\{x : f(x) \leq c\}$ is measurable for all real numbers $c$.*
(d) *$\{x : f(x) < c\}$ is measurable for all real numbers $c$.*

*Proof* Suppose that Statement (a) is true. If $\chi$ is the characteristic function of a closed bounded interval $[a, b]$, then

$$\chi \circ f = \lim_{n\to\infty} (\chi_{A(a)} - \chi_{A(b+1/n)})$$

where $A(c)$ denotes the set referred to in Statement (a), so $\chi \circ f$ is measurable. Since by Corollary 1.1.4 every step function is a linear combination of characteristic functions of bounded closed intervals, it follows that $\varphi \circ f$ is measurable for every step function $\varphi$ or, by Proposition 3.2.4, that $f$ is measurable. In the same way we find that each of statements (b), (c), and (d) implies the measurability of $f$. Conversely, if we suppose that $f$ is measurable and let $\chi_n$ denote the characteristic function of the set $\{x : c \leq x \leq c + n\}$, then by Propositions 3.1.4 and 3.2.4

$$\chi_{A(c)} = \lim_{n \to \infty} \chi_n \circ f$$

is measurable, so that $A(c)$ is indeed a measurable set for all real numbers $c$. In the same way we prove the remaining statements (b), (c), and (d), which concludes the proof of Theorem 3.3.4.

We are now in a position to introduce the counterpart of one of the most common features in ordinary calculus, namely the integral sign with limits, $\int_a^b f\,dx$.

**3.3.5 DEFINITION** *Let $E$ be a measurable set and let $f$ be a function defined on $E$. We say that $f$ is measurable on $E$ if the function $F$ defined by*

$$F(x) = \begin{cases} f(x) & \text{if } x \in E \\ 0 & \text{if } x \notin E \end{cases}$$

*is measurable, and we say that $f$ is integrable on $E$ if $F$ is integrable. The integral of $f$ on $E$ is defined and denoted by*

$$\int_E f\,dx = \int F\,dx.$$

*In particular, if $E$ is an interval with endpoints $a < b$, we write $\int_a^b f\,dx$ instead of $\int_E f\,dx$.*

Before we go on with abstract considerations, we want to give two examples for measurable sets on the real line. Namely, every open set and every closed set on the real line is measurable, as we shall prove below. Recall that a set $E$ is open if every point $x \in E$ is contained in an open interval $(a, b) \subset E$, and a set $F$ is closed if

$$R - F = \{x : x \notin F\}$$

is open. Open sets have the following property.

**3.3.6 LEMMA** *Every open set $E$ on the real line is the union of a sequence $(a_k, b_k)$ of pairwise disjoint intervals,*

$$E = \bigcup_{k \geq 1} (a_k, b_k).$$

*Proof* For each $x \in E$ let

$$a_x = \inf \{y : y < x, (y, x) \subset E\},$$
$$b_x = \sup \{y : y > x, (x, y) \subset E\};$$

$a_x$ and $b_x$ may be $-\infty$ or $+\infty$, respectively. We have certainly

$$(a_x, b_x) \subset E.$$

We claim that $a_x$ and $b_x$ are not in $E$, that is, $(a_x, b_x)$ is the largest open interval contained in $E$ and containing $x$. Namely, if say $a_x \in E$, then there are $a < a_x$, $b > a_x$ with $a_x \in (a, b) \subset E$ since $E$ is open, and hence

$$(a, x) \subset (a, b) \cup (a_x, x) \subset E,$$

which is a contradiction to the definition of $a_x$.

Furthermore, if $y$ is any other point, then either $(a_x, b_x) = (a_y, b_y)$ or $(a_x, b_x)$ and $(a_y, b_y)$ are disjoint; for if $(a_x, b_x) \neq (a_y, b_y)$ and $(a_x, b_x) \cap (a_y, b_y) \neq \varnothing$, then one of the following holds:

$$a_x \in (a_y, b_y) \subset E, \qquad a_y \in (a_x, b_x) \subset E,$$
$$b_x \in (a_y, b_y) \subset E, \qquad b_y \in (a_x, b_x) \subset E,$$

each of which is impossible. We have also

$$E = \bigcup_{x \in E} (a_x, b_x)$$

since $x \in (a_x, b_x)$ if $x \in E$. One can enumerate now the different intervals among the $(a_x, b_x)$ in the following way. There are at most $2n^2$ different intervals $(a_x, b_x)$ contained in $(-n, n)$ and of length greater than or equal to $1/n$. If we list these intervals first for $n = 1$, then for $n = 2$ and so on, we get an enumeration of all the bounded intervals among the $(a_x, b_x)$. But there are at most two unbounded intervals, one with a left end point $-\infty$ and another with a right end point $\infty$. This completes the proof.

3.3.7 COROLLARY *Every open set is measurable, and every closed set is measurable.*

*Proof* This is immediate for open sets. If $F$ is closed, then $\chi_F = 1 - \chi_{R-F}$ so that $F$ is measurable since the open set $R - F$ is measurable.

We shall now prove two theorems that demonstrate how the theory of measurable sets is applied in analysis. The first of these theorems, called Egoroff's theorem, gives a precise meaning to the statement that a sequence of measurable functions which converges pointwise almost everywhere is "nearly uniformly convergent."

## Egoroff's Theorem

**3.3.8 Theorem** *Let $E$ be an integrable set and let the functions $f, f_n$ be measurable on $E$ and satisfy*

$$f = \lim_{n \to \infty} f_n \text{ a.e.}$$

*on $E$ (that is, there exists a set $A$ such that $E - A$ is a null set and*

$$f(x) = \lim_{n \to \infty} f_n(x)$$

*for all $x \in A$). For each $\varepsilon > 0$ there is then a measurable set $A(\varepsilon)$ with measure at most $\varepsilon$ such that $\{f_n\}$ converges uniformly to $f$ on $E - A(\varepsilon)$.*

*Proof* Define the double sequence $\{A_{nk}\}$ of sets by

$$A_{nk} = \left\{x : x \in E, |f(x) - f_k(x)| \geq \frac{1}{n}\right\}.$$

Keep $n$ fixed and consider the sequence $\{B_{nN} : N \geq 1\}$,

$$B_{nN} = \bigcup_{k=N}^{\infty} A_{nk}.$$

This sequence of integrable sets decreases as $N$ increases and

$$\bigcap_{N=1}^{\infty} B_{nN} \subset E - A,$$

so that

$$\lim_{n \to \infty} \sigma(B_{nN}) = 0$$

by Proposition 3.3.3. Now choose $N(n)$ so large that $\sigma(B_{nN(n)}) \leq \varepsilon \cdot 2^{-n}$ and put

$$A(\varepsilon) = \bigcup_{n=1}^{\infty} B_{nN(n)}.$$

Again, by Proposition 3.3.3, $A(\varepsilon)$ is a measurable set and

$$\sigma(A(\varepsilon)) \leq \sum_{n=1}^{\infty} \sigma(B_{nN(n)}) \leq \varepsilon,$$

whereas if $x \in E - A(\varepsilon)$ and $k \geq N(n)$, then

$$|f(x) - f_k(x)| \leq \frac{1}{n}$$

so that $\{f_n\}$ does indeed converge uniformly to $f$ on $E - A(\varepsilon)$.

Next we prove a theorem due to Steinhaus about the set of distances between points of a measurable set.

## STEINHAUS THEOREM

3.3.9 THEOREM *Let $A$ be a closed bounded set on the real line with $\sigma(A) > 0$. Then there is a $\delta > 0$ such that every number $z$ satisfying $|z| < \delta$ can be expressed as the difference $x - y$ of two points $x$ and $y$ in $A$.*

*Proof* Let $U_n$ be the open bounded set of points $u$ such that $|u - a| < 1/n$ for some $a \in A$. The sequence $\{U_n\}$ is decreasing and $\bigcap_{n=1}^{\infty} U_n = A$ because $A$ is closed. (The set $R - A$ is open; thus for every point $b \notin A$ there is an integer $n \geq 1$ such that $(b - 1/n, b + 1/n)$ contains no point of $A$, whence $b \notin U_n$). Since

$$\lim_{n\to\infty} \sigma(U_n) = \sigma(A) > 0,$$

we can find an $n$ such that

$$\tfrac{2}{3}\sigma(U_n) < \sigma(A).$$

Let $\delta = 1/n$. If $|z| < \delta$, then the set

$$A_z = \{a - z : a \in A\}$$

is contained in $U_n$. Since the measure of $A_z$ is the same as that of $A$, we get

$$\begin{aligned}\sigma(U_n - (A \cap A_z)) &= \sigma((U_n - A) \cup (U_n - A_z)) \\ &\leq \sigma(U_n - A) + \sigma(U_n - A_z) \\ &= 2\sigma(U_n) - 2\sigma(A) \\ &< \tfrac{2}{3}\sigma(U_n),\end{aligned}$$

that is, $A \cap A_z$ has a positive measure and thus is not empty. Therefore there is $x \in A$ such that $y = x - z \in A$. This proves the theorem.

### *EXERCISES*

*3.3.1* Prove part (a) of Proposition 3.3.3 and give an example of a decreasing sequence $\{A_n\}$ of measurable sets with $\bigcap_{n=1}^{\infty} A_n = \varnothing = A$ but $\sigma(A_n) = \infty$, so that $\lim_{n\to\infty} \sigma(A_n) \neq \sigma(A) = 0$ in this case.

*3.3.2* A subset $E$ of the real line is said to be dense in $R$ if every real number is the limit of some sequence of points in $E$. For instance, the set of rational numbers is dense in $R$. Show that a function $f$ is measurable if and only if the set $\{x : f(x) > r\}$ is measurable for each $r$ in a dense subset $E$ of the real line.

*3.3.3* Show that if $f$ is integrable on the interval with endpoints $a$ and $c$, $a < c$, then if $a < b < c$, $f$ is integrable on each of the intervals $(a, b)$ and $(b, c)$ and

$$\int_a^c f\,dx = \int_a^b f\,dx + \int_b^c f\,dx.$$

*3.3.4* Show that if $E(k)$, $k = 1, 2, \cdots$ is a sequence of disjoint measurable sets, that is, $E(h) \cap E(k) = \varnothing$ if $h \neq k$, and if $f$ is integrable on $E = \bigcup_{k=1}^{\infty} E(k)$, then $f$ is integrable on each set $E(k)$ and

$$\int_E f\,dx = \sum_{k=1}^{\infty} \int_{E(k)} f\,dx.$$

*3.3.5* Let $E$ be the closed interval $[0, 1]$ and let $C$ be the Cantor set defined in Example 1.4.3. Define the sequence $\{f_n\}$ of functions on $E$ by

$$f_n(x) = (1 - n\,\text{dist}\,(x, C))^+,$$
$$\text{dist}\,(x, C) = \inf\,\{|x - y| : y \in C\}.$$

For each $\varepsilon > 0$ construct explicitly a set $A(\varepsilon)$ such that $\sigma(A(\varepsilon)) \leq \varepsilon$ and $\{f_n\}$ tends to zero uniformly on $E - A(\varepsilon)$.

*3.3.6* Show by an example that you cannot take $A(\varepsilon)$ in Egoroff's theorem to be a null set, and that the theorem is false if $E$ is a measurable set of infinite measure.

## 3.4 AXIOMATIC MEASURE THEORY

Suppose that we have started with the abstract setup of a family $L$ of functions on a set $S$ and an integral $\int \varphi\,d\mu$ defined for $\varphi \in L$, all subject to the postulated conditions (1) to (5). Then we define in analogy with the concrete case the concept of measurable functions. Finally we define the family $\mathscr{M}$ of measurable sets and the measure $\mu(A)$ of each set $A \in \mathscr{M}$. The measure is then a function on $\mathscr{M}$ whose values are nonnegative real numbers or $\infty$. The following three properties of $\mathscr{M}$ and $\mu$ are characteristic.

(a) If $A, B \in \mathscr{M}$, then $A \cup B$ and $S - A$ are also in $\mathscr{M}$.
(b) $\mu(\varnothing) = 0$.
(c) If $\{A_n\}$ is a sequence of sets in $\mathscr{M}$ such that $A_n \cap A_k = \varnothing$ for $n \neq k$, and if

$$\bigcup_{n=1}^{\infty} A_n \in \mathscr{M},$$

then

$$\mu\left(\bigcup_{n=1}^{\infty} A_n\right) = \sum_{n=1}^{\infty} \mu(A_n).$$

We will now assume that a nonempty family $\mathscr{M}$ of subsets of a set $S$ is given, together with a function $\mu$ on $\mathscr{M}$ with values that are either nonnegative real numbers or $\infty$, such that the three properties (a), (b) and (c) are satisfied. Since

$$A \cap B = S - [(S - A) \cup (S - B)],$$

it follows that if $A$ and $B$ are in $\mathscr{M}$, then so is $A \cap B$, and that

$$S = (S - A) \cup A \text{ and } \varnothing = (S - A) \cap A$$

are in $\mathscr{M}$. Hence Property (b) makes sense. Furthermore,

$$A - B = (S - B) \cap A$$

belongs to $\mathscr{M}$ if $A$ and $B$ do. In particular, if $B \subset A$, then by (c)

$$\mu(A) = \mu(B) + \mu(A - B)$$

whence

$$\mu(B) \leq \mu(A) \qquad \text{if } B \subset A.$$

An example of a family $\mathscr{M}$ satisfying the three properties is the family of all finite disjoint unions of intervals on the real line, with $\mu(A)$ the total length of $A$. The verification of Property (c) requires a short argument using the Heine-Borel covering theorem, whereas (a) and (b) are immediate (see Exercise 3.4.1).

We can now define a class $L$ of elementary functions and an integral for them that are in a natural way connected with $\mathscr{M}$ and $\mu$.

**3.4.1 DEFINITION** *Let $L$ be the set of all finite linear combinations of characteristic functions of pairwise disjoint sets in $\mathscr{M}$ with finite measure. In other words, if $\varphi \in L$, then*

$$\varphi = \sum_{k=1}^{n} a_k \chi_k$$

*where the $a_k$ are real numbers and $\chi_k$ is the characteristic function of $A_k \in \mathscr{M}$ with $A_h \cap A_k = \varnothing$ for $h \neq k$ and $\mu(A_k) < \infty$ for $k = 1, \cdots, n$. Also, define $\int \varphi \, d\mu$ by*

$$\int \varphi \, d\mu = \sum_{k=1}^{n} a_k \, \mu(A_k)$$

*for $\varphi \in L$. Then $L$ and $\int \varphi \, d\mu$ are said to be generated by $\mathscr{M}$ and $\mu$.*

We remark that if $b_1 < b_2 < \cdots < b_m$ is the set of all different values of $\varphi$, then the sets on which $\varphi$ assumes the value $b_h$ is

$$B_h = \bigcup \{A_k : a_k = b_h\}.$$

These sets $B_h$ are in $\mathscr{M}$ and

$$\int \varphi \, d\mu = \sum_{h=1}^{m} b_h \mu(B_h),$$

by Property (c). Hence the definition of $\int \varphi \, d\mu$ does not depend on the choice of the sets $A_k$. Next we remove the restriction $A_h \cap A_k = \varnothing$ in the definition.

**3.4.2 PROPOSITION** *If*

$$\varphi = \sum_{k=1}^{n} a_k \chi_k$$

*where $\chi_k$ are characteristic functions of sets $A_k \in \mathcal{M}$ with $\mu(A_k) < \infty$ (and $A_h \cap A_k$ may be nonempty for $h \neq k$), then $\varphi \in L$ and*

$$\int \varphi \, d\mu = \sum_{k=1}^{n} a_k \mu(A_k).$$

3.4.3 COROLLARY *The set L satisfies Properties (1), (2), (3), and (5) of a set of elementary functions.*

*Proof* To prove Proposition 3.4.2 it suffices by induction to show that if $\varphi \in L$ and $A \in \mathcal{M}$, $\mu(A) < \infty$, then $\varphi + a\chi_A$ is also in $L$ and

$$\int (\varphi + a\chi_A) \, d\mu = \int \varphi \, d\mu + a\mu(A).$$

Hence let $\varphi \in L$, $\varphi = \sum_{k=1}^{n} a_k \chi_k$ with all conditions of Definition 3.4.1 satisfied. Then

$$\varphi + a\chi_A = \sum_{k=1}^{n} (a_k + a)\chi_k \chi_A + \sum_{k=1}^{n} a_k \chi_k (1 - \chi_A) + a\left(1 - \sum_{k=1}^{n} \chi_k\right)\chi_A$$

where $\chi_k \chi_A$ is the characteristic function of $A_k \cap A \in \mathcal{M}$, $\chi_k(1 - \chi_A)$ that of $A_k \cap (S - A) \in \mathcal{M}$, and $(1 - \sum_{k=1}^{n} \chi_k)\chi_A$ is the characteristic function of $(S - \bigcup_{k=1}^{n} A_k) \cap A$, which is again a set in $\mathcal{M}$. The sets in the collection

$$\left\{A_k \cap A,\ A_k \cap (S - A),\ \left(S - \bigcup_{k=1}^{n} A_k\right) \cap A\right\}$$

are pairwise disjoint and $\mu$ has a finite value on each of them. Thus $\varphi + a\chi_A \in L$; we now use property $c$ again to compute

$$\begin{aligned}
&\int (\varphi + a\chi_A) \, d\mu \\
&= \sum_{k=1}^{n} (a_k + a)\mu(A_k \cap A) + \sum_{k=1}^{n} a_k \mu(A_k \cap (S - A)) + a\mu\left(\left(S - \bigcup_{k=1}^{n} A_k\right) \cap A\right) \\
&= \sum_{k=1}^{n} a_k[\mu(A_k \cap A) + \mu(A_k \cap (S - A))] \\
&\qquad + a\left[\sum_{k=1}^{n} \mu(A_k \cap A) + \mu\left(A - \bigcup_{k=1}^{n} A_k \cap A\right)\right] \\
&= \sum_{k=1}^{n} a_k \mu(A_k) + a\mu(A) = \int \varphi \, d\mu + a\mu(A).
\end{aligned}$$

Here ends the proof of Proposition 3.4.2. The proof of Corollary 3.4.3 is left to the reader as Exercise 3.4.2.

Finally we now verify the continuity property (4) for the setup $L$, $\int \varphi \, d\mu$ defined in Definition 3.4.1.

**3.4.4 PROPOSITION** *If $\{\varphi_n\}$ is a sequence of functions in $L$ satisfying $\varphi_n \geq \varphi_{n+1} \geq 0$ for all $n$ and $\lim_{n\to\infty} \varphi_n(x) = 0$ for all $x \in S$, then*

$$\lim_{n\to\infty} \int \varphi_n \, d\mu = 0$$

*Proof* There exists a real number $m$ and a set $A \in \mathscr{M}$ such that

$$\varphi_n \leq m\chi_A \qquad \text{for all } n;$$

one need only take

$$A = \{x : \varphi_1(x) > 0\}, \qquad m = \max_{x\in S} \varphi(x).$$

Given an arbitrary $\varepsilon > 0$, define the sequence of sets $\{B_n\}$ in $\mathscr{M}$ by

$$B_n = \{x : \varphi_n(x) \geq \varepsilon/(\mu(A) + 1)\}.$$

We have $B_n \supset B_{n+1}$ for all $n$ and $\bigcap_{n=1}^{\infty} B_n = \varnothing$. Thus

$$B_1 = \bigcup_{k=1}^{\infty} (B_k - B_{k+1}), \qquad B_n = \bigcup_{k=n}^{\infty} (B_k - B_{k+1})$$

so that by Property (c)

$$\mu(B_1) = \sum_{k=1}^{\infty} \mu(B_k - B_{k+1}), \qquad \mu(B_n) = \sum_{k=n}^{\infty} \mu(B_k - B_{k+1}).$$

Evidently

$$\lim_{n\to\infty} \mu(B_n) = 0.$$

We have then the following estimate

$$\varphi_n \leq \left[\frac{\varepsilon}{\mu(A) + 1}\right]\chi_A + m\chi_n$$

if $\chi_n$ denotes the characteristic function of $B_n$. Hence

$$\lim_{n\to\infty} \int \varphi_n \, d\mu \leq \lim_{n\to\infty} \left(\frac{\varepsilon\mu(A)}{\mu(A) + 1} + m\mu(B_n)\right) \leq \varepsilon.$$

We have thus proved that $\lim_{n\to\infty} \int \varphi_n \, d\mu = 0$, since $\varepsilon$ was arbitrary.

As a consequence of the validity of the properties (1) to (5) for the set $L$ and the integral $\int \varphi \, d\mu$, we get an integration theory with a class of integrable functions, a class of measurable functions, and finally a class of measurable sets which is in general larger than the original family $\mathscr{M}$ (as for instance in the concrete example given in the beginning of this section). It will however always contain $\mathscr{M}$.

## *EXERCISES*

*3.4.1* Let $\mathscr{M}$ be the family of all finite disjoint unions of intervals and $\sigma(A)$, $A \in \mathscr{M}$, the total length of $A$. Without reference to the theory of Lebesgue integration show that Properties (a) to (c) hold.

*Hint* In proving Property (c) show first that it suffices to consider the case when $\bigcup_{n=1}^{\infty} A_n$ is a bounded and closed interval $[a, b]$, and then enlarge each $A_n$ into a union of open intervals so that $\sigma(A_n)$ is increased by at most $\varepsilon 2^{-n}$; then the Heine-Borel theorem applies saying that a finite number of the enlarged $A_n$ already cover $[a, b]$. (For a statement and proof of the Heine-Borel theorem, see Lemma 7.3.6.)

*3.4.2* Prove that the set $L$ in Definition 3.4.1 has the properties (1), (2), (3), and (5).

*3.4.3* In this exercise we shall give another proof of Proposition 3.4.2. Suppose that the sum representation

$$\varphi = \sum_{k=1}^{n} a_k \chi_k$$

is the one with the shortest length $n$, subject to the condition that $A_h \cap A_k = \varnothing$ if $h \neq k$ and $a_h \neq a_k$ for $h \neq k$. The set $A$ corresponding to the new added term $a\chi_A$ now intersects a certain number, say $p$, of the $A_k$, $k = 1, \cdots, n$. Suppose that we have proved that $\varphi + a\chi_A \in L$ if $p < r$ $(r \geq 1)$ and that

$$\int (\varphi + a\chi_A)\, d\mu = \int \varphi\, d\mu + a\mu(A)$$

in that case. Note that the induction starts naturally at $r = 1$, since $p = 0$ means that $A$ is disjoint from all $A_k$, so that Property (c) applies.

Prove that $\varphi + a\chi_A \in L$ and

$$\int (\varphi + a\chi_A)\, d\mu = \int \varphi\, d\mu + a\mu(A)$$

if $p = r$.

*3.4.4* Show that the product of two functions in $L$ is in $L$.

*3.4.5* Show that if $f$ is any real-valued function such that $f(0) = 0$ and $\varphi \in L$, then $f \circ \varphi \in L$.

## 3.5 OUTER MEASURE

In this section we will give one more definition of measurability and at the same time introduce a new function, the outer measure, defined on all subsets of the real line $R$ without exception. We let $\mathscr{M}$ be the family of all finite unions of intervals on the real line with $\sigma(A)$ the Lebesgue measure for $A \in \mathscr{M}$, which is nothing else but the total length of $A$ if we decompose $A$ into a union of a finite number of disjoint intervals. Notice that the step functions are just the linear combinations of characteristic functions of sets $A \in \mathscr{M}$ with $\sigma(A) < \infty$.

As such this section is independent of the previous one. But the main part (up to and including Theorem 3.5.5) is also valid for the setup of the previous section where $\mathscr{M}$ is a family of subsets of a set $S$, together with an elementary measure $\mu(A)$ for $A \in \mathscr{M}$ subject to the conditions (a), (b), and (c) of Section 3.4. One has only to replace $\sigma$ by $\mu$, and $R$ by $S$ and instead of step functions one has the elementary functions that are the linear combinations of characteristic functions of sets $A \in \mathscr{M}$ with $\mu(A) < \infty$. As we have seen in the last section, the existence of such a family $\mathscr{M}$ of subsets of $S$ and a function $\mu$ satisfying the prescribed conditions led naturally to the existence of an integration theory so that we have also in this abstract case defined the concepts almost everywhere, integrable function, integral, measurable set, and integrable set.

**3.5.1 DEFINITION** *The outer measure of a set $A \subset R$ is defined and denoted by*

$$\sigma^*(A) = \inf \left[ \sum_{k=1}^{\infty} \sigma(A_k) : A_k \in \mathscr{M},\ A \subset \bigcup_{k=1}^{\infty} A_k \right].$$

It is easily verified that

$$\sigma^*(A) \leq \sigma^*(B) \qquad \text{if } A \subset B$$

(Exercise 3.5.1). An alternate description of the outer measure is given in the following proposition.

**3.5.2 PROPOSITION** *If $A \subset R$, then*

$$\sigma^*(A) = \inf \{\sigma(B) : B \textit{ is measurable}, B \supset A\}.$$

*Proof* Denote the above infimum provisionally by $m^*(A)$. Suppose that $m^*(A) = \infty$, that is, that there is no integrable set $B \supset A$. Then if $A \subset \bigcup_{k=1}^{\infty} A_k$, $A_k \in \mathscr{M}$, one must have $\sum_{k=1}^{\infty} \sigma(A_k) = \infty$; since otherwise

$$B = \bigcup_{k=1}^{\infty} A_k$$

is an integrable set satisfying $A \subset B$. Hence $\sigma^*(A) = \infty$, so that in this case $\sigma^*(A) = m^*(A)$.

Now suppose $m^*(A) < \infty$. Then, given an arbitrary $\varepsilon > 0$, there exists an integrable set $B \supset A$ such that

$$\sigma(B) < m^*(A) + \varepsilon.$$

By Lemma 2.2.5 there is some number $k > 1$ and a series $\sum \varphi_n$ of step functions such that

$$\sum_{n=1}^{\infty} \varphi_n = k\chi_B \geq k\chi_A \text{ a.e.,}$$

$$\sum_{n=1}^{\infty} \int |\varphi_n| \, dx \leq \sigma(B) + \varepsilon \leq m^*(A) + 2\varepsilon.$$

We can rid ourselves of the proviso "almost everywhere" by adding another series of nonnegative step functions with an integral less than $\varepsilon$ that diverges on the null set in question. Hence there exists a series $\sum \psi_n$ of step functions satisfying

$$\sum_{n=1}^{\infty} \psi_n \geq k\chi_A \qquad \text{everywhere},$$

$$\sum_{n=1}^{\infty} \int |\psi_n| \, dx \leq m^*(A) + 3\varepsilon.$$

Now put

$$A_1 = \{x : |\psi_1(x)| \geq 1\}$$

$$A_n = \left\{x : \sum_{k=1}^{n-1} |\psi_k(x)| < 1 \leq \sum_{k=1}^{n} |\psi_k(x)|\right\}, \qquad n \geq 2.$$

Then $\{A_n\}$ is a sequence of pairwise disjoint sets in $\mathscr{M}$, and

$$A_1 \cup \cdots \cup A_n = \left\{x : \sum_{k=1}^{n} |\psi_k(x)| \geq 1\right\}$$

whence

$$\sigma(A_1) + \cdots + \sigma(A_n) \leq \sum_{k=1}^{n} \int |\psi_k| \, dx \leq m^*(A) + 3\varepsilon.$$

We have therefore

$$A \subset \bigcup_{n=1}^{\infty} A_n, \qquad \sum_{n=1}^{\infty} \sigma(A_n) \leq m^*(A) + 3\varepsilon.$$

Hence $\sigma^*(A) < \infty$ and, since $\varepsilon$ was arbitrary, $\sigma^*(A) \leq m^*(A)$. But the opposite inequality follows for $\sigma^*(A) < \infty$ from

$$\begin{aligned} m^*(A) &= \inf\{\sigma(B) : B \text{ measurable}, A \subset B\} \\ &\leq \inf\left\{\sigma\left(\bigcup_{k=1}^{\infty} A_k\right) : A_k \in \mathscr{M}, A \subset \bigcup_{k=1}^{\infty} A_k\right\} \\ &\leq \inf\left\{\sum_{k=1}^{\infty} \sigma(A_k) : A_k \in \mathscr{M}, A \subset \bigcup_{k=1}^{\infty} A_k\right\} = \sigma^*(A). \end{aligned}$$

Hence $m^*(A) = \sigma^*(A)$ for all subsets $A$ of $R$, as claimed.

3.5.3 COROLLARY *If $\sigma^*(A) < \infty$, then there exists an integrable set $B \supset A$ such that $\sigma^*(A) = \sigma(B)$.*

*Proof* For each $n$ we can find an integrable set $B_n \supset A$ with

$$0 \leq \sigma(B_n) - \sigma^*(A) \leq \frac{1}{n}.$$

Let $C_n = B_1 \cap \cdots \cap B_n$, then $\{C_n\}$ is a decreasing sequence of integrable sets and

$$0 \leq \sigma(C_n) - \sigma^*(A) \leq \frac{1}{n}.$$

If $B = \bigcap_{n=1}^{\infty} C_n$, then

$$\sigma(B) = \lim_{n \to \infty} \sigma(C_n) = \sigma^*(A),$$

and hence $B \supset A$ is an integrable set with $\sigma(B) = \sigma^*(A)$.

3.5.4 COROLLARY *If $A$ is a measurable set then $\sigma(A) = \sigma^*(A)$.*

We can now formulate the new definition of measurability and measure that we announced in the beginning of this section and can prove its equivalence with the old definition.

3.5.5 THEOREM *A set $E \subset R$ is measurable if and only if for every set $A \in \mathcal{M}$*

$$\sigma^*(A) = \sigma(A) = \sigma^*(A \cap E) + \sigma^*(A - E)$$

*in which case $\sigma(E) = \sigma^*(E)$.*

*Proof* Suppose that $E \subset R$ satisfies the condition of Theorem 3.5.5. By Definition 3.1.1 it suffices to prove that $A \cap E$ is integrable for each $A \in \mathcal{M}$ with finite measure in order to show that $E$ is measurable. But by Corollary 3.5.3 there exist integrable sets $B$ and $C$ satisfying

$$A \cap E \subset B, \sigma(B) = \sigma^*(A \cap E),$$
$$A - E \subset C, \sigma(C) = \sigma^*(A - E).$$

Hence $A \subset B \cup C$ and it follows that $A \cap B \cap C$ is a null set, because

$$\begin{aligned} \sigma(B) + \sigma(C) &= \sigma^*(A \cap E) + \sigma^*(A - E) \\ &= \sigma(A) = \sigma(A \cap B) + \sigma(A \cap C) - \sigma(A \cap B \cap C) \\ &\leq \sigma(B) + \sigma(C) - \sigma(A \cap B \cap C) \end{aligned}$$

so that $\sigma(A \cap B \cap C) = 0$. But

$$A \cap B - A \cap E \subset A \cap B \cap C$$

since, if $x \in A$ and $x \notin E$, then $x \in C$; thus

$$A \cap E = A \cap B - \text{null set}$$

is an integrable set for all $A \in \mathcal{M}$ of finite measure and consequently $E$ is measurable.

Now that we have proved the measurability of $E$, the relation $\sigma(E) = \sigma^*(E)$ follows immediately from Corollary 3.5.4. Conversely, if we assume that $E$ is measurable, then $\sigma(E) = \sigma^*(E)$, and since $A \cap E$ and $A - E$ are measurable, the condition in Theorem 3.5.5 follows from the equalities $\sigma(A \cap E) = \sigma^*(A \cap E)$ and $\sigma(A - E) = \sigma^*(A - E)$.

We shall now deduce some corollaries of Theorem 3.5.5 that are valid only on the real line and cannot be generalized to the setting of the last section.

**3.5.6 PROPOSITION**

$$\sigma^*(A) = \inf\left\{\sum_{k=1}^{\infty} \sigma(I_k) : A \subset \bigcup_{k=1}^{\infty} I_k,\ I_k \in \mathscr{I}\right\}$$

*where $\mathscr{I}$ is the family of open intervals.*

*Proof* The sets $A_k \in \mathscr{M}$ used in Definition 3.5.1 are all finite unions of intervals, so that Proposition 3.5.6 would have been trivial were it not for the condition that all intervals have to be open. If the $k$th interval were not open, then it could, however, be covered by an open interval whose length is at most $\varepsilon \cdot 2^{-k}$ greater. Since $\varepsilon > 0$ can be chosen arbitrarily, it follows that the infimum with the restriction to open intervals is the same as the infimum without that restriction. This proves Proposition 3.5.6.

**3.5.7 COROLLARY** *To every integrable set $E$ of real numbers and every $\varepsilon > 0$ there is an open set $A \supset E$ with*

$$\sigma(A) \geq \sigma(E) \geq \sigma(A) - \varepsilon.$$

**3.5.8 COROLLARY** *To every integrable set $E$ of real numbers and every $\varepsilon > 0$ there is a compact (that is, closed and bounded) set $A \subset E$ such that*

$$\sigma(A) \leq \sigma(E) \leq \sigma(A) + \varepsilon.$$

*Proof* To prove the last corollary we first observe that by the monotone convergence theorem

$$\sigma(E) = \lim_{n \to \infty} \sigma(E \cap [-n, n])$$

so that we may choose an $n$ for which

$$\sigma(E \cap [-n, n]) + \frac{\varepsilon}{2} \geq \sigma(E).$$

Then by Corollary 3.5.7 there exists an open set $B \supset [-n, n] - E$ such that

$$\sigma([-n, n] - E) + \frac{\varepsilon}{2} \geq \sigma(B).$$

Adding the two inequalities, we get

$$2n + \varepsilon \geq \sigma(B) + \sigma(E).$$

Now $A = [-n, n] - B$ is a compact set such that $A \subset E$ and

$$\sigma(A) + \varepsilon \geq 2n - \sigma(B) + \varepsilon \geq \sigma(E)$$

as required.

## *EXERCISES*

*3.5.1* Show that if $A \subset B$, then $\sigma^*(A) \leq \sigma^*(B)$.

*3.5.2* Show that $\sigma^*(A \cup B) \leq \sigma^*(A) + \sigma^*(B)$ for all subsets $A, B$ of the real line.

*3.5.3* Show that if $E$ is an arbitrary subset of the real line $R$, and $A$ is a measurable subset, then

$$\sigma^*(E) = \sigma^*(A \cap E) + \sigma^*((R - A) \cap E).$$

*3.5.4* Prove that there is a compact subset of the real line which has positive (Lebesgue) measure but does not contain any nonempty open interval. (A closed set that does not contain any nonempty open interval is said to be nowhere dense.)

*Hint* Apply Corollary 3.5.8 to the set of irrational numbers in [0, 1].

# 3.6 EXERCISES

Most of the following problems are formulated for the real line $R$ and the ordinary Lebesgue measure $\sigma$. However, we have indicated those problems that use the special properties of $R$ and $\sigma$ by an asterisk. The other problems can hence be reformulated for an abstract set $S$ with measure $\mu$.

## A. Measurable Functions and Measurable Sets

**3.6.1*** Let $(-\infty, a_1), (a_1, a_2), \cdots, (a_n, \infty)$ be a finite number of intervals. Suppose the function $f$ is constant on each of these intervals. Prove that $f$ is measurable.

**3.6.2*** Prove that the set $K$ of Example 1.4.4 is not measurable.

**3.6.3***

(a) Give an example of a nonmeasurable function $f$ such that $f^2$ is measurable.

(b) Show that a function $f$ is measurable if and only if $f^2$ and $\{x : f(x) > 0\}$ are measurable.

**3.6.4*** A function $f$ on the real line is upper semicontinuous if it is bounded above on every bounded interval and if it satisfies the relation

$$f(x) = \lim_{n \to \infty} \sup \left\{ f(y) : x - \frac{1}{n} \leq y \leq x + \frac{1}{n} \right\}$$

for all real numbers $x$. Show that an upper semicontinuous function is measurable.

*Hint* Define the sequence $\{f_n\}$ of functions by

$$f_n\left(\frac{k}{n}\right) = \sup \left\{ f(y) : \frac{k-1}{n} \leq y \leq \frac{k+1}{n} \right\}$$

for integer values of $k$ and by

$$f_n(x) = \sum_{k=-\infty}^{\infty} (1 - |nx - k|)^+ f_n\left(\frac{k}{n}\right)$$

for all real numbers $x$. Notice that all but two summands vanish if you restrict $x$ to any of the intervals $[(j-1)/n, (j+1)/n], j = 0, \pm 1, \cdots$. Show that $\{f_n\}$ is a sequence of continuous functions that tends to $f$ everywhere. Another method would be to show that the set $\{x : f(x) < c\}$ is open for every real number $c$.

**3.6.5*** Show that the characteristic function of a closed set is upper semi-continuous (as defined in the preceding exercise), and hence it is measurable.

**3.6.6*** Show that a function $f$ which is continuous almost everywhere is measurable.

*Hint* Apply Theorem 2.6.10 to $f_n = \text{mid}\,(-n, f, n)\chi_{[-n,n]}$; or prove that $\{x : f(x) > c\}$ differs from an open set by only a null set.

**3.6.7** Suppose $L$ is a space of elementary functions on a set $S$ with integral $\int \varphi \, d\mu$, $\varphi \in L$, satisfying Properties (1) to (5). Prove that the following are equivalent:

(a) There is a sequence $\{S_n\}$ of integrable sets such that $S = \bigcup_{n=1}^{\infty} S_n$.
(b) Every measurable function is the limit almost everywhere of a sequence of integrable generalized step functions.
(c) Every measurable function is the limit almost everywhere of a sequence of integrable functions.
(d) There is a sequence $\{\varphi_n\}$ of elementary functions with $\lim \varphi_n = 1$ everywhere.

*Hint* To prove that (c) implies (d), let $\{f_n\}$ be a sequence of integrable functions that converges to 1 a.e. You may assume $f_n \leq 1$, replacing $f_n$ by $f_n \wedge 1$ if necessary. For each $n$, let $\{\psi_{nk} : k \geq 1\}$ be a sequence of elementary functions converging to $f_n$ a.e. Again you may assume $0 \leq \psi_{nk} \leq 1$. Then the sequence $\{\phi_m\}$ defined by

$$\phi_m = \bigvee_{n=1}^{m} \bigvee_{k=1}^{m} \psi_{nk}$$

tends to 1 a.e. Now let

$$\varphi_m = (\phi_m + \eta_m) \wedge 1$$

where $\{\eta_n\}$ is a sequence of elementary functions that diverges to infinity on the null set on which $\{\phi_m\}$ does not converge to 1.

**3.6.8** Suppose $L$ is a linear space of elementary functions on an abstract set $S$ with an integral $\int \varphi \, d\mu$, $\varphi \in L$. Suppose $A$ is a subset of $S$ such that $\varphi(x) = 0$ for all $x \in A$ and $\varphi \in L$. Prove that $A$ is not measurable.

## B. Relation between Measurability and Integrability

**3.6.9*** Show that a function $f$ on the real line is measurable if and only if the function

$$h = \frac{fg}{|f| + g}$$

is integrable, where $g$ is the function defined in Exercise 3.1.6.

*Hint* Show first that

$$h^+ = \frac{f^+g}{f^+ + g}, \qquad h^- = \frac{f^-g}{f^- + g}.$$

**3.6.10** Suppose the functions $f$ and $g$ are integrable. Which of the following functions are integrable and which are not?

(a) $f^2$ (b) $f^{1/3}$ (c) $[\text{mid}\,(-1, f, 1)]^{1/3}$

(d) $\arctan f$ (e) $\sqrt{|f|} + \sqrt{|g|}$ (f) $fg$

(g) $\sqrt{|fg|}$ (h) $\sin\,[1/(1 + |f|)]$ (i) $f/(1 + |g|)$

*Hint* Theorem 3.1.8 is useful here. In (d), for instance, you have the inequality

$$|\arctan y| \leq |y|.$$

**3.6.11** Suppose $f$ and $g$ are measurable. Prove that $f$ and $g$ are integrable if and only if $(f^2 + g^2)^{1/2}$ is integrable.

*Hint* Use Theorem 3.1.8.

**3.6.12** Suppose $f$ and $g$ are measurable. If $f^2$ and $g^2$ are integrable, then $fg$ is also integrable.

*Hint* Use Theorem 3.1.8.

## C. Baire Classes of Functions of $k$ Variables

Let ${}_k\mathscr{C}_0$ be the vector space of continuous functions in $k$ variables. Define the $n$th Baire class by induction on $n$ as follows. A function $F$ belongs to ${}_k\mathscr{C}_n$, $n \geq 1$, if and only if it is the limit (everywhere) of a sequence $\{F_n\}$ of functions in ${}_k\mathscr{C}_{n-1}$,

$$F = \lim_{n\to\infty} F_n, \qquad F_n \in {}_k\mathscr{C}_{n-1}.$$

${}_k\mathscr{C}_n$ is a vector space.

**3.6.13*** Prove that the functions in ${}_1\mathscr{C}_n$ are measurable for any $n$.

**3.6.14*** Show that all functions of the kind defined in Exercise 3.6.1 are in ${}_1\mathscr{C}_1$, hence in particular all ordinary step functions.

**3.6.15*** Show that a function $F$ of one variable that is discontinuous only at a finite number of points is in ${}_1\mathscr{C}_1$.

*Hint* Prove first that a function $F$ which is continuous on an open interval $(a, b)$ and vanishes outside $(a, b)$ belongs to ${}_1\mathscr{C}_1$.

**3.6.16*** Show that a function $F$ of one variable that is discontinuous at only a countable number of points is in ${}_1\mathscr{C}_1$.

*Hint* If $\{a_n\}$ is a sequence enumerating the points of discontinuity of $F$ and, for $k = 1, 2, \cdots$,

$$\cdots < a_{k,\,-m} < \cdots < a_{k,\,0} < \cdots < a_{k,\,m} < \cdots$$

is the infinite and increasing sequence that enumerates

$$\left\{a_1, \cdots, a_k, \frac{n}{k} : n = 0, \pm 1, \cdots\right\},$$

then let $f_k$ be the continuous function that satisfies

$$f_k(a_{k,\,n}) = f(a_{k,\,n}), \qquad n = 0, \pm 1, \cdots$$

and which is linear on each interval $[a_{k,\,n}, a_{k,\,n+1}]$. Show that $f(x) = \lim_{k\to\infty} f_k(x)$ for all $x$.

**3.6.17*** Prove that a function $F$ of two variables that is continuous in each variable separately belongs to ${}_2\mathscr{C}_1$. Give an example of such a function $F$ that is not continuous.

*Hint* Consider the sequence $\{F_n\}$ in ${}_2\mathscr{C}_0$ defined by

$$F_n(x, y) = \sum_{k=-\infty}^{\infty} (1 - |k - ny|)^+ F\left(x, \frac{k}{n}\right)$$

and prove that $\{F_n(x, y)\}$ tends to $F(x, y)$ for all $x, y$.

**3.6.18*** Consider the binary expansion

$$a = 0 \cdot a_1 a_2 \cdots$$

of the real number $a \in [0, 1)$. In order to avoid ambiguities, we put

$$a_n = [2^n a] - 2[2^{n-1} a]$$

for all natural numbers $n$. Define the function $g$ by

$$g(a) = \begin{cases} 2\sum_{n=1}^{\infty} a_n 3^{-n} & \text{if} \quad a \in [0, 1) \\ 0 & \text{if} \quad a \notin [0, 1) \end{cases}$$

or in other words, $g(a) = 0$ unless $a \in [0, 1]$ in which case $g(a)$ equals the ternary expansion

$$g(a) = 0 \cdot b_1 b_2 \cdots$$

with $b_j = 0$ if $a_j = 0$ and $b_j = 2$ if $a_j = 1$. Prove that $g$ belongs to ${}_1\mathscr{C}_2$; thus $g$ is measurable.

*Hint* Define

$$g_n(a) = \begin{cases} 0 \cdot b_1 b_2 \cdots b_n & \text{if} \quad a \in [0 \cdot a_1 \cdots a_n, 0 \cdot a_1 \cdots a_n 11 \cdots) \\ 0 & \text{if} \quad a \notin [0, 1) \end{cases}$$

and show $\lim_{n \to \infty} g_n = g$ everywhere.

**3.6.19*** Show that the characteristic function $\chi$ of the rational numbers belongs to ${}_1\mathscr{C}_2$.

*Remark* One can show that $\chi$ does not belong to ${}_1\mathscr{C}_1$, but the proof uses a Baire category argument, the discussion of which would go beyond the scope of these exercises.

**3.6.20*** Show that every measurable function on the real line is equivalent to a function in ${}_1\mathscr{C}_2$. (But there are measurable functions that are not equivalent to a function in ${}_1\mathscr{C}_1$.)

*Hint* If the measurable function $f$ is nonnegative and bounded, then $f$ is equivalent to a function in ${}_1\mathscr{C}_1$. To show this, let $\{f_n\}$ be a bounded sequence of continuous functions converging to $f$ a.e. and consider $g = \limsup f_n$. For an unbounded function, apply Proposition 3.2.4.

## D. Composition of Measurable Functions with Functions in ${}_k\mathscr{C}_n$

**3.6.21** Suppose $f_1, \cdots, f_k$ are measurable. Prove that, for any $F \in {}_k\mathscr{C}_n$, $F(f_1, \cdots, f_k)$ is measurable.

**3.6.22** Let $R$ be a rational function of one variable and $f$ a measurable function. Define the function $g$ by

$$g(x) = \begin{cases} R(f(x)) & \text{if } R \text{ is regular at } y = f(x) \\ 0 & \text{if } R \text{ is not defined at } y = f(x). \end{cases}$$

Show that $g$ is measurable.

*Hint* Either use Exercise 3.6.16, or show that the rational functions

$$R_n = \frac{nR}{n + R^2}$$

are continuous, and that $g(x) = \lim_{n\to\infty} R_n(f(x))$ for all $x$.

**3.6.23** Let $f$ be a measurable function. Define $g$ by

$$g(x) = \begin{cases} 0 & \text{if } f(x) \text{ is rational} \\ 1 & \text{if } f(x) \text{ is irrational.} \end{cases}$$

Prove that $g$ is measurable.

*Hint* Use Exercise 3.6.19.

**3.6.24** Let $A$ be a subset of $[0, 1)$ whose characteristic function is not integrable; for instance, if we choose the set $K$ of Example 1.4.4 in $[0, 1)$, then $K$ is such a set (Exercise 2.7.2). Define the function $F$ by

$$F(x) = \begin{cases} 1 & \text{if } x = g(a) \text{ for some } a \in A \\ 0 & \text{if } x \neq g(a) \text{ for all } a \in A \end{cases}$$

where $g$ is the function of Exercise 3.6.18. Prove that $F$ is measurable.

*Hint* Prove that $F$ is a null function (see Example 1.4.3).

**3.6.25** Prove that the function $F$ defined in the previous exercise does not belong to any of the classes ${}_1\mathscr{C}_n$.

*Hint* Show that $F \circ g$ is not measurable.

**3.6.26** Show that, if $h$ is a generalized step function and $F$ is the function defined in Exercise 3.6.24, then $F \circ h$ is a generalized step function and hence measurable.

## E. Lusin's Theorem

**3.6.27*** Prove Lusin's theorem: Let $f$ be a measurable function defined on a measurable set $E$. For each $\varepsilon > 0$ there is a set $A \subset E$ with $\sigma(A) \leq \varepsilon$ such that $f$ is continuous on $E - A$.

*Hint* Prove this theorem first under the assumption $E \subset [n, n + 1]$ for some $n$; then $E$ is integrable. Let $\{\psi_n\}$ be any sequence of step functions that converges to $f$ a.e. Construct $A$ in such a way that each $\psi_n$ is continuous on $E - A$ and $\{\psi_n\}$ converges uniformly to $f$ on $E - A$. (Use Theorem 3.3.8.)

## F. Outer and Inner Measure

**3.6.28** Show that if $A$ is an arbitrary subset of $R$ and $E$ is measurable, then

$$\sigma^*(A) = \sigma^*(A \cap E) + \sigma^*(A - E)$$

(compare Theorem 3.5.5).

*Hint* If $\sigma^*(A) < \infty$, choose an integrable set $B \subset A$ with $\sigma(B) = \sigma^*(A)$ and use the fact that $B \cap E$ and $B - E$ are integrable.

We define the inner measure $\sigma_*$ associated to the outer measure $\sigma^*$ by

$$\sigma_*(A) = \sup \{\sigma(B) : B \text{ is measurable, } A \supset B\}$$

for each subset $A \subset R$.

**3.6.29** Show that if $\sigma_*(A) < \infty$, then there exists an integrable set $B \subset A$ such that $\sigma_*(A) = \sigma(B)$.

**3.6.30** Show that if $E$ is an integrable subset of $R$ and $A$ is an arbitrary subset of $E$, then

$$\sigma_*(A) = \sigma(E) - \sigma^*(E - A).$$

**3.6.31** Show that if $\sigma^*(A) < \infty$, then $A$ is measurable—and hence integrable—if and only if $\sigma_*(A) = \sigma^*(A)$.

**3.6.32** Show that if $\{A_n\}$ is a sequence of disjoint subsets of $R$, then

$$\sigma^*\left(\bigcup_{n=1}^{\infty} A_n\right) \geq \sum_{n=1}^{\infty} \sigma_*(A_n).$$

**3.6.33*** A set is called a $G_\delta$ ($G$-delta) if it is equal to the intersection of a sequence of open sets, and it is called an $F_\sigma$ ($F$-sigma) if it is equal to the union of a sequence of closed sets. Show that, for every subset $A$ of the real line, there is a $G_\delta$ set $B$ and an $F_\sigma$ set $C$ with $B \supset A \supset C$ and

$$\sigma(B) = \sigma^*(A), \sigma(C) = \sigma_*(A).$$

## G. The Cauchy Functional Equation

In the following exercises we discuss the Cauchy functional equation

$$f(x + y) = f(x) + f(y), \quad x, y \in R.$$

**3.6.34*** Show that a function $f$ on the real line that satisfies the Cauchy functional equation also satisfies

$$f(rx) = rf(x), \quad x \in R,$$

for all rational numbers $r$.

*Hint* Prove this first for positive integers. Then observe that $f(0) = f(2 \cdot 0) = 2f(0)$ implies $f(0) = 0$ and conclude from $0 = f(0) = f(x - x) = f(x) + f(-x)$ that the above equation holds for all integers. Now suppose $r = p/q$ is a rational number, where $p$ and $q \neq 0$ are integers. Prove that

$$qf\left(\frac{px}{q}\right) = pf(x).$$

**3.6.35*** Suppose the function $f$ satisfies the Cauchy functional equation and is bounded on some interval $(-\delta, \delta)$, $\delta > 0$. Prove that

$$f(x) = xf(1), \qquad x \in R.$$

*Hint* Let $x$ be fixed and let $r$ be a rational number such that $|x - r| < \delta/n$, $n > 0$. Then estimate

$$|f(x) - xf(1)| = |f(x - r) - (x - r)f(1)|.$$

**3.6.36*** Suppose the function $f$ satisfies the Cauchy functional equation and is bounded on some measurable set of positive measure. Prove that

$$f(x) = xf(1), \qquad x \in R.$$

*Hint* Show that, by Corollary 3.5.8, $f$ is in fact bounded on a closed bounded set of positive measure. Then apply the Steinhaus theorem to show that $f$ is bounded on some interval $(-\delta, \delta)$, $\delta > 0$.

**3.6.37*** Apply the previous exercise to show that a measurable function $f$ which satisfies the Cauchy functional equation also satisfies

$$f(x) = xf(1), \qquad x \in R.$$

## H. Vitali's Covering Theorem

In the following exercise we present a version of a theorem in real analysis known as Vitali's theorem. It says, roughly, that, if a bounded set is covered by a family of nondegenerate intervals, so that to each point in the set there are arbitrarily small intervals in the family containing the point, then the set is almost covered by a subfamily of mutually disjoint intervals. In many treatises this statement is used as a lemma in the development of the theory of differentiation for monotone functions (which is presented in Chapter 6 of this book), but in our presentation Vitali's theorem will not be used anywhere in the sequel.

In the following, let $E$ be a set contained in an open bounded interval $(a, b)$. *The set $E$ is said to be covered in the sense of Vitali* by a family $\mathscr{I}$ of nondegenerate closed intervals if, for each $x$ in $E$ and each $\varepsilon > 0$, there is an interval $I$ in $\mathscr{I}$ such that $x$ belongs to $I$ and $\sigma(I) < \varepsilon$.

**3.6.38*** Show that the subfamily $\mathscr{I}'$ of $\mathscr{I}$ consisting of those intervals in $\mathscr{I}$ that are contained in $(a, b)$ covers $E$ in the sense of Vitali.

**3.6.39*** Show that, unless $E$ is covered by a finite subfamily of mutually disjoint intervals in $\mathscr{I}'$, there exists a sequence $\{I_n\}$ of mutually disjoint intervals in $\mathscr{I}'$ with the following property:

$$\sigma(I_{n+1}) > \tfrac{1}{2} \sup \left\{\sigma(I) : I \in \mathscr{I}', I \cap \left(\bigcup_{k=1}^{n} I_k\right) = \varnothing\right\}.$$

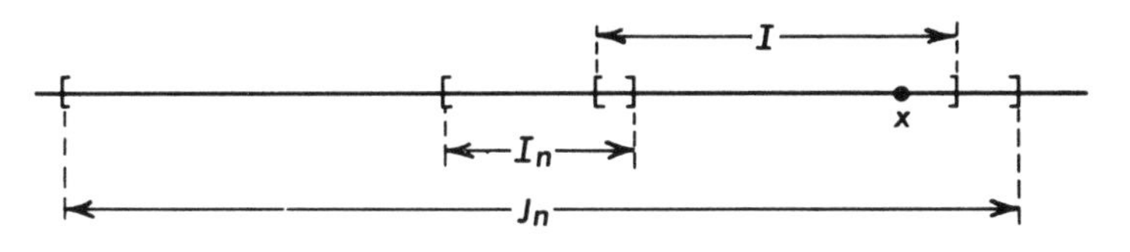


Figure 3.4

*Hint* Observe that, inductively for each $n$, unless $E$ is contained in $\bigcup_{k=1}^{n} I_k$, there are points in $E$ which are not in this union. Since this union is a closed set, the family

$$\left\{I : I \in \mathscr{I}', I \cap \left(\bigcup_{k=1}^{n} I_k\right) = \varnothing\right\}$$

is not empty.

**3.6.40*** Show that $\lim_{n\to\infty} \sigma(I_n) = 0$.

*Hint* Observe that $\sum_{n=1}^{\infty} \sigma(I_n) \leq b - a$.

**3.6.41*** Let $x$ be a point in $E$ and $x \in I \in \mathscr{I}'$. Show that, if $I \cap I_i = \varnothing$ for $i < n$, $n > 1$, then

$$\sigma(I) \leq 2\sigma(I_n).$$

Hence deduce that $I$ must meet $I_n$ for some $n$.

**3.6.42*** Let $x$ and $I$ be as in the previous exercise and suppose that $n$ is the smallest integer such that $I \cap I_n \neq \varnothing$ (so that $I \cap I_i = \varnothing$ for $i < n$). Show that if $J_n$ is the closed interval with the same midpoint as $I_n$ and five times its length, then $x$ belongs to $J_n$.

*Hint* Consider Figure 3.4.

**3.6.43*** *(Vitali's covering theorem). There is a sequence $\{I_n\}$ of pairwise disjoint intervals in $\mathscr{I}$ such that $E - \bigcup_{n=1}^{\infty} I_n$ is a null set.*

*Hint* Use the information in the hint to Exercise 3.6.40 together with the following consequence of the last exercise: for each integer $N \geq 2$,

$$E \subset \left(\bigcup_{n=1}^{N} I_n\right) \cup \left(\bigcup_{n=N+1}^{\infty} J_n\right), \qquad \sum_{n=N+1}^{\infty} \sigma(J_n) = 5 \sum_{n=N+1}^{\infty} \sigma(I_n).$$

## SUMMARY

In the development of the theory of measurable functions and measurable sets, a fifth property of step functions (Stone's axiom) plays an important role:

(5) If $\varphi \in L$, then $1 \wedge \varphi \in L$.

If a Daniell integral also satisfies Property (5), then all considerations in this chapter hold for it with the exception of most of the examples.

A function $f$ is measurable if and only if $\text{mid}(-\varphi, f, \varphi)$ is integrable for all non-negative $\varphi \in L$ (Definition 3.1.1). In this definition the condition $\varphi \in L$ may be replaced by $\varphi \in L^1$ (Proposition 3.1.6); thus the concept of a measurable function does not depend on the particular choice of the linear space $L$ of elementary functions with which a certain integration theory is built up (Corollary 3.1.7).

For instance, all integrable functions and the constant functions are measurable (Proposition 3.1.2). Other basic properties of measurable functions are these:

(a) If $f$ and $g$ are measurable, then so are

$$af + bg, |f|, f \vee g, f \wedge g$$

(Proposition 3.1.3).

(b) If $\{f_n\}$ is a sequence of measurable functions and

$$= \lim_{n \to \infty} f_n \text{ a.e.}$$

for some function $f$, then $f$ is measurable (Proposition 3.1.4).

(c) If $f$ is measurable and if there is an integrable function $g$ with $|f| \leq g$, then $f$ is integrable.

The measurable functions that take on only a finite number of different values are called generalized step functions (Definition 3.2.1). They are exactly the linear combinations of measurable characteristic functions (Proposition 3.2.3). The integrable generalized step functions form a class of elementary functions suitable to be taken as a basis for the development of the integral (Proposition 3.2.6). A function $f$ is measurable if and only if $\varphi \circ f$ is a generalized step function for every step function $\varphi$ (Proposition 3.2.4).

If $F$ is a continuous function of $k$ variables and if $f_1, \cdots, f_k$ are measurable functions, then so is

$$F(f_1, \cdots, f_k)$$

(Theorem 3.2.5).

A set $A$ is measurable (integrable) if its characteristic function $\chi_A$ is measurable (integrable) and the measure of a measurable set $A$ is defined as

$$\sigma(A) = \begin{cases} \int \chi_A \, dx & \text{if } A \text{ is integrable} \\ \infty & \text{if } A \text{ is not integrable} \end{cases}$$

(Definitions 3.3.1 and 3.3.2).

Among the most important properties of measurable sets are the following (Proposition 3.3.3):

(a) If $\{A_n\}$ is an increasing sequence of measurable sets, then $A = \bigcup_{n=1}^{\infty}$ is measurable and

$$\sigma(A) = \lim_{n\to\infty} \sigma(A_n).$$

(b) If $\{A_n\}$ is a decreasing sequence of measurable sets, then $A = \bigcap_{n=1}^{\infty} A_n$ is measurable and if at least one of the $A_n$ has finite measure, then

$$\sigma(A) = \lim_{n\to\infty} \sigma(A_n).$$

(c) If $\{A_n\}$ is any sequence of measurable sets, then $A = \bigcup_{n=1}^{\infty} A_n$ is measurable and

$$\sigma(A) \le \sum_{n=1}^{\infty} \sigma(A_n)$$

with equality holding if the $A_n$ are pairwise disjoint.

A function $f$ is measurable if and only if the sets in any one of the four categories

$$\{x:f(x) \ge c\}, \{x:f(x) > c\}, \{x:f(x) \le c\}, \{x:f(x) < c\}$$

are measurable for all real numbers $c$ (Theorem 3.3.4).

A function $f$ on a measurable set $E$ is said to be integrable if the function $F$,

$$F(x) = \begin{cases} f(x) & \text{if } x \in E \\ 0 & \text{if } x \notin E \end{cases}$$

is integrable, and one defines (Definition 3.3.5):

$$\int_E f \, dx = \int F \, dx;$$

if $E$ is an interval with end points $a$, $b$,

$$\int_a^b f \, dx = \int_E f \, dx.$$

Suppose $\mathscr{M}$ is any collection of subsets of a set $S$ together with a measure $\mu(A)$ for $A \in \mathscr{M}$ (which may be infinite) subject to the conditions:

(a) If $A, B \in \mathscr{M}$ then $A \cup B \in \mathscr{M}$ and $S - A \in \mathscr{M}$.
(b) $\mu(\varnothing) = 0$.

(c) If $\{A_n\}$ is a sequence of pairwise disjoint sets in $\mathscr{M}$ and if $\bigcup_{n=1}^{\infty} A_n \in \mathscr{M}$, then

$$\mu\left(\bigcup_{n=1}^{\infty} A_n\right) = \sum_{n=1}^{\infty} \mu(A_n).$$

If $L$ denotes the set of functions

$$\varphi = \sum_{k=1}^{n} a_k \chi_{A_K}, \qquad A_k \in \mathscr{M}, \qquad \sigma(A_k) < \infty$$

with integral

$$\int \varphi \, d\mu = \sum_{k=1}^{n} a_k \mu(A_k)$$

(Definition 3.4.1 and Proposition 3.4.2), then Properties (1) to (5) are satisfied and a theory of integration can be developed (Corollary 3.4.3 and Proposition 3.4.4).

The outer measure of a set $A$ is defined as

$$\sigma^*(A) = \inf\left\{\sum_{k=1}^{\infty} \sigma(A_k) : A_k \in \mathscr{M}, A \subset \bigcup_{k=1}^{\infty} A_k\right\}$$

where $\mathscr{M}$ is the collection of all finite unions of intervals (or a collection of sets having Properties (a), (b), and (c) above, in which case $\sigma$ has to be replaced by $\mu$) (Definition 3.5.1). One may interpret $\mathscr{M}$ in this formula also as the collection of all open intervals (Proposition 3.5.6). Another formula for $\sigma^*(A)$ is

$$\sigma^*(A) = \inf\{\sigma(B) : B \text{ is measurable, } B \supset A\}$$

(Proposition 3.5.2). For a measurable set $B$, $\sigma^*(B) = \sigma(B)$ (Corollary 3.5.4), and for any set $A$ with $\sigma^*(A) < \infty$, there is always a measurable set $B \supset A$ with $\sigma^*(A) = \sigma(B)$ (Corollary 3.5.3).

The measurable sets $E$ can be characterized by the equation

$$\sigma^*(A) = \sigma^*(A \cap E) + \sigma^*(A - E), A \in \mathscr{M}$$

(Theorem 3.5.5).

# 4

# Integration of Functions of Several Variables

In this chapter we are going to discuss the counterpart of the elementary calculus of integrals in two and more real variables. To do this, we construct in Section 4.1 an integral on a product set $S = S_1 \times S_2$ when, on each of the two sets $S_1$ and $S_2$, there is defined an integral in the sense of Section 2.5. Then, in Section 4.2 we specialize this to the most important case, namely, the ordinary Lebesgue integral of Euclidean space $R^n$. The definitions in this case are slightly different from those of the general theory in Section 4.1. This is done because of the importance of having a simple and customary class of elementary functions on $R^n$, whereas in the general case certain complications arise from the need to insure an easy operability within the classes of elementary functions on $S_1$ and $S_2$. For students who are mainly interested in the theory of Lebesgue integration, we have arranged our discussion in Section 4.2 to be independent of Section 4.1.

In Sections 4.3 and 4.4 we study the behavior of the Lebesgue integral under certain transformations. In Section 4.3 translations and linear transformations are discussed. For this a certain amount of linear algebra is needed. The student should especially be familiar with the elementary theory of matrices and determinants. Section 4.4, in which continuously differentiable transformations are considered, is even more advanced. In order to obtain any real profit from it the student must have some experience with the calculus of several variables.

## 4.1 DEFINITIONS AND FUBINI'S THEOREM

We will now develop the theory of Lebesgue integration in the $n$-dimensional Euclidean space $R^n$. Here we will be able to make use of our abstract theory of Section 2.5 by specializing the set $S$ to $R^n$. On the other hand, the process whereby we obtain $R^n$ from the real line $R$, namely forming Cartesian products, is a general set theoretic operation. Given two sets $S_1$ and $S_2$, the set $S$ whose elements consist of all ordered pairs with their first component from $S_1$ and their second from $S_2$,

$$S = S_1 \times S_2 = \{(x, y): x \in S_1, y \in S_2\}$$

is called the Cartesian product of $S_1$ and $S_2$. The Cartesian product is associative up to a natural isomorphism; hence we can speak of $R^n$ as the $n$-fold Cartesian product of $R$ with itself, without ambiguity. Because of this we will first develop a general theory of integration on product sets and then specialize the theory to $R^n$.

Suppose that $L_1$ is a class of elementary functions on the set $S_1$, with the integral

$$\int \xi \, d\mu_1 \quad \text{for} \quad \xi \in L_1$$

and that $L_2$ is a class of elementary functions on $S_2$ with the integral

$$\int \eta \, d\mu_2 \qquad \text{for} \quad \eta \in L_2.$$

Because of the investigation at the end of Section 3.2 (Proposition 3.2.7), it is possible to suppose that $L_1$ and $L_2$ are the respective classes of integrable generalized step functions, without changing the integration theories on $S_1$ and $S_2$. We shall see later why this choice of the spaces of elementary functions is necessary.

4.1.1 **Definition** *The class $L$ of elementary functions on the Cartesian product $S = S_1 \times S_2$ is the set of all functions $\varphi$ that can be written*

$$\varphi(x, y) = \sum_{k=1}^{m} \xi_k(x)\eta_k(y), \quad \xi_k \in L_1, \quad \eta_k \in L_2, \quad k = 1, \cdots, m \tag{4.1.2}$$

*where $L_1$ and $L_2$ are the spaces of generalized step functions on $S_1$ and $S_2$, respectively.*

It is easy to see that $L$ is a vector space, that is, that $L$ is closed under linear operations. It is not so easy to see that $L$ is also closed under order operations, that if $\varphi$ and $\psi$ belong to $L$, then $\varphi \wedge \psi$ and $\varphi \vee \psi$ also belong to $L$, or, what amounts to the same according to Equation (2.2.2), to show that if $\varphi$ is in $L$, then so is $|\varphi|$. Here we have to use the fact that each function in $L_1$ has only finitely many different values; it is possible to construct counterexamples in the opposite case (Exercise 4.1.1).

4.1.3 **Lemma** *If $\varphi \in L$, then $|\varphi| \in L$ also.*

*Proof* To see that $|\varphi| \in L$ if $\varphi$ is the function given by Equation (4.1.2), consider the possible positions of the point $(\xi_1(x), \cdots, \xi_m(x))$ in $R^m$ as $x$ varies over $S_1$. These points are finite in number, so we can denote the ones that are different from the origin by

$$(a_{i1}, \cdots, a_{ik}, \cdots, a_{im}), \qquad i = 1, 2, \cdots, n.$$

To each of them there corresponds a measurable set $E_i$, namely, the set on which the measurable function $\rho_i$ defined by

$$\rho_i(x) = \sum_{k=1}^{m} (\xi_k(x) - a_{ik})^2$$

vanishes. Let $\chi_i$ be the characteristic function of $E_i$. There is at least one $a_{ik}$ different from zero, since $(a_{i1}, \cdots, a_{im})$ is not the origin. Since $\xi_k$ equals $a_{ik}$ on $E_i$, we have

$$\chi_i \leq |a_{ik}^{-1}| \, |\xi_k|$$

which shows that $\chi_i$ is integrable. Furthermore,

$$\xi_k = \sum_{i=1}^{n} a_{ik}\chi_i, \qquad k = 1, \cdots, m$$

whence

$$\varphi(x, y) = \sum_{k=1}^{m} \left[ \sum_{i=1}^{n} a_{ik} \chi_i(x) \right] \eta_k(y)$$
$$= \sum_{i=1}^{n} \chi_i(x) \zeta_i(y)$$

where

$$\zeta_i = \sum_{k=1}^{m} a_{ik} \eta_k \in L_2, \qquad i = 1, \cdots, n.$$

It is easily seen from the definition that the sets $E_i$ are disjoint. Thus

$$|\varphi(x, y)| = \sum_{i=1}^{n} \chi_i(x) \, |\zeta_i(y)|$$

so that $|\varphi|$ belongs to $L$, since $|\zeta_i| \in L_2$, $i = 1, \cdots, n$.

If $\varphi \in L$, then, for each $y$ in $S_2$,

$$\varphi_y(x) = \varphi(x, y)$$

is a function in $L_1$. The function $\eta$ defined by

$$\eta(y) = \int \varphi_y \, d\mu_1 \qquad \text{for} \quad y \in S_2$$

is in $L_2$, because if $\varphi$ is given by Equation (4.1.2), then

$$\eta = \sum_{k=1}^{m} \left[ \int \xi_k \, d\mu_1 \right] \eta_k.$$

Consequently,

$$\int \eta \, d\mu_2 = \sum_{k=1}^{m} \int \xi_k \, d\mu_1 \int \eta_k \, d\mu_2 = \int \xi \, d\mu_1 \tag{4.1.4}$$

where $\xi$ is the function in $L_1$ defined by

$$\xi(x) = \int \varphi_x \, d\mu_2 = \sum_{k=1}^{m} \left[ \int \eta_k \, d\mu_2 \right] \xi_k(x) \qquad \text{for } x \in S_1,$$

with $\varphi_x(y) = \varphi(x, y)$.

4.1.5 DEFINITION *The integral $\int \varphi \, d\mu$ of a function $\varphi \in L$ given by Equation (4.1.2) is defined as the common value of the three expressions (4.1.4). This integral is also denoted by*

$$\int \varphi \, d\mu = \int \varphi \, d\mu_1 \otimes \mu_2.$$

Note that in the simple case $S_1 = S_2 = R$, $\mu_1 = \mu_2 = \sigma$, $m = 1$, and $\xi_1$, $\eta_1$ characteristic functions of bounded intervals, the integral of $\varphi$ becomes the area of the rectangle whose characteristic function is $\varphi$.

4.1.6 PROPOSITION *The linear space $L$ with the integral $\int \varphi \, d\mu$, $\varphi \in L$, as defined in Definition 4.1.5, satisfies the fundamental properties (1) to (5).*

*Proof* If $\varphi$ and $\psi$ belong to $L$, then so do $\varphi \vee \psi$ and $\varphi \wedge \psi$ as a consequence of Lemma 4.1.3. We leave the proof of the remainder of (1) and the verification of (2) and (3) to the reader (Exercise 4.1.2). To prove (4), let $\{\varphi_n\}$ be a decreasing sequence of nonnegative functions in $L$ such that

$$\lim_{n\to\infty} \varphi_n(x, y) = 0$$

for all $(x, y) \in S$. Then for each $y \in S_2$, $\{\varphi_{ny}\}$ is a decreasing sequence of nonnegative functions in $L_1$ and

$$\lim_{n\to\infty} \varphi_{ny}(x) = 0$$

for all $x \in S_1$. Thus by Property (4) for $L_1$,

$$\lim_{n\to\infty} \int \varphi_{ny} \, d\mu_1 = 0$$

for each $y \in S_2$. Now $\{\eta_n\}$,

$$\eta_n(y) = \int \varphi_{ny} \, d\mu_1,$$

is a decreasing sequence of nonnegative functions in $L_2$ with

$$\lim_{n\to\infty} \eta_n(y) = 0$$

for all $y \in S_2$. Hence, by Property (4) for $L_2$,

$$\lim_{n\to\infty} \int \varphi_n \, d\mu = \lim_{n\to\infty} \int \eta_n \, d\mu_2 = 0.$$

In the proof of (5) we apply the result of the proof of Lemma 4.1.3 where we have seen that each $\varphi \in L$ can be written as

$$\varphi(x, y) = \sum_{i=1}^{m} \chi_i(x)\zeta_i(y)$$

where $\zeta_i \in L_2$, and $\chi_i \in L_1$ are characteristic functions of disjoint (integrable) sets. Therefore

$$\varphi(x, y) \wedge 1 = \sum_{i=1}^{\infty} \chi_i(x)[\zeta_i(y) \wedge 1].$$

This shows $\varphi \wedge 1 \in L$, because $\zeta_i \wedge 1 \in L_2$ by Property (5) for $L_2$.

Equation (4.1.4) gives a procedure for computing $\int \varphi \, d\mu$ by integrating first with respect to one variable, then with respect to the other, which is consistent with the procedure known from elementary calculus. Such considerations lie behind the assertion that Definition 4.1.5 is more natural than any other one that also satisfies Properties (1) to (5); but this, of course, is not a mathematical statement.

When we want to emphasize the computational procedures indicated in Equation (4.1.4), we write

$$\int \varphi \, d\mu = \int \eta \, d\mu_2 = \iint \varphi \, d\mu_1 \, d\mu_2$$

and

$$\int \varphi \, d\mu = \int \xi \, d\mu_1 = \iint \varphi \, d\mu_2 \, d\mu_1.$$

The most important statement of this chapter is the assertion, known as Fubini's theorem, that these computational procedures—with only some very obvious modifications—remain valid for all functions in $L^1$, the class of integrable functions on $S = S_1 \times S_2$. In the following, the expressions "integrable," "measurable," "null set," "null function," "almost everywhere" (a.e.), and "almost all" (a.a.) are understood to be with respect to $d\mu_1$ when used on objects associated with $S_1$, with respect to $d\mu_2$ when used on objects associated with $S_2$, and with respect to $d\mu$ when used on objects associated with $S$.

4.1.7 DEFINITION *If, for a function $f$ on $S$, $f_y(x) = f(x, y)$ is integrable for a.a. $y \in S_2$, and if there is an integrable function $H$ on $S_2$ satisfying*

$$H(y) = \int f_y \, d\mu_1 \qquad \text{for a.a. } y,$$

*then we say that the iterated integral*

$$\iint f \, d\mu_1 \, d\mu_2 = \int H \, d\mu_2$$

*exists. Similarly, if $f_x(y) = f(x, y)$ is integrable for a.a. $x \in S_1$, and if there is an integrable function $G$ on $S_1$ satisfying*

$$G(x) = \int f_x \, d\mu_2 \qquad \text{for a.a. } x,$$

*then we say that the iterated integral*

$$\iint f \, d\mu_2 \, d\mu_1 = \int G \, d\mu_1$$

*exists.*

### 4.1.8 THEOREM

FUBINI'S THEOREM *If the function $f$ on $S$ is integrable, then the iterated integrals $\iint f\,d\mu_1\,d\mu_2$ and $\iint f\,d\mu_2\,d\mu_1$ both exist and are equal to $\int f\,d\mu$,*

$$\int f\,d\mu = \iint f\,d\mu_1\,d\mu_2 = \iint f\,d\mu_2\,d\mu_1.$$

*Proof* By Mikusiński's lemma there is a series $\sum \varphi_n$ of functions in $L$ which satisfies $\sum_{n=1}^{\infty} \int |\varphi_n|\,d\mu < \infty$ and

$$f(x, y) = \sum_{n=1}^{\infty} \varphi_n(x, y)$$

for all those $(x, y)$ for which the last series converges absolutely. Let

$$\zeta_n(y) = \int |\varphi_{ny}|\,d\mu_1, \qquad \varphi_{ny}(x) = \varphi_n(x, y).$$

Then $\sum \zeta_n$ is a series of nonnegative functions in $L_2$ and

$$\sum_{n=1}^{\infty} \int \zeta_n\,d\mu_2 = \sum_{n=1}^{\infty} \iint |\varphi_n|\,d\mu_1\,d\mu_2 < \infty.$$

Hence there is a null set $F \subset S_2$ such that

$$\sum_{n=1}^{\infty} \zeta_n(y) = \sum_{n=1}^{\infty} \int |\varphi_{ny}|\,d\mu_1 < \infty$$

for $y \notin F$. Consequently $\sum \varphi_{ny}(x)$ converges absolutely for a.a. $x$ if $y \notin F$, whence

$$f_y = \sum_{n=1}^{\infty} \varphi_{ny} \text{ a.e.}$$

if $y \notin F$. Thus $f_y$ is integrable on $S_1$ for $y \notin F$ and

$$\int f_y\,d\mu_1 = \sum_{n=1}^{\infty} \int \varphi_{ny}\,d\mu_1.$$

Furthermore, if $H$ is a function on $S_2$ satisfying

$$H(y) = \int f_y\,d\mu_1$$

for $y \notin F$, and if we define

$$\vartheta_n(y) = \int \varphi_{ny}\,d\mu_1$$

then $\sum \vartheta_n$ is a series of functions in $L_2$ satisfying

$$\sum_{n=1}^{\infty} \int |\vartheta_n|\,d\mu_2 \le \sum_{n=1}^{\infty} \int \zeta_n\,d\mu_2 < \infty$$

and for $y \notin F$

$$H(y) = \sum_{n=1}^{\infty} \vartheta_n(y).$$

Hence $H$ is an integrable function on $S_2$ with integral

$$\int H \, d\mu_2 = \sum_{n=1}^{\infty} \int \vartheta_n \, d\mu_2 = \sum_{n=1}^{\infty} \int \varphi_n \, d\mu = \int f \, d\mu.$$

Since $\int H \, d\mu_2$ is the iterated integral $\iint f \, d\mu_1 \, d\mu_2$, we have proved one half of Theorem 4.1.8 and the other half follows by symmetry.

### 4.1.9 COROLLARY

TONELLI'S THEOREM *A function $f$ on $S$ is integrable if and only if it is measurable, vanishes off some set that is the union of a sequence of integrable sets, and furthermore one of the two iterated integrals,*

$$\iint |f| \, d\mu_1 \, d\mu_2, \qquad \iint |f| \, d\mu_2 \, d\mu_1,$$

*exists.*

*Proof* We observe first that the conditions are necessary. The sets

$$E_n = \left\{(x, y) : |f(x, y)| \geq \frac{1}{n}\right\}$$

outside whose union $f$ vanishes are integrable since, if $\chi_n$ is the characteristic function of $E_n$, then $\chi_n \leq n\,|f|$. The iterated integrals exist by Fubini's theorem.

For the converse, suppose $f$ is a measurable function on $S$, vanishing off $\bigcup_{n=1}^{\infty} E_n$, where the $E_n$ are integrable sets. Let $\chi_n$ be the characteristic function of $\bigcup_{i=1}^{n} E_i$. Suppose, for instance, that $\iint |f| \, d\mu_1 \, d\mu_2$ exists. The increasing sequence $\{n\chi_n \wedge |f|\}$ consists of integrable functions, and

$$|f| = \lim_{n \to \infty} n\chi_n \wedge |f|$$

everywhere. By Theorem 4.1.8 we have the estimate

$$\int n\chi_n \wedge |f| \, d\mu = \iint n\chi_n \wedge |f| \, d\mu_1 \, d\mu_2$$
$$\leq \iint |f| \, d\mu_1 \, d\mu_2.$$

Thus the monotone convergence theorem applies, proving that $|f|$ is integrable and, since $f$ is measurable, $f$ is integrable also.

## *EXERCISES*

*4.1.1* Show that if $S_1 = S_2 = R$ and $L_1$ and $L_2$ are both equal to the class of piecewise linear functions on $R$ (defined in part D of the exercise section

1.6), then the functions $\varphi(x, y)$ in $L$ are given piecewise by expressions of the type $a + bx + cy + dxy$, and the boundaries of the regions of validity for the different expressions are always broken straight lines consisting of segments parallel to either the $x$-axis or the $y$-axis. Define the two piecewise linear functions $\varphi$ and $\psi$ by

$$\varphi(x) = (1 - |x - 1|)^+,$$
$$\psi(x) = (1 - |x - \tfrac{1}{2}|)^+ - (\tfrac{1}{2} - |x - \tfrac{1}{2}|)^+.$$

Show that the function $\eta$ defined by

$$\eta(x, y) = \varphi(x)\varphi(y) - \psi(x)\psi(y)$$

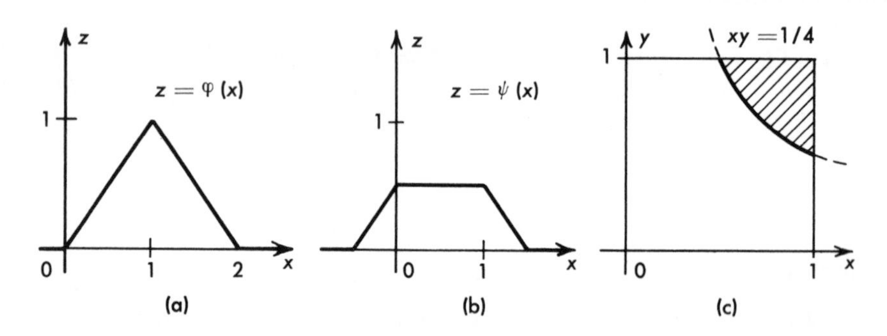


Figure 4.1 The region of validity of $\varphi(x)\varphi(y) = xy$ as well as that of $\psi(x)\psi(y) = \frac{1}{4}$ is the square in the diagram (c). However, $|\eta(x, y)| = xy - \frac{1}{4}$ holds only in the shaded region where $xy - \frac{1}{4} \geq 0$.

is in $L$ and equals $xy - \frac{1}{4}$ in the rectangle $\{(x, y) : 0 \leq x, y \leq 1\}$. Hence $|\eta|$ cannot be in $L$, since the region of validity of $|\eta(x, y)| = xy - \frac{1}{4}$ is bounded in part by the hyperbola $\{(x, y) : xy = \frac{1}{4}\}$ (see Figure 4.1).

*4.1.2* Show that the class $L$ and the integral $\int \varphi \, d\mu$ defined in Definitions 4.1.1 and 4.1.5, respectively, satisfies the fundamental properties (2) and (3) of a class of elementary functions.

*4.1.3* Show that in constructing the class $L$ from the classes of elementary functions on $S_1$ and $S_2$, one does not have to pass to the classes of integrable generalized step functions in order that $|\varphi| \in L$ for each $\varphi \in L$, provided at least one of the classes $L_1$ and $L_2$ of elementary functions has the property that each individual function in it takes on only finitely many different values.

*Hint* Suppose each of the functions in $L_1$ takes on only a finite number of different values. Let $\varphi \in L$,

$$\varphi(x, y) = \sum_{k=1}^{m} \xi(x)\eta(y), \qquad \xi \in L_1, \qquad \eta \in L_2.$$

Let $(a_{i1}, \cdots, a_{im})$, $1 \leq i \leq n$ be the values of $(\xi_1(x), \cdots, \xi_m(x))$ different from zero as $x$ ranges over $S_1$. Show that the functions

$$q_i = \sum_{k=1}^{m} |a_{ik}| - \sum_{k=1}^{m} |\xi_k - a_{ik}|$$

belong to $L_1$, using the equations

$$\alpha - |\alpha - \varphi| = 2(\varphi \wedge \alpha) - \varphi,$$
$$-\alpha - |\alpha - \varphi| = -2(\varphi \vee \alpha) + \varphi.$$

Then show that for sufficiently small $\varepsilon > 0$,

$$\chi_i = \left(q_i - q_i \wedge \left(\sum_{k=1}^{m} |a_{ik}| - \varepsilon\right)\right) \Big/ \varepsilon$$

is the characteristic function of the set of $x \in S_1$ such that

$$(\xi_1(x), \cdots, \xi_m(x)) = (a_{i1}, \cdots, a_{im}).$$

Note that $\chi_i$ belongs to $L_1$.

*4.1.4* Show that, in the case of the conditions of the previous exercise, the resulting class of integrable functions on $S = S_1 \times S_2$ coincides with the one previously obtained.

## 4.2 THE LEBESGUE INTEGRAL ON $R^n$

The construction of the Lebesgue integral for the $n$-dimensional Euclidean space $R^n$ is intimately related to the construction of an integral on a product space, as discussed in the preceding section. However, we prefer to proceed independently, using step functions instead of generalized step functions, since step functions seem to be more natural in the context of Lebesgue integration. Only at the end of this section will we point out the relation to the discussion in the previous section.

A point $x$ in the $n$-dimensional Euclidean space $R^n$ is given by an $n$-tuple $(x_1, \cdots, x_n)$ of real numbers,

$$x = (x_1, \cdots, x_n),$$

$x_k$, $k = 1, \cdots, n$, being the coordinates of $x$.

4.2.1 DEFINITION *A function $\varphi$ on $R^n$ is called a step function if there are step functions*

$$\varphi_{1k}, \cdots, \varphi_{nk}, \qquad k = 1, \cdots, m$$

*of one real variable, such that*

$$\varphi(x) = \varphi(x_1, \cdots, x_n) = \sum_{k=1}^{m} \varphi_{1k}(x_1) \cdots \varphi_{nk}(x_n) \tag{4.2.2}$$

*for all* $x \in R^n$. *The set of all step functions on* $R^n$ *is denoted by* ${}_nL$ *or, if no confusion is possible, just by* $L$ (see Figure 4.2).

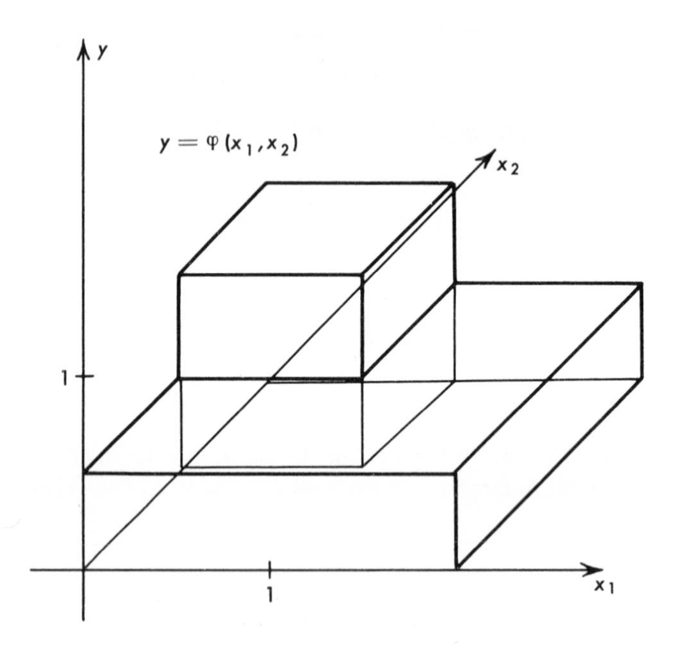


Figure 4.2 Example of a step function on $R^2$; $\varphi(x_1, x_2) = \varphi_{11}(x_1)\varphi_{21}(x_2) + \varphi_{12}(x_1)\varphi_{22}(x_2)$ where $\varphi_{11} = (1/\sqrt{2})\chi_{(0,2)} = \varphi_{21}$ and $\varphi_{12} = (1/\sqrt{2})\chi_{(1,2)} = \varphi_{22}$. The integral of $\varphi$ is the volume under the graph $y = \varphi(x_1, x_2)$.

Thus, if $n \geq 2$, and if we fix $x_2, \cdots, x_n$ and consider the step function $\varphi$ on $R^n$ as a function of $x_1$ alone, then we obtain a step function of one variable that we can integrate; let us denote its integral by $\int \varphi \, dx_1$, or by

$$\int \varphi(\cdot, x_2, \cdots, x_n) \, dx_1$$

to indicate that the integral still depends on the choice of $x_2, \cdots, x_n$. We have

$$\int \varphi(\cdot, x_2, \cdots, x_n) \, dx_1 = \sum_{k=1}^{m} \left[ \int \varphi_{1k} \, dx_1 \right] \varphi_{2k}(x_2) \cdots \varphi_{nk}(x_n)$$

if $\varphi$ is given by Equation (4.2.2). The last equation shows that $\int \varphi \, dx_1$ is a step function on $R^{n-1}$ where we consider the points in $R^{n-1}$ as $(n-1)$-tuples $(x_2, \cdots,$

$x_n$). Thus we can repeat the process of integration, finally obtaining an iterated integral,

$$\int \cdots \int \varphi \, dx_1 \cdots dx_n.$$

If $\varphi$ is given by Equation (4.2.2), then

$$\int \cdots \int \varphi \, dx_1 \cdots dx_n = \sum_{k=1}^{m} \int \varphi_{1k} \, dx_1 \cdots \int \varphi_{nk} \, dx_n. \tag{4.2.3}$$

For any permutation $(\pi 1, \cdots, \pi n)$ of $(1, \cdots, n)$, we can define an iterated integral $\int \cdots \int \varphi \, dx_{\pi 1} \cdots dx_{\pi n}$ of $\varphi$ in the same manner, and we have

$$\int \cdots \int \varphi \, dx_{\pi 1} \cdots dx_{\pi n} = \sum_{k=1}^{m} \int \varphi_{\pi 1,k} \, dx_{\pi 1} \cdots \int \varphi_{\pi n,k} \, dx_{\pi n}. \tag{4.2.4}$$

Obviously, the right-hand sides of (4.2.3) and (4.2.4) are the same, whence

$$\int \cdots \int \varphi \, dx_1 \cdots dx_n = \int \cdots \int \varphi \, dx_{\pi 1} \cdots dx_{\pi n}$$

for any permutation $(\pi 1, \cdots, \pi n)$ of $(1, \cdots, n)$.

4.2.5 DEFINITION *The Lebesgue integral $\int \varphi \, dx$ of a step function $\varphi$ on $R^n$ is defined by*

$$\int \varphi \, dx = \int \cdots \int \varphi \, dx_1 \cdots dx_n.$$

Conforming with common usage, we let the same notation $\int \varphi \, dx$ stand for the Lebesgue integral in all spaces $R^n$. This convention demands that the dimension of the domain of definition of the concerned function be carefully declared beforehand. On the other hand, we may use similar notations like

$$\int \varphi \, dy, \qquad \int \varphi \, dz \cdots$$

for the same integral.

Since every step function on the real line is a linear combination of characteristic functions of closed bounded intervals, every step function on $R^n$ is a linear combination of characteristic functions of closed bounded cubes

$$\{x \in R^n : a_k \leq x_k \leq b_k, k = 1, \cdots, n\}.$$

The integral of the characteristic function $\chi$ of such a cube, according to Definition 4.2.5 is the volume of the cube,

$$\int \chi \, dx = (b_1 - a_1) \cdots (b_n - a_n).$$

In order to be able to develop a theory of integration on $R^n$ we must, of course, convince ourselves that the integral $\int \varphi\, dx$, $\varphi \in L$, satisfies the basic properties (1) to (5).

4.2.6 PROPOSITION *The integral $\int \varphi\, dx$, $\varphi \in {}_nL$, defined in Definitions 4.2.1 and 4.2.5 satisfies Properties (1) to (5).*

*Proof* We proceed by induction on the dimension $n$ of $R^n$. For $n = 1$, we just have the Lebesgue integral on the real line for which we have established Properties (1) to (5) already. Now suppose $n > 1$ and assume that Properties (1) to (5) have been proved for the Lebesgue integral on $R^{n-1}$.

It is an immediate consequence of the definitions that ${}_nL$ is a linear space and that properties (2) and (3) hold for $\int \varphi\, dx$, $\varphi \in {}_nL$.

Let us show now that $|\varphi|$ is a step function on $R^n$ if $\varphi$ is. The proof is almost identical to that of Lemma 4.1.3. We can write

$$\varphi(x_1, \cdots, x_{n-1}, x_n) = \sum_{k=1}^{m} \psi_k(x_1, \cdots, x_{n-1})\varphi_{nk}(x_n)$$

where the $\psi_k$ are step functions on $R^{n-1}$ and the $\varphi_{nk}$ are step functions on the real line. As $x_n$ runs through the real numbers, the point

$$(\varphi_{n1}(x_n), \cdots, \varphi_{nm}(x_n))$$

can assume only finitely many different positions in $R^m$. Let

$$(a_{j1}, \cdots, a_{jm}) \qquad j = 1, \cdots, s$$

be the positions different from the origin $(0, \cdots, 0)$. For each $j$, the set

$$E_j = \{x_n : \varphi_{nk}(x_n) = a_{jk},\ k = 1, \cdots, m\}$$

is a union of a finite number of bounded intervals; the characteristic function $\chi_j$ of $E_j$ is therefore a step function. Notice also that the sets $E_j$ are pairwise disjoint. We have

$$\varphi_{nk}(x_n) = \sum_{j=1}^{s} a_{jk}\chi_j(x_n)$$

by the very definition of the $\chi_j$. Thus

$$\text{(4.2.7)} \qquad \varphi(x_1, \cdots, x_{n-1}, x_n) = \sum_{k=1}^{m} \psi_k(x_1, \cdots, x_{n-1})\left[\sum_{j=1}^{s} a_{jk}\chi_j(x_n)\right]$$

$$= \sum_{j=1}^{s} \psi_j'(x_1, \cdots, x_{n-1})\chi_j(x_n)$$

where

$$\psi_j' = \sum_{k=1}^{m} a_{jk}\psi_k$$

are step functions on $R^{n-1}$; hence by induction hypothesis, $|\psi_j'|$ is a step function on $R^{n-1}$ for each $j$. Since the $\chi_j$ are characteristic functions of disjoint sets, we have

$$|\varphi(x_1, \cdots, x_{n-1}, x_n)| = \sum_{j=1}^{s} |\psi_j'(x_1, \cdots, x_{n-1})| \chi_j(x_n)$$

proving that $|\varphi|$ is a step function on $R^n$. Equations (2.2.2) tell us now that $\varphi \vee \psi$ and $\varphi \wedge \psi$ are step functions on $R^n$ whenever $\varphi$ and $\psi$ are. This proves Property (1).

Equation (4.2.7) yields also a proof of Property (5):

$$\varphi(x_1, \cdots, x_{n-1}, x_n) \wedge 1 = \sum_{j=1}^{s} [\psi_j'(x_1, \cdots, x_{n-1}) \wedge 1]\chi_j(x_n)$$

where $\psi_j' \wedge 1$ is a step function on $R^{n-1}$ by induction hypothesis.

Finally, let us verify Property (4). Suppose $\{\varphi_m\}$ is a decreasing sequence of step functions on $R^n$ with

$$\lim_{m\to\infty} \varphi_m(x) = 0$$

for all $x \in R^n$. Considered as a function of $x_n$ alone, $\varphi_m$ is a step function on the real line, whence

$$\lim_{m\to\infty} \int \varphi_m \, dx_n = 0.$$

Now $\{\int \varphi_m \, dx_n\}$ is a decreasing sequence of step functions on $R^{n-1}$, and we have therefore by induction hypothesis

$$\begin{aligned} 0 &= \lim_{m\to\infty} \int \cdots \int \left( \int \varphi_m \, dx_n \right) dx_1 \cdots dx_{n-1} \\ &= \lim_{m\to\infty} \int \varphi_m \, dx. \end{aligned}$$

This completes the proof of Proposition 4.2.6.

Thus the space ${}_nL$ of step functions on $R^n$ with the integral $\int \varphi \, dx$, $\varphi \in {}_nL$ is suitable for the construction of a theory of integration. The integrable functions on $R^n$ with respect to this theory are also called *Lebesgue integrable*.

Now suppose $n \geq 2$, and let $j$ be an integer with $1 \leq j < n$. If we denote the points in $R^j$ by

$$y = (x_1, \cdots, x_j)$$

and the points in $R^{n-j}$ by

$$z = (x_{j+1}, \cdots, x_n),$$

then we can think of $R^n$ as the Cartesian product

$$R^n = R^j \times R^{n-j}.$$

To a point $x = (x_1, \cdots, x_n)$ in $R^n$ corresponds the point $(y, z)$ in $R^j \times R^{n-j}$.

4.2.8 DEFINITION *Suppose $f$ is a function on $R^n$. For each $z \in R^{n-j}$ let $f_z$ be the function defined by*

$$f_z(y) = f(y, z).$$

*If $f_z$ is integrable on $R^j$ for a.a. $z$ in $R^{n-j}$, and if there is an integrable function $H$ on $R^{n-j}$ such that*

$$H(z) = \int f_z \, dy$$

*for a.a. $z$ in $R^{n-j}$, then we say that the iterated integral $\int\int f \, dy \, dz$ exists and we let*

$$\int\int f \, dy \, dz = \int H \, dz.$$

*Similarly we define what it means that the iterated integral $\int\int f \, dz \, dy$, or the iterated integral $\int \cdots \int f \, dx_1 \cdots, dx_n$ exists.*

4.2.9 THEOREM

FUBINI'S THEOREM *Suppose $f$ is an integrable function on $R^n$, $n \geq 2$. For any $j$, $1 \leq j < n$, let $R^n = R^j \times R^{n-j}$ where the point $x = (x_1, \cdots, x_n)$ in $R^n$ corresponds to the point*

$$(y, z), \qquad y = (x_1, \cdots, x_j), \qquad z = (x_{j+1}, \cdots, x_n)$$

*in $R^j \times R^{n-j}$. Then the iterated integrals $\int\int f \, dy \, dz$ and $\int\int f \, dz \, dy$ both exist, and*

$$\int f \, dx = \int\int f \, dy \, dz = \int\int f \, dz \, dy.$$

*Proof* Let $L$ be the space of step functions on $R^n$, and $L_1$ and $L_2$ the spaces of step functions on $R^j$ and $R^{n-j}$, respectively. The step functions $\varphi \in L$ are exactly the functions on $R^n$ that admit a representation

$$\varphi(x_1, \cdots, x_n) = \sum_{k=1}^{m} \xi_k(x_1, \cdots, x_j)\eta_k(x_{j+1}, \cdots, x_n)$$

$$\xi_k \in L_1, \qquad \eta_k \in L_2, \qquad k = 1, \cdots, m.$$

If we make now the substitutions

$$S = R^n, \; S_1 = R^j, \; S_2 = R^{n-j},$$
$$d\mu = dx, \; d\mu_1 = dy, \; d\mu_2 = dz,$$

then a word by word transcription of the proof of Theorem 4.1.8 yields the proof for the present theorem.

Notice that Fubini's theorem for $R^n$ as stated above is not a direct consequence of Theorem 4.1.8 unless we show that Lebesgue integration on $R^n$ is the same as product integration on $R^j \times R^{n-j}$, as defined in the preceding section. This will be done in Lemma 4.2.12 below. (Note, however, that in the proof of Theorem 4.2.9 we did not use Theorem 4.1.8, but merely transcribed the proof of Theorem 4.1.8.)

We list now two corollaries to Theorem 4.2.9, the first one of which is established easily using induction on $n$.

### 4.2.10 COROLLARY

FUBINI'S THEOREM *Suppose the function $f$ on $R^n$ is Lebesgue integrable. Then for any permutation $(\pi 1, \cdots, \pi n)$ of $(1, \cdots, n)$, the iterated integral $\int \cdots \int f\, dx_{\pi 1} \cdots dx_{\pi n}$ exists and*

$$\int f\, dx = \int \cdots \int f\, dx_{\pi 1} \cdots dx_{\pi n}.$$

### 4.2.11 COROLLARY

TONELLI'S THEOREM *If the function $f$ on $R^n$ is measurable and if the iterated integral $\int \cdots \int |f|\, dx_{\pi 1} \cdots dx_{\pi n}$ exists for some permutation $(\pi 1, \cdots, \pi n)$ of $(1, \cdots, n)$, then $f$ is integrable.*

*Proof* Let $\chi_m$ be the characteristic function of the cube

$$\{x : |x_j| \leq m, j = 1, \cdots, n\}.$$

$\{m \wedge |f|\, \chi_m\}$ is an increasing sequence of integrable functions satisfying

$$\lim_{m \to \infty} m \wedge |f|\, \chi_m = |f|$$

everywhere. Because

$$\begin{aligned} \int m \wedge |f|\, \chi_m\, dx &= \int \cdots \int m \wedge |f|\, \chi_m\, dx_{\pi 1} \cdots dx_{\pi n} \\ &\leq \int \cdots \int |f|\, dx_{\pi 1} \cdots dx_{\pi n} \end{aligned}$$

for all $m$, we conclude that $|f|$ is integrable according to the monotone convergence theorem; and since $f$ is measurable, $f$ is in fact integrable.

We shall now prove the promised lemma, which will show us that Theorem 4.2.9 is actually a consequence of the general Theorem 4.1.8.

**4.2.12 LEMMA** *Suppose $n \geq 2$ and $1 \leq j < n$. Then Lebesgue integration on $R^n$ is the product integration on $R^j \times R^{n-j}$ as defined in Definition 4.1.1 and 4.1.5.*

*Proof* Let $L_1$, $L_2$, and $L$ be the step functions on $R^j$, $R^{n-j}$, and $R^n$, respectively. $K_1$ and $K_2$ are the Lebesgue integrable generalized step functions on $R^j$ and $R^{n-j}$, respectively. $K$ denotes the space of all functions $\varphi$ on $R^n$ of the form

$$\varphi(x) = \varphi(y, z) = \sum_{k=1}^{m} \xi_k(y)\eta_k(z), \qquad \xi_k \in K_1, \qquad \eta_k \in K_2$$

with the integral

$$\int \varphi \, d\mu = \sum_{k=1}^{m} \int \xi_k \, dy \int \eta_k \, dz.$$

We have, obviously, $L \subset K$ and

$$\int \varphi \, dx = \int \varphi \, d\mu \qquad \text{for } \varphi \in L.$$

If we prove that $K \subset L^1$ and

$$\int \varphi \, d\mu = \int \varphi \, dx \qquad \text{for } \varphi \in K \tag{4.2.13}$$

then the general comparison theorem (Corollary 2.5.8) implies that $L$ with the integral $\int \psi \, dx$, $\psi \in L$, and $K$ with the integral $\int \varphi \, d\mu$, $\varphi \in K$ yield the same theory of integration, thus proving the lemma.

In order to prove (4.2.13) it suffices to show that each function $\varphi$ of the form

$$\varphi(y, z) = \xi(y)\eta(z), \qquad \xi \in K_1, \ \eta \in K_2,$$

is Lebesgue integrable on $R^n$ and that we have

$$\int \varphi \, d\mu = \int \varphi \, dx.$$

By Mikusiński's lemma there are two series $\sum \xi_k$ and $\sum \eta_k$ of step functions on $R^j$ and $R^{n-j}$, respectively, such that

$$\sum_{k=1}^{\infty} \int |\xi_k| \, dy < \infty, \qquad \sum_{k=1}^{\infty} \int |\eta_k| \, dz < \infty,$$

$$\xi(y) = \sum_{k=1}^{\infty} \xi_k(y) \quad \text{if } \sum_{k=1}^{\infty} |\xi_k(y)| < \infty,$$

$$\eta(z) = \sum_{k=1}^{\infty} \eta_k(z) \quad \text{if } \sum_{k=1}^{\infty} |\eta_k(z)| < \infty.$$

Let $\varphi_{hk}$ be the step function on $R^n$ defined by

$$\varphi_{hk}(y, z) = \xi_h(y)\eta_k(z).$$

If $\{\varphi_m\}$ is any enumeration of the doubly indexed sequence $\{\varphi_{hk}\}$, then, by the theorem on double series (Theorem 1.0.5),

$$\begin{aligned}
\sum_{m=1}^{\infty} \int |\varphi_m| \, dx &= \sum_{h=1}^{\infty} \left( \sum_{k=1}^{\infty} \int |\varphi_{hk}| \, dx \right) \\
&= \sum_{h=1}^{\infty} \left( \sum_{k=1}^{\infty} \int |\xi_h| \, dy \int |\eta_k| \, dz \right) \\
&= \left( \sum_{h=1}^{\infty} \int |\xi_h| \, dy \right) \left( \sum_{k=1}^{\infty} \int |\eta_k| \, dz \right) < \infty.
\end{aligned}$$

We claim that if $\sum |\varphi_m(y, z)|$ converges, then

(4.2.14) $$\varphi(y, z) = \sum_{m=1}^{\infty} \varphi_m(y, z).$$

In fact, the theorem on double series implies that $\sum_h |\xi_h(y)\eta_k(z)|$ converges for each $k$ and $\sum_k |\xi_h(y)\eta_k(z)|$ converges for each $h$. Thus $\sum |\xi_h(y)|$ converges if $\eta_k(z) \neq 0$ for at least one $k$, and $\sum |\eta_k(z)|$ converges if $\xi_h(y) \neq 0$ for at least one $h$. Under these conditions we find

$$\sum_{m=1}^{\infty} \varphi_m(y, z) = \sum_{h=1}^{\infty}\left(\sum_{k=1}^{\infty} \xi_h(y)\eta_k(z)\right)$$
$$= \left(\sum_{h=1}^{\infty} \xi_h(y)\right)\left(\sum_{k=1}^{\infty} \eta_k(z)\right) = \xi(y)\eta(z)$$

as desired. But (4.2.14) is trivial if $\xi_h(y) = 0$ for all $h$ or $\eta_k(z) = 0$ for all $k$, because then $\varphi(y, z) = 0 = \varphi_m(y, z)$ for all $m$. Thus Mikusiński's lemma implies that $\varphi$ is Lebesgue integrable and

$$\int \varphi \, dx = \sum_{m=1}^{\infty} \int \varphi_m \, dx = \sum_{m=1}^{\infty} \int \varphi_m \, d\mu = \int \varphi \, d\mu.$$

This completes the proof of the lemma.

We conclude this section with the discussion of some examples. A rectangle $Q$ in $R^n$ is a set of the form

$$Q = \{x : x_i \in I_i, \ 1 \leq i \leq n\}$$

where $I_i$, $1 \leq i \leq n$, are intervals on the real line. Such a rectangle is measurable; its measure is

$$\sigma(Q) = |I_1| \cdot \cdots \cdot |I_n|$$

where $|I_i|$ is the length of $I_i$. $Q$ is called bounded if all the intervals $I_i$ are bounded. It is called closed (open) if all the intervals $I_i$ are closed (open). Let $a_i$, $b_i$ be the endpoints of $I_i$, $1 \leq i \leq n$. To the rectangle $Q$ we associate an open rectangle

$$Q^0 = \{x : x_i \in (a_i, b_i), \ 1 \leq i \leq n\},$$

called the interior of $Q$, and if $Q$ is bounded the closed rectangle

$$\bar{Q} = \{x : x_i \in [a_i, b_i], \ 1 \leq i \leq n\}$$

is called the closure of $Q$. We say that the bounded rectangle $Q$ is a cube if $|I_1| = |I_i|$, $1 \leq i \leq n$.

4.2.15 DEFINITION *A set $D \subset R^n$ is said to be open if every point in $D$ is contained in an open cube contained in $D$.*

For instance every open cube is an open set.

4.2.16 **Proposition** *Let $D$ be an open set in $R^n$. Then $D$ is the union of a sequence of pairwise disjoint cubes with closure contained in $D$. In particular, $D$ is measurable.*

*Proof* For each integer $m \geq 1$ let $\mathscr{F}^m$ be the family of cubes

$$Q = \{x : x_i \in I_i, 1 \leq i \leq n\}$$

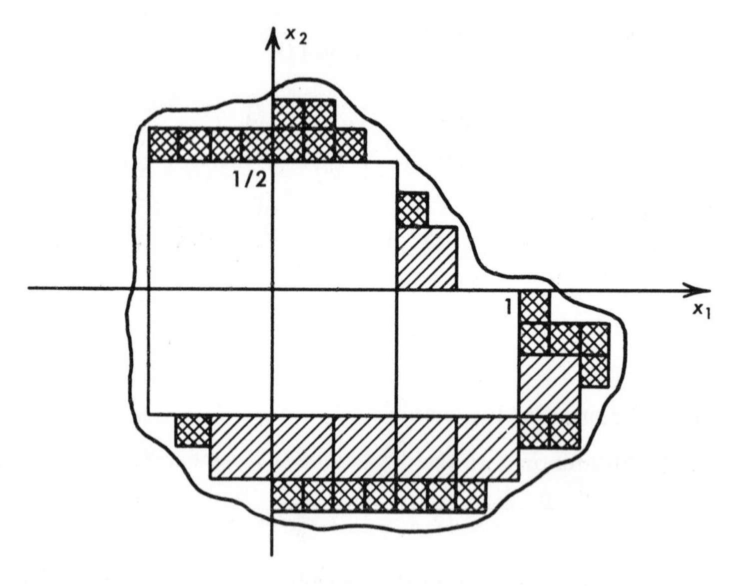


Figure 4.3 Example of an open set in $R^2$ which is exhausted by cubes. The blank cubes belong to $\mathscr{G}^1$, the lightly shaded ones to $\mathscr{G}^2$, and the darker shaded ones to $\mathscr{G}^3$.

where $I_i$ are intervals of the form

$$(k2^{-m}, (k+1)2^{-m}], \qquad k = 0, \pm 1, \cdots$$

The cubes in $\mathscr{F}^m$ cover $R^n$ and are pairwise disjoint. If $Q^m$ is a cube in $\mathscr{F}^m$ and $Q^{m+1}$ is a cube in $\mathscr{F}^{m+1}$, then either $Q^m$ and $Q^{m+1}$ are disjoint or $Q^{m+1} \subset Q^m$. Now define for each $m \geq 1$ a subfamily $\mathscr{G}^m$ of $\mathscr{F}^m$ by induction on $m$. For $m = 1$, $\mathscr{G}^1$ is the collection of all cubes in $\mathscr{F}^1$ with closure contained in $D$. For $m > 1$, $\mathscr{G}^m$ is the set of all cubes in $\mathscr{F}^m$ with closure contained in $D$ and not contained in any of the cubes in $\mathscr{G}^r$ for $r < m$ (see Figure 4.3). We claim that

$$D = \bigcup_{m=1}^{\infty} \bigcup \{Q : Q \in \mathscr{G}^m\},$$

which is certainly a union of pairwise disjoint cubes by construction. Namely, let $z \in D$. We can find a bounded open cube

$$P = \{x : x_i \in (a_i, b_i), 1 \leq i \leq n\}$$

with $z \in P \subset D$. There is also an integer $m \geq 1$ such that

$$2^{-m} < z_i - a_i, \qquad 2^{-m} < b_i - z_i, \qquad 1 \leq i \leq n.$$

For each $i$ we can find an integer $k_i$ with the property

$$a_i < k_i 2^{-m} < z_i \leq (k_i + 1)2^{-m} < b_i.$$

Then

$$Q = \{x : x_i \in (k_i 2^{-m}, (k_i + 1)2^{-m}], 1 \leq i \leq n\}$$

is a cube in $\mathscr{F}^m$ with closure contained in $D$ and $z \in Q$. Let $m$ be the smallest integer with this property, then certainly $Q \in \mathscr{G}^m$. This completes the proof.

4.2.17 COROLLARY *Suppose $f$ is a continuous function on an open set $D$ in $R^n$. Then $f$ is measurable.*

*Proof* We interpret $f$ to be equal to zero outside $D$. To prove that $f$ is measurable we need only show that $\{x : f(x) > c\}$ is a measurable set for each real number $c$. Since

$$\{x : f(x) > c\} = \begin{cases} \{x : f(x) > c, x \in D\} & \text{if } c \geq 0 \\ \{x : f(x) > c, x \in D\} \cup (R^n - D) & \text{if } c < 0 \end{cases}$$

and $R^n - D$ is measurable by Proposition 4.2.16, we need only show that $C = \{x : x \in D, f(x) > c\}$ is measurable. In fact, this set is open because $f$ is continuous on $D$; if $z \in C$, we can find a $\delta > 0$ such that

$$Q = \{x : x_i \in (z_i - \delta, z_i + \delta), 1 \leq i \leq n\} \subset D,$$

$$|f(x) - f(z)| < f(z) - c \qquad \text{if } |x - z| < \delta.$$

Then clearly $z \in Q \subset C$.

4.2.18 COROLLARY *If $f$ is a continuous function on a closed bounded rectangle $Q$, then $f$ is integrable on $Q$.*

*Proof* Since $|f| \leq M\chi_Q$ where $M$ is the maximum of $|f|$ on $Q$, we need only show that $f$ is measurable on $Q$. By the previous corollary, $f$ is measurable on the interior $Q^0$ of $Q$, and $\sigma(Q) = \sigma(Q^0)$ so that $Q - Q^0$ is a null set. Thus $f$ is indeed measurable on $Q$.

## *EXERCISES*

*4.2.1*

(a) Let $R^n = R^j \times R^{n-j}$, $1 \leq j < n$, and suppose $E$ is a null set in $R^j$. Show that

$$E \times R^{n-j} = \{x = (y, z): y \in E, z \in R^{n-j}\}$$

is a null set in $R^n$.

(b) Suppose $g$ is an integrable function on $R^j$ and $h$ is an integrable function on $R^{n-j}$. Prove that the function $f$, defined by

$$f(x) = f(y, z) = g(y)h(z),$$

is integrable on $R^n$.

*Hint* Show first that $f$ is measurable by using the fact that $g$ and $h$ each are the limit almost everywhere of a sequence of step functions. Then apply Tonelli's theorem.

(c) Suppose $g$ and $h$ in (b) are only measurable. Show that $f$ is measurable.

*4.2.2* Suppose $\varphi$ and $\psi$ are continuous functions on the closed interval $[a, b]$, $a < b$ on the real line such that

$$\varphi(a) = \psi(a), \qquad \varphi(b) = \psi(b),$$

$$\varphi(t) > \psi(t) \qquad \text{for } t \in (a, b).$$

Show that

$$E = \{x = (x_1, x_2): x_1 \in (a, b), \psi(x_1) < x_2 < \varphi(x_1)\}$$

is an open subset of $R^2$ and that for any integrable function $f$ on $R^2$,

$$\int_E f\,dx = \int_a^b \int_{\psi(x_1)}^{\varphi(x_1)} f\,dx_2\,dx_1$$

(see Figure 4.4).

*4.2.3* Suppose $f$ and $g$ are continuous functions on $R^2$ with continuous partial derivatives

$$f_i = \frac{\partial}{\partial x_i} f, \qquad g_i = \frac{\partial}{\partial x_i} g, \qquad i = 1, 2.$$

Let $a, b, c, d$ be real numbers such that $a \leq b$, $c \leq d$. Prove Green's formula

$$\int_E (g_1 - f_2)\,dx = \int_a^b [f(x_1, c) - f(x_1, d)]\,dx_1 + \int_c^d [g(b, x_2) - g(a, x_2)]\,dx_2$$

where $E$ is the rectangle

$$E = \{x = (x_1, x_2): a \leq x_1 \leq b, c \leq x_2 \leq d\}.$$

The expression on the right of Green's formula is also denoted by $\int_\Gamma (f\,dx_1 + g\,dx_2)$ where $\Gamma$ is the boundary of $E$.

*Hint* Compute $\iint_E f_2\,dx_2\,dx_1$ and $\iint_E g_1\,dx_1\,dx_2$ separately.

*4.2.4* Suppose $f$ and $g$ are continuous functions on $R^2$ with continuous partial derivatives such that

$$\frac{\partial}{\partial x_2} f = \frac{\partial}{\partial x_1} g.$$

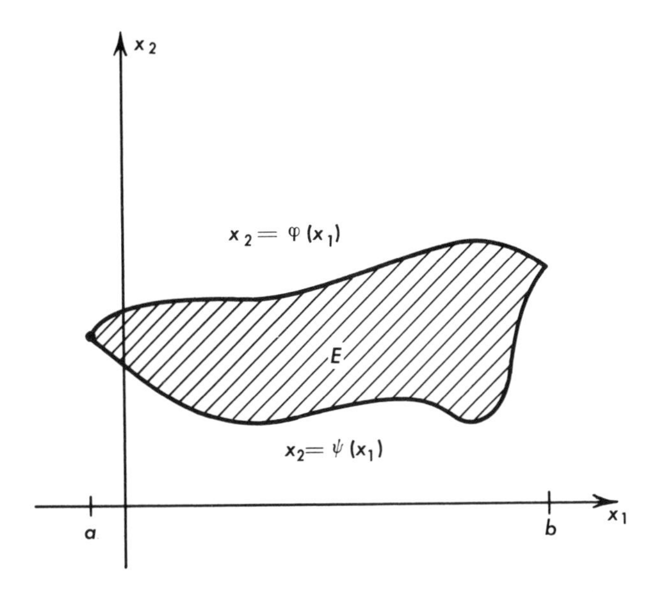


Figure 4.4 An open set in $R^2$ bounded by two curves.

Prove that there is a function $F$ on $R^2$ with

$$\frac{\partial}{\partial x_1} F = f, \qquad \frac{\partial}{\partial x_2} F = g.$$

*Hint* Define

$$F(x_1, x_2) = \int_0^{x_1} f(y_1, 0)\,dy_1 + \int_0^{x_2} g(x_1, y_2)\,dy_2.$$

Use the previous exercise to show that

$$F(x_1, x_2) = \int_0^{x_2} g(0, y_2)\,dy_2 + \int_0^{x_1} f(y_1, x_2)\,dy_1.$$

Then compute the partial derivatives of $F$, using the second and first formula respectively.

*4.2.5* Let $f$ be a nonnegative integrable function of one variable. Prove that

$$E = \{z = (x, y): 0 \leq y \leq f(x)\}$$

is an integrable subset of $R^2$ and that

$$\int f\,dx = \int_E dz,$$

that is, the integral of $f$ is the area under its graph.

*Hint* Use Tonelli's theorem. To prove that $E$ is measurable represent $f$ as the limit almost everywhere of a sequence of step functions $\varphi_n$ and show

$$\chi_E = \lim_{n\to\infty} \chi_{E_n} \text{ a.e.},$$

where $E_n$ is defined similarly as $E$ with $f$ replaced by $\varphi_n$.

## 4.3 LINEAR CHANGE OF VARIABLES

In this and the following section we study the behavior of integrable functions on $R^n$ under certain transformations acting on $R^n$. In each case we prove the relevant theorem first for step functions and then extend it to integrable functions. This extension of the result to integrable functions follows a routine pattern. We are actually able to establish a lemma which will apply in each of the cases that we will consider in the following discussion, thus saving us some work.

4.3.1 LEMMA *Suppose $\Phi$ maps the open subset $D$ of $R^n$ onto the open subset $E$ of $R^n$. Furthermore, assume there is a nonnegative measurable function $h$ on $D$ such that $h(\varphi \circ \Phi)$ is an integrable function on $D$ for any step function $\varphi$ and*

$$\int_E \varphi\,dx = \int_D h(\varphi \circ \Phi)\,dx.$$

*Then, if $f$ is an integrable function on $R^n$, $h(f \circ \Phi)$ is integrable on $D$ and*

$$\int_E f\,dx = \int_D h(f \circ \Phi)\,dx.$$

*Proof* By Mikusiński's lemma, there is a series $\sum \varphi_m$ of step functions such that $\sum_{m=1}^{\infty} \int |\varphi_m|\,dx < \infty$ and

$$f(x) = \sum_{m=1}^{\infty} \varphi_m(x)$$

for all $x$ for which the last series converges absolutely. We have

$$\sum_{m=1}^{\infty} \int_D h\,|\varphi_m \circ \Phi|\,dx = \sum_{m=1}^{\infty} \int_E |\varphi_m|\,dx < \infty,$$

whence $\sum h(\varphi_m \circ \Phi)$ converges absolutely almost everywhere on $D$. Since

$$h(x)f(\Phi(x)) = \sum_{m=1}^{\infty} h(x)\varphi_m(\Phi(x))$$

for all $x \in D$ for which the last series converges absolutely, $h(f \circ \Phi)$ is indeed integrable and

$$\int_D h(f \circ \Phi)\, dx = \sum_{m=1}^{\infty} \int_D h(\varphi_m \circ \Phi)\, dx = \sum_{m=1}^{\infty} \int_E \varphi_m\, dx = \int_E f\, dx.$$

We turn now to the discussion of some special transformations $\Phi$ of $R^n$. Let us first assume that $\Phi$ is the translation by a vector $c = (c_1, \cdots, c_n)$,

$$\Phi(x) = x + c.$$

4.3.2 **PROPOSITION** *Suppose $\Phi$ is a translation. If $f$ is an integrable function, then $f \circ \Phi$ is also integrable and*

$$\int f\, dx = \int f \circ \Phi\, dx, \tag{4.3.3}$$

*that is, the Lebesgue integral is translation-invariant.*

*Proof* Suppose first that $n = 1$ and $f$ is the characteristic function of a closed bounded interval $[a, b]$. If $\Phi$ is a translation by $c$, then $f \circ \Phi$ is the characteristic function of $[a - c, b - c]$. Clearly, Equation (4.3.3) holds in this case. Thus it holds also for every step function on $R$. Now suppose $\Phi$ is a translation by $c = (c_1, \cdots, c_n)$ in $R^n$. Let $\varphi$ be any step function on $R^n$,

$$\varphi(x_1, \cdots, x_n) = \sum_{k=1}^{m} \varphi_{k1}(x_1) \cdots \varphi_{kn}(x_n).$$

$\varphi \circ \Phi$ is again a step function and

$$\varphi(\Phi(x)) = \sum_{k=1}^{m} \varphi_{k1}(\Phi_1(x_1)) \cdots \varphi_{kn}(\Phi_n(x_n))$$

where $\Phi_j$ is a translation on $R$ by $c_j$, $1 \le j \le n$. Thus

$$\int \varphi \circ \Phi\, dx = \sum_{k=1}^{m} \int \varphi_{k1} \circ \Phi_1\, dx_1 \cdots \int \varphi_{kn} \circ \Phi_n\, dx_n$$

$$= \sum_{k=1}^{m} \int \varphi_{k1}\, dx_1 \cdots \int \varphi_{kn}\, dx_n = \int \varphi\, dx.$$

This proves the proposition for step functions; it holds then also for integrable functions by Lemma 4.3.1 (with $D = E = R^n$ and $h = 1$).

Next we consider a linear transformation $\Phi$ on $R^n$. Such a linear transformation is given by a matrix $A = (a_{ij})$; the $i$th component of $\Phi(x)$ is

$$\Phi_i(x) = \sum_{j=1}^{n} a_{ij}x_j.$$

It is clear that the functions $\Phi_i$ are continuous on $R^n$. This is also expressed by saying that a linear transformation on $R^n$ is continuous. More generally, we say that a (not necessarily linear) map $\Phi$ from an open subset $D$ in $R^n$ into $R^n$ is continuous if the $i$th component $\Phi_i(x)$ of $\Phi(x)$ defines a continuous function on $D$ for $1 \leq i \leq n$. For such continuous maps the following lemma holds.

4.3.4 LEMMA *Suppose $\Phi$ is a continuous map from an open subset $D$ in $R^n$ into $R^n$. If $Q$ is an open subset of $R^n$, then*

$$\Phi^{-1}(Q) = \{x : x \in D, \Phi(x) \in Q\}$$

*is also open.*

*Proof* Let $x \in \Phi^{-1}(Q)$. Since $Q$ is open and $\Phi(x) \in Q$, there is an $\varepsilon > 0$ such that

$$\{y : |\Phi_i(x) - y_i| < \varepsilon, 1 \leq i \leq n\} \subset Q.$$

Since $D$ is open and $x \in D$, we can find a $\delta$ such that

$$P = \{x' : |x_i - x_i'| < \delta, 1 \leq i \leq n\} \subset D.$$

Furthermore, we can choose $\delta$ so small that

$$|\Phi_i(x) - \Phi_i(x')| < \varepsilon \qquad \text{for } 1 \leq i \leq n \text{ and } x' \in P.$$

Then we have $P \subset \Phi^{-1}(Q)$ which proves that $\Phi^{-1}(Q)$ is open.

4.3.5 COROLLARY *Suppose $\Phi$ is a one-to-one linear transformation; then $\varphi \circ \Phi$ is integrable for every step function $\varphi$.*

*Proof* Every step function is a linear combination of characteristic functions of bounded open rectangles, because every step function on the real line is a linear combination of characteristic functions of bounded open intervals. Thus we need to prove the corollary only for the characteristic function $\chi$ of a bounded open rectangle $Q$. Here $\chi \circ \Phi$ is the characteristic function of $\Phi^{-1}(Q)$ which is open, by the last lemma, and hence measurable. Also, $\Psi = \Phi^{-1}$ is a linear transformation and therefore continuous. Each of the functions $\Psi_i$, $1 \leq i \leq n$ is therefore bounded on the closure $\bar{Q}$ of $Q$ which implies that $\Psi(Q) = \Phi^{-1}(Q)$ is a bounded set; it is thus integrable. This completes the proof.

If $\Phi$ and $\Psi$ are linear transformations on $R^n$ given by matrices $A = (a_{ij})$ and $B = (b_{ij})$, respectively, then $\Phi \circ \Psi$ is a linear transformation described by the product $AB = (c_{ij})$ of the two matrices $A$ and $B$, where

$$c_{ij} = \sum_{k=1}^{n} a_{ik}b_{kj}.$$

In linear algebra one shows that every matrix can be written as the product of triangular matrices and a diagonal matrix. In these triangular matrices the entries on the diagonal are all equal to 1, while all other entries save one are equal to zero. If the nonzero entry $d$ off the diagonal is at the intersection of the $i$th row with the $j$th column ($i \neq j$), then we denote the triangular matrix by $D_{ij}(d)$,

$$D_{ij}(d) = \begin{pmatrix} 1 & 0 & \cdot & \cdot & \overset{j}{0} & \cdot & \cdot & 0 \\ 0 & 1 & & & \cdot & & & \cdot \\ \cdot & \cdot & & & \cdot & & & \cdot \\ \cdot & & & \cdot & d & \cdot & \cdot & 0 \\ \cdot & & & & \cdot & & & \cdot \\ \cdot & & & & & \cdot & & \cdot \\ \cdot & & & & & & \cdot & \cdot \\ \cdot & & & & & & 1 & \cdot \\ 0 & \cdot & \cdot & \cdot & \cdot & \cdot & \cdot & 1 \end{pmatrix} \begin{matrix} \\ \\ \\ i \\ \\ \\ \\ \\ \\ \end{matrix}$$

In a diagonal matrix all entries off the diagonal are zero, while the entries on the diagonal can have any value. The theorem of linear algebra to which we are referring reads precisely as follows.

**4.3.6 PROPOSITION** *Every matrix $A$ can be written as a product of matrices*

$$A = D_1 \cdots D_r D D_1' \cdots D_s',$$

*where $D$ is a diagonal matrix and $D_1, \cdots, D_r$ and $D_1', \cdots, D_s'$ are triangular matrices.*

*Proof* We will sketch here a proof of this proposition. Notice that multiplication of $A$ on the left by $D_{ij}(d)$ has the effect of adding $d$ times the $j$th row to the $i$th row, while multiplication on the right by $D_{ij}(d)$ has the effect of adding $d$ times the $i$th column to the $j$th column. If $A$ is multiplied by $D_{ij}(-1)D_{ji}(1)D_{ij}(-1)$ on the left, then the $i$th row is interchanged with the negative of the $j$th row. Similarly, if $A$ is multiplied by $D_{ij}(-1)D_{ji}(1)D_{ij}(-1)$ on the right, then the $j$th column is interchanged with the negative of the $i$th column. Having made these preliminary remarks, we can now give the proof of the proposition.

If $A = (a_{ij})$ is already a diagonal matrix, then there is nothing to prove. Otherwise we can find a nonzero entry $a_{k\ell}$ with $k \neq \ell$ in $A$. Multiplying $A$ by $D_{k1}(-1)D_{1k}(1)D_{k1}(-1)$ on the left and by $D_{1\ell}(-1)D_{\ell 1}(1)D_{1\ell}(-1)$ on the right, we obtain a matrix $A^1 = (a_{ij}{}^1)$ with $a_{11}{}^1 = a_{k\ell} \neq 0$. If $A^1$ is a diagonal matrix, we are finished. If not, then we multiply $A^1$ on the left by

$$D_{21}\left(\frac{-a_{21}^{\ 1}}{a_{11}^{\ 1}}\right)\cdots D_{n1}\left(\frac{-a_{n1}^{\ 1}}{a_{11}^{\ 1}}\right)$$

and on the right by

$$D_{12}\left(\frac{-a_{12}^{\ 1}}{a_{11}^{\ 1}}\right)\cdots D_{1n}\left(\frac{-a_{1n}^{\ 1}}{a_{11}^{\ 1}}\right).$$

The result is a matrix $A^2 = (a_{ij}^{\ 2})$ of the form

$$\begin{pmatrix} a_{11}^{\ 2} & 0 & 0 & \cdots & 0 \\ 0 & a_{22}^{\ 2} & a_{23}^{\ 2} & \cdots & a_{2n}^{\ 2} \\ 0 & a_{32}^{\ 2} & \cdot & & \cdot \\ \cdot & \cdot & & & \cdot \\ \cdot & \cdot & & \cdot & \cdot \\ \cdot & \cdot & & \cdot & \cdot \\ 0 & a_{n2}^{\ 2} & \cdot & \cdots & a_{nn}^{\ 2} \end{pmatrix}$$

If $A^2$ is not already a diagonal matrix, we can find an entry $a_{k\ell}^{\ 2} \neq 0$ with $k \neq \ell$. Multiplying $A^2$ by $D_{k2}(-1)D_{2k}(1)D_{k2}(-1)$ on the left and by $D_{2\ell}(-1)D_{\ell 2}(1)D_{2\ell}(-1)$ on the right, we obtain a matrix $A^3 = (a_{ij}^{\ 3})$ of the same form as $A^2$ and with $a_{22}^{\ 3} = a_{k\ell}^{\ 2} \neq 0$. Similarly as above, we multiply $A^3$ on the left by

$$D_{32}\left(\frac{-a_{32}^{\ 3}}{a_{22}^{\ 3}}\right)\cdots D_{32}\left(\frac{-a_{n2}^{\ 3}}{a_{22}^{\ 3}}\right)$$

and on the right by

$$D_{23}\left(\frac{-a_{23}^{\ 3}}{a_{22}^{\ 3}}\right)\cdots D_{2n}\left(\frac{-a_{2n}^{\ 3}}{a_{22}^{\ 3}}\right),$$

thus obtaining a matrix $A^4 = (a_{ij}^{\ 4})$ of the form

$$\begin{pmatrix} a_{11}^{\ 4} & 0 & 0 & & \cdots & 0 \\ 0 & a_{22}^{\ 4} & 0 & & \cdots & 0 \\ 0 & 0 & a_{33}^{\ 4} & a_{34}^{\ 4} & & a_{3n}^{\ 4} \\ \cdot & \cdot & a_{43} & \cdot & & \cdot \\ \cdot & \cdot & & & \cdot & \cdot \\ \cdot & \cdot & & & \cdot & \cdot \\ 0 & 0 & a_{n3}^{\ 4} & & \cdots & a_{nn}^{\ 4} \end{pmatrix}$$

Repeating these steps again and again, we finally obtain a diagonal matrix $D$,

$$D_1 \cdots D_r A D_1' \cdots D_s' = D$$

where $D_1, \cdots, D_r$ and $D_1' \cdots D_s'$ are triangular matrices. Now we have only to notice that the inverse of a triangular matrix $D_{ij}(d)$ is again a triangular matrix, namely $D_{ij}(-d)$. Thus

$$A = D_r^{-1} \cdots D_1^{-1} D D_s'^{-1} \cdots D_1'^{-1}$$

as claimed.

Recall that a linear transformation $\Phi$ given by the matrix $A$ is one-to-one if and only if the determinant of $A$ is not zero,

$$\det \Phi = \det A \neq 0.$$

In this case, the inverse $\Psi$ of $\Phi$ is again a linear transformation given by the matrix $A^{-1}$.

4.3.7 THEOREM *Suppose $\Phi$ is a linear transformation of $R^n$ with* $\det \Phi \neq 0$. *If $f$ is an integrable function on $R^n$, then $f \circ \Phi$ is also integrable and*

$$\int f\,dx = |\det \Phi| \int f \circ \Phi\,dx.$$

*Proof* Suppose we have established the theorem for two linear transformations $\Phi^{(1)}$ and $\Phi^{(2)}$; it also holds obviously for the linear transformation $\Phi = \Phi^{(1)} \circ \Phi^{(2)}$, because of the multiplicativity of the determinant,

$$\det \Phi = (\det \Phi^{(1)})(\det \Phi^{(2)}).$$

Thus, by Proposition 4.3.6, it suffices to prove the theorem for a transformation that can be described by a diagonal matrix or a triangular matrix. By Lemma 4.3.1 it suffices to establish the theorem for a step function $\varphi$. Since $\varphi \circ \Phi$ is integrable by Corollary 4.3.5, it suffices to check the equation in the theorem.

Suppose first that $\Phi$ is given by a triangular matrix $D_{ij}(c)$, $i \neq j$. Then $\det \Phi = 1$. We have

$$\varphi(\Phi(x)) = \varphi(x_1, \cdots, x_i + cx_j, x_{i+1}, \cdots, x_n).$$

If we integrate first with respect to $dx_i$, we obtain

$$\int \varphi \circ \Phi\,dx_i = \int \varphi\,dx_i,$$

because the Lebesgue integral is translation invariant. Consequently,

$$\begin{aligned}\int \varphi \circ \Phi\,dx &= \int \cdots \int \varphi \circ \Phi\,dx_i\,dx_1 \cdots [dx_i] \cdots dx_n \\ &= \int \cdots \int \varphi\,dx_i\,dx_1 \cdots [dx_i] \cdots dx_n = \int \varphi\,dx\end{aligned}$$

where the term in brackets is to be omitted. This establishes the theorem if $\Phi$ is given by a triangular matrix.

Next suppose $\Phi$ is given by a diagonal matrix $D$ with entries $a_1, \cdots, a_n$ in the diagonal. Then

$$0 \neq \det \Phi = a_1 \cdots a_n$$

whence in particular $a_i \neq 0$, $1 \leq i \leq n$. Let us prove the theorem first for the real line, which corresponds to $n = 1$. It suffices to check it for the characteristic function $\chi$ of a closed bounded interval $[\alpha, \beta]$. Here $\chi \circ \Phi$ is the characteristic function of $[a_1^{-1}\alpha, a_1^{-1}\beta]$ if $a_1 > 0$ and of $[a_1^{-1}\beta, a_1^{-1}\alpha]$ if $a_1 < 0$. In either case,

$$\int \chi \circ \Phi \, dx = |a_1|^{-1}(\beta - \alpha) = |a_1|^{-1} \int \chi \, dx$$

which proves the theorem for the real line. If $n > 1$ we use iterated integration:

$$\int \varphi \circ \Phi \, dx = \int \cdots \int \varphi \circ \Phi \, dx_1 \cdots dx_n$$

$$= |a_1|^{-1} \cdots |a_n|^{-1} \int \varphi \, dx_1 \cdots dx_n$$

$$= |\det \Phi|^{-1} \int \varphi \, dx.$$

This completes the proof of Theorem 4.3.7.

A linear transformation $\Phi$ with determinant equal to $+1$ or $-1$ is also called unimodular. The last theorem implies, in particular, the following.

4.3.8 COROLLARY *The Lebesgue integral on $R^n$ is invariant under unimodular transformations.*

## *EXERCISES*

*4.3.1* Let $x^1, \cdots, x^j$ be $j$ linearly independent vectors in $R^n$. Show that the linear subspace $E$ spanned by $x^1, \cdots, x^j$ is a null set if $j < n$. (See Exercise 4.2.1.)

*4.3.2* Let $x^1, \cdots, x^n$ be $n$ linearly independent vectors in $R^n$ and $P$ the parallelotope spanned by $x^1, \cdots, x^n$; $P$ is the convex set

$$\left\{x \in R^n : x = \sum_{j=1}^{n} \lambda_j x^j, \; 0 \leq \lambda_j \leq 1\right\}.$$

Show that $P$ is integrable and

$$\int_P dx = |\det (x_i^j)| .$$

*4.3.3* Compute the volume of the ellipsoid

$$E = \left\{x \in R^3 : \frac{{x_1}^2}{a^2} + \frac{{x_2}^2}{b^2} + \frac{{x_3}^2}{c^2} \leq 1\right\} \qquad (a, b, c > 0)$$

by finding the linear map that maps $E$ onto the unit ball $B = \{x \in R^3 : |x| \leq 1\}$.

*4.3.4* Suppose $F$ is an integrable function on $R^2$. For each $y$ on the real line, define the function $G_y$ on the real line by

$$G_y(z) = F(z, z - y).$$

Prove that $G_y$ is integrable for a.a.y, and if $H$ is any function on the real line that equals $\int G_y \, dz$ a.e., then $H$ is integrable and

$$\int H \, dy = \int F \, dx.$$

## 4.4 NONLINEAR CHANGE OF VARIABLES

The transformations discussed in this section are continuously differentiable transformations. For the reader who is not familiar with this concept, we include a brief discussion of differentiable mappings. However, he should know about partial derivatives of functions of several variables when entering upon this section, since a little experience is needed in handling such functions.

4.4.1 **Definition** *A mapping $\Phi$ from an open subset $D$ of $R^n$ into $R^n$ is called differentiable at $z \in D$ if there is a linear transformation $T$, a $\delta > 0$ such that*

$$S = \{z' : |z_i - z_i'| \leq \delta, 1 \leq i \leq n\} \subset D,$$

*and for $x, y \in S$ a linear transformation $\varepsilon_{xy}$ given by a matrix $(\varepsilon_{xy}{}^{ij})$ such that*

(a) $$\lim_{x,y \to z} \varepsilon_{xy}{}^{ij} = 0 = \varepsilon_{zz}{}^{ij}, \qquad 1 \leq i, j \leq n,$$

(b) $$\Phi(x) - \Phi(y) = T(x - y) + \varepsilon_{xy}(x - y).$$

*$\Phi$ is said to be differentiable on $D$ if it is differentiable at every point of $D$.*

Let us denote the $i$th component of $\Phi$ again by $\Phi_i$. We see immediately from (b) that for $1 \leq i \leq n$,

$$\lim_{x \to z} (\Phi_i(x) - \Phi_i(z)) = \lim_{x \to z} \sum_{j=1}^{n} (t_{ij} + \varepsilon_{xz}{}^{ij})(x_j - z_j) = 0.$$

Thus a differentiable mapping from an open subset $D$ of $R^n$ into $R^n$ is continuous.

4.4.2 **Proposition** *Suppose $\Phi$ is a differentiable mapping from an open subset $D$ of $R^n$ into $R^n$. Then the partial derivatives of $\Phi_i$, $1 \leq i \leq n$ exist at every point $z$ of $D$. The linear transformation $T$ in Definition 4.4.1 is given by the matrix*

$$\left(\frac{\partial \Phi_i}{\partial x_j}(z)\right).$$

*Proof* We have from (b) of Definition 4.4.1,

$$\Phi_i(x) - \Phi_i(z) = \sum_{j=1}^{n} (t_{ij} + \varepsilon_{xz}{}^{ij})(x_j - z_j)$$

where $(t_{ij})$ is the matrix describing $T$. If we take, in particular, $x = (z_1, \cdots, z_j + h, z_{j+1}, \cdots, z_n)$, then

$$\frac{1}{h}[\Phi_i(x) - \Phi_i(z)] = t_{ij} + \varepsilon_{xz}{}^{ij}.$$

The last term tends to zero as $h$ approaches zero, whence

$$\frac{\partial \Phi_i}{\partial x_j}(z) = \lim_{h \to 0} \frac{1}{h}[\Phi_i(x) - \Phi_i(z)] = t_{ij}.$$

The last proposition shows in particular that the linear transformation $T$ in Definition 4.4.1 is uniquely determined by $\Phi$.

4.4.3 **Definition** *The linear transformation $T$ in Definition 4.4.1 is called the derivative of $\Phi$ at $z$; it is also denoted by $\Phi_z'$. We have*

$$\Phi_z' = \left(\frac{\partial \Phi_i}{\partial x_j}(z)\right).$$

*We say that the mapping $\Phi$ from the open set $D$ in $R^n$ into $R^n$ is continuously differentiable if it is differentiable, and if in addition*

$$\frac{\partial \Phi_i}{\partial x_j}, \qquad 1 \le i, \quad j \le n$$

*are continuous functions on $D$.*

For instance, if $\Phi$ is translation by a vector $c$, then $\Phi$ is continuously differentiable and $\Phi_z'$ is the identity transformation for all $z$. If $\Phi$ is a linear transformation, then (a) and (b) of Definition 4.4.1 are satisfied with $T = \Phi$ and $\varepsilon_{xy} \equiv 0$. Thus $\Phi$ is continuously differentiable and $\Phi_z' = \Phi$ for all $z$.

4.4.4 **Proposition** *Suppose $\Phi$ maps the open subset $D$ of $R^n$ into $R^n$. If the partial derivatives*

$$\frac{\partial \Phi_i}{\partial x_j}, \qquad 1 \le i, \quad j \le n,$$

*exist and are continuous on $D$, then $\Phi$ is continuously differentiable on $D$.*

*Proof* Let $z \in D$ and choose a $\delta > 0$ such that

$$S = \{z' : |z_i - z_i'| < \delta, 1 \le i \le n\} \subset D.$$

For any two points $x, y \in S$, define

$$x^j = (x_1, \cdots, x_j, y_{j+1}, \cdots, y_n) \qquad 0 \le j \le n.$$

In particular, $x^0 = y$ and $x^n = x$. Notice also that

$$|z_i - x_i^j| < \delta, 1 \le i \le n, 0 \le j \le n,$$

since either $x_i^j = x_i$ or $x_i^j = y_i$. Consequently,

$$|z_i - \lambda x_i^j - (1-\lambda)x_i^{j-1}| = |\lambda(z_i - x_i^j) + (1-\lambda)(z_i - x_i^{j-1})|$$
$$\leq \lambda\,|z_i - x_i^j| + (1-\lambda)|\,z_i - x_i^{j-1}| < \delta$$

for $0 \leq \lambda \leq 1$. Thus the line segment connecting $x^j$ and $x^{j-1}$ is contained in $S \subset D$. By the mean value theorem for functions of one variable, there is a point $\xi^{ij}$ on this line segment such that

$$\Phi_i(x^j) - \Phi_i(x^{j-1}) = \frac{\partial \Phi_i}{\partial x_j}(\xi^{ij})(x_j - y_j).$$

Now define

$$\varepsilon_{xy}{}^{ij} = \frac{\partial \Phi_i}{\partial x_j}(\xi^{ij}) - \frac{\partial \Phi_i}{\partial x_j}(z)$$

for $x, y \in S$. We have

$$\lim_{x,y\to z} \varepsilon_{xy}{}^{ij} = 0$$

since $\xi^{ij}$ tends to $z$ as $x$ and $y$ tend to $z$. Furthermore,

$$\Phi_i(x) - \Phi_i(y) = \sum_{j=1}^{n} [\Phi_i(x^j) - \Phi_i(x^{j-1})]$$
$$= \sum_{j=1}^{n} \left(\frac{\partial \Phi_i}{\partial x_j}(z) + \varepsilon_{xy}{}^{ij}\right)(x_j - y_j)$$

which proves our proposition.

Suppose $\Phi$ is a differentiable mapping from an open subset $D$ of $R^n$ into $R^n$. *The function h, defined by*

$$h(x) = \det \Phi_x'$$

*is called the Jacobian of* $\Phi$; it is sometimes also denoted

$$h = \det \Phi'.$$

The Jacobian of $\Phi$ is a continuous function on $D$ if $\Phi$ is continuously differentiable on $D$, because $\det \Phi'$ is a linear combination of certain products of the functions $\partial\Phi_i/\partial x_j$. We can now state our main theorem as follows.

4.4.5 THEOREM *Suppose $\Phi$ is a one-to-one continuously differentiable mapping from an open set D in $R^n$ onto an open set E in $R^n$ such that its inverse $\Psi = \Phi^{-1}$ is a continuously differentiable mapping from E onto D. If f is an integrable function on $R^n$, then $f \circ \Phi\,|\det \Phi'|$ is an integrable function on D and*

$$\int_E f\,dx = \int_D (f \circ \Phi)\,|\det \Phi'|\,dx.$$

We postpone the proof of this theorem for a while.

Suppose $\Phi^1$ is a differentiable mapping from an open set $D$ in $R^n$ into an open set $E$ in $R^n$ and $\Phi^2$ is a differentiable mapping from $E$ into $R^n$. Then $\Phi = \Phi^2 \circ \Phi^1$ is a differentiable mapping from $D$ into $R^n$ and

$$\Phi_z' = (\Phi^2)_w' \circ (\Phi^1)_z', \qquad w = \Phi^1(z). \tag{4.4.6}$$

Namely, according to Definition 4.4.1,

$$\begin{aligned} \Phi^1(x) - \Phi^1(y) &= (\Phi^1)_z'(x - y) + \varepsilon_{xy}^1(x - y) \qquad \text{for } x, y \in S^1, \\ \Phi^2(u) - \Phi^2(v) &= (\Phi^2)_w'(u - v) + \varepsilon_{uv}^2(u - v) \qquad \text{for } u, v \in S^2. \end{aligned}$$

Since $\Phi^1$ is continuous, we can choose $S^1$ so small that $\Phi^1(S^1) \subset S^2$. Now let $u = \Phi^1(x)$ and $v = \Phi^2(y)$ in the above equations. This yields for $x, y \in S^1$

$$\begin{aligned} \Phi(x) - \Phi(y) &= \Phi^2(\Phi^1(x)) - \Phi^2(\Phi^1(y)) \\ &= (\Phi^2)_w' \circ (\Phi^1)_z'(x - y) + \varepsilon_{xy}(x - y) \end{aligned}$$

where

$$\varepsilon_{xy} = (\Phi^2)_w' \circ \varepsilon_{xy}^1 + \varepsilon_{uv}^2 \circ (\Phi^1)_z' + \varepsilon_{uv}^2 \circ \varepsilon_{xy}^1, \quad u = \Phi^1(x), \quad v = \Phi^1(y).$$

It is easily checked that $\varepsilon_{xy}$ satisfies (a) of Definition 4.4.1. This establishes Equation (4.4.6).

We can apply Equation (4.4.6) to the mapping $\Phi$ and its inverse $\Psi$ occurring in Theorem 4.4.5. Then $\Psi \circ \Phi = I$ is the identity mapping that maps each point of $D$ into itself. Thus

$$I_x' = I = \Psi_w' \circ \Phi_x', \qquad w = \Phi(x),$$

that is, $\Phi_z'$ is invertible for every $z \in D$, and consequently

$$\det \Phi_z' \neq 0, \qquad z \in D. \tag{4.4.7}$$

One can in fact show that the requirement in Theorem 4.4.5 that the inverse $\Psi$ of $\Phi$ be continuously differentiable may be replaced by the condition $\det \Phi_z' \neq 0$ (which implies that $\Psi$ is continuously differentiable). But this is not so easy, and since we do not want to prove it here, we have preferred to choose the stronger hypothesis that $\Psi$ be continuously differentiable.

We prepare now for the proof of Theorem 4.4.5 by a sequence of lemmas. In the following we say that a sequence $\{Q^k\}$ of cubes tends to a point $z$ if, for every $\varepsilon > 0$, there is an integer $k_0$ such that

$$Q^k \subset \{z' : |z_i - z_i'| < \varepsilon, 1 \leq i \leq n\} \qquad \text{for } k \geq k_0.$$

A cube $Q$ is called nondegenerate if its Lebesgue measure $\sigma(Q)$ is different from 0.

4.4.8 LEMMA *Suppose $h$ is a continuous function on an open set $D$ in $R^n$. Let $z \in D$ and suppose $\{Q^k\}$ is a sequence of bounded nondegenerate cubes tending to $z$. Assume also that the closure of each $Q^k$ is contained in $D$ so that $h$ is integrable on each $Q^k$. Then*

$$h(z) = \lim_{k \to \infty} [\sigma(Q^k)]^{-1} \int_{Q^k} h \, dx$$

*where $\sigma(Q^k)$ denotes the Lebesgue measure of $Q^k$.*

*Proof* Let $\varepsilon > 0$. Since $h$ is continuous at $z$, we can find a $\delta$ such that

$$|h(z) - h(z')| \leq \varepsilon \quad \text{if } z' \in D, |z_i - z_i'| \leq \delta \text{ for } 1 \leq i \leq n.$$

Now choose an integer $k_0$ with

$$Q^k \subset \{z' : |z_i - z_i'| < \delta, 1 \leq i \leq n\} \qquad \text{for } k \geq k_0.$$

Then, for $k \geq k_0$,

$$\begin{aligned}\left| h(z) - [\sigma(Q^k)]^{-1} \int_{Q^k} h \, dx \right| &= [\sigma(Q^k)]^{-1} \left| \int_{Q^k} (h(z) - h) \, dx \right| \\ &\leq [\sigma(Q^k)]^{-1} \int_{Q^k} |h(z) - h| \, dx \\ &\leq [\sigma(Q^k)]^{-1} \int_{Q^k} \varepsilon \, dx = \varepsilon.\end{aligned}$$

This completes the proof.

4.4.9 LEMMA *Suppose $h$ is a continuous function on an open set $D$ in $R^n$. Assume, furthermore, that to every bounded nondegenerate cube $Q$ with $\bar{Q} \subset D$ there is attached a number $m(Q)$ such that*

$$m(Q) = \sum_{k=1}^{s} m(Q_k) \qquad \text{if } Q = Q_1 \cup \cdots \cup Q_s$$

*is a decomposition of $Q$ into disjoint cubes,*

$$\lim_{k \to \infty} \frac{m(Q^k)}{\sigma(Q^k)} = h(z)$$

*if $\{Q^k\}$ is a sequence of nondegenerate bounded cubes tending to $z$ and with closure contained in $D$. Then*

$$m(Q) = \int_Q h \, dx$$

*for every bounded nondegenerate cube $Q$ with $\bar{Q} \subset D$.*

*Proof* Assume first that $h = 0$. We have to show that $m(Q) = 0$ for all $Q$. Suppose this is not the case; then $m(Q) \neq 0$ for some nondegenerate cube

$$Q = \{x : x_j \in I_j, 1 \leq j \leq n\} \quad [\sigma(I_j) = \sigma(I_i), 1 \leq i, j \leq n]$$

with closure contained in $D$. There is a positive number $q$ such that

$$|m(Q)| \geq q \, \sigma(Q).$$

We subdivide $Q$ into $2^n$ disjoint cubes of the same size in the following way. We write each $I_j$, $1 \leq j \leq n$, as the disjoint union of two intervals of the same length,

$$I_j = I_j^1 \cup I_j^2, \ 1 \leq j \leq n.$$

Then there are $2^n$ cubes of the form

$$\{x : x_j \in J_j, 1 \leq j \leq n, J_j = I_j^1 \text{ or } J_j = I_j^2\}.$$

They are disjoint, their union is $Q$, and they all have the same Lebesgue measure. Because of the first condition on $m$ there must be at least one cube $Q^1$ among them such that

$$|m(Q^1)| \geq q\sigma(Q^1).$$

If $d$ denotes the diameter of $Q$,

$$d = \sqrt{n}\sigma(I_1),$$

then the diameter $d_1$ of $Q^1$ is clearly $d/2$.

Now we subdivide $Q^1$ in the same manner as $Q$ and find a cube $Q^2 \subset Q^1$ with diameter $d_2 = d_1/2$ satisfying

$$|m(Q^2)| \geq q\sigma(Q^2),$$

and so forth. Thus we obtain a sequence $\{Q^k\}$ of cubes with closures in $D$ such that

$$Q^k \supset Q^{k+1}, \qquad m(Q^k) \geq q\sigma(Q^k),$$

$$d_k = \text{diameter of } Q^k = \frac{d_{k-1}}{2} = \cdots = \frac{d}{2^k}.$$

We claim that $\{Q^k\}$ converges to a point $z$ in $D$. Namely, for each $k$ pick $z^k \in Q^k$. $\{z^k\}$ is a Cauchy sequence, since $z^m \in Q^k$ for $m \geq k$, and hence

$$|z^m - z^k| \leq \frac{d}{2^k} \qquad \text{for } m \geq k.$$

Let $z$ be the limit of the sequence $\{z^k\}$. Then $\{Q^k\}$ converges to $z$; namely, for $\varepsilon > 0$ we can find an integer $k_0$ such that

$$|z - z^k| \leq \frac{\varepsilon}{2} \qquad \text{and} \qquad d_k = \frac{d}{2^k} \leq \frac{\varepsilon}{2}$$

for $k \geq k_0$. Thus

$$\begin{aligned} |z - z'| &\leq |z - z^k| + |z^k - z'| \\ &\leq \frac{\varepsilon}{2} + d_k \leq \varepsilon \end{aligned}$$

for $z' \in Q^k$, $k \geq k_0$.

But if $\{Q^k\}$ converges to $z$ we should have

$$\lim_{k \to \infty} \frac{m(Q^k)}{\sigma(Q^k)} = h(z) = 0$$

which contradicts $|m(Q^k)| \geq q\sigma(Q^k)$ for all $k$. Thus indeed $m(Q) = 0$ for all $Q$. This proves the lemma if $h = 0$.

If $h$ is not the zero function, we let

$$m'(Q) = m(Q) - \int_Q h\, dx.$$

$m'$ clearly satisfies the first condition in the lemma. It also satisfies the second condition with $h$ replaced by 0; in fact, we have by Lemma 4.4.8,

$$\lim_{k\to\infty} \frac{m'(Q^k)}{\sigma(Q^k)} = \lim_{k\to\infty} \left[\frac{m(Q^k)}{\sigma(Q^k)} - [\sigma(Q^k)]^{-1}\int_{Q^k} h\,dx\right]$$
$$= h(z) - h(z) = 0.$$

Thus $m'(Q) = 0$ for all $Q$ by the first part of the proof, or

$$m(Q) = \int_Q h\,dx$$

as asserted.

**4.4.10 LEMMA** *Suppose $\Phi$ is a continuously differentiable mapping as described in Theorem 4.4.5. Then $\Phi(Q)$ is integrable and*

$$\int_{\Phi(Q)} dx = \int_Q |\det \Phi'|\,dx$$

*for every bounded nondegenerate cube $Q$ with $\bar{Q} \subset D$.*

*Proof* First let us show that $\Phi(Q)$ is measurable. There is a decreasing sequence $Q^k$ of open rectangles with

$$Q = \bigcap_{k=1}^{\infty} Q^k.$$

In fact, if $Q = \{x : x_j \in I_j,\ 1 \leq j \leq n\}$, then we choose the $Q^k$,

$$Q^k = \{x : x_j \in (a_j^k, b_j^k),\ 1 \leq j \leq n\}$$

such that

$$I_j = \bigcap_{k=1}^{\infty} (a_j^k, b_j^k), \qquad 1 \leq j \leq n.$$

If for instance $I_j = (a_j, b_j]$, then we could take

$$a_j^k = a_j,\ b_j^k = b_j + \frac{1}{k}, \qquad k \geq 1.$$

Each of the sets $\Phi(Q^k \cap D) = \Psi^{-1}(Q^k \cap D)$ is open by Lemma 4.3.4, and hence measurable. Therefore

$$\Phi(Q) = \bigcap_{k=1}^{\infty} \Phi(Q^k \cap D)$$

is also measurable. Here $\Phi(Q)$ is a bounded set, because the components $\Phi_i$ of $\Phi$ are continuous functions on $D$ and thus bounded on $\bar{Q}$. This shows that $\Phi(Q)$ is integrable.

Now define

$$m(Q) = \sigma(\Phi(Q))$$

for bounded nondegenerate cubes $Q$ with $\bar{Q} \subset D$. Then $m$ clearly satisfies the first condition of Lemma 4.4.9. Lemma 4.4.10 is therefore a consequence of Lemma 4.4.9 if we can show that the second condition of that lemma holds for $m$ with $h = |\det \Phi'|$.

Let $\{Q^k\}$ be a sequence of bounded nondegenerate cubes with closures contained in $D$ which tends to $z \in D$. Then we have to prove

$$\lim_{k\to\infty} \frac{\sigma(\Phi(Q^k))}{\sigma(Q^k)} = |\det \Phi_z'| . \tag{4.4.11}$$

Let $\Phi^1$ be the translation by $z$ and $\Phi^2$ the translation by $-\Phi(z)$. Then $\tilde{\Phi} = \Phi^2 \circ \Phi \circ \Phi^1$ is a mapping from $(\Phi^1)^{-1}(D)$ onto $\Phi^2(E)$ with all the properties of $\Phi$. Furthermore,

$$\tilde{\Phi}(0) = 0, \ \tilde{\Phi}_x' = \Phi_y', \qquad \text{where } y = \Phi^1(x) = x + z.$$

In order to prove Equation (4.4.11), it suffices to establish

$$\lim_{k\to\infty} \frac{\sigma(\tilde{\Phi}(\tilde{Q}^k))}{\sigma(\tilde{Q}^k)} = |\det \tilde{\Phi}_0'| = |\det \Phi_z'|$$

where $\tilde{Q}^k = (\Phi^1)^{-1}(Q^k)$, because Lebesgue measure is translation-invariant. Thus we may as well assume right from the beginning that $\{Q^k\}$ tends to 0 and $\Phi(0) = 0$.

Now let $T = (\Phi_0')^{-1}$. Then $\Phi^0 = T \circ \Phi$ is a mapping from $D$ into $T(E)$ with all the properties of $\Phi$. Also $(\Phi^0)_x' = T \circ \Phi_x'$ and in particular $(\Phi^0)_0' = I$. Furthermore, by Theorem 4.3.7 we have

$$\begin{aligned}\sigma(\Phi(Q^k)) &= \sigma(T^{-1} \circ \Phi^0(Q^k)) \\ &= |\det T^{-1}|\, \sigma(\Phi^0(Q^k)) = |\det \Phi_0'|\, \sigma(\Phi^0(Q^k)).\end{aligned}$$

Thus (4.4.11) follows, once we establish

$$\lim_{k\to\infty} \frac{\sigma(\Phi^0(Q^k))}{\sigma(Q^k)} = 1 = \det I.$$

Or, we may assume right away that $\Phi_0' = I$. Then also $\Psi_0' = (\Phi_0')^{-1} = I$.

Let $S = \{z' : |z_i'| \le \delta, 1 \le i \le n\}$ and $(\varepsilon_{xy}^{ij})$, $x, y \in S$ be as in Definition 4.4.1, corresponding to $z = 0$:

$$\Phi_i(x) - \Phi_i(y) = x_i - y_i + \sum_{j=1}^{n} \varepsilon_{xy}^{ij}(x_j - y_j) \qquad \text{for } x, y \in S. \tag{4.4.12}$$

We may assume that $\delta$ is chosen so small that

$$\Psi_i(x) - \Psi_i(y) = x_i - y_i + \sum_{j=1}^{n} \eta_{xy}^{ij}(x_j - y_j) \qquad \text{for } x, y \in S \tag{4.4.13}$$

where $(\eta_{xy}^{ij})$ is a matrix with similar properties as $(\varepsilon_{xy}^{ij})$. Let $\alpha > 0$ be given, and choose a $\delta_1$, $0 < \delta_1 \le \delta$ such that

$$|\varepsilon_{xy}^{ij}| \le \frac{\alpha}{n} \quad \text{for } 1 \le i, j \le n \text{ and } x, y \in S_1 = \{z : |z_i| \le \delta_1, 1 \le i \le n\}.$$

If $Q = \{z : z_i \in I_i,\ 1 \leq i \leq n\}$ is any cube in $S_1$, then we have from Equation (4.4.12) for $x, y \in Q$:

$$|\Phi_i(x) - \Phi_i(y)| \leq |x_i - y_i| + \sum_{j=1}^{n} |\varepsilon_{xy}{}^{ij}|\,|x_j - y_j| \leq (1 + \alpha)\ell$$

where $\ell = \sigma(I_1) = \sigma(I_i)$, $1 \leq i \leq n$ is the "length" of the cube $Q$. This shows that $\Phi(Q)$ is contained in a cube of length $(1 + \alpha)\ell$; namely

$$\Phi(Q) \subset \{z : z_i \in [a_i, b_i],\ 1 \leq i \leq n\}$$

where

$$a_i = \inf\{\Phi_i(x) : x \in Q\}, \qquad b_i = a_i + (1 + \alpha)\ell.$$

Thus we conclude

$$\sigma(\Phi(Q)) \leq (1 + \alpha)^n \ell^n = (1 + \alpha)^n \sigma(Q) \tag{4.4.14}$$

if $Q$ is a cube in $S_1$. Now choose $\delta_2$, $0 < \delta_2 \leq \delta$ such that

$$|\eta_{xy}{}^{ij}| \leq \frac{\alpha}{n} \qquad \text{for } 1 \leq i, j \leq n \quad \text{and} \quad x, y \in S_2.$$

If $P$ is any cube in $S_2$, we conclude as above that

$$\sigma(\Psi(P)) \leq (1 + \alpha)^n \sigma(P), \tag{4.4.15}$$

this time using Equation (4.4.13).

We may assume that $\delta_1$ is chosen so small that the continuous mapping $\Phi$ maps $S_1$ into $S_2$. Again let $Q$ be any cube in $S_1$ and denote by $Q^0$ the interior of $Q$, then $\sigma(Q) = \sigma(Q^0)$. By Lemma 4.3.4, $\Phi(Q^0) = \Psi^{-1}(Q^0)$ is an open set and contained in $S_2$. By Proposition 4.2.16, $\Phi(Q^0)$ is the union of a sequence $\{P_k\}$ of pairwise disjoint cubes. By Equation (4.4.15),

$$\sigma(\Psi(P_k)) \leq (1 + \alpha)^n \sigma(P_k), \qquad k \geq 1,$$

whence

$$\begin{aligned}
\sigma(Q) = \sigma(Q^0) = \sigma\left(\bigcup_{k=1}^{\infty} \Psi(P_k)\right) &= \sum_{k=1}^{\infty} \sigma(\Psi(P_k)) \\
&\leq (1 + \alpha)^n \sum_{k=1}^{\infty} \sigma(P_k) = (1 + \alpha)^n \sigma(\Phi(Q^0)) \\
&\leq (1 + \alpha)^n \sigma(\Phi(Q)).
\end{aligned}$$

Combining this with Equation (4.4.14), we find

$$\frac{1}{(1 + \alpha)^n} \leq \frac{\sigma(\Phi(Q))}{\sigma(Q)} \leq (1 + \alpha)^n$$

if $Q$ is any cube in $S_1$. If $k_0$ is any integer such that $Q^k \subset S_1$ for $k \geq k_0$, then the last inequality holds for $Q^k$, $k \geq k_0$, instead of $Q$. Since $\alpha$ was arbitrary, we conclude

$$\lim_{k\to\infty} \frac{\sigma((\Phi Q^k))}{\sigma(Q^k)} = 1.$$

This completes the proof of Lemma 4.4.10.

*Proof of Theorem 4.4.5* By Lemma 4.3.1 it suffices to prove the theorem for step functions, and since every step function is a linear combination of characteristic functions of bounded open rectangles, we need in fact establish the theorem only for the characteristic function $\chi$ of a bounded open rectangle $P$. Further, $\chi \circ \Phi$ is the characteristic function of $\Phi^{-1}(P \cap E)$, which is open by Lemma 4.3.4. Hence, by Proposition 4.2.16,

$$\Phi^{-1}(P \cap E) = \bigcup_{k=1}^{\infty} Q^k$$

where $\{Q^k\}$ is a sequence of bounded pairwise disjoint nondegenerate cubes with closures contained in $\Phi^{-1}(P \cap E) \subset D$. Thus by Lemma 4.4.10,

$$\begin{aligned}\sum_{k=1}^{\infty} \int_{Q^k} |\det \Phi'| \, dx &= \sum_{k=1}^{\infty} \sigma(\Phi(Q^k)) \\ &= \sigma(P \cap E) < \infty.\end{aligned}$$

Beppo Levi's theorem implies now that $|\det \Phi'|$ is integrable on $\Phi^{-1}(P \cap E)$ and

$$\begin{aligned}\int_D \chi \circ \Phi \, |\det \Phi'| \, dx &= \int_{\Phi^{-1}(P\cap E)} |\det \Phi'| \, dx \\ &= \sum_{k=1}^{\infty} \int_{Q^k} |\det \Phi'| \, dx = \sigma(P \cap E) \\ &= \int_E \chi \, dx.\end{aligned}$$

This completes the proof.

## *EXERCISES*

*4.4.1* Give an example of a function $f$ on the interval $(-1, 1)$ which is differentiable at 0, but which is not differentiable at 0 in the sense of Definition 4.4.1 if considered as a mapping from $(-1, 1)$ into $R$.

*4.4.2* Formulate a definition of differentiability for a mapping $\Phi$ from an open subset $D$ of $R^n$ into $R^m$ and prove a theorem analogous to Proposition 4.4.4.

*4.4.3* Let $\Phi$ be the following mapping from the open set

$$D = \{(r, \theta) : r > 0, -\pi < \theta < \pi\}$$

in $R^2$ into $R^2$:

$$\Phi_1(r, \theta) = r \cos \theta, \qquad \Phi_2(r, \theta) = r \sin \theta.$$

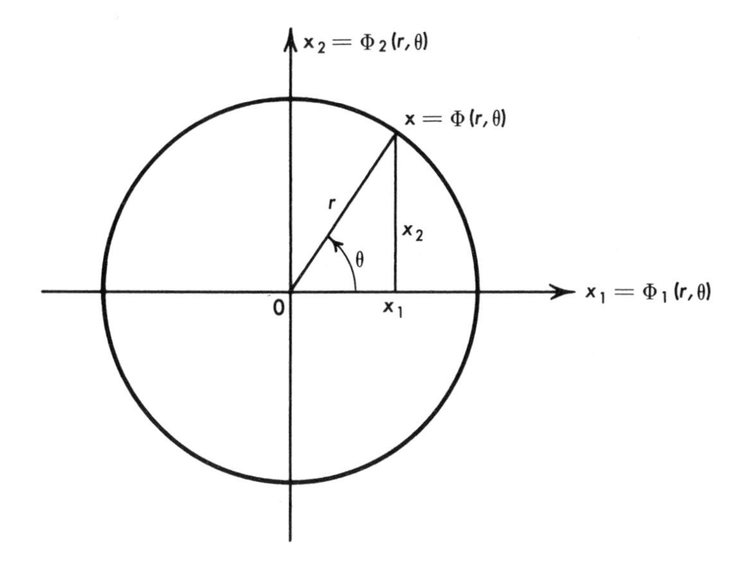


Figure 4.5 Polar coordinates for $R^2$ are related to cartesian coordinates by the equations

$$x_1 = r\cos\theta \qquad r = (x_1^2 + x_2^2)^{1/2}$$
$$x_2 = r\sin\theta \qquad \theta = \arctan x_2/x_1$$

Prove that a function $f$ on $R^2$ is integrable if and only if the function $F$,

$$F(r, \theta) = rf(\Phi(r, \theta)),$$

is integrable on $D$ and then

$$\int f\,dx = \int_0^\infty \int_{-\pi}^{\pi} rf(\Phi(r, \theta))\,d\theta\,dr.$$

Here $(r, \theta)$ are called polar coordinates for $R^2$ (see Figure 4.5).

*4.4.4* Let $r$ be the function $r(x_1, x_2) = (x_1^2 + x_2^2)^{1/2}$ on $R^2$. Use the previous exercise to show that $1/r^s$ is integrable on the set $E = \{(x_1, x_2): 0 < x_1^2 + x_2^2 \leq 1\}$ if $s < 2$. Compute

$$\int_E \left(\frac{1}{r^s}\right) dx.$$

## 4.5 EXERCISES

### A. Product Integration

4.5.1 Show that, if $S = S_1 \times S_2 \times S_3$ and $L_i$, $\int \varphi\,d\mu_i$ for $\varphi \in L_i$ is a class of elementary functions and an integral on $S_i$ ($i = 1, 2, 3$), then equivalent integrals are obtained on $S$ by using Definitions 4.1.1 and 4.1.5 first on $S_1$ and $S_2$, and then on $S_1 \times S_2$ and $S_3$, and by using them first on $S_2$ and $S_3$ and then on $S_1$ and $S_2 \times S_3$, that is,

$$\int \varphi \, d(\mu_1 \otimes \mu_2) \otimes \mu_2 = \int \varphi \, d\mu_1 \otimes (\mu_2 \otimes \mu_3).$$

**4.5.2**

(a) Let $\int \varphi \, d\mu_i$ ($i = 1, 2$) be two integrals for the step functions $\varphi \in L$ on the real line such that the constant function 1 is integrable for $d\mu_1$ and $d\mu_2$. Such integrals are called finite. Show that for $\varphi \in L$

$$\Phi(x, y) = \varphi(x + y)$$

defines a $d(\mu_1 \otimes \mu_2)$-integrable function $\Phi$ on $R^2$. Furthermore, show that

$$\int \varphi \, d\mu_1 * \mu_2 = \iint \Phi \, d\mu_1 \, d\mu_2$$

defines an integral on $L$.

(b) Suppose $\int \varphi \, d\mu_i$ ($i = 1, 2, 3$) are finite integrals on $L$. Show

$$\int \varphi \, d\mu_1 * \mu_2 = \int \varphi \, d\mu_2 * \mu_1,$$

$$\int \varphi \, d(\mu_1 * \mu_2) * \mu_3 = \int \varphi \, d\mu_1 * (\mu_2 * \mu_3).$$

## B. The Lebesgue Integral for $R^n$

**4.5.3** Compute the measure (volume) of the following sets in $R^3$.

(a) $\{(x, y, z) : x^2 + y^2 + z^2 \leq 1\}$,

(b) $\{(x, y, z) : 0 \leq z \leq 2 - x^2 - y^2\}$,

(c) $\{(x, y, z) : x + y + z \leq 1, x \geq 0, y \geq 0, z \geq 0\}$.

**4.5.4** Define the function $r$ on $R^n$ by

$$r(x) = r(x_1, \cdots, x_n) = (x_1{}^2 + \cdots + x_n{}^2)^{1/2}.$$

Show that the function $r^{-p}$ is integrable on $\{x \in R^n : 0 < r(x) \leq 1\}$ if $p$ is any real number strictly less than $n$.

**4.5.5** Let $(\xi, \eta)$, $\eta > 0$, be a point in the (open) upper half plane of $R^2$ and let $E$ be a measurable subset of the $\xi$-axis. We define the angle subtended by $E$ at $(\xi, \eta)$ by the integral

$$\alpha(\xi, \eta, E) = \int_E \frac{\eta \, dx}{(\xi - x)^2 + \eta^2}.$$

Show that, if $f \geq 0$ is an integrable function of one variable and $E(y) = \{x : f(x) \geq \log y\}$, then

$$\int \frac{\eta f(x) \, dx}{(\xi - x)^2 + \eta^2} = \int_1^\infty y^{-1} \alpha(\xi, \eta, E(y)) \, dy.$$

*Hint* Apply Fubini's theorem to the function:

$$F(x, y) = \frac{\eta\chi(x, y}{y[(\xi - x)^2 + \eta^2]}$$

where $\chi$ is the characteristic function of the set $\{(x, y):0 \leq \log y \leq f(x)\}$.

**4.5.6** Let $f$ be a function on $R^2$ which is measurable as a function of the second variable for each value of the first variable, and continuous as a function of the first variable for each value of the second variable. Prove that $f$ is measurable.

*Hint*

$$f(x, y) = \lim_{n\to\infty} f([nx]/n, y).$$

## C. Linear Change of Variables

**4.5.7** Let $f$ be an integrable function on $R^2$. Justify the following formulas:

$$\iint f(x + y, x - y)\,dx\,dy = \frac{1}{2}\iint f(x, y)\,dx\,dy,$$

$$\iint f(2x + y, x + y)\,dx\,dy = \iint f(x, y)\,dx\,dy,$$

$$\iint (x + y)^2 f((x + y)^3, x - y)\,dy\,dx = \frac{1}{6}\iint f(x, y)\,dx\,dy.$$

**4.5.8** Let $f$ and $g$ be integrable functions of one variable. Show that the integral

$$\int f(x - y)g(y)\,dy$$

exists for a.a.$x$. Define the function $f * g$ by

$$f * g(x) = \begin{cases} \int f(x - y)g(y)dy & \text{when this integral exists} \\ 0 & \text{otherwise.} \end{cases}$$

Show that $f * g$ is integrable and

$$\int f * g\,dx = \int f\,dx \int g\,dy.$$

*Hint* See Exercise 4.2.1.

**4.5.9** Suppose $f$ and $g$ are integrable functions of one variable. Define

$$\hat{f}_c(t) = \int f(x) \cos tx\,dx,$$

$$\hat{f}_s(t) = \int f(x) \sin tx\,dx.$$

Let $f * g$ be defined as in the previous exercise. Show that

$$(f * g)_c^\wedge = \hat{f}_c \hat{g}_c - \hat{f}_s \hat{g}_s,$$
$$(f * g)_s^\wedge = \hat{f}_s \hat{g}_c + \hat{f}_c \hat{g}_s.$$

## D. Nonlinear Change of Variables

4.5.10 Define the mapping $\Phi$ from the open subset

$$E = \{(r, \theta, z) : r > 0, -\pi < \theta < \pi, z \in R\}$$

of $R^3$ into $R^3$ by

$$\Phi_1(r, \theta, z) = r \cos \theta, \quad \Phi_2(r, \theta, z) = r \sin \theta, \quad \Phi_3(r, \theta, z) = z.$$

Prove that a function $f$ on $R^3$ is integrable if and only if $r(f \circ \Phi)$ is integrable on $E$, and then

$$\int f\, dx = \int_{-\infty}^{\infty} \int_0^{\infty} \int_{-\pi}^{\pi} rf(\Phi(r, \theta, z))\, d\theta\, dr\, dz.$$

Here $(r, \theta, z)$ are called cylindrical coordinates for $R^3$ (see Figure 4.6).

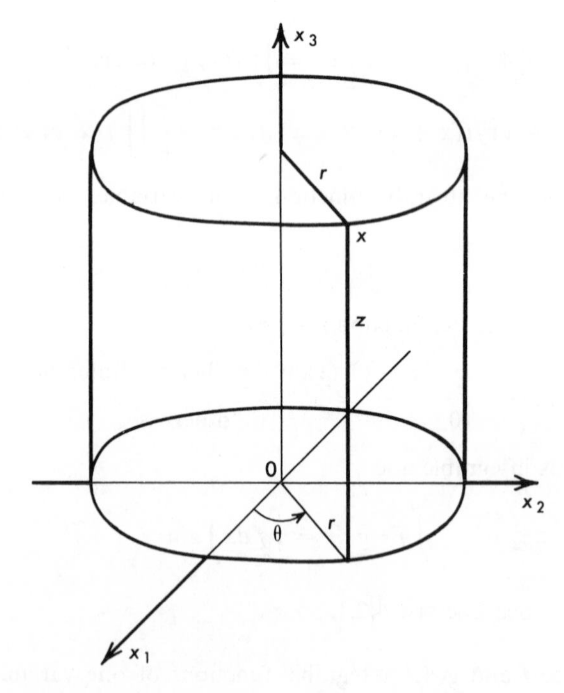


Figure 4.6 Cylindrical coordinates for $R^3$ are related to cartesian coordinates by the equations

$$x_1 = r \cos \theta \qquad r = (x_1^2 + x_2^2)^{1/2}$$
$$x_2 = r \sin \theta \qquad \theta = \text{arc tan } x_2/x_1$$
$$x_3 = z \qquad z = x_3$$

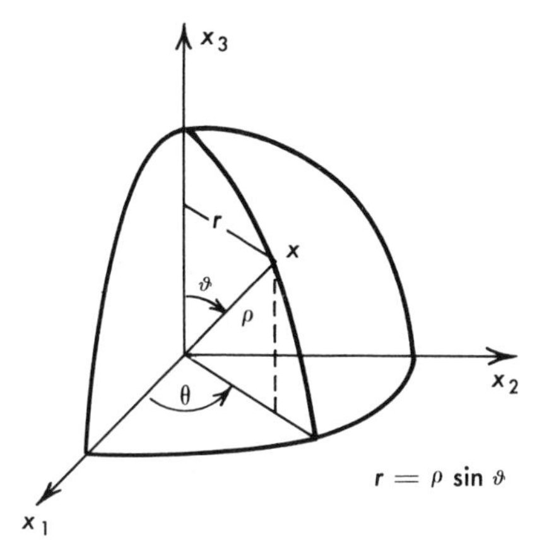


Figure 4.7 Spherical coordinates for $R^3$ are related to cartesian coordinates by the equations

$$x_1 = \rho \sin \vartheta \cos \theta, \qquad x_2 = \rho \sin \vartheta \sin \theta, \qquad x_3 = \rho \cos \vartheta.$$

**4.5.11** Define the mapping $\Phi$ from the open subset

$$E = \left\{(\rho, \theta, \vartheta) : \rho > 0, -\pi < \theta < \pi, -\frac{\pi}{2} < \vartheta < \frac{\pi}{2}\right\}$$

of $R^3$ into $R^3$ by

$$\begin{aligned} \Phi_1(r, \theta, \vartheta) &= \rho \cos \theta \sin \vartheta, \\ \Phi_2(r, \theta, \vartheta) &= \rho \sin \theta \sin \vartheta, \\ \Phi_3(r, \theta, \vartheta) &= \rho \cos \vartheta. \end{aligned}$$

Prove that a function $f$ on $R^3$ is integrable if and only if $\rho^2 \sin \vartheta (f \circ \Phi)$ is integrable on $E$, and then

$$\int f\, dx = \int_0^\infty \int_{-\pi/2}^{\pi/2} \int_{-\pi}^{\pi} \rho^2 \sin \vartheta (f \circ \Phi)\, d\theta\, d\vartheta\, d\rho.$$

Here $(\rho, \theta, \vartheta)$ are called spherical coordinates for $R^3$ (see Figure 4.7).

**4.5.12** Use the previous exercise to show that the function $r^{-p}$ $(r(x) = (x_1^2 + x_2^2 + x_3^2)^{1/2})$ is integrable on $\{x : 0 < r(x) \leq 1\}$ if $p < 3$.

**4.5.13** Prove that

$$\int_0^\infty e^{-x^2}\, dx = \frac{\sqrt{\pi}}{2}.$$

*Hint* Notice that

$$\left(2\int_0^\infty e^{-x^2}\, dx\right)^2 = \iint e^{-(x^2+y^2)}\, dx\, dy.$$

Use polar coordinates to evaluate the second integral (see Exercise 4.4.3).

4.5.14 Suppose $f$ and $g$ are continuous functions on $R^2$ with continuous partial derivatives

$$f_i = \frac{\partial}{\partial x_i} f, \qquad g_i = \frac{\partial}{\partial x_i} g, \qquad i = 1, 2.$$

Let $\Phi$ be the map from $\{(r, \theta): r > 0, -\pi < \theta < \pi\}$ into $R^2$ defined by

$$\Phi_1(r, \theta) = r \cos \theta, \qquad \Phi_2(r, \theta) = r \sin \theta$$

(see Exercise 4.4.3). Prove Green's formula for the disk:

$$\iint_{\{x_1^2+x_2^2 \leq 1\}} (g_1 - f_2)\, dx_1\, dx_2$$
$$= \int_{-\pi}^{\pi} [g(\cos \theta, \sin \theta) \cos \theta - f(\cos \theta, \sin \theta) \sin \theta]\, d\theta.$$

## E. Integration on the Unimodular Group

The set of $2 \times 2$ matrices

$$\begin{pmatrix} x_1 & x_2 \\ x_3 & x_4 \end{pmatrix}$$

can be regarded as $R^4$. We will study the unimodular group $SL(R, 2)$ defined by

$$SL(R, 2) = \left\{ \begin{pmatrix} x_1 & x_2 \\ x_3 & x_4 \end{pmatrix} : x_1 x_4 - x_2 x_3 = 1 \right\}.$$

The group operation is, of course, the ordinary matrix multiplication. We will denote the elements of $SL(R, 2)$ by letters $g, h, k$ and the elements of $R^4$ by $x, y, z$, even when they are regarded as $2 \times 2$ matrices. As such, the determinant function, $\det x$, is defined on $R^4$ and satisfies the relation

$$\det xy = \det x \det y.$$

The definition of the unimodular group can then also be written

$$SL(R, 2) = \{g : g \text{ is a real } 2 \times 2 \text{ matrix}, \det g = 1\}.$$

Let $f$ be a function on $SL(R, 2)$ and define the function $F$ on $R^4$ by

$$F(x) = \begin{cases} f\left[\dfrac{x}{(\det x)^{1/2}}\right] & \text{if } \tfrac{1}{2} \leq \det x \leq 2 \\ 0 & \text{otherwise.} \end{cases}$$

In the sequel we write $S$ instead of $SL(R, 2)$ for the unimodular group. We say that the function $f$ is integrable on $S$ if the function $F$ is integrable on $R^4$; we define and denote the integral of $f$ on $S$ by

$$\int f\, dg = \int F\, dx.$$

We denote the class of functions on $S$ that are integrable in this sense by $L^1(S)$.

**4.5.15** Show that $L^1(S)$ and $\int f\,dg$ satisfy the fundamental properties (1) to (5) and that $L^1(S)$ is also complete in the sense that if $f = \sum_{n=1}^{\infty} f_n$ a.e., $f_n \in L^1(S)$, and $\sum_1^{\infty} \int |f_n|\,dg < \infty$, then $f \in L^1(S)$ and $\int f\,dg = \sum_{n=1}^{\infty} \int f_n\,dg$.

**4.5.16** If $h \in S$ and $f$ is a function on $S$, define the left translated function ${}_hf$ of $f$ and the right translated function $f_h$ of $f$ by

$$ {}_hf(g) = f(h^{-1}g), \qquad f_h(g) = f(gh^{-1}) \qquad \text{for } g \in S. $$

Show that, if $f$ is in $L^1(S)$, then so are ${}_hf$ and $f_h$ and

$$ \int {}_hf\,dg = \int f_h\,dg = \int f\,dg. $$

*Hint* Suppose the matrix representation of $h$ is

$$ h = \begin{pmatrix} \alpha & \beta \\ \gamma & \delta \end{pmatrix}, \qquad \alpha\delta - \beta\gamma = 1. $$

Show that the function that corresponds to ${}_hf$ in the same way as $F$ corresponds to $f$ is $F \circ A$, where $A : R^4 \to R^4$ is a linear transformation with the matrix

$$ \begin{pmatrix} \delta & 0 & -\beta & 0 \\ 0 & \delta & 0 & -\beta \\ -\gamma & 0 & \alpha & 0 \\ 0 & -\gamma & 0 & \alpha \end{pmatrix}. $$

Verify that $\det A = (\alpha\delta - \beta\gamma)^2 = 1$.

**4.5.17** Show that, if $f \in L^1(S)$, then so is the function $\check{f}$ defined by

$$ (\check{f}g) = f(g^{-1}) \qquad \text{for } g \in S $$

and

$$ \int \check{f}\,dg = \int f\,dg. $$

*Hint* Show that $\int \check{f}\,dg = \int \check{F}\,dx$ with $\check{F} = F \circ A$ and

$$ A = \begin{pmatrix} 0 & 0 & 0 & 1 \\ 0 & -1 & 0 & 0 \\ 0 & 0 & -1 & 0 \\ 1 & 0 & 0 & 0 \end{pmatrix} $$

by using the fact that $f((x/(\det x)^{1/2})^{-1}) = F((\det x)x^{-1})$.

## SUMMARY

Suppose we start out with an integration theory on a set $S_1$ and another integration theory on a set $S_2$. Let us denote the integral of an integrable function $f$ on $S_i$ by $\int f\, d\mu_i$ $(i = 1, 2)$. We designate the linear space of generalized step functions on $S_i$ by $L_i$ $(i = 1, 2)$. Then we can obtain an integration theory on $S = S_1 \times S_2$ in the following way. The set $L$ of elementary functions on $S$ consists of functions $\varphi$ of the form

$$\varphi(x, y) = \sum_{k=1}^{m} \xi_k(x)\eta_k(y), \qquad \xi_k \in L_1, \qquad \eta_k \in L_2$$

with the integral

$$\int \varphi\, d\mu = \sum_{k=1}^{m} \int \xi_k\, d\mu_1 \int \eta_k\, d\mu_2$$

(Definitions 4.1.1 and 4.1.5). The integral $\int \varphi\, d\mu$ is also denoted by $\int \varphi\, d\mu_1 \otimes \mu_2$. The fundamental properties (1) to (5) are satisfied for this integral (Proposition 4.1.6). If $f$ is a function on $S$ and if $f_y(x) = f(x, y)$ is an integrable function on $S_1$ for a.a. $y \in S_2$, and if there exists an integrable function $H$ on $S_2$ such that $H(y) = \int f_y\, d\mu_1$ for a.a.$y$, then we say that the iterated integral

$$\iint f\, d\mu_1\, d\mu_2 = \int H\, d\mu_2$$

exists. The iterated integral $\iint f\, d\mu_2\, d\mu_1$ is defined similarly (Definition 4.1.7). Fubini's theorem (Theorem 4.1.8) tells us that for an integrable function $f$ on $S$, the iterated integrals $\iint f\, d\mu_1\, d\mu_2$ and $\iint f\, d\mu_2\, d\mu_1$ both exist and

$$\int f\, dx = \iint f\, d\mu_1\, d\mu_2 = \iint f\, d\mu_2\, d\mu_1.$$

The step functions on $n$-dimensional Euclidean space $R^n$ are the functions $\varphi$ of the form

$$\varphi(x) = \varphi(x_1, \cdots, x_n) = \sum_{k=1}^{m} \varphi_{1k}(x_1) \cdots \varphi_{nk}(x_n)$$

where $\varphi_{jk}$ are step functions on the real line. The linear space of step functions on $R^n$ is denoted by ${}_nL$ or also simply by $L$ (Definition 4.2.1). The Lebesgue integral of a function $\varphi \in {}_nL$, represented as above, is given by the equation

$$\int \varphi\, dx = \sum_{k=1}^{m} \int \varphi_{1k}\, dx_1 \cdots \int \varphi_{nk}\, dx_n$$

(Definition 4.2.5 and Equation (4.2.3)). The fundamental properties (1) to (5) are satisfied for the Lebesgue integral (Proposition 4.2.6).

Suppose $f$ is a function on $R^n$, $n > 2$. For any $j$, $1 \leq j < n$, let $R^n = R^j \times R^{n-j}$ where the point $x = (x_1, \cdots, x_n)$ in $R^n$ corresponds to the point

$$(y, z), \qquad y = (x_1, \cdots, x_j), \qquad z = (x_{j+1}, \cdots, x_n)$$

in $R^j \times R^{n-j}$. For each $z$ let $f_z$ be the function on $R^j$ defined by $f_z(y) = f(y, z)$. If $f_z$ is integrable for a.a.$z$ in $R^{n-j}$, and if there is an integrable function $H$ on $R^{n-j}$ such that $H(z) = \int f_z\, dy$ for a.a.$z$ in $R^{n-j}$, then we say that the iterated integral $\iint f\, dy\, dz$ exists and we let

$$\iint f\, dy\, dz = \int H\, dz.$$

The iterated integrals $\iint f\, dz\, dy$ and $\int \cdots \int f\, dx_1, \cdots, dx_n$ are defined in a similar way (Definition 4.2.8). Fubini's theorem (Theorem 4.2.9 and Corollary 4.2.10) says that, for an integrable function $f$ on $R^n$, $n > 2$, the iterated integrals $\iint f\, dy\, dz$, $\iint f\, dz\, dy$, and more generally, for any permutation $(\pi 1, \cdots, \pi n)$ of $(1, \cdots, n)$, $\int \cdots \int f\, dx_{\pi 1} \cdots dx_{\pi n}$ exist and

$$\int f\, dx = \iint f\, dy\, dz = \iint f\, dz\, dy = \int \cdots \int f\, dx_{\pi 1} \cdots dx_{\pi n}.$$

There is a partial converse to this theorem which asserts that, for a measurable function $f$ on $R^n$, the existence of one of the iterated integrals $\int \cdots \int |f|\, d_{\pi 1} \cdots dx_{\pi n}$ implies the integrability of $f$ (Corollary 4.2.11).

For instance, every open subset of $R^n$ is measurable (Proposition 4.2.16), a continuous function on an open set is measurable, and a continuous function on a closed bounded rectangle is integrable (Corollaries 4.2.17 and 4.2.18).

If the mapping $\Phi$ of $R^n$ into $R^n$ is a translation, then for any integrable function $f$ on $R^n$, $f \circ \Phi$ is again integrable and (Proposition 4.3.2):

$$\int f\, dx = \int f \circ \Phi\, dx.$$

If the mapping $\Phi$ from $R^n$ into $R^n$ is a linear mapping with $\det \Phi \neq 0$, then for any integrable function $f$ on $R^n$, $f \circ \Phi$ is also integrable and (Theorem 4.3.7):

$$\int f\, dx = |\det \Phi| \int f \circ \Phi\, dx.$$

Suppose the mapping $\Phi$ from an open subset $D$ of $R^n$ onto an open subset $E$ on $R^n$ is one-to-one and the components $\Phi_i (i = 1, \cdots, n)$ of $\Phi$ have continuous partial derivatives. Suppose furthermore that the inverse mapping $\Psi = \Phi^{-1}$ from $E$ onto $D$ has the same property. If $f$ is an integrable function on $R^n$, then $f \circ \Phi\, |\det \Phi'|$ is an integrable function on $D$ and (Theorem 4.4.5):

$$\int_E f\, dx = \int_D f \circ \Phi\, |\det \Phi'|\, dx$$

where $\det \Phi'$ is the Jacobian of $\Phi$ defined by

$$\det \Phi_x' = \det\left(\frac{\partial \Phi_i}{\partial x_j}(x)\right).$$

# 5

# $L^2$ and $L^p$ Spaces

This chapter is by far not so simple as the previous ones. Not that it contains any difficult computations or wearisome arguments; in fact, the proofs are not at all complicated, though tricky at times. The difficulty lies in the new concepts like norm, scalar product, and linear functional, which are introduced in this chapter and which are farther removed from the familiar concepts of function and integral known from calculus. Nevertheless, the present chapter can be mastered by any reader who has a good understanding of the material so far presented and who had little difficulty in doing the exercises in part F of Section 2.7.

A knowledge of the scalar product in Euclidean space $R^n$ and its fundamental properties certainly will help one to understand the notion of scalar product for the space $L^2$ of measurable functions with an integrable square. This scalar product is defined by $(f, g) = \int fg \, dx$ for $f, g \in L^2$. In fact, most of the theorems on the space $L^2$ have their counterpart in the theory of Euclidean space $R^n$ with its scalar product.

In Sections 5.1 and 5.2 we will be discussing geometric and metric properties of the space $L^2$, most of which are generalized in Section 5.4 to the space $L^p$ of measurable functions with an integrable $p$th power $1 \leq p < \infty$. This means that we treat a special case first and generalize afterwards, conforming with the spirit of this book. Another special case, $p = 1$, has already been discussed in part F of the exercise section 2.7. Accordingly, there is much duplication in the results and constructions, and the reader is recommended to look for, and try to follow up, analogies even where they are not expressly indicated.

Section 5.3 presents the characterization of bounded linear functionals on $L^2$, a result that will be used in Chapter 9 to give a proof of the Radon-Nikodym theorem for abstract Daniell integrals.

With a mastery of these sections the student will be prepared to enter upon the study of the more advanced theory of functional analysis for Hilbert and Banach spaces.

A special application of the functional analysis for $L^2$ is given in Section 5.6 which presents a short introduction to the theory of Fourier transformations for functions of a real variable. The use of $L^2$ as the underlying space gives a neat symmetry to the Fourier theory, which it is very rewarding to exploit. But we need an $L^2$ space of complex-valued functions. Hence Section 5.5 is inserted to clear up the obstacles presented by this generalization. Those who do not want to read Section 5.6 do not have to read Section 5.5 either, since its results are not used elsewhere.

## 5.1 THE SPACE $L^2$

In the following, let $L$ be the set of step functions on the real line or, more generally, on Euclidean space $R^n$. The integral $\int f \, dx$ is the Lebesgue integral of an integrable function $f$. Or, we may interpret $L$ as a set of elementary functions on a set $S$ with an integral $\int \varphi \, d\mu$, $\varphi \in L$, subject to the conditions (1) to (5) of

Sections 2.5 and 3.1. The theory that is now being developed for the Lebesgue integral will hold also for this more general setting. In any case, $L^1$ will denote the space of integrable functions.

5.1.1 DEFINITION *The set of all measurable functions that have an integrable square is denoted by $L^2$. The functions in $L^2$ are sometimes also referred to as square integrable functions.*

In particular, all null functions are in $L^2$. But there are also plenty of less trivial functions in $L^2$. We have, for instance:

5.1.2 PROPOSITION *Every bounded function in $L^1$ belongs to $L^2$.*

*Proof* Suppose $f \in L^1$ and $|f| \leq M$; then $f^2 \leq M|f|$ so that $f^2$ is indeed integrable (by Theorem 3.1.8).

5.1.3 DEFINITION *The norm $\|f\|$ of a function $f \in L^2$ is defined by*

$$\|f\| = \left\{\int f^2\,dx\right\}^{1/2}.$$

If $f$ and $g$ belong to $L^2$, then $fg$ is measurable, and since

$$|fg| \leq \tfrac{1}{2}(f^2 + g^2),$$

$fg$ is in fact integrable by Theorem 3.1.8. For any two real numbers $a$, $b$, we have now

$$(af + bg)^2 = a^2f^2 + 2abfg + b^2g^2$$

so that $(af + bg)^2$ is integrable. Hence

$$af + bg \in L^2.$$

We have just proved:

5.1.4 PROPOSITION *$L^2$ is a linear space.*

We see immediately from the definition that the norm $\|f\|$ on $L^2$ has the following homogeneity property,

$$\|af\| = |a|\,\|f\|$$

for any real number $a$. It also satisfies a triangle inequality,

$$\|f + g\| \leq \|f\| + \|g\|$$

for $f, g \in L^2$. Before we can give the proof, we need some more information on another operation on $L^2$, called the scalar product.

5.1.5 DEFINITION *For $f, g \in L^2$,*

$$(f, g) = \int fg\,dx$$

*is the scalar product of $f$ and $g$. The scalar product is sometimes also called the inner product.*

We have the following relations between the scalar product and the norm on $L^2$:

(5.1.6)
$$\|f\| = [(f, f)]^{1/2},$$
$$(f, g) = \tfrac{1}{4}(\|f+g\|^2 - \|f-g\|^2).$$

The scalar product is a bilinear functional, which is to say that it has these properties:

$$(a_1 f_1 + a_2 f_2, g) = a_1(f_1, g) + a_2(f_2, g),$$
$$(f, b_1 g_1 + b_2 g_2) = b_1(f, g_1) + b_2(f, g_2).$$

It is also symmetric,

$$(f, g) = (g, f).$$

### 5.1.7 PROPOSITION

PARALLELOGRAM IDENTITY *If $f, g \in L^2$, then*

$$\|f+g\|^2 + \|f-g\|^2 = 2\|f\|^2 + 2\|g\|^2.$$

The proof of this proposition is left to the exercises (Exercise 5.1.1). We come now to a fundamental inequality that is usually labeled with some combination of the names Cauchy, Schwarz, and Buniakowsky. For brevity, we will call it the Schwarz inequality.

### 5.1.8 PROPOSITION

SCHWARZ INEQUALITY *If $f, g \in L^2$, then*

$$|(f, g)| \leq \|f\| \, \|g\|$$

*with equality only if either $f = 0$ a.e. or $g = 0$ a.e. or else $f = kg$ a.e. for some real number $k$.*

*Proof* The cases $f = 0$ a.e. and $g = 0$ a.e. are evident, so we assume that neither $f$ nor $g$ vanishes almost everywhere, which (by Corollary 2.2.6) implies that $\|f\|, \|g\| > 0$. Let

$$f' = f \cdot \|f\|^{-1}, \qquad g' = g \cdot \|g\|^{-1}.$$

Then we have $\|f'\| = 1 = \|g'\|$. Using Equation (5.1.6) and the parallelogram identity, we obtain

$$\begin{aligned} \frac{1}{\|f\| \cdot \|g\|} |(f, g)| = |(f', g')| &= \tfrac{1}{4} \left| \, \|f' + g'\|^2 - \|f' - g'\|^2 \right| \\ &\leq \tfrac{1}{4} (\|f' + g'\|^2 + \|f' - g'\|^2) \\ &= \tfrac{1}{2} (\|f'\|^2 + \|g'\|^2) = 1, \end{aligned}$$

which proves the inequality. Equality can happen only if $f' + g' = 0$ or $f' - g' = 0$ a.e., proving the second claim.

The parallelogram identity can be interpreted in relation to elementary geometry as stating that there exists a parallelogram with sides of lengths $\|f\|$ and $\|g\|$ and with diagonals of length $\|f + g\|$ and $\|f - g\|$. It is shown in trigonometry that the cosine of the angle $\alpha$ in Figure 5.1 is related to the sides of the triangle $ABD$ by

$$\|f - g\|^2 = \|f\|^2 + \|g\|^2 - 2\|f\|\,\|g\| \cos \alpha.$$

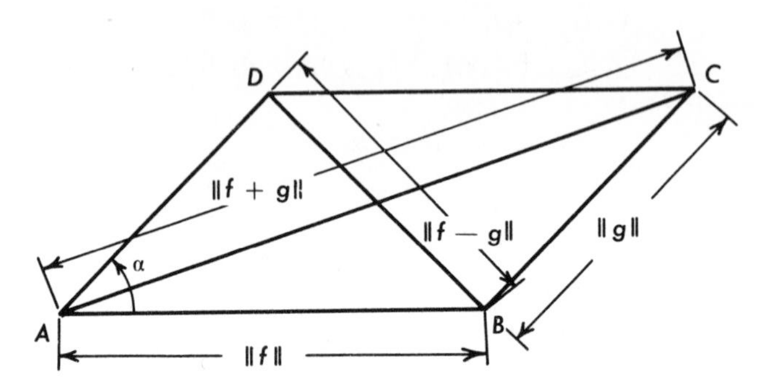


Figure 5.1 The parallelogram identity.

If we express $\|f\|^2 + \|g\|^2$ by the parallelogram identity, we obtain

$$2\|f\|\,\|g\| \cos \alpha = \tfrac{1}{2}(\|f + g\|^2 - \|f - g\|^2)$$

which by Equation (5.1.6) yields

$$(f, g) = \|f\| \cdot \|g\| \cdot \cos \alpha.$$

The Schwarz inequality can then be interpreted as stating that the cosine of the angle between the sides $AB$ and $AD$ of the parallelogram has an absolute value at the most one. The triangle inequality between the lengths of the sides of the triangle $ABC$ in Figure 5.1 gives the relation

$$\|f + g\| \leq \|f\| + \|g\|.$$

We also give an analytic proof of this inequality, which is alternatively called Minkowski's inequality, or the triangle inequality.

### 5.1.9 PROPOSITION

MINKOWSKI'S INEQUALITY *If $f, g \in L^2$, then*

$$\|f + g\| \leq \|f\| + \|g\|$$

*with equality only if either $f = 0$ or $g = 0$ a.e., or else $f = kg$ a.e. for some positive number $k$.*

*Proof* By the parallelogram identity and by Equation 5.1.6,

$$\begin{aligned}\|f+g\|^2 - \|f\|^2 - \|g\|^2 &= \|f+g\|^2 - \tfrac{1}{2}\|f+g\|^2 - \tfrac{1}{2}\|f-g\|^2 \\ &= \tfrac{1}{2}(\|f+g\|^2 - \|f-g\|^2) \\ &= 2(f,g);\end{aligned}$$

hence by the Schwarz inequality

$$\begin{aligned}\|f+g\|^2 &\leq \|f\|^2 + \|g\|^2 + 2\|f\|\cdot\|g\| \\ &= (\|f\| + \|g\|)^2.\end{aligned}$$

A necessary condition for equality is then the equality condition of the Schwarz inequality, and if $f = kg$, we see immediately that $k$ has to be nonnegative if equality is to hold in

$$|k+1|\cdot\|g\| = \|kg+g\| \leq \|kg\| + \|g\| = (1+|k|)\|g\|.$$

We now collect some of the results of this section in a final theorem.

**5.1.10 THEOREM** *The space $L^2$ of measurable square integrable functions is a linear space with a norm*

$$\|f\| = \left\{\int f^2\,dx\right\}^{1/2}$$

*satisfying*

$$\begin{aligned}\|f\| &= 0 \quad \text{if and only if } f = 0 \quad \text{a.e.}, \\ \|af\| &= |a|\,\|f\|, \\ \|f+g\| &\leq \|f\| + \|g\|.\end{aligned}$$

*$L^2$ is also an inner product space with an inner product*

$$(f,g) = \int fg\,dx$$

*satisfying*

$$\begin{aligned}&(f,f) \geq 0 \text{ and } (f,f) = 0 \text{ if and only if } f = 0 \quad \text{a.e.}, \\ &(a_1 f_1 + a_2 f_2, g) = a_1(f_1,g) + a_2(f_2,g),\ a_1 a_2 \textit{ real}, \\ &(f, b_1 g_1 + b_2 g_2) = b_1(f,g_1) + b_2(f,g_2),\ b_1, b_2 \textit{ real}, \\ &(f,g) = (g,f).\end{aligned}$$

## *EXERCISES*

*5.1.1* Verify the second of Equation (5.1.6) and the parallelogram identity (Proposition 5.1.7).

*5.1.2* Use the fact that the quadratic function

$$\|f\|^2 + 2\lambda(f,g) + \lambda^2\|g\|^2 = \|f+\lambda g\|^2$$

of $\lambda$ has a nonnegative minimum to get another proof of the Schwarz inequality (Proposition 5.1.8).

*5.1.3* Show that

$$\int f^2\,dx \int g^2\,dx - \left\{\int fg\,dx\right\}^2 = \frac{1}{2}\iint \{f(x)\,g(y) - f(y)\,g(x)\}^2\,dx\,dy$$

for $f, g \in L^2$ to obtain another proof of the Schwarz inequality.

*5.1.4* The points $x = (x_1, \cdots, x_n)$ in Euclidean space $R^n$ can be considered as functions on the finite set $\{1, \cdots, n\}$. Define an integral for these functions by

$$\int x\,d\mu = \sum_{k=1}^{n} x_k.$$

Then all functions on $\{1, \cdots, n\}$ are integrable and these functions are just the points in $R^n$; so are the square integrable functions. Interpret the norm, the scalar product, and the Schwarz inequality for this setting.

*5.1.5* The ball $B(f, r)$ in $L^2$ with center $f \in L^2$ and radius $r > 0$ is the subset

$$B(f, r) = \{g : \|f - g\| < r\}$$

of $L^2$. Show that the intersection of two different balls with the same radius is either empty or is contained in a ball of strictly smaller radius.

## 5.2 METRIC PROPERTIES OF $L^2$

It is extremely important that Minkowski's inequality can be generalized to infinite sums yielding a proposition which is similar to Beppo Levi's theorem (Theorem 2.2.4).

5.2.1 PROPOSITION *If $\sum f_n$ is a series of functions in $L^2$ and $\sum_{n=1}^{\infty} \|f_n\| < \infty$, then $\sum f_n$ converges absolutely almost everywhere, and if $f$ is a function such that*

$$f = \sum_{n=1}^{\infty} f_n \text{ a.e.}$$

*then $f \in L^2$ and*

$$\|f\| = \lim_{n\to\infty} \left\| \sum_{k=1}^{n} f_k \right\| \le \sum_{n=1}^{\infty} \|f_n\|.$$

*Proof* We obtain, using the trivial generalization of Minkowski's inequality to finite sums,

$$\int \left(\sum_{k=1}^{n} |f_k|\right)^2 dx \le \left(\sum_{k=1}^{n} \|f_k\|\right)^2 \le \left(\sum_{k=1}^{\infty} \|f_k\|\right)^2.$$

By the monotone convergence theorem the sequence $\{(\sum_{k=1}^{n} |f_k|)^2\}$ converges almost everywhere, and if we define the function $h$ by

$$h(x) = \begin{cases} \left(\sum_{k=1}^{\infty} |f_k(x)|\right)^2 & \text{if the sum is finite} \\ 0 & \text{otherwise} \end{cases}$$

then $h$ is integrable and

$$\int h\, dx = \lim_{n\to\infty} \int \left(\sum_{k=1}^{n} |f_k|\right)^2 dx \leq \left(\sum_{k=1}^{\infty} \|f_k\|\right)^2.$$

Now Lebesgue's dominated convergence theorem shows that $f^2$ is integrable, since

$$f^2 = \lim_{n\to\infty} \left(\sum_{k=1}^{n} f_k\right)^2 \text{ a.e.,}$$

$$\left(\sum_{k=1}^{n} f_k\right)^2 \leq h \text{ a.e.}$$

But $f$ is measurable, hence $f \in L^2$ and

$$\|f\|^2 = \int f^2\, dx = \lim_{n\to\infty} \int \left(\sum_{k=1}^{n} f_k\right)^2 dx$$

$$\leq \int h\, dx \leq \left(\sum_{n=1}^{\infty} \|f_n\|\right)^2$$

as claimed.

The norm $\|f\|$ for $L^2$ can be used to introduce a notion of distance $\|f - g\|$ between elements $f$ and $g$ of $L^2$. This distance has the properties

$$\|f - g\| = 0 \text{ if and only if } f = g \text{ a.e.,}$$
$$\|f - g\| = \|g - f\|,$$
$$\|f - g\| \leq \|f - h\| + \|h - g\|.$$

The latter triangle inequality is a consequence of Minkowski's inequality. The distance in turn leads to the notion of convergence. We say that *a sequence* $\{f_n\}$ *in* $L^2$ *converges in norm (or strongly) to* $f \in L^2$ *if*

$$\lim_{n\to\infty} \|f - f_n\| = 0.$$

A convergent sequence $\{f_n\}$ in $L^2$ is always a Cauchy sequence in the sense that

$$\lim_{n,m\to\infty} \|f_n - f_m\| = 0$$

because we have by the triangle inequality

$$\|f_n - f_m\| \leq \|f_n - f\| + \|f - f_m\|.$$

We will prove now that the converse is true also.

### 5.2.2 THEOREM

RIESZ-FISCHER *The space $L^2$ is complete; that is, if $\{f_n\}$ is a Cauchy sequence,*

$$\lim_{n,m\to\infty} \|f_n - f_m\| = 0,$$

*then $\{f_n\}$ converges strongly to an element $f \in L^2$,*

$$\lim_{n\to\infty} \|f - f_n\| = 0.$$

*Proof* Choose a sequence

$$n(1) < n(2) < \cdots < n(k) < \cdots$$

of natural numbers with the property

$$\|f_m - f_{n(k)}\| \leq 2^{-k} \qquad \text{if } m \geq n(k).$$

Then define the series $\Sigma\, g_n$ by

$$g_1 = f_{n(1)}, \qquad g_k = f_{n(k)} - f_{n(k-1)} \qquad \text{for } k \geq 2.$$

By construction

$$\sum_{k=1}^{\infty} \|g_k\| \leq \|f_{n(1)}\| + \sum_{k=2}^{\infty} 2^{-(k-1)} = \|f_{n(1)}\| + 1,$$

so that, by Proposition 5.2.1, the series $\sum g_k$ converges absolutely almost everywhere. Now we can define the function $f$ in a familiar way

$$f(x) = \begin{cases} \displaystyle\sum_{k=1}^{\infty} g_k(x) = \lim_{k\to\infty} f_{n(k)}(x) & \text{if } \displaystyle\sum_{k=1}^{\infty} |g_k(x)| < \infty \\ 0 & \text{otherwise.} \end{cases}$$

Again using Proposition 5.2.1, $f \in L^2$ and we can estimate $\|f - f_m\|$ as follows:

$$\begin{aligned} \|f - f_m\| &\leq \|f - f_{n(k)}\| + \|f_{n(k)} - f_m\| \\ &\leq \sum_{h=k+1}^{\infty} \|f_{n(h)} - f_{n(h-1)}\| + 2^{-k} \\ &\leq \sum_{h=k+1}^{\infty} 2^{-(h-1)} + 2^{-k} = 3 \cdot 2^{-k} \end{aligned}$$

for $m \geq n(k)$; hence, in fact,

$$\lim_{m\to\infty} \|f - f_m\| = 0,$$

completing the proof of Theorem 5.2.2.

Note that we have constructed $f$ as the almost everywhere limit of a subsequence $\{f_{n(k)}\}$ of $\{f_n\}$ but we do not claim that

$$f = \lim_{n\to\infty} f_n \text{ a.e.;}$$

this is in fact false in general. As an example, let $f_n$ be the characteristic function of the interval $[n2^{-k} - 1, (n + 1)2^{-k} - 1]$ where $k$ is the unique integer for which $2^k \leq n < 2^{k+1}$. Then

$$\lim_{n\to\infty} \|0 - f_n\| = 0$$

but $\{f_n(x)\}$ does not tend to zero for any $x$ in the interval $[0, 1]$.

We conclude this section with two theorems on the approximation of functions in $L^2$ by functions in a space $L$ of elementary functions, which may be step functions or piecewise linear functions in the case of Lebesgue integration on the real line. But we will not employ any special properties of $L$, as for instance $L \subset L^2$, which happens to be true if $L$ is the space of step functions. We will, however, make use of a similar approximation of functions in $L^1$ by functions in $L$ which we obtained in Lemma 2.2.5:

5.2.3 LEMMA *Suppose $f$ is an integrable function. For every $\varepsilon > 0$ there is a function $\varphi \in L$ such that*

$$\int |f - \varphi| \, dx \leq \varepsilon.$$

5.2.4 THEOREM *If $f \in L^2$ and $\varepsilon > 0$ are given, then there exists a square integrable function $\varphi \in L$ such that*

$$\|f - \varphi\| \leq \varepsilon.$$

*Proof* Let us first assume that $f$ is nonnegative. For each integer $n \geq 1$, the function

$$h_n = n \wedge nf^2 \wedge f$$

is integrable, since $0 \leq h_n \leq nf^2$; it is also square integrable because $h_n^2 \leq f^2$. The sequence $\{(f - h_n)^2\}$ decreases to zero, since $\{h_n\}$ tends to $f$. The monotone convergence theorem shows therefore

$$\lim_{n\to\infty} \|f - h_n\|^2 = \lim_{n\to\infty} \int (f - h_n)^2 \, dx = 0.$$

Choose $n$ so large that

$$\|f - h_n\| \leq \varepsilon.$$

By Lemma 5.2.3 we can find a function $\psi \in L$ such that

$$\int |h_n - \psi| \, dx \leq \frac{\varepsilon^2}{2n}.$$

$\varphi = n \wedge \psi^+$ is a function in $L$ by our basic property (5) and it is square integrable by Proposition 5.1.2. (This is of course trivial if $L$ is the space of step functions.) Notice that

$$|h_n - \varphi| \leq |h_n - \psi|$$

because $0 \leq h_n \leq n$. Hence

$$\|h_n - \varphi\|^2 = \int |h_n - \varphi| \cdot |h_n - \varphi| \, dx$$

$$\leq 2n \int |h_n - \psi| \, dx \leq \varepsilon^2,$$

and consequently,

$$\|f - \varphi\| \leq \|f - h_n\| + \|h_n - \varphi\| \leq 2\varepsilon$$

which completes the proof for a nonnegative $f$.

If $f$ is not nonnegative, then we can decompose $f$ into its positive and negative parts, $f = f^+ - f^-$, where $f^+$ and $f^-$ both belong to $L^2$, since

$$f^+ = \tfrac{1}{2}(f + |f|), \qquad f^- = f^+ - f.$$

By the preceding argument we can approximate $f^+$ and $f^-$ by square integrable functions $\varphi_1 \in L$ and $\varphi_2 \in L$, respectively,

$$\|f^+ - \varphi_1\| \leq \frac{\varepsilon}{2}, \qquad \|f^- - \varphi_2\| \leq \frac{\varepsilon}{2},$$

and thus

$$\|f - (\varphi_1 - \varphi_2)\| \leq \|f^+ - \varphi_1\| + \|f^- - \varphi_2\| \leq \varepsilon.$$

As a corollary we obtain a characterization of square integrable functions that is similar to the definition of integrable functions (Definition 2.1.3).

5.2.5 THEOREM *A function $f$ is in $L^2$ if and only if there is a series $\sum \varphi_n$ of square integrable elementary functions such that*

$$f = \sum_{n=1}^{\infty} \varphi_n \text{ a.e.}$$

$$\sum_{n=1}^{\infty} \|\varphi_n\| < \infty.$$

*Proof* The sufficiency of the condition follows from Proposition 5.2.1. So we need only show that the condition is necessary.

Since $\varepsilon$ was arbitrary in Theorem 5.2.4, we may first choose a square integrable function $\varphi_1 \in L$ so that

$$\|f - \varphi_1\| \leq 2^{-1}$$

then $\varphi_2$, so that

$$\|(f - \varphi_1) - \varphi_2\| \leq 2^{-2},$$

and so on successively, and in general for $n \geq 2$ a square integrable function $\varphi_n \in L$ such that

$$\left\| \left( f - \sum_{k=1}^{n-1} \varphi_k \right) - \varphi_n \right\| \leq 2^{-n}.$$

Then it follows from the Minkowski inequality that

$$\|\varphi_n\| \leq \left\| f - \sum_{k=1}^{n-1} \varphi_k - \varphi_n \right\| + \left\| f - \sum_{k=1}^{n-1} \varphi_k \right\| \leq 3 \cdot 2^{-n} \qquad \text{for } n \geq 2$$

so that

$$\sum_{n=1}^{\infty} \|\varphi_n\| < \|\varphi_1\| + 2 < \infty.$$

Hence it follows from Proposition 5.2.1 that there exists a function $g \in L^2$ such that $g = \sum_{k=1}^{\infty} \varphi_k$ a.e., and then

$$\|f - g\| \leq \left\| f - \sum_{k=1}^{n} \varphi_k \right\| + \left\| \sum_{k=n+1}^{\infty} \varphi_k \right\|$$

$$\leq 2^{-n} + \sum_{k=n+1}^{\infty} \|\varphi_k\| \leq 4 \cdot 2^{-n}$$

so that, in fact, $\|f - g\| = 0$ and thus

$$f = \sum_{n=1}^{\infty} \varphi_n \text{ a.e.},$$

as claimed.

## *EXERCISES*

*5.2.1* Show that for $f, g \in L^2$,

$$|\|f\| - \|g\|| \leq \|f - g\|.$$

*Hint* Apply Minkowski's inequality to $f = (f - g) + g$ and to $g = (g - f) + f$.

*5.2.2* Use Exercise 5.2.1 to prove that

$$\lim_{n \to \infty} \|f_n\| = \|f\|$$

if $\{f_n\}$ is a sequence in $L^2$ that converges strongly to $f \in L^2$.

*5.2.3* If $\{f_n\}$ converges strongly to $f$, then we denote this by

$$\{f_n\} \to f.$$

Show that if $\{f_n\} \to f$ and $\{g_n\} \to g$, then

$$\{f_n + g_n\} \to f + g, \qquad \{(f_n, g_n)\} \to (f, g).$$

*5.2.4* Show that if $f$ is a nonnegative function in $L^2$, then for every $\varepsilon > 0$ there is a nonnegative elementary function $\varphi$ such that $\|f - \sqrt{\varphi}\| \leq \varepsilon$. In particular, if we take the step functions as our elementary functions, then $\sqrt{\varphi}$ is again a step function and we have another proof of Theorem 5.2.4.

*Hint* Apply Lemma 5.2.3 to choose $\varphi$ such that

$$\int |f^2 - \varphi| \, dx \leq \varepsilon^2.$$

Then use the inequality

$$|x - y|^2 \leq |x^2 - y^2|,$$

which is valid for $x, y \geq 0$.

## 5.3 LINEAR FUNCTIONALS ON $L^2$

For historical reasons, certain functions defined on spaces like $L^2$ are conventionally called *functionals*. This was originally motivated by the risk of confusing the functional with the elements of $L^2$ themselves, which are also functions, albeit on another set. Since then, the use of the term functional has been extended to the corresponding functions on linear spaces in general.

5.3.1 DEFINITION *A bounded linear functional on $L^2$ is a function $F$ that assigns to every $f \in L^2$ a real number $F(g)$ and satisfies in addition the two following conditions:*

(a) *$F(af + bg) = aF(f) + bF(g)$ for $f, g \in L^2$ and $a, b$ real;*
(b) *there is a real number $M$ such that*

$$|F(f)| \leq M \, \|f\| \qquad \text{for } f \in L^2.$$

The first of these two conditions is of course the linearity condition; it implies for instance that $F(0) = 0$. The second one is a continuity condition, though this is not immediately apparent in the given formulation. We have, in fact:

5.3.2 PROPOSITION *For a linear functional $F$ on $L^2$ satisfying* (a) *of Definition 5.3.1,* (b) *is satisfied if and only if the following condition holds:*

(c) $$\lim_{n\to\infty} F(f_n) = F(f) \quad \text{if} \quad \lim_{n\to\infty} \|f_n - f\| = 0.$$

*Proof* Namely, if Condition (b) of Definition 5.3.1 holds, then so does Condition (c), since

$$|F(f_n) - F(f)| \leq M \, \|f_n - f\|.$$

Conversely, if Condition (b) of Definition 5.3.1 is not satisfied, then one can find for each natural number $n$ an element $f_n \in L^2$ different from zero such that

$$|F(f_n)| > n\|f_n\|.$$

Now

$$g_n = \frac{1}{n} \|f_n\|^{-1} f_n$$

is a sequence in $L^2$ satisfying

$$\lim_{n\to\infty} \|g_n\| = \lim_{n\to\infty} \frac{1}{n} = 0,$$

$$|F(g_n)| = \frac{1}{n} \|f_n\|^{-1} \cdot |F(f_n)| > 1$$

so that Condition (c) does not hold either.

A bounded linear functional is therefore also called a *continuous linear functional.* As an example of a bounded linear functional, we have the functional $F_g$ generated by an element $g$ in $L^2$:

$$F_g(f) = (f, g) = \int fg\, dx \qquad \text{for } f \in L^2.$$

It is obvious that $F_g$ satisfies the linearity condition (a) of Definition 5.3.1 and the Schwarz inequality shows that

$$|F_g(f)| \leq M \|f\| \qquad \text{with } M = \|g\|.$$

Putting $f = g$, we find $F_g(g) = (g, g) = \|g\| \cdot \|g\|$ so that the smallest $M$ for which this inequality holds is

$$M = \|g\|.$$

5.3.3 DEFINITION *If $F$ is a bounded linear functional on $L^2$, then the norm $\|F\|$ of $F$ is defined as the smallest possible $M$ in the continuity condition (b) of Definition 5.3.1. We have then*

$$|F(f)| \leq \|F\| \cdot \|f\|.$$

Hence, in particular,

$$\|F_g\| = \|g\|.$$

It is easily verified that for any bounded linear functional $F$,

$$\|F\| = \sup \{\|f\|^{-1} \cdot |F(f)| : f \in L^2, \|f\| \neq 0\}$$

We now consider the following problem. Suppose that we have a functional $F_g$, which has been generated by some element $g$ of $L^2$; can we regain the generator $g$ from the information contained in the functional $F_g$?

5.3.4 PROPOSITION *If $g \neq 0$, then the generator $g$ of the continuous linear functional $F_g$ is an element of smallest norm in the "hyperplane,"*

$$H = \{f : F_g(f) = \|F_g\|^2\},$$

*and any other element of smallest norm in $H$ is equal to $g$ a.e.*

*Proof* This is essentially the statement about equality in the Schwarz inequality. We have for $f \in H$,

$$\|g\|^2 = \|F_g\|^2 = F_g(f) = (f, g) \leq \|f\| \cdot \|g\| \tag{5.3.5}$$

that is, $\|f\| \geq \|g\|$ so that $g$ is an element of the smallest norm in $H$. If $f \in H$ also has the smallest norm, then $\|f\| = \|g\|$ and equality holds in (5.3.5). Since $g \neq 0, f = kg$ by Proposition 5.1.8, which in this case implies

$$\|g\|^2 = \|f\|\,\|g\| = k\|g\|\,\|g\|,$$

or $k = 1$ so that $f = g$ a.e. as claimed.

We are now ready to prove the main statement of this section, namely that all continuous linear functionals are generated by elements $g$ of $L^2$ in the way described above. Since obviously the trivial functional that assigns the value zero to every element of $L^2$ can be thought of as generated by the zero function in $L^2$, we may assume that $F \neq 0$, or in other words that $\|F\| > 0$.

5.3.6 THEOREM *If $F \neq 0$ is a continuous linear functional on $L^2$, then there exists an element $g$ of smallest norm in the hyperplane,*

$$H = \{f: F(f) = \|F\|^2\}$$

*which is unique in the sense that any other element of smallest norm in $H$ equals $g$ a.e. For this $g$ we have $F = F_g$, that is,*

$$F(f) = (f, g) = \int fg\, dx$$

*for all $f \in L^2$.*

*Proof* $H$ is not empty, since $[F(f)]^{-1}\|F\|^2 f \in H$ if $F(f) \neq 0$. Let

$$A = \inf\{\|f\|: f \in H\}.$$

For any element $f \in H$,

$$\|F\|^2 = F(f) \leq \|F\| \cdot \|f\|$$

whence $\|F\| \leq \|f\|$, since $\|F\| \neq 0$ by hypothesis. Thus $\|F\| \leq A$ and therefore $A \neq 0$. One can actually show that $A = \|F\|$, but this is immaterial at present and it will be found anyway at the end of the proof.

To establish the existence of an element $g_0$ in $H$ with the smallest norm, we pick a sequence $\{g_n\}$ in $H$ such that

$$\lim_{n\to\infty} \|g_n\| = A.$$

Since $2^{-1}(g_n + g_m)$ belongs also to $H$, we have

$$\tfrac{1}{2}\|g_n + g_m\| \geq A.$$

The parallelogram identity now yields

$$\begin{aligned}\|g_n - g_m\|^2 &= 2\|g_n\|^2 + 2\|g_m\|^2 - \|g_n + g_m\|^2 \\ &\leq 2\|g_n\|^2 + 2\|g_m\|^2 - 4A.\end{aligned}$$

The right-hand side tends to zero as $n$ and $m$ tend to infinity; hence

$$\lim_{n,m\to\infty} \|g_n - g_m\| = 0.$$

By the Riesz-Fischer theroem, there is an element $g_0$ in $L^2$ such that

$$\lim_{n\to\infty} \|g_0 - g_n\| = 0.$$

Since $F$ is continuous,

$$F(g_0) = \lim_{n\to\infty} F(g_n) = \|F\|^2$$

so that $g_0 \in H$. Also

$$\|g_0\| = \lim_{n\to\infty} \|g_n\| = A$$

because $|\|g_0\| - \|g_n\|| \leq \|g_0 - g_n\|$ (Exercise 5.2.1). Hence $g_0$ is of smallest norm.

If $h \in L^2$ satisfies $F(h) = 0$, then $g_0 + th$ belongs to $H$ for all real numbers $t$.

$$\begin{aligned}\|g_0 + th\|^2 &= (g_0 + th, g_0 + th)\\ &= \|g_0\|^2 + 2t(h, g_0) + t^2\|h\|^2\end{aligned}$$

is a quadratic polynomial in $t$. The left-hand side has a minimum for $t = 0$ because $g_0$ is of smallest norm in $H$; but the right-hand side can have a minimum at zero only if the linear term vanishes; hence

$$(h, g_0) = 0.$$

For any $f \in L^2$, let

$$h = f - \frac{F(f)}{\|F\|^2} g_0;$$

we have $F(h) = 0$ and therefore

$$\begin{aligned}0 = (h, g_0) &= (f, g_0) - \frac{F(f)}{\|F\|^2} \|g_0\|^2\\ &= (f, g_0) - F(f)\frac{A^2}{\|F\|^2}.\end{aligned}$$

Consequently, $F = F_g$ where

$$g = \frac{\|F\|^2}{A^2} g_0.$$

Since $g_0$ is an element of smallest norm in the hyperplane

$$\{f: F(f) = \|F\|^2 = \|F_g\|^2\} = \{f: F_g(f) = \|F_g\|^2\},$$

$g = g_0$ a.e. by Proposition 5.3.4, which proves the theorem. This implies also $\|F\| = A$.

In the proof of the existence of $g_0$ we have used only the following properties of $H$:

(a) if $f, g \in H$, then $\frac{1}{2}(f + g) \in H$,

(b) $H$ is closed in the sense that if $\{f_n\}$ is a sequence in $H$ and $\lim_{n\to\infty} \|f_n - f\| = 0$, then $f \in H$.

Hence we have proved that *any closed set $H$ in $L^2$ with Property (a) contains an element $g_0$ of smallest norm. And if $g$ is another element in $H$ with the same norm* *as $g_0$ then $g = g_0$ a.e.* Namely, we have $\frac{1}{2}(g + g_0) \in H$ whence $\|g_0\| \leq \frac{1}{2}\|g + g_0\|$ and therefore by the parallelogram identity

$$\begin{aligned}\|g - g_0\|^2 &= 2\|g\|^2 + 2\|g_0\|^2 - \|g + g_0\|^2 \\ &\leq 4\|g_0\|^2 - 4\|g_0\|^2 = 0.\end{aligned}$$

## *EXERCISES*

*5.3.1* A set $C$ in $L^2$ is convex if

$$\lambda f + (1 - \lambda)g \in C$$

whenever $f, g \in C$ and $0 \leq \lambda \leq 1$. Suppose the set $C$ in $L^2$ is closed and has the property that the midpoint $\frac{1}{2}(f + g)$ between any two elements $f$ and $g$ of $C$ belongs to $C$. Prove that $C$ is convex.

*Hint* Prove first that $\lambda f + (1 - \lambda)g \in C$ for dyadic numbers $\lambda = k2^{-n}$, where $n \geq 1$ and $k$, $0 \leq k \leq 2^n$ are integers.

*5.3.2* Let $C$ be a closed convex subset of $L^2$ and $f \in L^2$. Show that there is $g \in C$ such that
(a) $\|f - g\| \leq \|f - h\|$ for all $h \in C$,
(b) if $g_0 \in C$ has the same property as $g$, then $g = g_0$ a.e.

*Hint* Apply the remark after Theorem 5.3.6 to the set

$$H = \{f - h : h \in C\}.$$

*5.3.3* Let $C$ be a closed convex subset of $L^2$ and $f \in L^2$. Define the distance of $f$ to $C$ by

$$\text{dist}\,(f, C) = \inf\,\{\|f - h\| : h \in C\}.$$

According to Exercise 5.3.2, there is $g \in C$ with

$$\text{dist}\,(f, C) = \|f - g\|.$$

Now fix $f_1, f_2 \in L^2$. Prove that

$$\varphi(t) = \text{dist}\,(tf_1 + (1 - t)f_2, C)$$

defines a convex function of $t$, that is,

$$\varphi(\lambda t_1 - (1 - \lambda)t_2) \leq \lambda\varphi(t_1) + (1 - \lambda)\varphi(t_2)$$

for all real numbers $t_1$ and $t_2$ and $0 \leq \lambda \leq 1$.

*5.3.4* A linear functional $F$ on $R^n$ assigns to each $x \in R^n$ a real number $F(x)$ and it satisfies the linearity condition

$$F(ax + by) = aF(x) + bF(y) \qquad \text{for } x, y \in R^n \text{ and } a, b \text{ real.}$$

Show that every linear functional on $R^n$ is bounded.

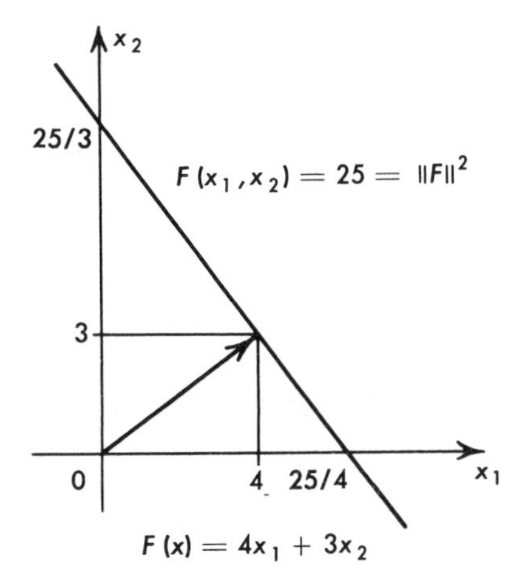


Figure 5.2 The linear functional $F(x) = 4x_1 + 3x_2$ on $R^2$ has a norm $(4^2 + 3^2)^{1/2} = 5$. $F(x)$ is the inner product of $x = (x_1, x_2)$ with (4, 3).

*Hint* Let $e_k$, $1 \leq k \leq n$ be the point in $R^n$ whose $k$th coordinate is 1, while all of its other coordinates are zero. Then

$$x = x_1e_1 + \cdots + x_ne_n,$$

$$F(x) = x_1F(e_1) + \cdots + x_nF(e_n).$$

Then $F(x)$ is the inner product of $x$ with which point in $R^n$?

*5.3.5* Explain Theorem 5.3.6 geometrically in the plane $R^2$ (see Figure 5.2).

## 5.4 $L^p$ SPACES

We are now going to study the properties of a family of spaces $L^p$ where $p$ is a parameter that can have any real value greater than, or equal to, one; there is also a conventional meaning attached to $p = \infty$. We have already studied the two special cases $p = 1$ and $p = 2$. Most of the results and proofs of this section are close analogies to the corresponding previous ones. As we have mentioned in the beginning of Section 5.1, the following theory is valid for any integral based on Properties (1) to (5), though we formulate everything only in terms of Lebesgue integration.

5.4.1 DEFINITION *For $1 \leq p < \infty$, $L^p$ is the space of all measurable functions $f$ such that $|f|^p$ is integrable. $L^\infty$ is the space of all measurable functions that are equivalent to bounded functions.*

In particular, all null functions are in $L^p$, $1 \leq p \leq \infty$, but there are also nontrivial functions in $L^p$.

**5.4.2 PROPOSITION** *Every bounded integrable function belongs to $L^p$, $1 \leq p \leq \infty$.*

*Proof* This is trivial for $p = \infty$, and for $p < \infty$ we have

$$|f|^p = |f|^{p-1} \cdot |f| \leq M^{p-1} |f|$$

if $|f| \leq M$, so that $|f|^p$ is integrable (by Theorem 3.1.8).

**5.4.3 PROPOSITION** *$L^p$ is a linear space for any $p$, $1 \leq p \leq \infty$.*

*Proof* This is trivial for $p = \infty$. It is also easily verified that $af \in L^p$ for any real number $a$ if $f \in L^p$. Now suppose $f, g \in L^p$, $p < \infty$. Then the inequality

$$|f + g|^p \leq [2(|f| \vee |g|)]^p \leq 2^p(|f|^p + |g|^p)$$

shows that $f + g \in L^p$ also.

The *essential supremum* of a function $f \in L^\infty$ is

$$\text{ess sup} f = \inf \{M : |f| \leq M \text{ a.e.}\}.$$

**5.4.4 DEFINITION** *The norm $\|f\|$ of a function $f \in L^p$ is defined by*

$$\|f\| = \left\{\int |f|^p \, dx\right\}^{1/p} \qquad \text{if } 1 \leq p < \infty,$$

$$\|f\| = \text{ess sup} f \qquad \text{if } p = \infty.$$

It is clear that this norm has the homogeneity property

$$\|af\| = |a| \, \|f\|$$

for $a$ real; the norm $\|f\|$ on $L^p$ satisfies also a triangle inequality

$$\|f + g\| \leq \|f\| + \|g\|$$

as we shall prove in Proposition 5.4.7.

We may denote the norm of an element $f \in L^p$ by $\|f\|_p$ at times when confusion between norms in different $L^p$ spaces is possible, but this will not usually be the case.

For $p \neq 2$ the concept of scalar product does not have a counterpart in the theory of a single $L^p$ space. Instead, it turns out that the $L^p$ spaces are paired together with respect to what is called conjugate exponents.

**5.4.5 DEFINITION** *A pair $p$, $q$, $1 \leq p, q \leq \infty$ is called a pair of conjugate exponents if either*

$$p = 1 \text{ and } q = \infty \quad \text{or} \quad p = \infty \text{ and } q = 1$$
$$\text{or} \quad 1 < p, q < \infty \text{ and } \frac{1}{p} + \frac{1}{q} = 1.$$

When in this section $p$ and $q$ occur together in a statement without further explanation, it is always assumed that they denote a pair of conjugate exponents. Obviously, the only pair of conjugate exponents for which $p = q$ is $p = 2$, $q = 2$ and this accounts for the special character of the scalar product in the case of $L^2$. In general, we have instead the following proposition.

**5.4.6 PROPOSITION**

**HÖLDER'S INEQUALITY** *If $f \in L^p$ and $g \in L^q$, then $fg \in L^1$ and*

$$\left| \int fg \, dx \right| \leq \|f\|_p \, \|g\|_q.$$

*Proof* The proposition is trivial if either $p = \infty$ or $q = \infty$. Therefore we assume $1 < p, q < \infty$. Since

$$y = \frac{1}{p} t + 1 - \frac{1}{p}$$

is the tangent line at 1 to the concave curve

$$y = t^{1/p}$$

in the $ty$-plane, we have

$$t^{1/p} \leq \frac{1}{p} t + 1 - \frac{1}{p} = \frac{1}{p} t + \frac{1}{q}$$

for all $t \geq 0$ (see Figure 5.3). If we replace $t$ by $x/y$, $x \geq 0$ and $y > 0$, and multiply by $y$, we obtain the inequality

$$x^{1/p} y^{1/q} \leq \frac{1}{p} x + \frac{1}{q} y,$$

which is valid also for $y = 0$.

Since the statement in the proposition is trivial if either $f = 0$ or $g = 0$, we assume $\|f\|_p \neq 0 \neq \|g\|_q$. If we replace $x$ by $(\|f\|_p^{-1} |f|)^p$ and $y$ by $(\|g\|_q^{-1} |g|)^q$ in the last inequality, we find

$$\frac{1}{\|f\|_p \cdot \|g\|_q} |fg| \leq \frac{1}{p \, \|f\|_p^p} |f|^p + \frac{1}{q \, \|g\|_q^q} |g|^q$$

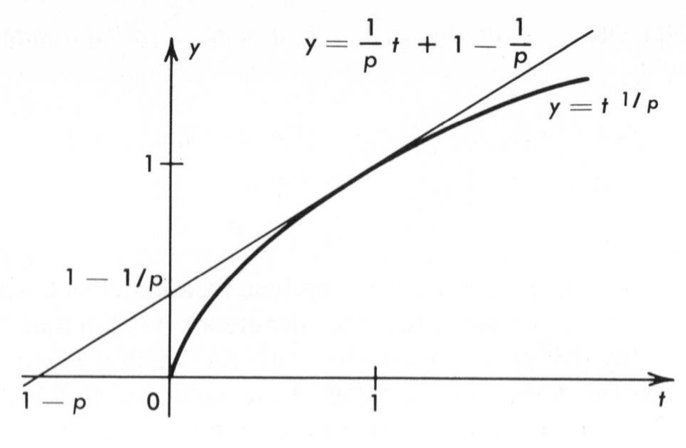


Figure 5.3

which shows in particular that $fg$ is integrable. Hölder's inequality is now obtained by integrating the last inequality:

$$\frac{1}{\|f\|_p \|g\|_q} \int |fg| \, dx \leq \frac{1}{p} + \frac{1}{q} = 1,$$

$$\left| \int fg \, dx \right| \leq \int |fg| \, dx \leq \|f\|_p \|g\|_q.$$

As in the case of the space $L^2$, Hölder's inequality can be used to prove Minkowski's inequality for $L^p$ spaces.

### 5.4.7 PROPOSITION

MINKOWSKI'S INEQUALITY *For $f, g \in L^p$,*

$$\|f + g\| \leq \|f\| + \|g\|.$$

*Proof* Again this is obvious for $p = 1$ or $p = \infty$. So we assume $1 < p < \infty$. Then

$$|f + g|^p = |f + g| \cdot |f + g|^{p-1} \leq |f| \cdot |f + g|^{p-1} + |g| \cdot |f + g|^{p-1}.$$

Since $(p - 1)q = (p - 1)(1 - 1/p)^{-1} = p$, the $q$th power of $|f + g|^{p-1}$ is integrable so that $|f + g|^{p-1}$ belongs to $L^q$. Therefore we can apply Hölder's inequality:

$$\begin{aligned}
\int |f + g|^p \, dx &\leq \int |f| \cdot |f + g|^{p-1} \, dx + \int |g| \cdot |f + g|^{p-1} \, dx \\
&\leq \left\{ \int |f|^p \, dx \right\}^{1/p} \left\{ \int |f + g|^{(p-1)q} \, dx \right\}^{1/q} \\
&\qquad + \left\{ \int |g|^p \, dx \right\}^{1/p} \left\{ \int |f + g|^{(p-1)q} \, dx \right\}^{1/q} \\
&= (\|f\| + \|g\|) \left\{ \int |f + g|^p \, dx \right\}^{1/q}.
\end{aligned}$$

If the integral on the right is nonzero, we can divide by it and obtain Minkowski's inequality. In the case $|f + g| = 0$ a.e., Minkowski's inequality is trivial.

Again we have the statement that generalizes Minkowski's inequality to infinite sums and which can be considered as one form of the Riesz-Fischer theorem.

5.4.8 PROPOSITION *If $\sum f_n$ is a series of functions in $L^p$ and $\sum_{n=1}^{\infty} \|f_n\| < \infty$, then $\sum f_n$ converges absolutely almost everywhere, and if*

$$f = \sum_{n=1}^{\infty} f_n \text{ a.e.,}$$

*then $f \in L^p$ and*

$$\|f\| \leq \sum_{n=1}^{\infty} \|f_n\| .$$

*Proof* The case $p = 1$ has already been proved (Theorem 2.2.4) and the case $p = \infty$ is trivial. Since by Minkowski's inequality

$$\int \left( \sum_{k=1}^{n} |f_k| \right)^p dx \leq \left( \sum_{k=1}^{n} \|f_k\| \right)^p \leq \left( \sum_{k=1}^{\infty} \|f_k\| \right)^p,$$

the monotone convergence theorem shows that $\sum |f_k|$ converges almost everywhere, and if we define the function $h$ by

$$h(x) = \begin{cases} \left( \sum_{k=1}^{\infty} |f_k(x)| \right)^p & \text{if the sum is finite} \\ 0 & \text{otherwise} \end{cases}$$

then $h$ is integrable. It now follows that

$$|f|^p = \lim_{n \to \infty} \left| \sum_{k=1}^{n} f_k \right|^p$$

is integrable, since $|\sum_{k=1}^{n} f_k|^p \leq h$ for all $n$, so that Lebesgue's dominated convergence theorem applies. Hence $f \in L^p$ and

$$\begin{aligned} \|f\|^p = \int |f|^p \, dx &= \lim_{n \to \infty} \int \left| \sum_{k=1}^{n} f_k \right|^p dx \\ &\leq \lim_{n \to \infty} \int \left( \sum_{k=1}^{n} |f_k| \right)^p dx \leq \left( \sum_{k=1}^{\infty} \|f_k\| \right)^p \end{aligned}$$

as claimed.

From Proposition 5.4.8 we deduce that if a sequence $\{f_n\}$ in $L^p$ satisfies

$$\lim_{n, m \to \infty} \|f_n - f_m\| = 0,$$

then there exists an element $f \in L^p$ such that

$$\lim_{n\to\infty} \|f - f_n\| = 0.$$

The proof of this completeness property is identical with the one in the $L^2$ case (Theorem 5.2.2) so that we omit it.

5.4.9 THEOREM

RIESZ FISCHER THEOREM *$L^p$ is complete (in the sense described above).*

Finally, we prove two theorems on the approximation of functions in $L^p$ by elementary functions. They are the theorems corresponding to Theorems 5.2.4 and 5.2.5 in the case $p = 2$. Since the proofs are almost identical to those in Section 5.2, we shall sketch them only.

5.4.10 THEOREM *If $f \in L^p$, $1 \leq p < \infty$, and $\varepsilon > 0$ are given, then there exists a function $\varphi \in L \cap L^p$ such that*

$$\|f - \varphi\| \leq \varepsilon.$$

*Proof* Since $f = f^+ - f^-$ and

$$f^+ = \tfrac{1}{2}(f + |f|) \in L^p, \qquad f^- = f^+ - f \in L^p,$$

we may restrict ourselves to the case in which $f$ is nonnegative. The function

$$h_n = n \wedge nf^p \wedge f$$

is integrable, since $0 \leq h_n \leq nf^p$; it is also in $L^p$ because $h_n{}^p \leq f^p$. The sequence $\{(f - h_n)^p\}$ decreases to zero, whence

$$\lim_{n\to\infty} \|f - h_n\|^p = \lim_{n\to\infty} \int (f - h_n)^p \, dx = 0$$

by the monotone convergence theorem. Now choose $n$ so large that

$$\|f - h_n\| \leq \varepsilon.$$

By Lemma 5.2.3 we can find a function $\psi \in L$ such that

$$\int |h_n - \psi| \, dx \leq \frac{\varepsilon^p}{(2n)^{p-1}}.$$

$\varphi = n \wedge \psi^+$ is a function in $L \cap L^p$ (Proposition 5.4.2). Notice that

$$|h_n - \varphi| \leq |h_n - \psi|$$

because $0 \leq h_n \leq n$. Hence

$$\|h_n - \varphi\|^p = \int |h_n - \varphi|^{p-1} |h_n - \varphi| \, dx$$
$$\leq (2n)^{p-1} \int |h_n - \varphi| \, dx \leq \varepsilon^p,$$
$$\|f - \varphi\| \leq \|f - h_n\| + \|h_n - \varphi\| \leq 2\varepsilon.$$

This completes the proof.

Note that the corresponding statement about $L^\infty$ is not true. In the case of the ordinary Lebesgue integral on the real line, the function constant equal to one is in $L^\infty$ but is certainly not approximable by step functions.

As a corollary of the last theorem we obtain a characterization of functions in $L^p$ in terms of series of functions in $L \cap L^p$. Since the proof is identical to the one of Theorem 5.2.5, we omit it here.

5.4.11 THEOREM *A function $f$ belongs to $L^p$, $1 \leq p < \infty$, if and only if there is a series $\sum \varphi_n$ of functions in $L \cap L^p$ such that*

$$f = \sum_{n=1}^{\infty} \varphi_n \text{ a.e. } \textit{and}$$
$$\sum_{n=1}^{\infty} \|\varphi_n\|_p < \infty.$$

The theory of continuous linear functionals on $L^p$ will only be touched on here. It is of course a consequence of the Hölder inequality, Proposition 5.4.6, that each element $g \in L^q$ generates a continuous linear functional $F_g$ on $L^p$, defined by

$$F_g(f) = \int fg \, dx \qquad \text{for } f \in L^p.$$

For $1 \leq p < \infty$ it is true, conversely, that every continuous linear functional on $L^p$ is generated in this way. The reason why we do not prove this result now is that we will do so in an application of a more general differentiation theory, notably the Radon-Nikodym theorem, which in turn will be derived using the $L^2$ theory—a nice interdependence. For $1 < p < \infty$ there is also a proof using "geometric" arguments related to those that worked in the case $p = 2$, which we outline in the exercise section 5.7.

## *EXERCISES*

*5.4.1* Convince yourself that

$$\|f + g\| \leq \|f\| + \|g\|$$

for $f, g \in L^\infty$.

*5.4.2* If $1 < p < \infty$ and $f \in L^p$ and $g \in L^q$, show that

$$\int fg\,dx = \|f\|_p \cdot \|g\|_q$$

if and only if $fg \geq 0$ a.e. and either $f = 0$ or $g = 0$ a.e, or else $|g|^q = k|f|^p$ for some real number $k$.

*Hint* Observe that in

$$x^{1/p}y^{1/q} \leq \frac{1}{p}x + \frac{1}{q}y$$

equality holds only for $x = y$ (see the proof of Proposition 5.4.6). In case $\|f\|_p \neq 0 \neq \|g\|_q$, conclude from this that equality can hold in

$$\int |fg|\,dx \leq \|f\|_p\,\|g\|_q$$

if and only if $(\|f\|_p^{-1}|f|)^p = (\|g\|_q^{-1}|g|)^q$ a.e.

*5.4.3* If $1 < p < \infty$ and $f, g \in L^p$, show that

$$\|f + g\| = \|f\| + \|g\|$$

if and only if $\|f\|g = \|g\|f$ a.e.

*Hint* Investigate the proof of Proposition 5.4.7 and use the previous exercise.

*5.4.4* Let $p$ and $q$ be any two real numbers, $0 < p < 1$ and $-\infty < q < 0$, such that $1/p + 1/q = 1$. Let $f$ and $g$ be positive measurable functions such that $f^p$ and $g^q$ are integrable. Furthermore, assume that $fg$ is integrable. Prove

$$\left\{\int f^p\,dx\right\}^{1/p} \cdot \left\{\int g^q\,dx\right\}^{1/q} \leq \int fg\,dx.$$

*Hint* Show that if $r = 1/p$ and $s = -q/p$, then $r, s$ is a pair of conjugate exponents and $(fg)^p \in L^r$, $g^{-p} \in L^s$. Now apply Hölder's inequality.

*5.4.5* Suppose $1 < p < \infty$. The norm of a bounded linear functional $F$ on $L^p$ is defined by

$$\|F\| = \sup\,\{|F(f)| \cdot \|f\|_p^{-1} : f \in L^p,\ \|f\| \neq 0\}.$$

$\|F\|$ is the smallest number such that

$$|F(f)| \leq \|F\| \cdot \|f\|_p \qquad \text{for } f \in L^p.$$

Show that the norm of the functional $F_g$,

$$F_g(f) = \int fg\,dx,$$

generated by a function $g \in L^q$ is $\|g\|_q$.

*Hint* Choose the function $f$ defined by

$$f(x) = \begin{cases} |g(x)|^{q/p} & \text{if } g(x) \geq 0 \\ -|g(x)|^{q/p} & \text{if } g(x) < 0 \end{cases}$$

in Hölder's inequality

$$\left| \int fg \, dx \right| \leq \left\{ \int |f|^p \, dx \right\}^{1/p} \left\{ \int |g|^q \, dx \right\}^{1/q}$$

and show that equality holds for this choice of $f$.

## 5.5 INTEGRATION OF COMPLEX-VALUED FUNCTIONS

We will now develop some integration theory for complex-valued functions on the real line. Indeed, what we say in this section will be valid for an arbitrary Daniell integral but we will apply it in Section 5.6 only to the ordinary integration theory on the real line.

We assume that the reader is familiar with the elementary properties of the complex number system, as presented in any book on the subject. We therefore skip such preliminaries here.

Every complex-valued function $f$ can be decomposed into its real part $\operatorname{Re} f$ and imaginary part $\operatorname{Im} f$,

$$f = \operatorname{Re} f + i \operatorname{Im} f.$$

Both $\operatorname{Re} f$ and $\operatorname{Im} f$ are real-valued functions. Thus the following definition offers itself as natural.

**5.5.1 DEFINITION** *A complex-valued function $f$ on the real line is said to be measurable if both $\operatorname{Re} f$ and $\operatorname{Im} f$ are measurable. The function $f$ is defined to be integrable if $\operatorname{Re} f$ and $\operatorname{Im} f$ are integrable; then we let*

$$\int f \, dx = \int \operatorname{Re} f \, dx + i \int \operatorname{Im} f \, dx.$$

It is easily verified that for any complex numbers $a$, $b$ and for any complex-valued integrable functions $f$, $g$, the function $af + bg$ is again integrable and

$$\int (af + bg) \, dx = a \int f \, dx + b \int g \, dx.$$

The following proposition permits us to prove for complex-valued integrable functions all those theorems of previous chapters that make sense for them. We have just to decompose the relevant functions into their real and imaginary parts and apply the known theorems about real-valued functions (see Exercises 5.5.1 and 5.5.2).

5.5.2 PROPOSITION *A measurable complex-valued function $f$ is integrable if and only if $|f|$ is integrable, and then*

$$\left|\int f\,dx\right| \leq \int |f|\,dx.$$

*Proof* If $f$ is measurable, then

$$|f| = \{(\operatorname{Re} f)^2 + (\operatorname{Im} g)^2\}^{1/2}$$

is measurable, and since

$$|\operatorname{Re} f|, |\operatorname{Im} f| \leq |f| \leq |\operatorname{Re} f| + |\operatorname{Im} f|,$$

$\operatorname{Re} f$ and $\operatorname{Im} f$ are integrable if and only if $|f|$ is.

To prove the inequality in Proposition 5.5.2 we assume first that $f$ attains only a finite number of nonzero values, say $c_1, \cdots, c_n$. Let $\chi_k$ be the characteristic function of the integrable set

$$\{x:f(x) = c_k\} = \{x:\operatorname{Re} f(x) = \operatorname{Re} c_k\} \cap \{x:\operatorname{Im} f(x) = \operatorname{Im} c_k\}.$$

Then

$$|f| = \sum_{k=1}^{n} |c_k|\,\chi_k$$

and hence

$$\left|\int f\,dx\right| = \left|\sum_{k=1}^{n} c_k \int \chi_k\,dx\right|$$

$$\leq \sum_{k=1}^{n} |c_k| \int \chi_k\,dx = \int |f|\,dx.$$

If $f$ is any complex-valued integrable function, we can find a sequence $\{\varphi_n\}$ of complex-valued integrable functions each of which attains only a finite number of values with the following properties:

$$f = \lim_{n\to\infty} \varphi_n \text{ a.e.,} \qquad \lim_{n,m\to\infty} \int |\varphi_n - \varphi_m|\,dx = 0,$$

$$\int f\,dx = \lim_{n\to\infty} \int \varphi_n\,dx.$$

Namely, by Proposition 2.2.8, there are sequences $\{\xi_n\}$ and $\{\eta_n\}$ of (real-valued) step functions such that

$$\operatorname{Re} f = \lim_{n\to\infty} \xi_n \text{ a.e.,} \qquad \operatorname{Im} f = \lim_{n\to\infty} \eta_n \text{ a.e.,}$$

$$\lim_{n,m\to\infty} \int |\xi_n - \xi_m|\,dx = 0 = \lim_{n,m\to\infty} \int |\eta_n - \eta_m|\,dx.$$

Now let $\varphi_n = \xi_n + i\eta_n$. We will call such functions whose real and imaginary parts are step functions, complex-valued step functions. Clearly $\lim_{n\to\infty} \varphi_n = f$ a.e., and

$$\int |\varphi_n - \varphi_m|\,dx \leq \int |\xi_n - \xi_m|\,dx + \int |\eta_n - \eta_m|\,dx$$

shows that $\{\int |\varphi_n - \varphi_m|\, dx\}$ tends to zero as $n$ and $m$ tend to infinity. Furthermore,

$$\int f\, dx = \int \operatorname{Re} f\, dx + i \int \operatorname{Im} f\, dx = \lim_{n\to\infty} \left[ \int \xi_n\, dx + i \int \eta_n\, dx \right].$$

In the case of an abstract Daniell integral we would have to take for $\xi_n$ and $\eta_n$ generalized step functions (see Proposition 3.2.7). Since

$$\int \big|\, |\varphi_n| - |\varphi_m| \,\big|\, dx \le \int |\varphi_n - \varphi_m|\, dx,$$

we have

$$|f| = \lim_{n\to\infty} |\varphi|\ \text{a.e.} \qquad \text{and} \qquad \lim_{n,m\to\infty} \int \big|\, |\varphi_n| - |\varphi_m| \,\big|\, dx = 0.$$

Thus again by Proposition 2.1.8,

$$\begin{aligned} \left| \int f\, dx \right| &= \lim_{n\to\infty} \left| \int \varphi_n\, dx \right| \\ &\le \lim_{n\to\infty} \int |\varphi_n|\, dx = \int |f|\, dx. \end{aligned}$$

Since we are dealing in this and the following section only with complex-valued functions, we shall leave out the qualifying term "complex-valued" in many cases from now on.

Let us discuss in somewhat more detail the generalization to complex-valued functions of the theorems in Sections 5.1 to 5.3, since these are relevant for the next section.

5.5.3 **DEFINITION** *The set of complex-valued measurable functions $f$ such that $|f|^2$ is integrable is denoted by $L_c^2$. The norm $\|f\|_c$ of $f \in L_c^2$ is defined by*

$$\|f\|_c = \left\{ \int |f|^2\, dx \right\}^{1/2}$$

*and the inner product (or scalar product) $(f, g)_c$ of functions $f, g \in L_c^2$ by*

$$(f, g)_c = \int f\bar{g}\, dx.$$

In this definition $\bar{g}$ is the complex conjugate of the function $g$,

$$\bar{g} = \operatorname{Re} g - i \operatorname{Im} g.$$

Since

$$|f|^2 = |\operatorname{Re} f|^2 + |\operatorname{Im} f|^2,$$

a measurable function $f$ belongs to $L_c^2$ if and only if $\operatorname{Re} f$ and $\operatorname{Im} f$ belong to $L^2$. From this remark it is immediate that $\bar{f}$ belongs to $L_c^2$ if $f$ does, and that $f\bar{g}$ is integrable if $f, \bar{g} \in L_c^2$. Thus the scalar product $(f, g)_c$ is indeed well defined. We will write $\|f\|$ instead of $\|f\|_c$ and $(f, g)$ instead of $(f, g)_c$ when no confusion can arise.

Because of the asymmetry introduced by the conjugation in the definition of $(f, g)_c$, the scalar product $(f, g)_c$ is also called *sesquilinear* (meaning "one-and-a half linear"). Here are the linearity rules it obeys:

$$(g, f) = \overline{(f, g)},$$

$$(a_1 f_1 + a_2 f_2, g) = a_1(f_1, g) + a_2(f_2, g), \tag{5.5.4}$$

$$(f, b_1 g_1 + b_2 g_2) = \bar{b}_1(f, g_1) + \bar{b}_2(f, g_2).$$

Here $a_1$, $a_2$, $b_1$, $b_2$ are complex numbers. We have also the following relations connecting the norm and the scalar product in $L_c^2$:

$$\|f\|_c = [(f, f)_c]^{1/2}, \tag{5.5.5}$$

$$(f, g)_c = \tfrac{1}{4}(\|f + g\|_c^2 + i\,\|f + ig\|_c^2 - \|f - g\|_c^2 - i\,\|f - ig\|_c^2).$$

The Schwarz inequality for $L_c^2$ follows easily from Schwarz's inequality for real functions. Namely, if $f, g \in L_c^2$, then

$$|(f, g)_c| = \left|\int f\bar{g}\,dx\right| \le \int |f|\,|\bar{g}|\,dx$$

$$= (|f|, |g|) \le \|\,|f|\,\|\,\|\,|g|\,\| = \|f\|_c\,\|g\|_c.$$

Similarly we prove Minkowski's inequality:

$$\|f + g\|_c = \left\{\int |f + g|^2\,dx\right\}^{1/2}$$

$$\le \left\{\int (|f| + |g|)^2\,dx\right\}^{1/2} = \|\,|f| + |g|\,\|$$

$$\le \|\,|f|\,\| + \|\,|g|\,\| = \|f\|_c + \|g\|_c.$$

The infinite sum version of Minkowski's inequality (Proposition 5.2.1) follows now as before; or we can deduce it also from Proposition 5.2.1.

**5.5.6 PROPOSITION** *Suppose $\{f_n\}$ is a sequence of functions in $L_c^2$ such that $\sum \|f_n\|_c$ converges. Then $\sum f_n$ converges almost everywhere to a function $f$ in $L_c^2$ and*

$$\|f\| = \lim_{n\to\infty}\left\|\sum_{k=1}^{n} f_k\right\| \le \sum_{n=1}^{\infty}\|f_n\|.$$

*Proof* Since $\sum \|f_n\|_c = \sum \|\,|f_n|\,\|$ converges, it follows from Proposition 5.2.1 that $\sum |f_n|$ converges almost everywhere to a function $h$ in $L^2$ and

$$\|h\| \le \sum_{n=1}^{\infty}\|\,|f_n|\,\| = \sum_{n=1}^{\infty}\|f_n\|_c.$$

Furthermore,

$$\|\mathrm{Re}\,f_n\| \le \|f_n\|_c, \quad \|\mathrm{Im}\,f_n\| \le \|f_n\|_c$$

so that, again by Proposition 5.2.1, $\sum \mathrm{Re}\,f_n$ and $\sum \mathrm{Im}\,f_n$ converge almost everywhere, respectively, to functions $g_1$ and $g_2$ in $L^2$. Let $f = g_1 + ig_2$. Then $\sum f_n$

converges almost everywhere to $f$, and since $|\sum_{k=1}^{n} f_k|^2 \leq h^2$ a.e., we get by Lebesgue's dominated convergence theorem

$$\|f\|_c^2 = \| \, |f| \, \|^2 = \lim_{n\to\infty} \left\| \left| \sum_{k=1}^{n} f_k \right| \right\|^2 \leq \|h\|^2$$

as desired.

Also, the Riesz-Fischer theorem (Theorem 5.2.2) is valid for $L_c^2$; one can either prove it as before using Proposition 5.5.6 instead of Proposition 5.2.1, or one could deduce it from Theorem 5.2.2 with the observation that $\{f_n\}$ is a Cauchy sequence in $L_c^2$ if and only if $\{\mathrm{Re}\, f_n\}$ and $\{\mathrm{Im}\, f_n\}$ are Cauchy sequences in $L^2$.

5.5.7 THEOREM *If $f \in L_c^2$ and $\varepsilon > 0$ are given, then there is a (complex-valued) step function $\varphi$ such that $\|f - \varphi\|_c \leq \varepsilon$.*

*Proof* By Theorem 5.2.4, there exist (real-valued) step functions $\varphi_1$ and $\varphi_2$, satisfying

$$\|\mathrm{Re}\, f - \varphi_1\| \leq \frac{\varepsilon}{\sqrt{2}}, \qquad \|\mathrm{Im}\, f - \varphi_2\| \leq \frac{\varepsilon}{\sqrt{2}}.$$

Let $\varphi = \varphi_1 + i\varphi_2$, then

$$\|f - \varphi\|_c^2 = \|\mathrm{Re}\, f - \varphi_1\|^2 + \|\mathrm{Im}\, f - \varphi_2\|^2 \leq \varepsilon^2.$$

As a corollary to this theorem and Proposition 5.5.6 we obtain as in Theorem 5.2.5:

5.5.8 THEOREM *A function $f$ belongs to $L_c^2$ if and only if there is a series $\sum \varphi_n$ of step functions converging to $f$ a.e. and satisfying*

$$\sum_{n=1}^{\infty} \|\varphi_n\| < \infty.$$

We will also say a few words about complex continuous linear functionals on $L_c^2$. By this we mean what we get from Definition 5.3.1 if we permit $F(g)$, $a$, and $b$ to be complex numbers. The complex linear functionals are determined by their values on the set of all real functions in $L_c^2$:

$$F(f) = F(\mathrm{Re}\, f + i\, \mathrm{Im}\, f) = F(\mathrm{Re}\, f) + iF(\mathrm{Im}\, f).$$

The set of all real-valued functions in $L_c^2$ is, of course, the same as $L^2$. Hence each complex linear functional $F$ on $L_c^2$ induces two real linear functionals $H$, $K$ on $L^2$, as follows:

$$\left.\begin{aligned} H(f) &= \operatorname{Re} F(f) \\ K(f) &= \operatorname{Im} F(f) \end{aligned}\right\} \quad f \in L^2 \ (f \text{ is real valued in } L_c^2).$$

We leave to the exercises the use of this reasoning for the extension of Theorem 5.3.6 to complex linear functionals on $L_c^2$.

## *EXERCISES*

*5.5.1* Show that a complex-valued function $f$ is integrable if and only if there is a series $\sum \varphi_n$ of (complex-valued) step functions which converges to $f$ a.e. and satisfies

$$\sum_{n=1}^{\infty} \int |\varphi_n| \, dx < \infty$$

and then

$$\int f \, dx = \sum_{n=1}^{\infty} \int \varphi_n \, dx.$$

*5.5.2* Prove Beppo Levi's theorem and Lebesgue's dominated convergence theorem for complex-valued functions.

*5.5.3* Prove the Schwarz inequality for $L_c^2$ in two different ways using (a) the hint for Exercise 5.1.2 and (b) the hint for Exercise 5.1.3.

*5.5.4* Show that if $F$ is a complex linear functional on $L_c^2$, then there exists an element $g$ in $L_c^2$ such that

$$F(f) = (f, g) = \int f\bar{g} \, dx \qquad \text{for all } f \in L_c^2.$$

*5.5.5* Show that if $F$ and $g$ are as in the previous exercise, then $g$ is the unique element of smallest norm in the set

$$H = \{f : F(f) = \|F\|^2\} \subset L_c^2.$$

# 5.6 THE FOURIER TRANSFORMATION

Recall that if $\xi$ is a real number, the function $e^{-i\xi x}$ of the real variable $x$ is defined by

$$e^{-i\xi x} = \cos \xi x - i \sin \xi x.$$

Thus $|e^{-i\xi x}| = 1$ for all $\xi$ and $x$. The function $e^{-i\xi x}$ shares many formal properties with the exponential function of a real argument, and the following elementary calculations may be done either using these properties or with the help of the above defining relation. Let $\chi$ be the characteristic function of an interval with end points

$a \le b$ and define the two transformations $\chi \to \mathscr{F}\chi$ and $\chi \to \mathscr{F}^*\chi$ by

(5.6.1)

$$\mathscr{F}\chi(\xi) = \frac{1}{C}\int \chi(x)e^{-i\xi x}\,dx = \frac{1}{C}\int_a^b e^{-i\xi x}\,dx = \frac{e^{-ib\xi} - e^{-ia\xi}}{-i\xi C} \quad \text{if } \xi \ne 0,$$

$$\mathscr{F}^*\chi(x) = \frac{1}{C}\int \chi(\xi)e^{i\xi x}\,d\xi = \frac{1}{C}\int_a^b e^{i\xi x}\,d\xi = \frac{e^{ibx} - e^{iax}}{ixC} \quad \text{if } x \ne 0,$$

where

$$C = \left\{2\int_{-\infty}^{\infty} \frac{\sin^2 x}{x^2}\,dx\right\}^{1/2}.$$

Notice that $(\sin^2 x)/x^2$ is nonnegative and improper Riemann integrable, and hence Lebesgue integrable by Proposition 2.4.3 (see Exercise 5.6.1). Later on we shall prove that $C = \sqrt{2\pi}$. We have here used the letter $\xi$ to denote a real variable, violating our convention that Greek letters denote elementary functions; however, we keep this convention for all other Greek letters.

5.6.2 DEFINITION *The transformation that takes $\chi$ into $\mathscr{F}\chi$ is called the Fourier transformation (sometimes the Fourier integral) and the transformation $\chi \to \mathscr{F}^*\chi$ is called the conjugate Fourier transformation. The function $\mathscr{F}\chi$ is called the Fourier transform of $\chi$.*

5.6.3 LEMMA *The functions $\mathscr{F}\chi$ and $\mathscr{F}^*\chi$ are in $L_c^2$ and*

(5.6.4)
$$\|\chi\| = \|\mathscr{F}\chi\| = \|\mathscr{F}^*\chi\| = (b - a)^{1/2}.$$

*Proof* Let us show for instance that $\|\chi\| = \|\mathscr{F}\chi\|$. We have

$$|\mathscr{F}\chi(\xi)|^2 = \left|\frac{e^{-ib\xi} - e^{-ia\xi}}{i\xi C}\right|^2 = \frac{2 - 2\cos\xi(b-a)}{\xi^2 C^2} = 4\,\frac{\sin^2 \tfrac{1}{2}\xi(b-a)}{\xi^2 C^2},$$

where we have made use of the relation

$$\sin^2\alpha = \tfrac{1}{2}(1 - \cos 2\alpha).$$

Thus $|\mathscr{F}\chi|^2$ is integrable and

$$\int |\mathscr{F}\chi|^2\,dx = (b - a).$$

We say that (5.6.4) expresses the fact that $\mathscr{F}$ and $\mathscr{F}^*$ are isometries of the set of characteristic functions of bounded intervals into $L_c^2$, and we will now start to extend these isometries into isometries of all of $L_c^2$ into $L_c^2$, which we will then denote by the same symbols and names. Along with (5.6.4) we will also extend the relation

$$(\mathscr{F}\chi, \omega) = (\chi, \mathscr{F}^*\omega) \tag{5.6.5}$$

valid when $\chi$ and $\omega$ are characteristic functions of intervals with real end points $a \leq b$ and $c \leq d$, respectively, since

$$\begin{aligned}(\mathscr{F}\chi, \omega) &= \int_c^d \left\{\frac{1}{C}\int_a^b e^{-i\xi x}\,dx\right\}\bar{1}\,d\xi \\ &= \int_a^b 1\overline{\left\{\frac{1}{C}\int_c^d e^{i\xi x}\,d\xi\right\}}\,dx = (\chi, \mathscr{F}^*\omega).\end{aligned}$$

Note that the values of the transformed functions as well as the relations (5.6.4) and (5.6.5) are independent of which end points, if any, are included in the intervals, so that our impreciseness in this respect is permissible.

The first step in carrying out this extension is to observe that if $\chi_1$ and $\chi_2$ are characteristic functions of intervals with end points $a$, $b$ and $b$, $c$, respectively, $a \leq b \leq c$, then

$$\|\mathscr{F}\chi_1 + \mathscr{F}\chi_2\|^2 = \|\mathscr{F}\chi_1\|^2 + \|\mathscr{F}\chi_2\|^2 \;(= c - a). \tag{5.6.6}$$

Since

$$\begin{aligned}\|\mathscr{F}\chi_1 + \mathscr{F}\chi_2\|^2 &= (\mathscr{F}\chi_1 + \mathscr{F}\chi_2, \mathscr{F}\chi_1 + \mathscr{F}\chi_2) \\ &= \|\mathscr{F}\chi_1\|^2 + 2\,\mathrm{Re}\,(\mathscr{F}\chi_1, \mathscr{F}\chi_2) + \|\mathscr{F}\chi_2\|^2\end{aligned}$$

we see that the relation (5.6.6) is equivalent with

$$\mathrm{Re}\,(\mathscr{F}\chi_1, \mathscr{F}\chi_2) = 0.$$

**5.6.7 DEFINITION** *Two functions $f$ and $g$ in $L_c^2$ are called orthogonal if*

$$\mathrm{Re}\,(f, g) = 0.$$

Thus, the Fourier transforms of the characteristic functions of two contiguous intervals, like $\mathscr{F}\chi_1$ and $\mathscr{F}\chi_2$ above, are orthogonal, and the same is of course true for the conjugate Fourier transforms. But it is easy to see that we have orthogonality also in the case when the closures of the intervals are disjoint. Namely, suppose that we have $a \leq b < c \leq d$ and let $\chi_1$, $\chi_2$, and $\chi_3$ be the characteristic functions of intervals with end points $a$, $b$; $b$, $c$ and $c$, $d$, respectively; then

$$\begin{aligned}\mathrm{Re}\,(\mathscr{F}\chi_1 + \mathscr{F}\chi_2, \mathscr{F}\chi_3) &= 0, \\ \mathrm{Re}\,(\mathscr{F}\chi_2, \mathscr{F}\chi_3) &= 0,\end{aligned}$$

so that, by subtracting the second equation from the first,

$$\mathrm{Re}\,(\mathscr{F}\chi_1, \mathscr{F}\chi_3) = 0,$$

proving our assertion. Similarly $\mathscr{F}^*\chi_1$ and $\mathscr{F}^*\chi_3$ are found to be orthogonal. The transformed functions $\mathscr{F}\chi$ and $\mathscr{F}^*\chi$, where $\chi$ is the characteristic function of an arbitrary bounded interval, have a special kind of symmetry called Hermitian symmetry; namely, they satisfy

$$f(-x) = \overline{f(x)}.$$

The scalar product of any two Hermitian symmetric functions is always a real number:

$$\overline{(f, g)} = \int \overline{f(x)}\, g(x)\, dx = \int f(-x)\overline{g(-x)}\, dx = (f, g).$$

Consequently,

$$(\mathscr{F}\chi, \mathscr{F}\omega) = (\mathscr{F}^*\chi, \mathscr{F}^*\omega) = 0 \tag{5.6.8}$$

whenever $\chi$ and $\omega$ are characteristic functions of disjoint bounded intervals.

For any complex-valued step function $\varphi$, we define the transforms $\mathscr{F}\varphi$ and $\mathscr{F}^*\varphi$ by

$$\begin{aligned} \mathscr{F}\varphi(\xi) &= \frac{1}{C}\int \varphi(x)e^{-i\xi x}\, dx, \\ \mathscr{F}^*\varphi(x) &= \frac{1}{C}\int \varphi(\xi)e^{i\xi x}\, d\xi. \end{aligned} \tag{5.6.9}$$

By Lemma 1.1.3 we can write

$$\varphi = \sum_{k=1}^{n} C_k\chi_k$$

where $\chi_k$, $k = 1, 2, \cdots, n$ are characteristic functions of mutually disjoint, bounded intervals. Hence

$$\begin{aligned} \|\mathscr{F}\varphi\|^2 &= \sum_{k,h=1}^{n} C_k\bar{C}_h(\mathscr{F}\chi_k, \mathscr{F}\chi_h) \\ &= \sum_{k=1}^{n} |C_k|^2\, \|\chi_k\|^2 = \int |\varphi|^2\, dx = \|\varphi\|^2 \end{aligned}$$

so that, together with the same computations carried out for $\mathscr{F}^*\varphi$, one has

$$\|\varphi\| = \|\mathscr{F}\varphi\| = \|\mathscr{F}^*\varphi\|. \tag{5.6.10}$$

Thus $\mathscr{F}$ and $\mathscr{F}^*$ defined by (5.6.9) are isometries. Also, relation (5.6.5) generalizes easily to step functions due to the linearity properties of the scalar product:

$$(\mathscr{F}\varphi, \psi) = (\varphi, \mathscr{F}^*\psi). \tag{5.6.11}$$

Now suppose that $f$ is an arbitrary function in $L_c^2$. By Theorem 5.5.8, there is a series $\sum\varphi_n$ of step functions such that

$$= \sum_{n=1}^{\infty} \varphi_n \text{ a.e.} \qquad \text{and} \qquad \sum_{n=1}^{\infty} \|\varphi_n\| < \infty.$$

Hence, by Proposition 5.5.6, the series $\sum_{n=1}^{\infty} \mathscr{F}\varphi_n$ converges a.e. to a function in $L_c^2$. Moreover, if also

$$f = \sum_{n=1}^{\infty} \psi_n \text{ a.e.} \qquad \text{and} \qquad \sum_{n=1}^{\infty} \|\psi_n\| < \infty$$

then

$$\sum_{n=1}^{\infty} (\varphi_n - \psi_n) = 0 \text{ a.e.} \qquad \text{and} \qquad \sum_{n=1}^{\infty} \|\varphi_n - \psi_n\| < \infty.$$

Thus again by Proposition 5.5.6,

$$\|g\| = \lim_{n\to\infty} \left\| \sum_{k=1}^{n} \mathscr{F}(\varphi_k - \psi_k) \right\| = \lim_{n\to\infty} \left\| \sum_{k=1}^{n} (\varphi_k - \psi_k) \right\| = 0,$$

where

$$g = \sum_{k=1}^{\infty} \mathscr{F}\varphi_k - \sum_{k=1}^{\infty} \mathscr{F}\psi_k \text{ a.e.}$$

Thus

$$\sum_{k=1}^{\infty} \mathscr{F}\varphi_k = \sum_{k=1}^{\infty} \mathscr{F}\psi_k \text{ a.e.}$$

The following is therefore a good definition.

5.6.12 DEFINITION *If $f$ is in $L_c^2$ and $\sum \varphi_n$ is a series of step functions satisfying*

$$f = \sum_{n=1}^{\infty} \varphi_n \text{ a.e.} \qquad \text{and} \qquad \sum_{n=1}^{\infty} \|\varphi_n\| < \infty,$$

*then the transformations $\mathscr{F}f$ and $\mathscr{F}^*f$ are any functions satisfying*

$$\mathscr{F}f = \sum_{n=1}^{\infty} \mathscr{F}\varphi_n \text{ a.e.,} \qquad \mathscr{F}^*f = \sum_{n=1}^{\infty} \mathscr{F}^*\varphi_n \text{ a.e.}$$

*The functions $\mathscr{F}f$ and $\mathscr{F}^*f$ are uniquely determined by $f$ up to the addition of a null function.*

Note that it is impossible to define $\mathscr{F}f$ and $\mathscr{F}^*f$ directly as in Equations (5.6.9), since the attempted integrations may be impossible to carry out, at least within the framework of the Lebesgue theory. As example take the functions in Exercise 5.6.2. However, in this case the integrals do exist as improper Riemann integrals.

Thanks to Proposition 5.5.6, Equations (5.6.10) and (5.6.11) extend almost effortlessly:

$$\begin{aligned} \|f\| &= \|\mathscr{F}f\| = \|\mathscr{F}^*f\| \\ (\mathscr{F}f, g) &= (f, \mathscr{F}^*g) \end{aligned} \qquad \text{(Parseval's relation)} \tag{5.6.13}$$

To see this for the latter relation, take series $\sum\varphi_n$, $\sum\psi_n$ of step functions satisfying

$$f = \sum_{n=1}^{\infty} \varphi_n, \qquad g = \sum_{n=1}^{\infty} \psi_n \qquad \text{a.e.,}$$

$$\sum_{n=1}^{\infty} \|\varphi_n\|, \sum_{n=1}^{\infty} \|\psi_n\| < \infty$$

and compute, using Proposition 5.5.6 and (5.5.5),

$$(\mathscr{F} f, g) = \tfrac{1}{4}(\|\mathscr{F} f + g\|^2 + i\,\|\mathscr{F} f + ig\|^2 - \|\mathscr{F} f - g\|^2 - i\,\|\mathscr{F} f - ig\|^2)$$

$$= \tfrac{1}{4}\left(\lim_{n\to\infty} \left\|\mathscr{F} \sum_{k=1}^{n} \varphi_k + \sum_{k=1}^{n} \psi_k\right\|^2 + \cdots\right)$$

$$= \lim_{n\to\infty} \left(\mathscr{F} \sum_{k=1}^{n} \varphi_k, \sum_{k=1}^{n} \psi_k\right)$$

$$= \lim_{n\to\infty} \left(\sum_{k=1}^{n} \varphi_k, \mathscr{F}^* \sum_{k=1}^{n} \psi_k\right) = (f, \mathscr{F}^* g).$$

The relations (5.6.13) that we have now proved have an extremely important consequence:

### 5.6.14 THEOREM

FOURIER-PLANCHEREL THEOREM *The transformations $\mathscr{F}$ and $\mathscr{F}^*$ defined on $L_c^2$ are inverses of one another, that is,*

$$\mathscr{F}^*\mathscr{F} f = \mathscr{F}\mathscr{F}^* f = f \text{ a.e. for all } f \in L_c^2.$$

*Proof* Using (5.6.13) and (5.5.5) we have, for all $f, g$ in $L_c^2$

$$\begin{aligned}(f, g) &= \tfrac{1}{4}(\|f + g\|^2 + i\,\|f + ig\|^2 - \|f - g\|^2 - i\,\|f - ig\|^2)\\ &= \tfrac{1}{4}(\|\mathscr{F} f + \mathscr{F} g\|^2 + i\,\|\mathscr{F} f + i\mathscr{F} g\|^2 - \|\mathscr{F} f - \mathscr{F} g\|^2 - i\,\|\mathscr{F} f - i\mathscr{F} g\|^2)\\ &= (\mathscr{F} f, \mathscr{F} g) = (\mathscr{F}^*\mathscr{F} f, g).\end{aligned}$$

In particular, we may put $g = \mathscr{F}^*\mathscr{F} f - f$:

$$(\mathscr{F}^*\mathscr{F} f - f, g) = 0 = \|\mathscr{F}^*\mathscr{F} f - f\|^2.$$

Hence $\mathscr{F}^*\mathscr{F} f = f$ a.e. Similarly, we find that $\mathscr{F}\mathscr{F}^* f = f$ a.e.

Note that we have arrived at the fundamental inversion theorem above with the barest minimum of concrete computations; in fact, the only thing of that sort that we have done so far was to compute the norm in $L_c^2$ of the transform of a characteristic function of a bounded interval. However, we are not quite through with the computations, since we must at some time determine the value of the constant $C$

in the definition. But when we see in the exercises the various, quite nontrivial formulas that flow out of Theorem 5.6.14, we must say that it is a good testimony of the effectiveness of the abstract functional analysis used in its derivation.

In principle, the Fourier transform of a function in $L_c^2$ could be computed using Definition 5.6.12. In many practical cases, however, the function satisfies additional restrictions so that the transformations can be written more "concretely." A reasonable condition of this kind is that the function $f$ in $L_c^2$ should also be integrable. In the following proposition we anticipate the promised proof of $C = \sqrt{2\pi}$.

5.6.15 PROPOSITION *If $f$ is integrable and in $L_c^2$, then $\mathscr{F}f$ and $\mathscr{F}^*f$ are given by*

$$\mathscr{F}f(\xi) = \frac{1}{\sqrt{2\pi}} \int f(x)e^{-ix\xi}\,dx$$

$$\mathscr{F}^*f(x) = \frac{1}{\sqrt{2\pi}} \int f(\xi)e^{i\xi x}\,d\xi.$$

*Proof* $f(x)e^{-ix\xi}$ is integrable because $|f(x)e^{-ix\xi}| = |f(x)|$. Thus

$$g(\xi) = \frac{1}{C} \int f(x)e^{-i\xi x}\,dx$$

exists for all values of $\xi$. However, one has to show that $g$ is the transform $\mathscr{F}f$, as defined by Definition 5.6.12. This is easy if $f$ vanishes outside a bounded interval whose characteristic function is $\chi$, because then $f = f\chi$ so that, if $\sum \varphi_n$ satisfies the conditions of Definition 5.6.12, then

$$f = \sum \chi\varphi_n \text{ a.e.,} \qquad \sum_{n=1}^{\infty} \int |\chi\varphi_n|\,dx \le \|\chi\| \sum_{n=1}^{\infty} \|\varphi_n\| < \infty.$$

Hence by the Beppo Levi theorem

$$\frac{1}{C} \int f(x)e^{-i\xi x}\,dx = \sum_{n=1}^{\infty} \frac{1}{C} \int \chi\varphi_n e^{-i\xi x}\,dx = \mathscr{F}f(\xi)$$

for a.a. values of $\xi$. Now let $\{a_n\}$ be an increasing sequence of positive numbers such that

$$\int_{-a_n}^{a_n} |f|^2\,dx \ge \int |f|^2\,dx - 2^{-2n}.$$

In other words, if $f_n$ is the function that equals $f$ in the interval $(-a_n, a_n)$ and zero outside, then

$$\|f - f_n\| \le 2^{-n}$$

and consequently

$$\|f_{n+1} - f_n\| \le \|f_n - f\| + \|f - f_{n+1}\| \le 2^{-n+1}.$$

Using the isometry property we have that

$$\|\mathscr{F} f_1\| + \sum_{n=1}^{\infty} \|\mathscr{F} f_{n+1} - \mathscr{F} f_n\| \leq \|f_1\| + 2 < \infty.$$

Hence by Theorem 5.5.6,

$$\mathscr{F} f(\xi) = \mathscr{F} f_1(\xi) + \sum_{n=1}^{\infty} (\mathscr{F} f_{n+1}(\xi) - \mathscr{F} f_n(\xi))$$

$$= \lim_{n\to\infty} \frac{1}{C} \int_{-a_n}^{a_n} f(x) e^{-i\xi x}\, dx = \frac{1}{C} \int f(x) e^{-i\xi x}\, dx$$

for almost all $\xi$, as asserted. The same computations can be made using $\mathscr{F}^*$ instead of $\mathscr{F}$.

If $f$ belongs to $L_c^2$, then

$$\lim_{a\to\infty} \|\mathscr{F} f - \mathscr{F}(f\chi_{(-a,a)})\| = \lim_{a\to\infty} \|f - f\chi_{(-a,a)}\| = 0.$$

and similarly for the conjugate transform $\mathscr{F}^*$. Since $f\chi_{(-a,a)}$ is integrable, we get:

**5.6.16 PROPOSITION** *If $f$ is in $L_c^2$, then $\mathscr{F} f$ and $\mathscr{F}^* f$ are the strong limits in $L_c^2$ (as a tends to infinity) of the functions $\mathscr{F}_a f$ and $\mathscr{F}^*_a f$ defined by*

$$\mathscr{F}_a f(\xi) = \frac{1}{\sqrt{2\pi}} \int_{-a}^{a} f(x) e^{-i\xi x}\, dx, \qquad \mathscr{F}^*_a f(x) = \frac{1}{\sqrt{2\pi}} \int_{-a}^{a} f(\xi) e^{i\xi x}\, d\xi.$$

Without making it formal, we will think of Proposition 5.6.15 as defining the transformations $\mathscr{F}$ and $\mathscr{F}^*$ on all integrable functions. For the transforms of integrable functions we have the following important statement, sometimes called the *Riemann-Lebesgue lemma*.

**5.6.17 THEOREM**

**RIEMANN LEBESGUE LEMMA** *If $f$ is an integrable function, then $\mathscr{F} f$ and $\mathscr{F}^* f$ are continuous functions tending to zero at infinity.*

*Proof* Let $\varepsilon > 0$ be given and choose a step function $\varphi$ so that

$$\frac{1}{C} \int |f - \varphi|\, dx < \varepsilon.$$

The transforms $\mathscr{F}\varphi$ and $\mathscr{F}^*\varphi$ are continuous functions, being finite linear combinations of transforms of characteristic functions of intervals, written out explicitly in the beginning of this section. They also tend to zero at infinity. Hence there is a number $M < \infty$ such that

$$|\mathscr{F}\varphi(\xi)| < \varepsilon \qquad \text{if } |\xi| > M.$$

Consequently, $|\xi| > M$ implies

$$|\mathscr{F} f(\xi)| \leq \frac{1}{C} \left| \int (f(x) - \varphi(x)) e^{-i\xi x} \, dx \right| + |\mathscr{F} \varphi(\xi)| < 2\varepsilon.$$

But this means that $\mathscr{F} f(\xi)$ tends to zero as $\xi$ tends to infinity. Now let $\xi_0$ be a fixed real number and choose $\delta > 0$ such that

$$|\mathscr{F} \varphi(\xi) - \mathscr{F} \varphi(\xi_0)| < \varepsilon \qquad \text{if } |\xi - \xi_0| < \delta.$$

As before, $|\xi - \xi_0| < \delta$ implies

$$\begin{aligned} |\mathscr{F} f(\xi) - \mathscr{F} f(\xi_0)| &\leq \frac{1}{C} \left| \int (f(x) - \varphi(x)) e^{-i\xi x} dx \right| + |\mathscr{F} \varphi(\xi) - \mathscr{F} \varphi(\xi_0)| \\ &+ \frac{1}{C} \left| \int (\varphi(x) - f(x)) e^{-i\xi_0 x} \, dx \right| \leq 3\varepsilon. \end{aligned}$$

Thus $\mathscr{F} f$ is continuous at $\xi_0$, as claimed. The same computations apply, of course, to $\mathscr{F}^*$.

At last, we show that $C = \sqrt{2\pi}$. Let $f$ be the function defined by

$$f(x) = e^{-|x|}.$$

This function is in $L_c^2$ and integrable, so its Fourier transform $\mathscr{F} f$ can be found from the computations of Exercise 5.6.3 (see Figure 5.4):

$$\mathscr{F} f(\xi) = \frac{2}{C(1 + \xi^2)}.$$

The function $\mathscr{F} f$ is also integrable so that its conjugate Fourier transform is, by Theorem 5.6.17, a continuous function which is, by Theorem 5.6.14, a.e. equal to $f$. But two continuous functions that are equal almost everywhere must coincide

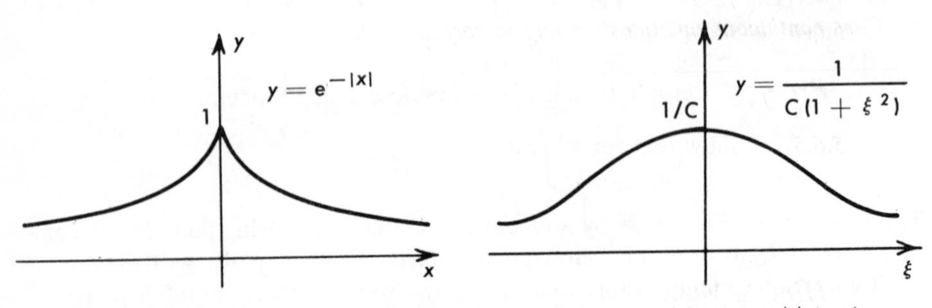


Figure 5.4 $[C(1 + \xi^2)]^{-1}$ is the Fourier transform of $e^{-|x|}$, and $e^{-|x|}$ is the inverse Fourier transform of $[C(1 + \xi^2)]^{-1}$. Both functions vanish at infinity since they are transforms of integrable functions.

everywhere; hence

$$\mathscr{F}^*\mathscr{F}f(0) = \frac{2}{C^2}\int \frac{d\xi}{1+\xi^2} = \frac{2\pi}{C^2} = f(0) = 1.$$

Here we have used the equation

$$\int_{-\infty}^{\infty} \frac{d\xi}{1+\xi^2} = \arctan(\infty) - \arctan(-\infty) = \pi.$$

## *EXERCISES*

*5.6.1* Show that $(\sin^2 x)/x^2$ is improper Riemann integrable and hence Lebesgue integrable.

*5.6.2* Show that the function $f_{ab}$,

$$f_{ab}(x) = \begin{cases} \dfrac{e^{-ibx} - e^{-iax}}{-ix} & \text{if } x = 0 \\ 0 & \text{if } x = 0 \end{cases}$$

where $a$ and $b$ are real and $a < b$, is in $L_c^2$ but not integrable, and prove that

$$\|f_{ab}\| = C(b-a)^{1/2}.$$

Also show that $f_{ab}$ is improper Riemann integrable.

*5.6.3* Show that, for each real value of the parameter $\xi$, the function $f_\xi$ defined by

$$f_\xi(x) = e^{-|x|}e^{-i\xi x}$$

is integrable and prove that

$$\int f_\xi \, dx = \frac{2}{1+\xi^2}.$$

*Hint* Notice that

$$-\frac{1}{\operatorname{sgn} x + i\xi} e^{-|x|}e^{-i\xi x}$$

is a primitive of $f_\xi$.

*5.6.4* Show that

$$\int \frac{\sin^2 x}{x^2}\, dx = \pi.$$

*5.6.5* Show that for all real $x$,

$$\int \frac{\cos \xi x}{1+\xi^2}\, d\xi = \pi e^{-|x|}.$$

*Hint* Notice that

$$\frac{2}{\pi}\int \frac{\cos \xi x}{1+\xi^2}\, dx = \operatorname{Re} \mathscr{F}\left(\frac{2}{\sqrt{2\pi}(1+\xi^2)}\right).$$

## 5.7 EXERCISES

### A. Strong and Weak Convergence

5.7.1 Suppose $\{B(f_n, r_n)\}$ is a sequence of balls in $L^2$ such that

$$B(f_n, r_n) \supset B(f_{n+1}, r_{n+1}).$$

Prove that there is an $f \in L^2$ which belongs to all $B(f_n, r_n)$.

*Hint* Use the definition of balls in Exercise 5.1.5. Prove that $\{f_n\}$ converges strongly by showing

$$\|f_n - f_m\| \leq r_m - r_n$$

for $m \leq n$. Notice that the sequence $\{r_n\}$ converges.

5.7.2 A sequence $\{\varphi_n\}$ of functions in $L^2$ is said to be a sequence of orthonormal elements if

$$(\varphi_n, \varphi_m) = \int \varphi_n \varphi_m \, dx = \begin{cases} 0 & \text{if } n \neq m \\ 1 & \text{if } n = m. \end{cases}$$

Suppose $\{\varphi_n\}$ is a sequence of orthonormal elements in $L^2$ and $f \in L^2$.

(a) Show that $\sum (f, \varphi_n)^2$ converges and

$$\sum_{n=1}^{\infty} (f, \varphi_n)^2 \leq \|f\|^2.$$

*Hint* Compute the square of the norm of

$$f - \sum_{n=1}^{k} (f, \varphi_n)\varphi_n$$

and notice that this value is nonnegative.

(b) Show that $\sum (f, \varphi_n)\varphi_n$ converges strongly to a $g \in L^2$.

5.7.3 A sequence $\{f_n\}$ in $L^2$ is said to converge weakly to $f \in L^2$ if

$$\lim_{n \to \infty} (f_n, g) = (f, g)$$

for each $g \in L^2$. We denote this by $\{f_n\} \rightharpoonup f$.

(a) Show that if $\{f_n\} \to f$, then $\{f_n\} \rightharpoonup f$.
(b) Show that if $\{f_n\} \rightharpoonup f$ and $\{\|f_n\|\} \to \|f\|$, then $\{f_n\} \to f$.

*Hint* In (b) notice that

$$\lim_{n \to \infty} \|f + f_n\|^2 = 4\,\|f\|^2.$$

Now use the parallelogram identity to prove

$$\lim_{n\to\infty} \|f_n - f\|^2 = 0.$$

**5.7.4** Show that if $\{\varphi_n\}$ is a sequence of orthonormal elements in $L^2$, then $\{\varphi_n\}$ converges weakly to zero but $\{\varphi_n\}$ does not converge strongly.

*Hint* Use Exercise 5.5.2.

## B. Orthonormal Systems

A subset $B$ of $L^2$ is called a set of orthonormal elements if for $f, g \in B$

$$(f, g) = \int fg\,dx = \begin{cases} 1 & \text{if } f = g \\ 0 & \text{otherwise.} \end{cases}$$

**5.7.5** Let $L^2$ be the space of square integrable functions on the real line and define step functions $\varphi_{nk}$ for $n \geq 0$ and $k = 0, \pm 1, \cdots$ by

$$\varphi_{0k} = \chi_{[k,k+1)}$$

$$\varphi_{nk}(x) = \begin{cases} 0 & \text{for } x \notin [k2^{-n+1}, (k+1)2^{-n+1}) \\ \dfrac{2^{(n-1)}}{2} & \text{for } x \in [k2^{-n+1}, (2k+1)2^{-n}) \\ \dfrac{-2^{(n-1)}}{2} & \text{for } x \in [(2k+1)2^{-n}, (k+1)2^{-n+1}) \end{cases}$$

if $n \geq 1$.

(a) Show that $\{\varphi_{nk}: n \geq 0,\ k = 0, \pm 1, \cdots\}$ is a set of orthonormal elements.
(b) Let $L_0$ be the set of all linear combinations of functions $\varphi_{nk}$. Show that $L_0$ is dense in $L^2$, that is, if $f \in L^2$ and $\varepsilon > 0$, then there is $\psi \in L_0$ with

$$\|f - \psi\| \leq \varepsilon.$$

*Hint* In (b) show first by induction on $n$ that the characteristic functions of $[k2^{-n+1}, (2k+1)2^{-n})$ and $[(2k+1)2^{-n}, (k+1)2^{-n+1})$ belong to $L_0$. Then observe that the characteristic function of any bounded interval, and hence every step function, can be approximated in the norm. Now use Theorem 5.2.4.

**5.7.6** Suppose $B$ is a set of orthonormal elements in $L^2$. Show that for any $f \in L^2$ there are only a countable number of $\varphi \in B$ with $(f, \varphi) \neq 0$.

*Hint* There are at most $n - 1$ elements $\varphi$ in $B$ with $(f, \varphi)^2 > n^{-1}\ \|f\|^2$ (see Exercise 5.7.2a).

**5.7.7** A set $B$ of orthonormal elements in $L^2$ is said to be complete (or to be a base for $L^2$) if there is no strictly larger set of orthonormal elements. Let $L_0$ be the set of all linear combinations of members of $B$. Prove the following are equivalent:

(a) $B$ is complete in $L^2$;
(b) $L_0$ is dense in $L^2$;
(c) If $f \in L^2$ and if $\{\varphi_k : k \geq 1\}$ is an enumeration of those $\varphi \in B$ for which $(f, \varphi) \neq 0$, then $\{\sum_{k=1}^n (f, \varphi_k)\varphi_k\}$ converges strongly to $f$ (by which we mean $f = \sum_{k\geq 1} (f, \varphi_k)\varphi_k$ if the set $\{\varphi_k : k \geq 1\}$ is finite), and

$$\|f\|^2 = \sum_{k\geq 1} (f, \varphi_k)^2.$$

*Hint* $\{\sum_{k=1}^n (f, \varphi_k)\varphi_k\}$ converges strongly to a $g \in L^2$ by Exercise 5.7.2. $\psi = f - g$ has the property that $(\psi, \varphi) = 0$ for all $\varphi \in B$. But then, also, $(\psi, h) = 0$ for all $h \in L_0$, which, if (b) holds, implies $(\psi, \psi) = 0$. Use this information to prove that (a) implies (b) and (b) implies (c). It is not difficult to show that (c) implies (a), and (c) implies (b) trivially.

5.7.8 Let $\{\varphi_k\}$ be a sequence of orthonormal elements in $L^2$. If $\{C_k\}$ is a sequence of numbers such that $\{\sum_{k=1}^n C_k\varphi_k\}$ converges strongly to $f \in L^2$, then we write

$$f \sim \sum_{k=1}^{\infty} C_k\varphi_k.$$

(Note that we do not claim $f = \sum_{k=1}^{\infty} C_k\varphi_k$ a.e.) Prove that $C_k = (f, \varphi_k)$ for all $k$.

5.7.9 Let $\{\varphi_{nk} : n \geq 1, k = 0, \pm 1, \cdots\}$ be the set of orthonormal elements that were introduced in Exercises 5.7.5 for the space $L^2$ of square integrable functions on the real line. For any $f \in L^2$ we have

$$\lim_{m\to\infty} \left\| f - \sum_{k=-m}^{m} \sum_{n=1}^{m} (f, \varphi_{nk})\varphi_{nk} \right\| = 0,$$

$$\|f\|^2 = \sum_{k=-\infty}^{\infty} \sum_{n=1}^{\infty} (f, \varphi_{nk})^2.$$

*Hint* This is just an application of Exercise 5.7.7.

5.7.10 In this exercise $L^2$ denotes the space of square integrable functions on the interval [0, 1]. Define functions $\varphi_0$, $\varphi_n$ and $\psi_n$, $n \geq 1$, on [0, 1] by

$$\varphi_0 = \chi_{[0,1]}$$

$$\varphi_n(x) = \begin{cases} 1 & \text{if } [2^n x] \text{ is even} \\ -1 & \text{if } [2^n x] \text{ is odd} \end{cases}$$

$$\psi_n(x) = \begin{cases} 1 & \text{if } [2^n x + \tfrac{1}{2}] \text{ is even} \\ -1 & \text{if } [2^n x + \tfrac{1}{2}] \text{ is odd} \end{cases}$$

where $[x]$ denotes the largest integer less than or equal to $x$. Prove that $\{\varphi_k, \psi_n: k \geq 0, n \geq 1\}$ is a complete set of orthonormal elements in $L^2$.

*Hint* Compare with Exercise 5.7.5 and the hint included there. To show that $\{\varphi_k, \psi_n\}$ is complete it suffices to prove, according to Exercise 5.7.7, that the set $L_0$ of all linear combinations of $\varphi_k$ and $\psi_n$ is dense in $L^2$.

**5.7.11** Show that the set of functions on $[0, 1]$

$$\{\chi_{[0,1]}, \sqrt{2}\sin 2\pi nx, \sqrt{2}\cos 2\pi kx : n, k \geq 1\}$$

is a set of orthonormal elements in the space $L^2$ of square integrable functions on $[0, 1]$. One can prove, in fact, that this set is complete, but this is not at all easy. For $f \in L^2$,

$$f \sim a_0\chi_{[0,1]} + 2\left(\sum_{n=1}^{\infty} a_n \sin 2\pi nx + \sum_{n=1}^{\infty} b_n \cos 2\pi nx\right),$$

$$a_0 = \int_0^1 f\,dx,$$

$$a_n = \int_0^1 f(x)\sin 2\pi nx\,dx, \qquad b_n = \int_0^1 f(x)\cos 2\pi nx\,dx,$$

is called the Fourier expansion of $f$ on $[0, 1]$. Find the Fourier expansions of $\chi_{[0,1/2]}$ and $x\chi_{[0,1/2]}$.

*Hint* Use the following formulas to prove orthogonality:

$$\begin{aligned}
\sin nx \sin mx &= \tfrac{1}{2}\{\cos(n-m)x - \cos(n+m)x\},\\
\sin nx \cos mx &= \tfrac{1}{2}\{\sin(n+m)x + \sin(n-m)x\},\\
\cos nx \cos mx &= \tfrac{1}{2}\{\cos(n+m)x + \cos(n-m)x\}.
\end{aligned}$$

These formulas can be found in most calculus textbooks.

## C. The Space $l^2$

**5.7.12** Let $L$ be the set of functions $\varphi$ on the positive integers that vanish at all but a finite number of points. $L$ can be thought of as the space of all finite sequences of real numbers. For $\varphi \in L$ define an integral

$$\int \varphi\,d\mu = \sum_{n=1}^{\infty} \varphi(n).$$

Notice that the sum is actually finite. We have seen in Example 2.5 that Properties (1) to (4) hold, and Property (5) holds trivially. In Exercise 2.5.3 it was shown that the space of integrable functions consists of all functions $\varphi$ for which $\sum |\varphi(n)|$ converges. This space of integrable functions is often denoted by $l^1$. The space of square integrable functions, which is denoted by $l^2$, consists therefore of all functions $\varphi$ for which

$$\sum_{n=1}^{\infty} |\varphi(n)|^2 < \infty.$$

Interpret the scalar product, Minkowski's inequality, and the Schwarz inequality for $l^2$.

5.7.13 Let $\varphi_k$ be the function in $l^2$ that satisfies $\varphi_k(n) = 0$ if $n \neq k$ and $\varphi_k(k) = 1$. Show that $\{\varphi_k\}$ is a set of orthonormal elements as defined in part B. If $\varphi \in l^2$, then

$$\varphi(n) = \sum_{k=1}^{\infty} (\varphi, \varphi_k)\varphi_k(n)$$

for all $n$.

5.7.14 Suppose that $S$ is an uncountable set. Let $L$ and $\int \varphi \, d\mu$, $\varphi \in L$, be defined as in Exercise 2.5.4. According to Exercise 2.5.5, a function $\varphi$ on $S$ is integrable if and only if it vanishes outside a denumerable set $\{a_n : n \geq 1\}$ and $\sum_{n\geq 1} |\varphi(a_n)| < \infty$. Determine the space $l^2(S)$ of square integrable functions on $S$ and show that there is no denumerable set of orthonormal elements in $l^2(S)$ that is complete.

## D. Continuous Quadratic Functionals on $L^2$

A continuous quadratic functional $Q$ on $L^2$ assigns to every $f \in L^2$ a real number $Q(f)$ such that

$Q(\lambda f) = \lambda^2 Q(f)$ for real $\lambda$ (homogeneity of second degree),
$Q(f+g) + Q(f-g) = 2Q(f) + 2Q(g)$ (parallelogram identity),
$Q(f_n) \to Q(f)$ whenever $f_n \to f$ (strong continuity).

For such a continuous quadratic functional on $L^2$ put

$$B(f, g) = \tfrac{1}{4}(Q(f+g) - Q(f-g)).$$

For instance $\|f\|^2$ is a continuous quadratic functional on $L^2$.

5.7.15 Prove the following relations

(a) $B(f,f) = Q(f)$, $B(f, g) = B(g, f)$,
(b) $B(f+g, h) = B(f, h) + B(g, h)$.

*Hint* In (b) combine the following four cases of the parallelogram identity:

$$\begin{aligned} Q(f+g+h) + Q(f-g+h) &= 2Q(g) + 2Q(f+h) \\ -Q(f+g-h) - Q(f-g-h) &= -2Q(g) - 2Q(f-h) \\ Q(f+g+h) + Q(-f+g+h) &= 2Q(f) + 2Q(g+h) \\ -Q(f+g-h) - Q(-f+g-h) &= -2Q(f) - 2Q(g-h). \end{aligned}$$

**5.7.16** Prove that

$$B(\lambda f, g) = \lambda B(f, g)$$

for all real numbers $\lambda$.

*Hint* Prove first that $B(pf, qg) = pqB(f, g)$ for all positive integers $p, q$, then use the homogeneity to show that $B((p/q)f, (q/q)g) = (p/q)B(f, g)$. The continuity of $Q$ will prove the assertion now for $\lambda > 0$. Finally, notice that the relation also holds for $\lambda = 0$ and $\lambda = -1$.

**5.7.17**

(a) Show that for each $g \in L^2$ there exists another element $g^*$ of $L^2$ such that

$$B(f, g) = (f, g^*)$$

for all $f \in L^2$.

*Hint* $B(f, g)$ is for fixed $g$ a continuous linear functional on $L^2$.

(b) For any $g \in L^2$ let $g^*$ be the element that corresponds to $g$ by (a). Show that

$$(af + bg)^* = af^* + bg^* \text{ a.e.}$$

for all real numbers $a$, $b$ and that $(f, g^*) = (f^*, g)$.

**5.7.18**

(a) Show that there exists a constant $M < \infty$ such that

$$|Q(f)| \leq M \|f\|^2 \qquad \text{for all } f \in L^2.$$

(b) For any $g \in L^2$ let $g^*$ be the element that corresponds to $g$ by Exercise 5.7.17a. Show that

$$\|g^*\| \leq M \|g\| \qquad \text{for all } g \in L^2,$$

with the same constant $M$ as in (a).

*Hint* (a) is proved in a way similar to the proof of Proposition 5.3.2. In (b) use

$$\frac{1}{M}\|g^*\|^2 = B\left(\frac{g^*}{M}, g\right) = \frac{1}{4}\left(Q\left(\frac{g^*}{M} + g\right) - Q\left(\frac{g^*}{M} - g\right)\right)$$

to estimate $\|g^*\|$.

## E. Continuous Linear Functionals on $L^p$

In this section we will always have $1 < p < \infty$. For $p > 1$,

$$f(x) = (1 + x^{1/p})^p + |1 - x^{1/p}|^p \qquad 0 < x < \infty$$

has a continuous first derivative

$$f'(x) = (x^{-1/p} + 1)^{p-1} + \operatorname{sgn}(x - 1)\,|x^{-1/p} - 1|^{p-1}$$

and a second derivative

$$f''(x) = -\frac{p-1}{p} x^{-1/p-1}[(x^{-1/p}+1)^{p-2} - |x^{-1/p}-1|^{p-2}]$$

which, for $x \neq 1$, is positive if $p < 2$ and negative if $p > 2$. Hence $f$ is convex if $1 < p < 2$ and concave if $2 < p < \infty$, that is,

$$f(x) \geq f(\xi) + f'(\xi)(x-\xi) \qquad \text{if } 1 < p < 2,$$
$$f(x) \leq f(\xi) + f'(\xi)(x-\xi) \qquad \text{if } 2 < p < \infty,$$

for $0 < x$, $\xi < \infty$, with equality if and only if $x = \xi$. Introducing the function

$$F(x, y) = xf\left(\frac{y}{x}\right) = (x^{1/p} + y^{1/p})^p + |x^{1/p} - y^{1/p}|^p,$$

we have the elementary inequalities

$$(x^{1/p} + y^{1/p})^p + |x^{1/p} - y^{1/p}|^p \geq x\frac{\partial F}{\partial x}(\xi, \eta) + y\frac{\partial F}{\partial y}(\xi, \eta) \qquad \text{if } 1 < p < 2,$$

$$(x^{1/p} + y^{1/p})^p + |x^{1/p} - y^{1/p}|^p \leq x\frac{\partial F}{\partial x}(\xi, \eta) + y\frac{\partial F}{\partial y}(\xi, \eta) \qquad \text{if } 2 < p < \infty,$$

for $0 < x, y, \xi, \eta < \infty$ with equality if and only if $x = k\xi$, $y = k\eta$ for some $k$. These inequalities hold also if either $x$ or $y$ or both are zero, since each side of each inequality is continuous in $x$ and $y$.

5.7.19 Prove Beurling's inequality for $f, g \in L^p$:

$$\|f+g\|^p + \|f-g\|^p \geq (\|f\| + \|g\|)^p + |\,\|f\| - \|g\|\,|^p \qquad \text{if } 1 < p < 2,$$
$$\|f+g\|^p + \|f-g\|^p \leq (\|f\| + \|g\|)^p + |\,\|f\| - \|g\|\,|^p \qquad \text{if } 2 < p < \infty.$$

*Hint* Prove the inequalities first for nonnegative functions $f$ and $g$ satisfying $\|f\| \neq 0 \neq \|g\|$ by introducing $x = f^p$, $y = g^p$, $\xi = \|f\|^p$, and $\eta = \|g\|^p$ and integrating in the above elementary inequalities. In the general situation apply the inequalities to $f\chi_i$ and $g\chi_i$, where $\chi_i$, $i = 1, 2, 3, 4$, are the characteristic functions of the disjoint sets $E_i$ defined by

$$E_1 = \{x : f(x) \geq 0, g(x) \geq 0\},\ E_2 = \{x : f(x) < 0, g(x) < 0\},$$
$$E_3 = \{x : f(x) \geq 0, g(x) < 0\},\ E_4 = \{x : f(x) < 0, g(x) \geq 0\}.$$

Then combine the four inequalities thus obtained.

5.7.20 Prove Clarkson's inequality for $f, g \in L^p$:

$$2\|f\|^p + 2\|g\|^p \geq \|f+g\|^p + \|f-g\|^p \qquad \text{if } 1 < p < 2,$$
$$2\|f\|^p + 2\|g\|^p \leq \|f+g\|^p + \|f-g\|^p \qquad \text{if } 2 < p < \infty.$$

*Hint* Apply Beurling's inequality to the two functions $\varphi$ and $\psi$ on a set of two elements defined by

$$\varphi(1) = \|f\|, \varphi(2) = \|g\|,$$
$$\psi(1) = \|g\|, \psi(2) = -\|f\|,$$

and with integral $\int \varphi \, d\mu = \varphi(1) + \varphi(2)$. This yields for $1 < p < 2$,

$$(\|f\| + \|g\|)^p + |\,\|f\| - \|g\|\,|^p \geq 2^{p-1}(\|f\|^p + \|g\|^p)$$

which has to be combined with the original Beurling inequality to yield Clarkson's inequality. Hence Beurling's inequality is in general sharper than Clarkson's.

5.7.21 Let $F$ be a nonzero continuous linear functional on $L^p$. Show that there exists an element $h$ of smallest norm in the hyperplane

$$H = \{f \in L^p, F(f) = \|F\|^q\},$$

and if $h_0$ is any other element of smallest norm in $H$, then $h = h_0$ a.e.

*Hint* Take a sequence $f_n \in H$ such that $\lim \|f_n\| = A$, where $A = \inf\{\|f\| : f \in H\}$; then estimate $\|f_n - f_m\|^p$, using Beurling's inequality if $1 < p < 2$ and Clarkson's inequality if $2 < p < \infty$. The proof is similar to that of Theorem 5.3.6. To prove $h = h_0$ a.e, estimate $\|h - h_0\|^p$ using Beurling's and Clarkson's inequalities.

5.7.22 Let $g \in L^q$ and define the continuous linear functional $F_g$ on $L^p$ by

$$F_g(f) = \int fg \, dx.$$

Define $h \in L^p$ by

$$h(x) = \begin{cases} |g(x)|^{q/p} & \text{if } g(x) \geq 0 \\ -|g(x)|^{q/p} & \text{if } g(x) < 0 \end{cases}$$

that is, $h = |g|^{q/p} \operatorname{sgn} g$. Show that $h$ is an element of smallest norm in the hyperplane

$$H = \{f : f \in L^p, F_g(f) = \|F_g\|^q\}$$

and $\|F_g\|^{q-1} = \|h\|_p$.

*Hint* According to Exercise 5.4.5, $\|F_g\| = \|g\|_q$. Thus for $f \in H$,

$$\|g\|_q^q = \|F_g\|^q = F_g(f) = \int fg \, dx \leq \|f\|_p \|g\|_q.$$

Now show $\|g\|_q^{q-1} = \|h\|_p$.

5.7.23 Suppose $F$ is a nonzero continuous linear functional on $L^p$. Let $h$ be an element of minimal norm in the hyperplane

$$H = \{f : f \in L^p, F(f) = \|F\|^q\}$$

Prove that $F = F_g$ where $g = |h|^{p/q} \operatorname{sgn} h \in L^q$.

*Hint* Prove first that $F_g(k) = 0$ whenever $F(k) = 0$. Suppose $F_g(k) \neq 0$ but $F(k) = 0$. You may then assume that $F_g(k) = \|F_g\|^q$, multiplying $k$ by a constant if necessary. Observe that for all real numbers $t$,

$$\|h - tk\| \geq \|h\|, \ \|(1-t)h + tk\| \geq \|h\|;$$

the first of these inequalities holds because $h - tk \in H$, and the second one follows from

$$\begin{aligned} \|F_g\| \, \|(1-t)h + tk\| &\geq F_g((1-t)h + tk) \\ &= (1-t)F_g(h) + tF_g(k) \\ &= (1-t)\,\|F_g\|^q + t\,\|F_g\|^q \\ &= \|F_g\|^q = \|F_g\| \, \|h\| \end{aligned}$$

where we have made use of $F_g(h) = \|F_g\|^q$ and $\|F_g\|^{q-1} = \|h\|$ (Exercise 5.7.22). In Beurling's inequalities (Exercise 5.7.19) replace $f$ by $h - tk$ and $g$ by $(1-t)h + tk$ if $p < 2$, and $f$ by $(2-t)h$ and $g$ by $t(h - 2k)$ if $p > 2$. You will obtain a contradiction for small values of $t$. For $p < 2$, for instance, we have

$$\begin{aligned} |2-t|^p \, \|h\|^p + |t|^p \, \|h - 2k\|^p &\geq (\|h - tk\| + \|(1-t)h + tk\|)^p \\ &\geq 2^p \, \|h\|^p \end{aligned}$$

which means

$$|2-t|^p + c\,|t|^p - 2^p \geq 0$$

for some constant $c > 0$; but this is not true since $p > 1$. If $f \in L^p$, then

$$k = f - \frac{F(f)}{\|F\|^q} h$$

has the property $F(k) = 0$. Hence $F_g(k) = 0$, or

$$F_g(f) = F(f)\frac{F_g(h)}{\|F\|^q} = F(f)\frac{\|F_g\|^q}{\|F\|^q}.$$

Consequently $F = F_{g_0}$ where $g_0 = (\|F\|/\|F_g\|)^q g$. Since, by Exercise 5.7.22, $h_0 = |g_0|^{q/p} \operatorname{sgn} g_0$ is an element of smallest norm in the hyperplane

$$\{f : F_{g_0}(f) = \|F_{g_0}\|^q = \|F\|^q\} = \{f : F(f) = \|F\|^q\},$$

$h = h_0$ a.e. by Exercise 5.7.21.

## F. Complex $L^2$ and Fourier Transforms

**5.7.24** Let $\omega$ be an $n$th root of unity, $n \geq 3$, that is, $\omega$ is a complex number such that $\omega^n = 1$. Show that

$$(f, g) = \frac{1}{n} \sum_{k=0}^{n-1} \omega^k \|f + \omega^k g\|^2, \qquad f, g \in L_c^2$$

if and only if $\omega$ is neither 1 nor $-1$.

*Hint* Use the relations

$$(1 - \omega) \sum_{k=0}^{n-1} \omega^k = 0 = (1 - \omega^2) \sum_{k=0}^{n-1} \omega^{2k}.$$

**5.7.25** For any function $f$ on the real line, its shift $f_h$ is defined by

$$f_h(x) = f(x + h).$$

Show that for $f \in L_c^2$,

$$\mathcal{F}(f_h)(\xi) = e^{i\xi h} \mathcal{F} f(\xi), \qquad \mathcal{F}^*(f_h)(x) = e^{-ihx} \mathcal{F}^* f(x) \qquad \text{a.e.}$$

**5.7.26** We say that a function in $L_c^2$ has a derivative $f'$ in $L_c^2$ if there is a function $f'$ in $L_c^2$ such that

$$\lim_{h \to 0} \left\| f' - \frac{1}{h}(f_h - f) \right\| = 0.$$

Show that $\mathcal{F} f'(\xi) = i\xi \mathcal{F} f(\xi)$ a.e..

*Hint* Choose a sequence $\{h(n)\}$, tending so fast to zero that

$$\left\| f' - \frac{1}{h(n)}(f_{h(n)} - f) \right\| \leq 2^{-n}.$$

Then show that

$$\lim_{n \to \infty} \frac{1}{h(n)} (\mathcal{F} f_{h(n)} - \mathcal{F} f) = \mathcal{F} f' \text{a.e.}$$

and apply the result of the previous exercise.

**5.7.27** SOBOLEV'S LEMMA If $f$ is a function in $L_c^2$ with a derivative $f'$ in $L_c^2$ (as defined in the previous exercise), then $f$ is (almost everywhere equal to) a continuous function.

*Hint* Show that $(1 + \xi^2) |\mathcal{F} f|^2$ is integrable and conclude that $\mathcal{F} f = (1 + \xi^2)^{-1/2} (1 + \xi^2)^{1/2} \mathcal{F} f$ is integrable.

**5.7.28** Let $f$ and $g$ be complex integrable functions. Show that the functions $\check{f}_{-y}g$ $(\check{f}_{-y}(x) = f(y - x))$ are integrable for almost all real numbers $y$ and that the function $f * g$ defined by

$$f * g\,(y) = \begin{cases} \int \check{f}_{-y}\, g\, dx & \text{if } \check{f}_{-y}\, g \text{ is integrable} \\ 0 & \text{otherwise} \end{cases}$$

is integrable. Furthermore $f * g = g * f$ a.e. and

$$\int f * g\, dx = \int f\, dx \int g\, dx.$$

*Hint* Use Fubini's theorem, or the result of Exercise 1.6.28 together with Definition 2.1.3.

**5.7.29** Let $f$ be a complex integrable function and $g \in L_c^2$, and let $\check{f}_{-y}g$ be defined as in the previous exercise. Show that if $\check{f}_{-y}g$ is integrable for some $y$, then so is $f\check{g}_{-y}$ and the two functions have the same integral. Then prove that $\check{f}_{-y}g$ is integrable for a.a. $y$, and that the function $f * g$ defined by

$$f * g(y) = \begin{cases} \int \check{f}_{-y}g\, dx & \text{if } \check{f}_{-y}g \text{ is integrable} \\ 0 & \text{otherwise} \end{cases}$$

is in $L_c^2$ and satisfies

$$\|f * g\|_2 \leq \|f\|_1\, \|g\|_2.$$

*Hint* Use Tonelli's theorem to show that the function of the three variables $x$, $y$, $z$

$$f(y)g(x - y)\overline{f(z)}\overline{g(x - z)}$$

is integrable. Then use Fubini's theorem, integrating first with respect to $y$ and $z$ for those $x$ for which the integral

$$h(x) = \iint f(y)g(x - y)\overline{f(z)}\,\overline{g(x - z)}\, dy\, dz$$

exists. Conclude that for these $x$, $f\check{g}_{-x}$ is integrable. Let $h$ be defined to be zero where the above integral does not exist (this is at most a null set). Show

$$\int h\, dx = \|f * g\|^2.$$

Finally, use repeated integration again to show that $\|f * g\|_2 \leq \|f\|_1\, \|g\|_2$, this time integrating first with respect to $x$.

**5.7.30** Show that in the last two exercises, $\mathscr{F}(f * g) = (\mathscr{F}f)(\mathscr{F}g)$ a.e.

## G. Fourier Transformations for Functions of Several Variables

In the following exercises $L_c^2$ denotes the set of complex measurable functions on $R^n$ whose modulus is square integrable. Let $x$ and $\xi$ be points in $R^n$,

$$x = (x_1, \cdots, x_n), \qquad \xi = (\xi_1, \cdots, \xi_n).$$

For the scalar product in $R^n$ we use the notation

$$\langle \xi, x \rangle = \sum_{k=1}^{n} \xi_k x_k$$

in order to avoid confusion with its counterpart in $L_c^2$. For complex step functions on $R^n$ and, more generally, for complex integrable functions on $R^n$ we define the Fourier transformation $\mathscr{F}$ and the conjugate Fourier transformation $\mathscr{F}^*$ by

$$\mathscr{F} f(\xi) = (2\pi)^{-n/2} \int f(x) e^{-i\langle \xi, x \rangle}\, dx,$$

$$\mathscr{F}^* f(x) = (2\pi)^{-n/2} \int f(\xi) e^{i\langle \xi, x \rangle}\, d\xi.$$

Finally, Definition 5.6.12 extends $\mathscr{F}$ and $\mathscr{F}^*$ to all of $L_c^2$ modulo the result of the following exercise:

**5.7.31** Show that $\mathscr{F}$ and $\mathscr{F}^*$ are isometries (with respect to the norm in $L_c^2$) on the set of complex-valued step functions of $n$ variables, and that $(\mathscr{F}\varphi, \psi) = (\varphi, \mathscr{F}^*\psi)$ for all such step functions $\varphi$ and $\psi$.

**5.7.32** Show that $\mathscr{F}^*\mathscr{F}f = \mathscr{F}\mathscr{F}^*f = f$ a.e. for $f \in L_c^2$.

**5.7.33** Generalize Exercise 5.7.30 to the present setting.

# SUMMARY

In this chapter $L^2$ is the space of measurable functions $f$ with an integrable square $f^2$ (Definition 5.1.1). $L^2$ is a linear space (Proposition 5.1.4).

If $f, g \in L^2$, then $fg$ is integrable. The scalar product $(f, g)$ of $f$ and $g$ is defined by

$$(f, g) = \int fg\, dx$$

(Definition 5.1.5). It has the following properties (Theorem 5.1.10):

$$(f, f) \geq 0 \text{ and } (f, f) = 0 \text{ if and only if } f = 0 \text{ a.e.},$$
$$(a_1 f_1 + a_2 f_2, g) = a_1(f_1, g) + a_2(f_2, g),\ a_1, a_2 \text{ real},$$
$$(f, b_1 g_1 + b_2 g_2) = b_1(f, g_1) + b_2(f, g_2),\ b_1, b_2 \text{ real},$$
$$(f, g) = (g, f).$$

The norm $\|f\|$ of a function $f$ in $L^2$ is defined by

$$\|f\| = \left\{\int f^2\, dx\right\}^{1/2}$$

(Definition 5.1.3). The norm is related to the scalar product by the following equations

$$\|f\| = [(f, f)]^{1/2},$$
$$(f, g) = \tfrac{1}{4}(\|f + g\|^2 - \|f - g\|^2)$$

(Equations 5.1.6). Basic properties of the norm $\|f\|$ are the following:

$$\|f\| = 0 \qquad \text{if and only if } f = 0 \text{ a.e.,}$$
$$\|af\| = |a| \cdot \|f\| \qquad \text{for } f \in L^2,\ a \text{ real,}$$
$$\|f + g\| \leq \|f\| + \|g\| \qquad \text{for } f, g \in L^2.$$

The latter inequality is Minkowski's inequality (Proposition 5.1.9). The parallelogram identity

$$\|f + g\|^2 + \|f - g\|^2 = 2\,\|f\|^2 + 2\,\|g\|^2$$

(Proposition 5.1.7) is of special importance for $L^2$.

For $1 \leq p < \infty$, $L^p$ is the space of measurable functions $f$ such that $|f|^p$ is integrable. $L^\infty$ is the space of those measurable functions that are equivalent to bounded functions (Definition 5.4.1). $L^p$ is a linear space (Proposition 5.4.3). For $f \in L^p$, a norm $\|f\|$ (or $\|f\|_p$) is defined:

$$\|f\| = \left\{\int |f|^p\, dx\right\}^{1/p} \qquad \text{if } 1 \leq p < \infty,$$
$$\|f\| = \inf\{M : |f| \leq M \text{ a.e.}\} \qquad \text{if } p = \infty$$

(Definition 5.4.4). This norm has the same basic properties as the norm for $L^2$ (but it does not satisfy the parallelogram identity). In particular, Minkowski's inequality holds for it (Proposition 5.4.7).

If $f, g \in L^2$, then

$$|(f, g)| \leq \|f\| \cdot \|g\|.$$

This is the Schwarz inequality (Proposition 5.1.8). Similarly, if $f \in L^p$ and $g \in L^q$ where $p$ and $q$ are conjugate indices,

$$p = \infty, q = 1 \quad \text{or} \quad p = 1, q = \infty$$

or

$$1 < p, q < \infty \quad \text{and} \quad \frac{1}{p} + \frac{1}{q} = 1,$$

then $fg$ is integrable and Hölder's inequality holds (Proposition 5.4.6):

$$\left|\int fg\, dx\right| \leq \|f\|_p \cdot \|g\|_q.$$

Every function $f$ in $L^2$ can be approximated by elementary functions; if $\varepsilon > 0$, then there is $\varphi \in L \cap L^2$ with

$$\|f - \varphi\| \leq \varepsilon$$

(Theorem 5.2.4). A function $f$ belongs to $L^2$ if and only if there is a series $\sum \varphi_n$ of functions $\varphi_n \in L \cap L^2$ such that

$$\sum_{n=1}^{\infty} \varphi_n = f \text{ a.e.,}$$

$$\sum_{n=1}^{\infty} \|\varphi_n\| < \infty$$

(Theorem 5.2.5). If $\{f_n\}$ is a sequence in $L^2$ such that

$$\lim_{n,m\to\infty} \|f_n - f_m\| = 0$$

then, by the Riesz-Fischer theorem (Theorem 5.2.6), there is a function $f \in L^2$ with

$$\lim_{n\to\infty} \|f - f_n\| = 0.$$

Similar theorems hold for the $L^p$ spaces (Theorems 5.4.11, 5.4.10, and 5.4.9).

A bounded (or continuous) linear functional $F$ on $L^2$ assigns to every $f \in L^2$ a real number $F(f)$, which has the following additional properties:
(a) $F(af + bg) = aF(f) + bF(g)$ for $f, g \in L^2$ and $a$, $b$ real,
(b) there is a number $M$ such that

$$|F(f)| \leq M \|f\| \qquad \text{for } f \in L^2$$

(Definition 5.3.1). For each bounded linear functional $F$, there is a function $g \in L^2$ such that

$$F(f) = (f, g) \qquad \text{for } f \in L^2$$

and $g$ is unique up to a null function (Theorem 5.3.6).

The theory of integration and measure discussed in the previous sections can be generalized to complex-valued functions with the exception of those statements that are obviously specific for real-valued functions. The generalizations are easy when they are possible.

The linear space of complex-valued measurable functions whose modulus is square integrable is denoted by $L_c^2$ (Definition 5.5.3). The norm of a function in $L_c^2$ is defined by

$$\|f\| = \left\{\int |f|^2\, dx\right\}^{1/2}.$$

A slightly different definition is used for the scalar product (Definition 5.5.4),

$$(f, g)_c = \int f\bar{g}\, dx, \qquad f, g \in L_c^2,$$

and this affects the formula expressing the scalar product in terms of the norm (Equation (5.5.5.)):

$$(f, g)_c = \tfrac{1}{4}(\|f+g\|^2 + i\,\|f+ig\|^2 - \|f-g\|^2 - i\,\|f-ig\|^2).$$

But, with this exception, the $L^2$ theory is as before.

If $f$ is a complex-valued integrable function, then its Fourier transform $\mathscr{F}f$ and conjugate Fourier transform $\mathscr{F}^*f$ are defined by

$$\mathscr{F}f(\xi) = (2\pi)^{-1/2}\int f(x)e^{-i\xi x}\,dx, \qquad \mathscr{F}^*f(x) = (2\pi)^{-1/2}\int f(\xi)e^{i\xi x}\,d\xi$$

(Proposition 5.6.15). These functions are continuous and tend to zero at infinity (Theorem 5.6.17); but, in general, they are neither integrable nor square integrable. However, the transforms $\mathscr{F}\varphi$ and $\mathscr{F}^*\varphi$ of a complex-valued step function $\varphi$ are in $L_c^2$ and have the same norm as $\varphi$ (Equations (5.6.10) and (5.6.11)). Generally, if $f$ belongs to $L_c^2$ and $\sum \varphi_n$ is a series of step functions converging to $f$ a.e. and satisfying $\sum_{n=1}^{\infty} \|\varphi_n\| < \infty$, then $\mathscr{F}f$ and $\mathscr{F}^*f$ can be defined by

$$\mathscr{F}f = \sum_{n=1}^{\infty} \mathscr{F}\varphi_n, \qquad \mathscr{F}^*f = \sum_{n=1}^{\infty} \mathscr{F}^*\varphi_n \quad \text{a.e.}$$

(Definition 5.6.12). The same functions in $L_c^2$ are the strong limits of

$$(2\pi)^{-1/2}\int_{-a}^{a} f(x)e^{-i\xi x}\,dx, \qquad (2\pi)^{-1/2}\int_{-a}^{a} f(\xi)e^{i\xi x}\,d\xi,$$

respectively, as $a$ tends to infinity (Proposition 5.6.16). Finally, $\mathscr{F}$ and $\mathscr{F}^*$ satisfy the following relations on $L_c^2$:

$$\|\mathscr{F}f\| = \|\mathscr{F}^*f\| = \|f\|,$$
$$(\mathscr{F}f, g) = (f, \mathscr{F}^*g),$$
$$\mathscr{F}^*\mathscr{F}f = \mathscr{F}\mathscr{F}^*f = f \text{ a.e.}$$

(Equation (5.6.13) and Theorem 5.6.14).

# 6

# The Differentiation of Functions of Locally Bounded Variation

The present chapter is wholly independent of the material discussed previously. It is concerned with the study of differentiability properties of monotone functions on the real line. Since, however, differentiation is a linear operation, any result for monotone functions will also hold for functions that can be written as a linear combination of monotone functions. These are the functions of locally bounded variation that are discussed in the first two sections of this chapter. They include the continuously differentiable functions on the real line, and thus differentiation as presented in this chapter and in the following one is an extension of classical calculus.

After some preparations in Section 6.3 we are then ready to prove the main theorem of this chapter in Section 6.4. It asserts that a monotone function possesses a derivative at almost all points. Section 6.5 applies this result to obtain theorems on term by term differentiation of series of monotone functions and series of functions of locally bounded variation.

As we have stressed above, this chapter does not depend on any previous one. In Section 6.7 it is shown how the results of this chapter can be used to develop the theory of Lebesgue integration on the real line as an inverse operation of differentiation. However, our discussion in Section 6.7 is rather brief. Most of the proofs are only indicated, the details being left as exercises to the reader. Thus this section can serve the eager student ideally in giving him an opportunity to develop a theory himself.

## 6.1 FUNCTIONS OF LOCALLY BOUNDED VARIATION

We begin our considerations in this section with a look at monotone functions, which will play a central role in the remainder of this book. Let us introduce these functions in a formal definition.

6.1.1 DEFINITION *A function $f$ on an interval $I$ is called monotone nondecreasing (monotone nonincreasing) if for any two points $x, y \in I$ with $x \leq y$ we have $f(x) \leq f(y)$, respectively $f(x) \geq f(y)$.*

Recall that an interval in our terminology may be open or closed, or right open and left closed, or left open and right closed. Any function on an interval that consists only of one point is monotone nondecreasing as well as monotone nonincreasing. On the other hand, the constant functions are monotone nondecreasing as well as monotone nonincreasing on every interval.

In the following we are considering only functions that are defined on the whole real line, though all of our discussion is also valid for functions that are defined on a fixed open interval and the proofs transfer to that case without significant modification.

Now let us look at the functions that can be expressed as the difference of two monotone nondecreasing functions. To characterize such functions, we need the concept of total variation of a function on a closed bounded interval.

**6.1.2 DEFINITION** *A function $f$ on the closed bounded interval $[a, b]$ is said to be of bounded variation on $[a, b]$ if the supremum*

$$T_{ab} = \sup\left\{\sum_{k=1}^{n} |f(a_k) - f(a_{k-1})| : a \leq a_0 \leq \cdots \leq a_n \leq b\right\},$$

*which is taken over all possible finite sequences $a_0, \cdots, a_n$, is finite. $T_{ab}$ is called the total variation of $f$ on $[a, b]$.*

Notice that $T_{ab} = f(b) - f(a)$ if $f$ is monotone nondecreasing.

**6.1.3 PROPOSITION** *Suppose the function $f$ on the real line is the difference of two monotone nondecreasing functions $g_1$ and $g_2$,*

$$f = g_1 - g_2.$$

*Then $f$ is of bonded variation on each closed bounded interval $[a, b]$; we have, in fact,*

$$T_{ab} \leq g_1(b) - g_1(a) + g_2(b) - g_2(a).$$

*Proof* Let $a_0, \cdots, a_n$ be any sequence of numbers such that $a \leq a_0 \leq \cdots \leq a_n \leq b$. Since $g_1$ and $g_2$ are monotone nondecreasing, we get

$$\begin{aligned}
\sum_{k=1}^{n} |f(a_k) - f(a_{k-1})| &\leq \sum_{k=1}^{n} |g_1(a_k) - g_1(a_{k-1})| + \sum_{k=1}^{n} |g_2(a_k) - g_2(a_{k-1})| \\
&= \sum_{k=1}^{n} [g_1(a_k) - g_1(a_{k-1})] + \sum_{k=1}^{n} [g_2(a_k) - g_2(a_{k-1})] \\
&= [g_1(a_n) - g_1(a_0)] + [g_2(a_n) - g_2(a_0)] \\
&\leq g_1(b) - g_1(a) + g_2(b) - g_2(a).
\end{aligned}$$

The converse of the above proposition holds also; a function that is of bounded variation on each bounded closed interval can be written as the difference of two monotone nondecreasing functions. Before we give a proof we introduce the total variation function, which will prove a useful tool in the following chapters.

**6.1.4 DEFINITION** *Suppose the function $f$ is of bounded variation on each closed bounded interval. The monotone nondecreasing function $Tf$, defined by*

$$Tf(x) = \begin{cases} f(0) + \sup\left\{\sum | f(a_k) - f(a_{k-1})| : 0 \leq a_0 \leq \cdots \leq a_n \leq x\right\} & \text{for } x \geq 0 \\ f(0) - \sup\left\{\sum | f(a_k) - f(a_{k-1})| : x \leq a_0 \leq \cdots \leq a_n \leq 0\right\} & \text{for } x \leq 0 \end{cases}$$

*is called the total variation function of $f$* (see Figure 6.1).

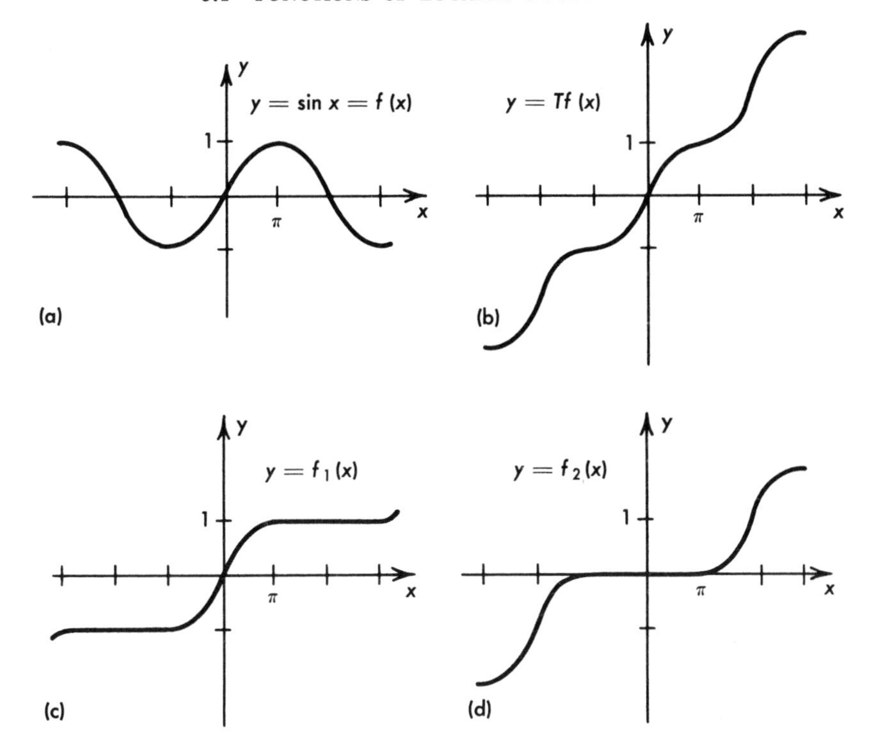


Figure 6.1 (b) shows the total variation function and (c) and (d) the parts of positive and negative variation of sin $x$.

If $T_{ab}$ denotes the total variation of $f$ on the bounded interval $[a, b]$, then we can also write the definition of $Tf$ as

$$Tf(x) = \begin{cases} f(0) + T_{0x} & \text{for } x \geq 0 \\ f(0) - T_{x0} & \text{for } x \leq 0. \end{cases}$$

For a monotone nondecreasing function $f$, $T_{ab} = f(b) - f(a)$; *thus* $Tf = f$ *if* $f$ *is monotone nondecreasing.*

6.1.5 PROPOSITION *For* $a \leq b$,

$$Tf(b) - Tf(a) = T_{ab} = \sup \left\{ \sum_{k=1}^{n} |f(a_k) - f(a_{k-1})| : a \leq a_0 \leq \cdots \leq a_n \leq b \right\}.$$

*Proof* From the definition of $Tf$ it is clear that the total variation of $f$ on an interval $[0, x]$ is $Tf(x) - f(0) = Tf(x) - Tf(0)$, since obviously $Tf(0) = f(0)$. Similarly, the total variation of $f$ on an interval $[x, 0]$ is $Tf(0) - Tf(x)$. From this we can conclude immediately that the total variation $T_{ab}$ of $f$ on any closed bounded interval $[a, b]$ is $Tf(b) - Tf(a)$ if we show that the total variation is additive, that is, if for any numbers $a \leq c \leq b$,

$$T_{ab} = T_{ac} + T_{cb}.$$

Suppose $a \leq c_0 \leq \cdots \leq c_s \leq b$, then $c_t \leq c \leq c_{t+1}$ for some integer $t$ if we make the convention $c_{-1} = a$ and $c_{s+1} = b$. We have

$$\begin{aligned}
\sum_{k=1}^{s} |f(c_k) - f(c_{k-1})| &\leq \sum_{k=1}^{t} |f(c_k) - f(c_{k-1})| + |f(c_{t+1}) - f(c_t)| \\
&\quad + \sum_{k=t+2}^{s} |f(c_k) - f(c_{k-1})| \\
&\leq \sum_{k=1}^{t} |f(c_k) - f(c_{k-1})| + |f(c) - f(c_t)| \\
&\quad + |f(c_{t+1}) - f(c)| + \sum_{k=t+2}^{s} |f(c_k) - f(c_{k-1})| \\
&\leq T_{ac} + T_{cb}.
\end{aligned}$$

Taking the sup on the left-hand side, we obtain

$$T_{ab} \leq T_{ac} + T_{cb}.$$

Similarly, we can derive the opposite inequality. Namely, if

$$a \leq a_0 \leq \cdots \leq a_n \leq c \leq b_0 \leq \cdots \leq b_m \leq b$$

and if we let $c_0, \cdots, c_s$ be the sequence $a_0, \cdots, a_n, c, b_0, \cdots, b_m$, then

$$\sum_{k=1}^{n} |f(a_k) - f(a_{k-1})| + \sum_{k=1}^{m} |f(b_k) - f(b_{k-1})| \leq \sum_{k=1}^{s} |f(c_k) - f(c_{k-1})| \leq T_{ab}$$

and hence $T_{ab} + T_{cb} \leq T_{ab}$. This completes the proof.

Now we are ready to prove the converse of Proposition 6.1.3.

**6.1.6 THEOREM** *Suppose $f$ is of bounded variation on each closed bounded interval $[a, b]$. The functions*

$$f_1 = \tfrac{1}{2}(Tf + f) \qquad \text{and} \qquad f_2 = \tfrac{1}{2}(Tf - f)$$

*are both monotone nondecreasing and*

$$\begin{aligned}
f = f_1 - f_2, &\qquad Tf = f_1 + f_2, \\
f(0) = f_1(0) = Tf(0), &\qquad f_2(0) = 0.
\end{aligned}$$

*Proof* We show that $f_1$ is monotone nondecreasing; the proof for $f_2$ is similar. Let $a \leq b$; then

$$\begin{aligned}
f_1(b) - f_1(a) &= \tfrac{1}{2}[Tf(b) - Tf(a)] + \tfrac{1}{2}[f(b) - f(a)] \\
&\geq \tfrac{1}{2}T_{ab} - \tfrac{1}{2}\,|f(b) - f(a)|.
\end{aligned}$$

It follows immediately from the definition of $T_{ab}$ that the last expression is nonnegative, and hence $f_1(b) \geq f_1(a)$. The formulas for $f$ and $Tf$ are obvious.

**6.1.7 DEFINITION** *The functions $f_1$ and $f_2$ in the last theorem are called the parts of positive and negative variation of $f$* (see Figure 6.1).

This nomenclature is perhaps made clearer by the equations in Exercise 6.1.1. Finally, let us also define the functions that we have been discussing so far in this chapter.

**6.1.8 DEFINITION** *A function is called of locally bounded variation if it has finite total variation on each bounded closed interval. The set of all functions of locally bounded variation is denoted by $V_{\text{loc}}$, and the subset of monotone nondecreasing functions by $V_{\text{loc}}^+$.*

Our last theorem says that *the functions in $V_{\text{loc}}$ are exactly those that can be expressed as the difference of two monotone nondecreasing functions.* From this characterization it follows easily that $V_{\text{loc}}$ is a linear space, that is, if $f, g \in V_{\text{loc}}$ and $a$ is any real number, then

$$f + g \in V_{\text{loc}} \qquad \text{and} \qquad af \in V_{\text{loc}}.$$

**6.1.9 COROLLARY** *$V_{\text{loc}}$ is a linear space.*

A function $f$ in $V_{\text{loc}}$ may, of course, equal several differences of monotone nondecreasing functions

$$f = g_1 - g_2 = h_1 - h_2 = \cdots.$$

We have already found one such pair $f_1, f_2$ that seems to distinguish itself among all others; namely, the pair of functions in Theorem 6.1.6, the parts of positive and negative variation of $f$. Here is another characterization of $f_1$ and $f_2$ which says that "$f_1$ and $f_2$ are of the smallest possible increase."

**6.1.10 THEOREM** *Let $f \in V_{\text{loc}}$. Among all the pairs $(g_1, g_2)$ of monotone nondecreasing functions satisfying*

$$(6.1.11) \qquad f = g_1 - g_2, \qquad g_2(0) = 0$$

*there is exactly one pair $(f_1, f_2)$, namely the parts of positive and negative variation of $f$, with the property*

$$(6.1.12) \qquad 0 \leq f_i(b) - f_i(a) \leq g_i(b) - g_i(a), \qquad i = 1, 2,$$

*for all pairs $a \leq b$ of real numbers and all pairs $(g_1, g_2)$ satisfying* (6.1.11).

*Proof* Looking at the formula for $f_2$ in Theorem 6.1.6, we see that $f_2(0) = 0$. In Proposition 6.1.3 we have noticed that if $f = g_1 - g_2$, then the total variation $Tf(b) - Tf(a)$ of $f$ on $[a, b]$ is bounded by $g_1(b) - g_1(a) + g_2(b) - g_2(a)$, that is,

$$(f_1(b) + f_2(b)) - (f_1(a) + f_2(a)) \leq (g_1(b) + g_2(b)) - (g_1(a) + g_2(a)).$$

On the other hand we have $f = f_1 - f_2 = g_1 - g_2$, and hence

$$(f_1(b) - f_2(b)) - (f_1(a) - f_2(a)) = (g_1(b) - g_2(b)) - (g_1(a) - g_2(a)).$$

Adding or subtracting this equality to or from the last inequality, we get

$$2(f_i(b) - f_i(a)) \leq 2(g_i(b) - g_i(a)), \qquad i = 1, 2,$$

which proves one part of the theorem. We leave it as an exercise (Exercise 6.1.5) to verify that the pair $(f_1, f_2)$ is uniquely determined by Condition (6.1.12).

## EXERCISES

*6.1.1* Let $f \in V_{\text{loc}}$, and let $f_1$ and $f_2$ be the parts of positive and negative variation of $f$. Prove that

$$f_1(x) = \begin{cases} f(0) + \sup\left\{\sum_{k=1}^{n} (f(a_k) - f(a_{k-1}))^+ : 0 \leq a_0 \leq \cdots \leq a_n \leq x\right\} & \text{if } x \geq 0 \\ f(0) - \sup\left\{\sum_{k=1}^{n} (f(a_k) - f(a_{k-1}))^+ : x \leq a_0 \leq \cdots \leq a_n \leq 0\right\} & \text{if } x \leq 0, \end{cases}$$

$$f_2(x) = \begin{cases} \sup\left\{\sum_{k=1}^{m} (f(b_k) - f(b_{k-1}))^- : 0 \leq b_0 \leq \cdots \leq b_m \leq x\right\} & \text{if } x \geq 0 \\ -\sup\left\{\sum_{k=1}^{m} (f(b_k) - f(b_{k-1}))^- : x \leq b \leq \cdots \leq b_m \leq 0\right\} & \text{if } x \leq 0. \end{cases}$$

*6.1.2* We say that a function on the real line is locally bounded if it is bounded on every closed bounded interval. Prove that every function of locally bounded variation is locally bounded.

*6.1.3* Suppose that $f$ is a differentiable function on the real line, and suppose the derivative $f'$ of $f$ is locally bounded. Prove that $f$ is of locally bounded variation.

*Hint* Use the mean value theorem.

*6.1.4* Give an example of a continuous function that is bounded, but not of locally bounded variation.

*Hint* Consider

$$g(x) = \begin{cases} x \cdot \sin \dfrac{1}{x} & \text{for } x \neq 0 \\ 0 & \text{for } x = 0. \end{cases}$$

*6.1.5* Prove the uniqueness of the pair $(f_1, f_2)$ in Theorem 6.1.10, that is, there is no other pair $(f_1^*, f_2^*)$ of functions such that $f = f_1^* - f_2^*, f_2^*(0) = 0$ and (6.1.12) holds for all real numbers $a \leq b$ and all pairs $(g_1, g_2)$, satisfying (6.1.11).

# 6.2 DECOMPOSITION OF FUNCTIONS OF LOCALLY BOUNDED VARIATION

The material in this section will give some intuitive idea of the behavior of monotone functions and functions of locally bounded variation.

Suppose $f$ is a monotone nondecreasing function. We claim that the limits

$$\lim_{\substack{h\to 0\\ h>0}} f(x+h) \quad \text{and} \quad \lim_{\substack{h\to 0\\ h>0}} f(x-h) \tag{6.2.1}$$

exist for every $x$. In fact, if for instance

$$b = \inf\{f(x+h): h > 0\},$$

then we claim that the first limit in (6.2.1) equals $b$. This infimum exists since, by the monotonicity of $f$, the set $\{f(x+h): h > 0\}$ is bounded below by $f(x)$. Given $\varepsilon > 0$, we can find $h_0$ with

$$0 \leq f(x+h_0) - b \leq \varepsilon$$

and hence

$$0 \leq f(x+h) - b \leq f(x+h_0) - b \leq \varepsilon$$

for $0 < h \leq h_0$. This means exactly that the first limit in (6.2.1) equals $b$. Similarly one proves that the second limit in (6.2.1) equals $\sup\{f(x-h): h > 0\}$. The expressions in (6.2.1) are called the right and the left limit of $f$ at $x$, respectively (see Figure 6.2). We let

$$f(x+0) = \lim_{\substack{h\to 0\\ h>0}} (x+h), \qquad f(x-0) = \lim_{\substack{h\to 0\\ h>0}} (x-h).$$

By linearity we can conclude now that in fact the right and left limits exist for every function in $V_{\text{loc}}$. This leads to the following proposition.

6.2.2 PROPOSITION *If $f \in V_{\text{loc}}$, then the right and left limits $f(x+0)$ and $f(x-0)$ exist at every point $x$.*

It is clear from the definition of continuity that a function $f$ is continuous at $x$ if and only if

$$f(x-0) = f(x) = f(x+0).$$

If $f$ is discontinuous at $x$ but $f(x-0) = f(x+0)$, then $f$ is said to have a removable discontinuity at $x$, since one can make $f$ continuous at $x$ by just redefining

$f$ to be equal $f(x-0)$ at $x$. If $f(x-0) \neq f(x+0)$, then $f$ is said to have a jump at $x$, and the difference

$$f(x+0) - f(x-0)$$

is called the jump of $f$ at $x$.

For a monotone nondecreasing function $f$ the inequality

$$f(x-0) \leq f(x) \leq f(x+0)$$

tells us that $f$ does not have any removable discontinuities; the only discontinuities are jumps. We claim that there are actually not so many of those discontinuities.

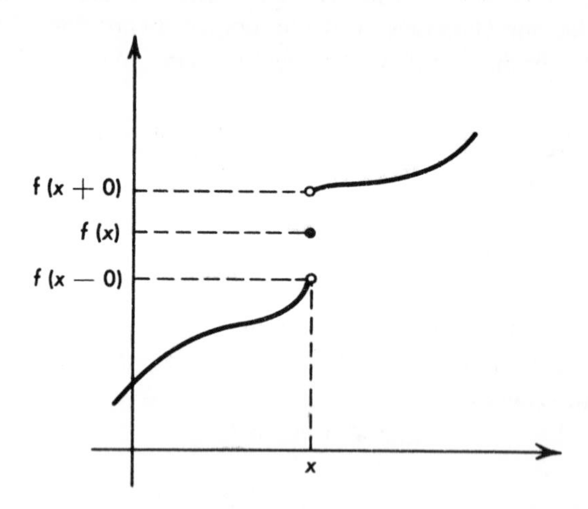


Figure 6.2 The figure characterizes the behavior of a monotone nondecreasing function at a jump.

**6.2.3 PROPOSITION** *A function of locally bounded variation can have at the most a countable number of discontinuities.*

*Proof* Since every function of locally bounded variation is the difference of two monotone nondecreasing functions, it suffices to verify the assertion for monotone nondecreasing functions. Let $f$ be such a function. We need to prove only that $f$ has at the most a countable number of discontinuities in each of the countably many open intervals $(-N, N)$, $N = 1, 2, \cdots$. The sum of any finite number of jumps of $f$ in $(-N, N)$ can never exceed the total increase $f(N) - f(-N)$ of $f$ on $[-N, N]$. Thus there can be at most $n$ points $x$ in $(-N, N)$ with

$$f(x+0) - f(x-0) \geq \frac{1}{n}(f(N) - f(-N)).$$

By counting first the discontinuities of $f$ in $(-N, N)$ with jumps greater than or equal to $\frac{1}{2}(f(N) - f(-N))$ and then those with jumps greater than or equal to $\frac{1}{3}(f(N) - f(-N))$, and so on, we get an enumeration of all the discontinuities of $f$ in $(-N, N)$.

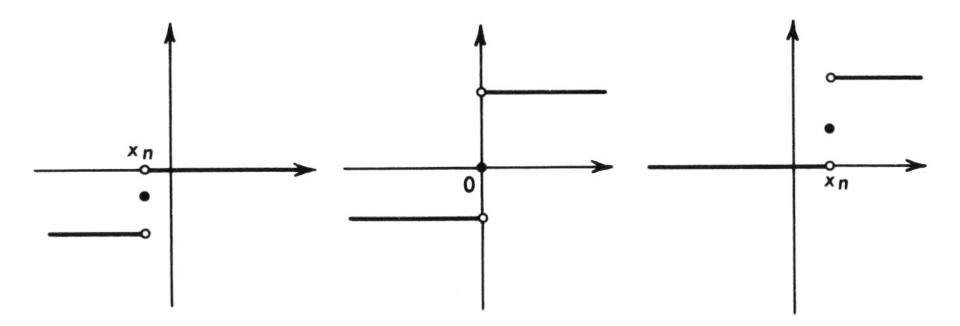


Figure 6.3 The elementary jump functions used in the construction of the jump part of a monotone nondecreasing function.

Let $f$ be a monotone nondecreasing function. We can enumerate the discontinuities of $f$ in a sequence $\{x_n\}$. To each discontinuity $x_n$ of $f$ we are going to assign an elementary jump function $s_n$, which describes the behavior of $f$ at $x_n$. The definition of $s_n$ will be different for each of the three cases $x_n > 0$, $x_n = 0$, and $x_n < 0$ (see Figure 6.3).

$$s_n(x) = \begin{cases} 0 & \text{for } x < x_n \\ f(x_n) - f(x_n - 0) & \text{for } x = x_n \\ f(x_n + 0) - f(x_n - 0) & \text{for } x > x_n \end{cases} \quad \text{if } x_n > 0,$$

$$(6.2.4) \qquad s_n(x) = \begin{cases} f(x_n - 0) - f(x_n) & \text{for } x < x_n \\ 0 & \text{for } x = x_n \\ f(x_n + 0) - f(x_n) & \text{for } x > x_n \end{cases} \quad \text{if } x_n = 0,$$

$$s_n(x) = \begin{cases} f(x_n - 0) - f(x_n + 0) & \text{for } x < x_n \\ f(x_n) - f(x_n + 0) & \text{for } x = x_n \\ 0 & \text{for } x > x_n \end{cases} \quad \text{if } x_n < 0.$$

6.2.5 LEMMA *The functions*

$$f_n = f - \sum_{k=1}^{n-1} s_k$$

*have the following properties:*

(a) $f_n$ *is monotone nondecreasing.*
(b) $f_n$ *is continuous at* $x_1, \cdots, x_{n-1}$ *and at every point at which* $f$ *is continuous.*
(c) $\left.\begin{aligned} f_n(x_k) - f_n(x_k - 0) &= f(x_k) - f(x_k - 0) \\ f_n(x_k + 0) - f_n(x_k) &= f(x_k + 0) - f(x_k) \end{aligned}\right\}$ *for* $k \geq n$.

*Proof* We proceed by induction on $n$. Since $f_1 = f$, the assertions in (a), (b), and (c) hold trivially for $n = 1$. Now suppose (a), (b), and (c) hold for $n = N$. Then (c) implies that $f_N$ has the same kind of jump at $x_N$ as $f$, and thus $f_N - s_N = f_{N+1}$ is going to be continuous at $x_N$; $f_{N+1}$ is continuous at $x_1, \cdots, x_{N-1}$ and at all points $x$ at which $f$ is continuous, since $f_N$ and $s_N$ have this property. This proves (b) for $n = N + 1$, and (a) is also easily verified. To prove (c) for $n = N + 1$, note that $s_N$ is continuous at all points $x \neq x_N$ and thus

$$\begin{aligned} f_{N+1}(x_k) - f_{N+1}(x_k - 0) &= f_N(x_k) - f_N(x_k - 0) - (s_N(x_k) - s_N(x_k - 0)) \\ &= f_N(x_k) - f_N(x_k - 0) \\ &= f(x_k) - f(x_k - 0) \end{aligned}$$

for $k \geq N + 1$. The second equation in (c) is proved similarly.

We will prove now that $\{f_n\}$ converges to a continuous function.

**6.2.6 Lemma** *The series $\sum s_k$ converges uniformly on every closed bounded interval.*

*Proof* First it will be proved that the series converges at every point. The functions $f_n$ are monotone nondecreasing, thus for $a \leq b$,

$$f(b) - f(a) - \sum_{k=1}^{n-1} s_k(b) + \sum_{k=1}^{n-1} s_k(a) = f_n(b) - f_n(a) \geq 0.$$

If we choose $a = 0$ and notice that $s_k(0) = 0$ for all $k$, we find that $\sum_{k=1}^{n-1} s_k(b)$ is bounded above by $f(b) - f(0)$ for $b \geq 0$. The series $\sum s_k(b)$ converges, therefore, because $s_k(b) \geq 0$ for $b \geq 0$. Similarly, if we choose $b = 0$, we find that $\sum_{k=1}^{n-1} s_k(a)$ is bounded below by $f(a) - f(0)$, and so $\sum s_k(a)$ converges also, since $s_k(a) \leq 0$ for $a \leq 0$. Thus

$$s(x) = \sum_{k=1}^{\infty} s_k(x)$$

exists for all $x$. Now it is true in general that every convergent series of monotone nondecreasing functions converges uniformly on every closed bounded interval $[a, b]$. Namely, if $\varepsilon > 0$ we can find an integer $N$ such that

$$\left| \sum_{k=n+1}^{\infty} s_k(a) \right| \leq \varepsilon \quad \text{and} \quad \left| \sum_{k=n+1}^{\infty} s_k(b) \right| \leq \varepsilon$$

for $n \geq N$. Thus

$$\begin{aligned} -\varepsilon \leq \sum_{k=n+1}^{\infty} s_k(a) \leq \sum_{k=n+1}^{\infty} s_k(x) &= s(x) - \sum_{k=1}^{n} s_k(x) \\ &\leq \sum_{k=n+1}^{\infty} s_k(b) \leq \varepsilon \end{aligned}$$

for $x \in [a, b]$ and $n \geq N$, which proves that $\sum s_k$ converges uniformly to $s$ on $[a, b]$.

**6.2.7 DEFINITION** *The monotone nondecreasing function*

$$s = \sum_{k=1}^{\infty} s_k$$

*is called the jump part of $f$. If $f$ is a function of locally bounded variation, $f = f_1 - f_2$ its decomposition into parts of positive and negative variation, and $s_i$ is the jump part of $f_i$, then $s = s_1 - s_2$ is called the jump part of $f$.*

**6.2.8 COROLLARY** *Let $f$ be a function of locally bounded variation and $s$ its jump part. The function*

$$g = f - s$$

*is of locally bounded variation and continuous. If $f$ is monotone nondecreasing, then so is $g$* (see Figure 7.1).

*Proof* Since $s$ is by definition the difference of two monotone nondecreasing functions, it is in $V_{\text{loc}}$ and hence $f - s$ is in $V_{\text{loc}}$. To prove that $g$ is continuous, we may restrict ourselves to the case in which $f$ is monotone nondecreasing. By Lemmas 6.2.5 and 6.2.6,

$$f_n = f - \sum_{k=1}^{n-1} s_k$$

is monotone nondecreasing and converges to $f - s$. This implies easily that $f - s = g$ is monotone nondecreasing. By Lemma 6.2.5, we can find an integer $N$ for any $x$ such that $f_n$ is continuous at $x$ for $n \geq N$ ($N = 1$ if $x$ is none of the $x_k$ and $N = k$ if $x = x_{k-1}$), and since $\{f_n\}$ converges uniformly to $g$ on the interval $[x - 1, x + 1]$, $g$ is continuous at $x$ also. This is a theorem usually proved in calculus. Let us recall how it is done. If $\varepsilon > 0$, we can find an integer $N$ such that $f_N$ is continuous at $x$ and

$$|g(y) - f_N(y)| \leq \frac{\varepsilon}{3}$$

for all $y \in [x - 1, x + 1]$, because $\{f_n\}$ tends to $g$ uniformly on that interval. Since $f_N$ is continuous at $x$, there is a $\delta < 1$ such that

$$|f_N(x) - f_N(y)| \leq \frac{\varepsilon}{3} \qquad \text{for } |x - y| \leq \delta.$$

If $|x - y| \leq \delta < 1$, then $y \in [x - 1, x + 1]$ so that

$$|g(x) - g(y)| \leq |g(x) - f_N(x)| + |f_N(x) - f_N(y)| + |f_N(y) - g(y)|$$
$$\leq 3 \cdot \frac{\varepsilon}{3} = \varepsilon$$

for $|x - y| \leq \delta$. This completes the proof.

## *EXERCISES*

*6.2.1* Observe that the jump part of a continuous function of locally bounded variation is zero. Use this to prove that the jump part of a function of locally bounded variation can be continuous only if it is zero.

*6.2.2* Prove the following lemma: Let $\sum s_n$ be a series of elementary jump functions (functions as in Equations (6.2.4)) that converges uniformly on every bounded interval. If $s = \sum_{n=1}^{\infty} s_n$ is continuous, then $s = 0$. (This lemma also solves the previous exercise.)

*Hint* Each $s_n$ is discontinuous at the most at one point. Let $x_k$ be an enumeration of all the different discontinuities of the $s_n$. Fix $k$ and let $s_{n(1)}, s_{n(2)}, \cdots$ be the elementary jump functions that are discontinuous at $x_k$ (this may be an infinite sequence). Then $t_k = \sum_j s_{n(j)}$ converges. Prove that $t_k$ is constant on $(-\infty, x_k)$ and $(x_k, \infty)$, so that $t_k$ is in fact constant. But $t_k(0) = 0$, whence $t_k = 0$.

*6.2.3* A function of locally bounded variation is said to be a jump function if it differs from its jump part by only a constant. Use Exercise 6.2.2 to prove that the set of jump functions is a linear space.

*6.2.4* Let $f$ be a function of locally bounded variation. Prove that there is only one way of writing $f$ as a sum $f = g + s$ of a continuous function $g$ of locally bounded variation and a jump function $s$ vanishing at 0.

*Hint* Use Exercise 6.2.2.

*6.2.5* Construct a jump function that is discontinuous at all rational numbers.

# 6.3 PREPARATIONS FOR THE DIFFERENTIATION THEOREM

For the remainder of this chapter we will be concerned with the theory of differentiation of functions of locally bounded variation. One of the main theorems that we will achieve in the next section states that a monotone nondecreasing function (and hence every function of locally bounded variation) has a derivative almost everywhere.

We recall that a function $f$ is differentiable at the point $x$ if the limit

$$\lim_{h \to 0} \frac{1}{h} (f(x + h) - f(x))$$

exists, and the limit is then called the derivative of $f$ at $x$ and is denoted by $f'(x)$. Note that differentiability is a local property; the behavior of $f$ in any (arbitrary small) open interval containing $x$ determines whether $f$ is differentiable at $x$ and what value the derivative has if it exists. A function is differentiable on an open interval if it is differentiable at all points in that interval; no knowledge of the behavior of the function outside the interval is needed.

Next we shall discuss differentiability almost everywhere, using the concept of a null set. Since we promised at the beginning of this chapter that we would not rely on any previous material, we will recall the definition and basic properties of null sets.

**6.3.1 DEFINITION** *A subset $E$ of the real line is called a null set if, for every $\varepsilon > 0$, there exists a sequence $\{I_k\}$, $I_k = (a_k, b_k)$, of open intervals such that*

(a) $E \subset \bigcup I_k$,

(b) $\sum_{k=1}^{\infty} |I_k| = \sum_{k=1}^{\infty} (b_k - a_k) \leq \varepsilon.$

The symbol $|I_k|$ denotes the length $b_k - a_k$ of the interval $I_k$. The sum in (b) is also called the total length of the system of intervals $\{I_k\}$. Thus the definition says that a set $E$ is a null set if and only if it can be covered by a countable system of open intervals of arbitrary small total length. For instance every finite set of points is clearly a null set. The main property of null sets that we are using follows.

**6.3.2 PROPOSITION** *Let $\{E_n\}$ be a sequence of null sets. Then*

$$E = \bigcup E_n$$

*is again a null set.*

*Proof* Let $\varepsilon > 0$ and choose for each $n$ a countable system $\{I_{nk}: k = 1, 2, \cdots\}$ of open intervals that covers $E_n$ and has a total length at the most of $2^{-n}\varepsilon$. The system of open intervals

$$\{I_{nk}: n, k = 1, 2, \cdots\}$$

is countable, covers $E$, and has a total length of at the most

$$\sum_{n=1}^{\infty} 2^{-n}\varepsilon = \varepsilon.$$

If a function is differentiable at all points of an open interval with the exception of those belonging to some null set, then we call the function "almost everywhere differentiable" on this interval, which is sometimes abbreviated to "a.e. differentiable"; or we may say that the function is differentiable at almost all points $x \in (a, b)$, which is often abbreviated to "differentiable at a.a. $x$." Since a nonopen interval can be made into an open interval by removing at the most two points, it is clear what one should mean by stating that a function is a.e. differentiable on an aribtrary interval, namely, that it is a.e. differentiable on the open interval which one obtains by removing the end point or end points of the nonopen interval.

The main lemma that we are using for the proof of the differentiability almost everywhere of a monotone nondecreasing function is sometimes referred to as the "rising sun lemma." Let us explain this name by giving first a pictorial statement and proof of this lemma for a continuous function $g$ on an open interval $(a, b)$. View the graph of $g$ as a mountain ridge and imagine the sun just rising at the right. Then the set of $x$ such that $g(x)$ is in the shade is a disjoint union of open intervals $(a_k, b_k)$ such that $g(b_k)$ is a peak obscuring the valley over $(a_k, b_k)$ (see Figure 6.4).

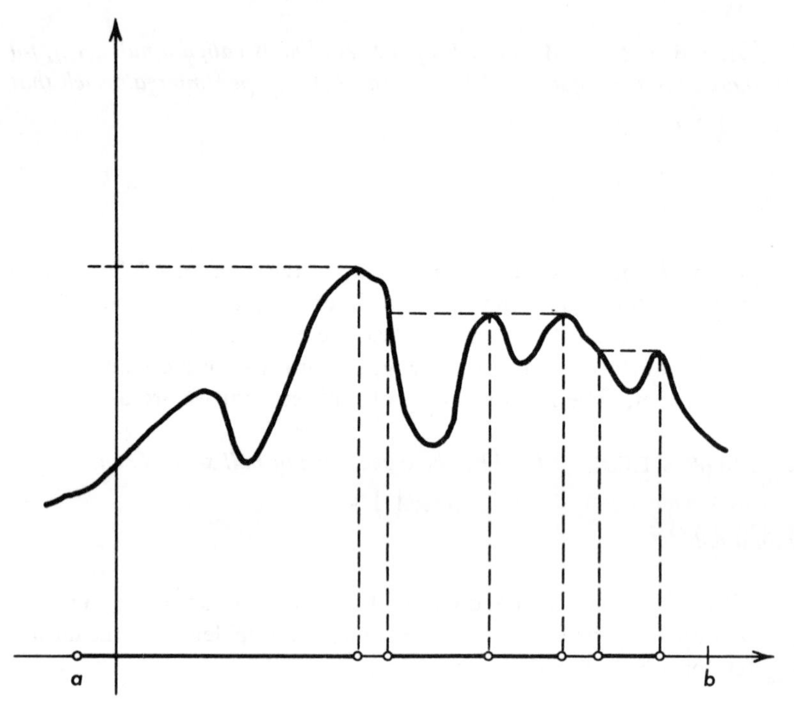


Figure 6.4 The set $E$ in the rising sun lemma is drawn in heavy lines on the $x$-axis.

The lemma is actually true and is needed for upper semicontinuous functions. A function $g$ on an open interval $(a, b)$ is upper semicontinuous at a point $x \in (a, b)$ if

$$g(x) \geq \limsup_{t\to 0} g(x + t) = \limsup_{t\to 0} \{g(x \pm h): 0 < h \leq t\}$$

(see Figure 6.5).

### 6.3.3 Lemma

**The Rising Sun Lemma** *Suppose $g$ is an upper semicontinuous function on the real line. Let $(a, b)$ be a bounded open interval and denote by $E$ the set of points $y \in (a, b)$ such that for some $z \in (y, b)$, $g(y) < g(z)$ holds. Then $E$ is open; hence the* *disjoint union of a sequence of open intervals* $\{(a_k, b_k)\}$, *and on each corresponding half-closed interval* $(a_k, b_k]$, $g$ *assumes its maximum at* $b_k$.

Before we give a proof of this lemma, we want to explain the concept of upper semicontinuity a bit. For instance, every continuous function $g$ on an open interval $(a, b)$ is upper semicontinuous; namely, if $\varepsilon > 0$, we can find a $\delta > 0$ (depending on $x$) such that for $y \in (a, b)$ with $|x - y| \leq \delta$,

$$g(x) - \varepsilon \leq g(y) \leq g(x) + \varepsilon$$

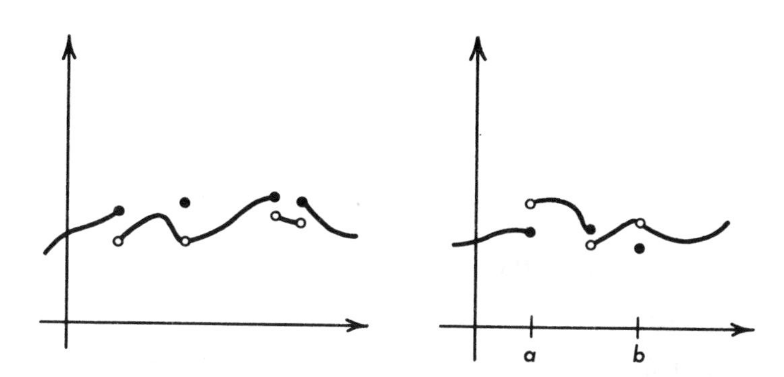


Figure 6.5 The first graph depicts an upper semicontinuous function. The function belonging to the second graph fails to be upper semicontinuous at the points $a$ and $b$.

whence

$$\limsup_{t\to 0} \{g(x \pm h) : 0 < h \leq t\} \leq \sup \{g(x \pm h) : 0 < h \leq \delta\} \leq g(x) + \varepsilon.$$

Since $\varepsilon$ was arbitrary, we find

$$\limsup_{t\to 0} \{g(x \pm h) : 0 < h \leq t\} \leq g(x).$$

(Equality holds here in fact; see Exercise 6.3.1.)

The properties of upper semicontinuous functions utilized here are summed up in the following proposition.

### 6.3.4 Proposition

(a) *If* $g$ *is an upper semicontinuous function on the open interval* $(a, b)$, *and* $[a_0, b_0]$ *is a closed bounded interval contained in* $(a, b)$, *then* $g$ *assumes its maximum on* $[a_0, b_0]$.

(b) *If* $f$ *is another upper semicontinuous function on* $(a, b)$, *then* $f + g$ *is also upper semicontinuous on* $(a, b)$.

*Proof* Let

$$G = \sup \{g(y) : y \in [a_0, b_0]\}$$

We show that $G$ is finite and that $g(x) = G$ for some $x \in [a_0, b_0]$. Let $\{x_n\}$ be any sequence in $[a_0, b_0]$ such that

$$G = \lim_{n\to\infty} g(x_n).$$

There is a subsequence $\{x_{n(k)}\}$ of $\{x_n\}$ which converges in the closed interval $[a_0, b_0]$, say to $x \in [a_0, b_0]$. Then we have also

$$G = \lim_{k\to\infty} g(x_{n(k)}).$$

Hence

$$G = \lim_{k\to\infty} g(x_{n(k)}) \leq \limsup_{t\to 0} \{g(x \pm h):0 < h \leq t\}$$
$$\leq g(x) \leq G$$

which means that $g(x) = G$.

To prove the assertion in (b), choose $\varepsilon > 0$ and find $t_0 > 0$ (dependent on $x$) such that

$$b_t = \sup \{g(x \pm h):0 < h \leq t\} \leq g(x) + \frac{\varepsilon}{2}$$

$$a_t = \sup \{f(x \pm h):0 \leq h \leq t\} \leq f(x) + \frac{\varepsilon}{2}$$

for $0 < t \leq t_0$. Then

$$\sup \{f(x \pm h) + g(x \pm h):0 < h \leq t\} \leq a_t + b_t \leq f(x) + g(x) + \varepsilon$$

for $0 < t \leq t_0$.

*Proof of the Rising Sun Lemma* To prove that $E$ is open, select $y \in E$ and $z \in (y, b)$ such that $g(y) < g(z)$. Then

$$\limsup_{t\to 0} g(y + t) \leq g(y) < g(z);$$

therefore we can find $\varepsilon > 0$ such that

$$g(y \pm h) < g(z) \qquad \text{for } 0 \leq h \leq \varepsilon,$$

and hence $(y - \varepsilon, y + \varepsilon) \subset E$. Thus $E$ is open and therefore it equals the union of a sequence of pair-wise disjoint open intervals $(a_k, b_k)$; this has been proved in Chapter 3 (Lemma 3.3.6); but the reader can prove the assertion himself, if he chooses, by using the hint in Exercise 6.4.5.

Now suppose $(a_k, b_k)$ is one of these intervals. If $g$ does not assume its maximum on $(a_k, b_k]$ at $b_k$, then there is $x \in (a_k, b_k)$ with $g(x) > g(b_k)$. Let $\bar{x}$ be a point in $[x, b_k]$ at which $g$ assumes its maximum value $G$ on $[x, b_k]$. We have

$$g(\bar{x}) = G \geq g(x) > g(b_k)$$

so that in fact $\bar{x} \in [x, b_k) \subset E$. Hence there is a point $\bar{z} \in (\bar{x}, b)$ with $g(\bar{x}) < g(\bar{z})$, and thus

$$g(b_k) < g(\bar{x}) < g(\bar{z}).$$

$\bar{z}$ cannot belong to $[\bar{x}, b_k]$, since $g$ assumes its maximum $G$ on $[x, b_k] \supset [\bar{x}, b_k]$ at $\bar{x}$. Therefore $\bar{z} > b_k$ and hence $b_k \in E$, a contradiction. This completes the proof.

Naturally, we can also let the sun set at the left and then obtain:

**6.3.5 COROLLARY** *Suppose $g$ is an upper semicontinuous function on the real line. Let $(a, b)$ be a bounded open interval and denote by $E$ the set of points $y \in (a, b)$ such that for some $z \in (a, y)$, $g(y) < g(z)$ holds. Then $E$ is open; hence the disjoint union of a sequence of open intervals $(a_k, b_k)$, and on each corresponding half-closed interval $[a_k, b_k)$, $g$ assumes its maximum at $a_k$.*

*Proof* We just have to apply the rising sun lemma to the upper semicontinuous function $g(-x)$ on the interval $(-b, -a)$.

### *EXERCISES*

*6.3.1* Let $g$ be a function on the real line. Prove that if $g$ is continuous at $x$, then $g(x) = \limsup g(x \pm h)$.

*6.3.2* Prove that a function $g$ on the real line is continuous if and only if $g$ and $-g$ are upper semicontinuous.

*6.3.3* Give a simple example of an upper semicontinuous function that does not assume its minimum on $[0, 1]$.

*6.3.4* A set $E$ is said to be open if for each $y \in E$ there is an open interval $(a, b)$ with $y \in (a, b) \subset E$. Prove that the union of a sequence of open sets is open, and that the intersection of any finite number of open sets is open.

*6.3.5* Let $E$ be an open set. Prove that $E$ is the union of a sequence of disjoint open intervals.

*Hint* For each $x \in E$, let $I_x$ be the union of all open intervals $(a, b)$ with $x \in (a, b) \subset E$. Prove that (a) $I_x$ is an open interval, (b) if $x, y \in E$, then either $I_x = I_y$ or $I_x$ and $I_y$ are disjoint, and (c) there are only a countable number of different $I_x$, $x \in E$ and $E$ is the union of them. (Observe that a bounded interval $(a, b)$ can contain at most $n$ different intervals $I_{x_1}, \cdots, I_{x_n}$ with

$$|I_{x_j}| \geq \frac{1}{n}(b - a), \qquad j = 1, \cdots, n.)$$

## 6.4 DIFFERENTIATION OF MONOTONE NONDECREASING FUNCTIONS

The rising sun lemma (Lemma 6.3.3) of the preceding section will now be employed to prove the differentiability almost everywhere of a monotone nondecreasing function.

**6.4.1 THEOREM** *A monotone nondecreasing function is almost everywhere differentiable.*

The proof consists of a series of simple lemmas that finally blend together to yield the asserted theorem.

We introduce the following notations for the four derivates of a function $f$:

*upper right derivate* $f^r$,

$$f^r(x) = \lim_{t \to 0} \sup \left\{ \frac{1}{h} (f(x+h) - f(x)) : 0 < h \le t \right\};$$

*lower right derivate* $f_r$,

$$f_r(x) = \lim_{t \to 0} \inf \left\{ \frac{1}{h} (f(x+h) - f(x)) : 0 < h \le t \right\};$$

*upper left derivate* $f^\ell$,

$$f^\ell(x) = \lim_{t \to 0} \sup \left\{ \frac{1}{h} (f(x) - f(x-h)) : 0 < h \le t \right\};$$

*lower left derivate* $f_\ell$,

$$f_\ell(x) = \lim_{t \to 0} \inf \left\{ \frac{1}{h} (f(x) - f(x-h)) : 0 < h \le t \right\}.$$

These derivates are well defined at every point $x$ provided that we admit $+\infty$ as a "value." Thus these derivates are not functions if we adhere to our convention that functions can have only real numbers as values. Notice that, since $f$ is monotone nondecreasing, the derivates are nonnegative at every point. Also, $f^r(x)$ equals $f_r(x)$ and is finite if and only if

$$\lim_{t > 0, t \to 0} \frac{1}{t} (f(x+t) - f(x))$$

exists (Exercise 6.4.1), and similarly for the left derivates of $f$. Hence the derivative $f'(x)$ of $f$ at $x$ exists if and only if all the derivates of $f$ at $x$ are finite and equal, and then we have

$$f'(x) = f^r(x) = f_r(x) = f^\ell(x) = f_\ell(x).$$

Thus to prove that a monotone nondecreasing function is differentiable almost everywhere, it suffices to show that the relation

$$f^r(x) = f_r(x) = f^\ell(x) = f_\ell(x) < \infty \tag{6.4.2}$$

holds for a.a. $x$.

**6.4.3 Lemma** *Suppose that for every monotone nondecreasing function $f$, the inequalities*

$$f^r(x) < \infty, \tag{6.4.4}$$

$$f^r(x) \le f_\ell(x), \tag{6.4.5}$$

*hold for a.a. $x$. Then Theorem 6.4.1 is a consequence.*

*Proof* It suffices to show that

$$f^r(x) \leq f_\ell(x) \leq f^\ell(x) \leq f_r(x) \leq f^r(x) < \infty$$

holds for a.a. $x$ because the relation (6.4.2) is then satisfied. The first and last of these inequalities hold for a.a. $x$ by the hypotheses of the lemma, and the second and fourth hold for all $x$ as is easily seen from the definition of the derivates of $f$. Thus we have to prove only that $f^\ell(x) \leq f_r(x)$ for a.a. $x$. Let $g$ be the function defined by

$$g(x) = -f(-x).$$

Here $g$ is also monotone nondecreasing. From the equations

$$\frac{1}{h}(g(-x+h) - g(-x)) = \frac{1}{h}(-f(x-h) + f(x))$$
$$= \frac{1}{h}(f(x) - f(x-h))$$
$$\frac{1}{h}(g(-x) - g(-x-h)) = \frac{1}{h}(f(x+h) - f(x))$$

we find that

$$g^r(-x) = f^\ell(x) \qquad \text{and} \qquad g_\ell(-x) = f_r(x)$$

for all $x$. Since $g^r(-x) \leq g_\ell(-x)$ for a.a. $x$ by the assumption in the lemma, we have $f^\ell(x) \leq f_r(x)$ for a.a. $x$, as asserted.

We have to concentrate now on the inequalities (6.4.4) and (6.4.5). It is here that the rising sun lemma of the previous section is needed. We want to apply it to the function $g$,

$$g(x) = f(x) + cx, \qquad c \text{ real}.$$

We could do so if $f$ were upper semicontinuous, since $g$ would then be upper semicontinuous by Proposition 6.3.4. Unfortunately, $f$ might not be upper semicontinuous. Thus another reduction step is needed which will allow us to restrict ourselves to upper semicontinuous monotone nondecreasing functions.

**6.4.6 Lemma** *Suppose $f$ is monotone nondecreasing and define $F$ by*

$$F(x) = f(x+0).$$

*Then $F$ is monotone nondecreasing, right continuous, and upper semicontinuous.*

*Proof* $F$ is certainly monotone nondecreasing, and it is right continuous since

$$F(x+0) = \lim_{t>0,t\to 0} F(x+t) = \lim_{t>0,t\to 0} f((x+t)+0)$$
$$\leq \lim_{t>0,t\to 0} f(x+2t) = f(x+0) = F(x)$$

and thus indeed $F(x + 0) = F(x)$. $F$ is also upper semicontinuous because

$$\begin{aligned}\limsup F(x \pm h) &= \limsup_{t\to 0} \{F(x+h) : 0 < h \leq t\} \\ &= \lim_{t>0, t\to 0} F(x+t) = F(x+0) = F(x).\end{aligned}$$

Notice that the function $F$ in the last lemma differs from $f$ at most at the points of discontinuity of $f$; this is a countable set and therefore a null set.

**6.4.7 LEMMA** *If $x$ is a point of continuity of $f$, then*

$$f^r(x) \leq F^r(x) \qquad \text{and} \qquad F_\ell(x) \leq f_\ell(x).$$

*Thus (6.4.4) and (6.4.5) hold almost everywhere for $f$ if they hold almost everywhere for $F$.*

*Proof* Notice that for all $y$,

$$f(y) \leq f(y+0) = F(y),$$

while $f(x) = F(x)$ if $f$ is continuous at $x$. Therefore,

$$\frac{1}{h}(f(x+h) - f(x)) \leq \frac{1}{h}(F(x+h) - F(x))$$

$$\frac{1}{h}(f(x) - f(x-h)) \geq \frac{1}{h}(F(x) - F(x-h))$$

for $h > 0$, whence the inequalities in the lemma follow immediately.

In order to prove Theorem 6.4.1, it suffices therefore to establish the inequalities (6.4.4) and (6.4.5) almost everywhere for an upper semicontinuous, right continuous, monotone nondecreasing function $f$.

**6.4.8 LEMMA** *Suppose $f$ is an upper semicontinuous, right continuous, monotone nondecreasing function and $(a, b)$ a bounded open interval. For any real number $t > 0$, the set*

$$G_t = \{x \in (a, b) : f^r(x) > t\}$$

*is contained in the union of a sequence of mutually disjoint open intervals of total length less than, or equal to,*

$$\frac{1}{t}(f(b-0) - f(a)),$$

*while the set*

$$H_t = \{x \in (a, b) : f_\ell(x) < t\}$$

*is contained in the union of a sequence $(a_k, b_k)$ of mutually disjoint open intervals satisfying*

$$t(b_k - a_k) \geq f(b_k - 0) - f(a_k).$$

*Proof* We apply the rising sun lemma to the function $g$ defined by

$$g(x) = [f(b-0) \wedge f(x)] - tx,$$

which is right continuous and upper semicontinuous by Proposition 6.3.4, and continuous for $x \geq b$. If $y \in G_t$, then there is $z \in (y, b)$ with

$$\frac{f(z) - f(y)}{z - y} > t.$$

We can rewrite this inequality in the following way:

$$g(z) = f(z) - tz > f(y) - ty = g(y),$$

which tells us that $g(y)$ is in the shade when the sun rises. Hence, by Lemma 6.3.3, $G_t$ is contained in the union of a sequence $\{(a_k, b_k)\}$ of disjoint open intervals and

$$g(b_k) \geq g(a_k + 0) = g(a_k)$$

since $g$ assumes its maximum on $(a_k, b_k]$ at $b_k$. The last inequality means that

$$f(b-0) \wedge f(b_k) - f(a_k) = (f(b-0) \wedge f(b_k)) - (f(b-0) \wedge f(a_k)) \geq tb_k - ta_k.$$

Summing over all $k$, we obtain

$$t\sum_{k=1}^{\infty}(b_k - a_k) \leq \sum_{k=1}^{\infty}(f(b-0) \wedge f(b_k) - f(a_k)) \leq f(b-0) - f(a)$$

the latter holds, since the intervals $(a_k, b_k)$ are disjoint. This proves the assertion for $G_t$.

We proceed similarly in proving the assertion for $H_t$. If $y \in H_t$, then there is $z \in (a, y)$ with

$$\frac{f(y) - f(z)}{y - z} < t,$$

whence

$$g(y) = f(y) - ty < f(z) - tz = g(z)$$

which tells us that $g(y)$ is in the shade when the sun sets at the left. Hence, by Corollary 6.3.5 to the rising sun lemma, $H_t$ is contained in the union of a sequence $\{(a_k, b_k)\}$ of disjoint open intervals, and

$$g(b_k - 0) \leq g(a_k).$$

The latter implies

$$f(b_k - 0) - f(a_k) \leq t(b_k - a_k)$$

as asserted in the lemma.

**6.4.9 COROLLARY** *Let $f$ be as in the last lemma. The set*

$$G = \{x : f^r(x) = \infty\}$$

*is a null set.*

*Proof* Let $(a, b)$ be any bounded interval; for any integer $n > 0$, $G \cap (a, b)$ is contained in the set

$$\{x \in (a, b) : f^r(x) > n\}$$

which, by Lemma 6.4.8, can be covered by a countable system of open intervals of total length less than, or equal to,

$$\frac{1}{n}(f(b) - f(a)).$$

Thus $G \cap (a, b)$ is a null set for every bounded interval $(a, b)$, which means that $G$ is itself a null set.

This establishes the validity almost everywhere of (6.4.4). The proof of (6.4.5) requires a little bit more work.

6.4.10 LEMMA *Let $f$ be as in Lemma* 6.4.8. *For any two rational numbers $q > p > 0$, define*

$$E_{pq} = \{x : f^r(x) > q > p > f_\ell(x)\}.$$

*If $(a, b)$ is any bounded interval, then $E_{pq} \cap (a, b)$ is contained in the union of a sequence of open intervals of total length less than, or equal to,*

$$\frac{p}{q}(b - a).$$

*Proof* $E_{pq} \cap (a, b)$ is contained in the set

$$\{x \in (a, b) : f_\ell(x) < p\}$$

which, by the second part of Lemma 6.4.8, is contained in the union of a sequence $\{(a_k, b_k)\}$ of disjoint open intervals satisfying

$$f(b_k - 0) - f(a_k) \leq p(b_k - a_k).$$

$E_{pq} \cap (a_k, b_k)$ is contained in the set

$$\{x \in (a_k, b_k) : f^r(x) > q\}$$

which, by the first part of Lemma 6.4.8 applied to the interval $(a_k, b_k)$, is contained in the union of a sequence $\{(a_{ki}, b_{ki}) : i \geq 1\}$ of open intervals such that

$$\sum_{i=1}^{\infty} (b_{ki} - a_{ki}) \leq \frac{1}{q}(f(b_k - 0) - f(a_k)).$$

Summing over $k$ and using the previous inequality, we obtain

$$\sum_{k=1}^{\infty}\sum_{i=1}^{\infty}(b_{ki}-a_{ki}) \le \frac{1}{q}\sum_{k=1}^{\infty}(f(b_k-0)-f(a_k))$$

$$\le \frac{p}{q}\sum_{k=1}^{\infty}(b_k-a_k)$$

$$\le \frac{p}{q}(b-a).$$

Thus $E_{pq}\cap(a,b)$ is contained in the union of the countable family $\{(a_{ki},b_{ki}): k,i=1,2,\cdots\}$ of open intervals of total length less, or equal to $p(b-a)/q$.

**6.4.11 COROLLARY** *Let $f$ be as in the last lemma. The set*

$$E=\{x:f^r(x)>f^\ell(x)\}$$

*is a null set.*

*Proof* Since a countable union of null sets is again a null set, and since

$$E=\bigcup E_{pq},$$

where the union runs over all rational numbers $q>p>0$, it suffices to show that each $E_{pq}$ is a null set. For $E_{pq}$ to be a null set, we need only prove that $E_{pq}\cap(a,b)$ is a null set for every bounded interval $(a,b)$. By the last lemma, $E_{pq}\cap(a,b)$ is contained in the union of a sequence $\{(a_k,b_k)\}$ of open intervals with

$$\sum_{k=1}^{\infty}(b_k-a_k)\le\frac{p}{q}(b-a).$$

Applying the lemma again to $E_{pq}\cap(a_k,b_k)$, we conclude that $E_{pq}\cap(a_k,b_k)$ is contained in the union of a sequence $\{(a_{ki},b_{ki}):i\ge 1\}$ of open intervals such that

$$\sum_{i=1}^{\infty}(b_{ki}-a_{ki})\le\frac{p}{q}(b_k-a_k).$$

Summing over $k$ and observing the previous inequality, we get

$$\sum_{k=1}^{\infty}\sum_{i=1}^{\infty}(b_{ki}-a_{ki})\le\frac{p}{q}\sum_{k=1}^{\infty}(b_k-a_k)\le\left(\frac{p}{q}\right)^2(b-a).$$

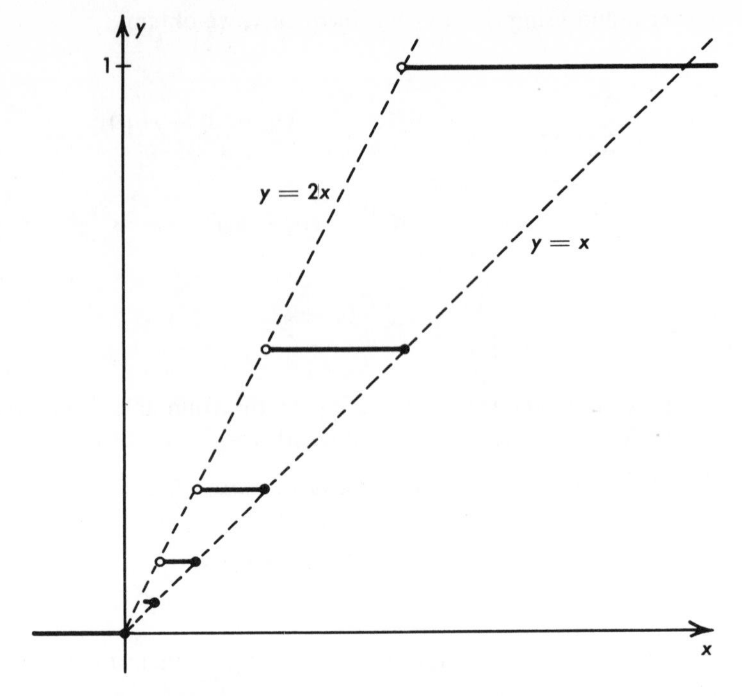


Figure 6.6 A jump function that is continuous at 0 but fails to have a derivative at 0.

Thus $E_{pq} \cap (a, b)$ is actually contained in the union of a countable system of open intervals (namely, $\{(a_{ki}, b_{ki}): i, k = 1, 2, \cdots\}$) of total length less than or equal to,

$$\left(\frac{p}{q}\right)^2 (b - a).$$

If we repeat this procedure over and over again we find that, for any $n$, $E_{pq} \cap (a, b)$ can be covered by a countable system of open intervals of total length less than, or equal to,

$$\left(\frac{p}{q}\right)^n (b - a).$$

Now $\lim (p/q)^n = 0$ since $p/q < 1$, and hence $E_{pq} \cap (a, b)$ is a null set.

This completes the proof of Theorem 6.4.1. The following theorem is a corollary.

6.4.12 THEOREM *A function of locally bounded variation is differentiable almost everywhere.*

Let $f$ be a function of locally bounded variation. In the following we denote by $f'$ the function with the property that $f'(x)$ is the derivative of $f$ at $x$ if it exists, and $f'(x) = 0$ if the derivative of $f$ at $x$ does not exist. $f'$ is called the derivative of $f$.

### *EXERCISES*

*6.4.1* Let $f$ be a monotone nondecreasing function. Prove that

$$\alpha = \lim_{t>0, t\to 0} \frac{1}{t}(f(x+t) - f(x))$$

exists if and only if $f^r(x) = f_r(x) < \infty$, and in this case

$$\alpha = f^r(x) = f_r(x).$$

*6.4.2* Construct a monotone nondecreasing jump function (a function that coincides with its jump part) whose derivative does not exist everywhere off the set of its discontinuities (jumps).

*Hint* Let the graph of the function oscillate at 0 between the lines $y = x$ and $y = 2x$ (see Figure 6.6).

## 6.5 DIFFERENTIATION OF INFINITE SERIES

The power and effectiveness of the seemingly innocent looking differentiation theorem (6.4.1) can be appreciated in the proof of Fubini's theorem on the differentiation of a series of monotone functions (Theorem 6.5.1). Let us recall here, for comparison, a theorem that is usually proved in calculus. Suppose $\sum f_n$ is a series of continuously differentiable functions that converges to a continuously differentiable function $f$. If the series $\sum f_n'$ is uniformly convergent on every bounded interval, then

$$f' = \sum_{n=1}^{\infty} f_n'$$

(see Exercise 6.5.1). Fubini's differentiation theorem requires the functions $f_n$ to be monotone nondecreasing, but it does not place any condition on the differentiated series $\sum f_n'$.

### 6.5.1 THEOREM

FUBINI'S DIFFERENTIATION THEOREM *Suppose*

$$f = \sum_{n=1}^{\infty} f_n$$

*is an everywhere-convergent series of monotone nondecreasing functions. Then*

(6.5.2)
$$f' = \sum_{n=1}^{\infty} f_n' \quad \text{a.e.}$$

*Proof* It immediately follows that the limit function $f$ is again monotone nondecreasing; thus $f$ is differentiable almost everywhere. Let $[a, b]$ be any bounded interval. In order to prove that (6.5.2) holds on $[a, b]$, it suffices to show that we may differentiate the series

$$f - f(a) = \sum_{n=1}^{\infty} (f_n - f_n(a))$$

termwise almost everywhere on $[a, b]$; the constants $f(a)$ and $f_n(a)$ drop out when differentiating. Thus, replacing $f_n$ by $f_n - f_n(a)$, we may as well assume that all the $f_n$ vanish at $a$. Then

$$f_n(x) \geq 0 \qquad \text{for} \quad x \geq a$$

since $f_n$ is monotone nondecreasing. For each integer $k \geq 1$, we can find an integer $n(k)$ such that

$$\sum_{m=n(k)}^{\infty} f_m(b) \leq 2^{-k},$$

because the series $\sum f_m(b)$ converges. We can also pick the integer $n(k)$ greater than $n(k-1)$. Now define a function $t_k$ by

$$t_k(x) = \begin{cases} 0 & \text{for } x \leq a \\ \sum_{m=n(k)}^{\infty} f_m(x) & \text{for } a \leq x \leq b \\ \sum_{m=n(k)}^{\infty} f_m(b) & \text{for } x \geq b. \end{cases}$$

It is clear that the functions $t_k$ are monotone nondecreasing and that

$$0 \leq t_k(x) \leq 2^{-k}$$

for all $x$. Thus the relation

$$t(x) = \sum_{k=1}^{\infty} t_k(x)$$

defines a monotone nondecreasing function $t$. Let $E$ be a null set outside of which all the monotone nondecreasing functions

$$f, f_m, t, t_k, s_n = \sum_{k=n+1}^{\infty} t_k, \qquad m, k, n = 1, 2, \cdots$$

are differentiable. Then for $x \notin E$,

$$t'(x) - s_n'(x) = \left(\sum_{k=1}^{n} t_k\right)'(x) = \sum_{k=1}^{n} t_k'(x),$$

and since $s_n'(x) \geq 0$ for all $n$,

$$t'(x) \geq \sum_{k=1}^{n} t_k'(x) \qquad \text{for } x \notin E, n \geq 1.$$

Consequently, the series $\sum t_k'(x)$ converges for $x \notin E$ as its terms $t_k'(x)$ are nonnegative. This implies that $t_k'(x)$ tends to zero for $x \notin E$. For $x \in (a, b) - E$ we get, therefore,

$$0 = \lim_{k\to\infty} t_k'(x) = \lim_{k\to\infty} \left(f - \sum_{m=1}^{n(k)-1} f_m\right)'(x)$$

$$= \lim_{k\to\infty} \left(f'(x) - \sum_{m=1}^{n(k)-1} f_m'(x)\right).$$

Since $f_m'(x) \geq 0$, the last equation tells us that

$$\sum_{m=1}^{n(k)-1} f_m'(x)$$

increases to $f'(x)$ for $x \in (a, b) - E$; on the other hand,

$$\sum_{m=1}^{n(k)-1} f_m'(x) \leq \sum_{m=1}^{n-1} f_m'(x) \leq \sum_{m=1}^{n(k+1)-1} f_m'(x)$$

for $n(k) \leq n \leq n(k + 1)$, and thus $\sum_{m=1}^{n-1} f_m'(x)$ increases to $f'(x)$ for $x \in (a, b) - E$ also. This completes the proof.

Of course, Theorem 6.5.1 does not include the theorem from calculus that we mentioned earlier, since we are assuming in Theorem 6.5.1 that all the functions $f_n$ are monotone nondecreasing. However, one can derive from Fubini's differentiation theorem a similar proposition for functions of locally bounded variation which, by Exercises 6.5.3 and 6.5.4, will include the theorem on termwise differentiation of series of continuously differentiable functions.

**6.5.3 THEOREM** *Suppose $\sum f_n$ is a series of functions of locally bounded variation such that the corresponding series $\sum Tf_n$ of total variation functions converges. Then $\sum f_n$ converges to a function $f$ of locally bounded variation and*

$$f' = \sum_{m=1}^{\infty} f_n' \qquad \text{a.e.}$$

*Proof* Let $f_n^1$ and $f_n^2$ be the parts of positive and negative variation, respectively. Recall that

$$Tf_n = f_n^1 + f_n^2, \qquad f_n = f_n^1 - f_n^2$$

$$Tf_n(0) = f_n(0) = f_n^1(0), \qquad f_n^2(0) = 0$$

(Theorem 6.1.6). By hypothesis,

$$\sum Tf_n(0) = \sum f_n(0) = \sum f_n^1(0)$$

converges. Furthermore, for $x \geq 0$ we have

$$\begin{aligned} Tf_n(x) - Tf_n(0) &= (f_n^1(x) - f_n^1(0)) + (f_n^2(x) - f_n^2(0)) \\ &\geq f_n^j(x) - f_n^j(0) \geq 0, \qquad j = 1, 2, \end{aligned}$$

and thus, since

$$\sum (Tf_n(x) - Tf_n(0)) = \sum Tf_n(x) - \sum Tf_n(0)$$

converges, $\sum (f_n^j(x) - f_n^j(0))$ converges also. Now $f_n^2(0) = 0$, so we obtain immediately that $\sum f_n^j(x)$ converges for $j = 2$; and for $j = 1$ we can conclude the same, since $\sum f_n^1(0)$ converges. A similar argument yields that $\sum f_n^j(x), j = 1, 2,$ converges for $x \leq 0$. Let

$$f^j(x) = \sum_{n=1}^{\infty} f_n^j(x).$$

$f^1$ and $f^2$ are monotone nondecreasing and

$$f^1 - f^2 = \sum_{n=1}^{\infty} (f_n^1 - f_n^2) = \sum_{n=1}^{\infty} f_n.$$

Thus $\sum f_n$ converges to the function $f = f^1 - f^2$ of locally bounded variation. By Theorem 6.5.1 we obtain finally

$$\begin{aligned} f' = f_1' - f_2' &= \sum_{n=1}^{\infty} (f_n^1)' - \sum_{n=1}^{\infty} (f_n^2)' \\ &= \sum_{n=1}^{\infty} (f_n^1 - f_n^2)' \\ &= \sum_{n=1}^{\infty} f_n' \qquad \text{a.e.} \end{aligned}$$

## *EXERCISES*

*6.5.1* Let $\sum f_n$ be a series of continuously differentiable functions $f_n$, and assume that $\sum f_n$ converges to a continuously differentiable function $f$. If $\sum_n f'$ converges uniformly on every bounded interval, then $f' = \sum_{n=1}^{\infty} f_n$.

***Hint*** Let $\sum_{n=1}^{\infty} f_n' = g$. Prove that for any bounded interval $(a, b)$, $\sum \int_a^t f_n'\, dx$ converges for $t \in (a, b)$ to $\int_a^t g\, dx$, and observe that $\sum_{n=1}^{\infty} \int_a^t f_n'\, dx$ differs on $(a, b)$ from $\sum_{n=1}^{\infty} f_n = f$ at most by a constant.

*6.5.2* Let $f$ be a continuously differentiable function. Prove that $f$ is of locally bounded variation. Prove also that

$$|Tf(x)| \leq |f(0)| + |x| \sup \{|f'(y)| : -x \leq y \leq x\}.$$

*6.5.3* Use Exercise 6.5.2 and Theorem 6.5.3 to prove the following. If $\sum f_n$ is a series of continuously differentiable functions that converges at 0, and if

$\sum f_n'$ converges uniformly on every bounded interval, then $\sum f_n$ converges to a function $f$ of locally bounded variation and $f' = \sum_{n=1}^{\infty} f_n'$ a.e.

*6.5.4* Deduce Exercise 6.5.1 from Exercise 6.5.3.

*Hint* $f'$ and $\sum_{n=1}^{\infty} f_n'$ are continuous in Exercise 6.5.1. Now prove that two continuous functions that are equal almost everywhere are actually identical.

*6.5.5* Use Fubini's differentiation theorem to prove that the derivative of the jump part of a function in $V_{\text{loc}}$ vanishes almost everywhere.

## 6.6 EXERCISES

### A. Functions of Locally Bounded Variation

**6.6.1** Suppose $f, g \in V_{\text{loc}}$. Prove that the following functions belong also to $V_{\text{loc}}$:

$$|f|, f \vee g, f \wedge g, f^+, f^-.$$

**6.6.2**

(a) Denote by $T(f, a, b)$ the total variation of $f \in V_{\text{loc}}$ on the bounded closed interval $[a, b]$. Prove

$$T(\alpha f + \beta g, a, b) \leq |\alpha|\, T(f, a, b) + |\beta|\, T(g, a, b)$$

for all real numbers $\alpha$, $\beta$.

(b) Suppose the series $\sum f_n$ of functions of locally bounded variation converges everywhere to a function $f \in V_{\text{loc}}$. Prove

$$T(f, a, b) \leq \sum_{n=1}^{\infty} T(f_n, a, b) \qquad \text{for } a \leq b.$$

(This is trivial if the right-hand side diverges to $\infty$.)

*Hint* Prove that

$$\sum_{k=1}^{m} |f(a_k) - f(a_{k-1})| \leq \sum_{n=1}^{\infty} T(f_n, a, b)$$

for all sequences $a \leq a_0 \leq \cdots \leq a_m \leq b$.

**6.6.3** Prove that

$$Tf(b - 0) - Tf(a + 0) = \sup\left\{\sum_{k=1}^{n} |f(a_k) - f(a_{k-1})| : a < a_0 \leq \cdots \leq a_n < b\right\}.$$

**6.6.4** Find the total variation function $Tf$ and the parts of positive and negative variation, $f_1$ and $f_2$, for the following functions $f$ of locally bounded variation:

(a) $f(x) = |x|$,
(b) $f(x) = x^2$,
(c) $f(x) = x(x^2 - 1)$,
(d) $f(x) = x^2(x - 1)$,
(e) $f$ is a step function.

**6.6.5** Let $f$ be a continuously differentiable function. We have seen in Exercise 6.5.2 that $f \in V_{\text{loc}}$. Suppose the set $\{x : f'(x) = 0\}$ can be enumerated as $\{a_n, n = 0, \pm 1, \cdots\}$ in such a way that $a_n < a_{n+1}$ for all integers $n$. Describe $Tf$ in terms of $f$ and observe that $Tf$ is also continuously differentiable.

**6.6.6** Let $\sum b_n$ be an absolutely convergent series and $\{a_n\}$ any sequence of distinct points on the real line. Define

$$f(x) = \begin{cases} b_n & \text{if } x = a_n \\ 0 & \text{if } x \neq a_n,\ n = 1, \cdots \end{cases}$$

Prove that $f \in V_{\text{loc}}$. Find a description for the total variation function $Tf$ and the parts of positive and negative variation, $f_1$ and $f_2$.

**6.6.7** Give an example of a convergent series $\sum b_n$ (which does not converge absolutely) and a sequence $\{a_n\}$ of points for which the function $f$ in Exercise 6.6.6 is not in $V_{\text{loc}}$.

## B. Convergence Theorems

**6.6.8** Let $f \in V_{\text{loc}}$ and $f_1$ and $f_2$ its parts of positive and negative variation. Prove

(a) $|f(x)| \leq |Tf(x)| + 2|f(0)|$,
(b) $|f_j(x)| \leq |Tf(x)| + 2\,|f(0)|, j = 1, 2$.

**6.6.9**

(a) For $g, h \in V_{\text{loc}}$ with $g(0) = h(0) = 0$, prove

$$|T(g + h)| \leq |Tg| + |Th|.$$

(b) Suppose $f_n \in V_{\text{loc}}$ and $f_n(0) = 0$ for all $n$. If $\sum f_n$ converges everywhere to $f \in V_{\text{loc}}$, then

$$|Tf| \leq \sum_{n=1}^{\infty} |Tf_n|$$

everywhere. (Note that the right-hand side may diverge to $\infty$ at some points.)

*Hint* Use Exercise 6.6.2(b).

**6.6.10** We say that a sequence $\{f_n\}$ in $V_{\text{loc}}$ converges to $f \in V_{\text{loc}}$ in $V_{\text{loc}}$ if

$$\lim_{n\to\infty} T(f - f_n) = 0$$

everywhere. Suppose the sequence $\{f_n\}, f_n \in V_{\text{loc}}$ tends to $f \in V_{\text{loc}}$ in $V_{\text{loc}}$. Prove that $\lim_{n\to\infty} f_n = f$ everywhere.

*Hint* Observe first that $Tf_n(0) = f_n(0)$ and that $\{f_n(0)\}$ converges to $f(0)$. Then apply Exercise 6.6.8(a) to $f - f_n$.

**6.6.11** If $\{f_n\}$ is a sequence in $V_{\text{loc}}$ such that

$$\lim_{n,m\to\infty} T(f_n - f_m) = 0$$

everywhere, then $\{f_n\}$ converges pointwise to a function $f \in V_{\text{loc}}$.

*Hint* First observe that $\{f_n(0)\}$ converges. Then apply Exercise 6.6.8(b) to $f^j - f_n^j, j = 1, 2$ (where $f_n^1$ and $f_n^2$ are the parts of positive and negative variation of $f_n$) to prove that $\{f_n^1\}$ and $\{f_n^2\}$ converge. (Compare with the proof of Theorem 6.5.3.)

**6.6.12** Let $f_n \in V_{\text{loc}}$ as in Exercise 6.6.11, and

$$f = \lim_{n\to\infty} f_n.$$

Prove that actually

$$\lim_{n\to\infty} T(f - f_n) = 0$$

that is, $f_n$ converges to $f$ in $V_{\text{loc}}$.

*Hint* First observe that $\lim T(f - f_n)(x) = 0$ for $x = 0$. Then explain why you may assume that $f(0) = f_n(0) = 0$ for all $n$, replacing $f_n$ by $f_n - f_n(0)$ if necessary. Let $a < b$ and pick a subsequence $f_{n(k)}$ with

$$|T(f_{n(k)}) - f_{n(k-1)})(x)| \leq 2^{-k} \qquad \text{for } x = a, b;$$

then this estimate holds for all $x \in [a, b]$. Use Exercise 6.6.9 to prove that $|T(f - f_{n(k)})(x)| \leq 2^{-k}$ for $x \in [a, b]$. Notice that $f - f_{n(k)} = \sum_{j=k}^{\infty}(f_{n(j+1)} - f_{n(j)})$, whence

$$\lim_{k\to\infty} T(f - f_{n(k)})(x) = 0$$

for $x \in [a, b]$. Now use Exercise 6.6.9 again to prove

$$\lim_{n\to\infty} T(f - f_n)(x) = 0$$

for $x \in [a, b]$. Notice: $f - f_{n(k)} = (f - f_n) + (f_n - f_{n(k)})$.

## C. Functions of Bounded Variation

*Definition* *A function $f \in V_{\text{loc}}$ is of bounded variation if $Tf$ is bounded.*

**6.6.13** Suppose $f$ is of bounded variation. Prove that in this case the following limits exist.

$$Tf(\infty) = \lim_{x\to\infty} Tf(x), \qquad Tf(-\infty) = \lim_{x\to-\infty} Tf(x),$$

$$f(\infty) = \lim_{x\to\infty} f(x), \qquad f(-\infty) = \lim_{x\to-\infty} f(x).$$

**6.6.14** Suppose that $f$ is of bounded variation. Prove that

$$Tf(\infty) - Tf(-\infty) = \sup\left\{\sum_{k=1}^{n} |f(a_k) - f(a_{k-1})| : a_0 \le \cdots \le a_n\right\}.$$

This is the total variation of $f$ (on the real line).

In the following let $V$ be the set of functions $f$ of bounded variation with $f(-\infty) = 0$, and define $\|f\|_V = Tf(\infty) - Tf(-\infty)$ for $f \in V$.

**6.6.15**

(a) Prove that $V$ is a linear space and that $\|f\|_V$ is a norm for $V$, that is,

$$\|\alpha f + \beta g\|_V \le |\alpha|\,\|f\|_V + |\beta|\,\|g\|_V$$

for $f, g \in V$ and all real numbers $\alpha, \beta$.

(b) Suppose the series $\sum f_n$ of functions $f_n \in V$ converges everywhere to $f \in V$. Prove that

$$\|f\|_V \le \sum_{n=1}^{\infty} \|f_n\|_V.$$

*Hint* The proof is identical to the one in Exercise 6.6.2(b).

**6.6.16** Let $g$ be of bounded variation. Define $g^1$ and $g^2$ by

$$g^1(x) = \tfrac{1}{2}(T(g, -\infty, x) + g(x))$$
$$g^2(x) = \tfrac{1}{2}(T(g, -\infty, x) - g(x))$$

where $T(g, -\infty, x)$ is the total variation of $g$ on $(-\infty, x]$. Then

$$g = g^1 - g^2, \qquad T(g, -\infty, x) = g^1(x) + g^2(x).$$

(a) Prove that

$$g^j(x) = g_j(x) + \tfrac{1}{2}(T(g, -\infty, 0) - g(0)), \qquad j = 1, 2$$

where $g_1$ and $g_2$ are the parts of positive and negative variation of $g$. Thus $g^1$ and $g^2$ are monotone nondecreasing.

(b) Prove that $g^j \in V$, $j = 1, 2$ if $g \in V$.

**6.6.17** If $g \in V$, then $0 \leq |g| \leq \|g\|_V$ and $0 \leq |g^j| \leq \|g\|_V$, $j = 1, 2$, where $g^1$ and $g^2$ are as in Exercise 6.6.16.

**6.6.18** Prove that if $f, f_n \in V$ and

$$\lim_{n\to\infty} \|f - f_n\|_V = 0,$$

then $\lim_{n\to\infty} f_n = f$ everywhere.

*Hint* Apply Exercise 6.6.17 to $f - f_n$.

**6.6.19** Suppose $\{f_n\}, f_n \in V$, is a Cauchy sequence, that is,

$$\lim_{n,m\to\infty} \|f_n - f_m\|_V = 0.$$

Then there is $f \in V$ such that $\lim_{n\to\infty} f_n = f$ everywhere.

*Hint* Let $f_n^j$, $j = 1, 2$, be defined as in Exercise 6.6.16. Use Exercise 6.6.17 to prove that $\{f_n^j\}$ converges to a bounded monotone nondecreasing function $f^j$ vanishing at $-\infty$.

**6.6.20** Prove that $V$ is complete: If $\{f_n\}, f_n \in V$ is a Cauchy sequence, then there is $f \in V$ with

$$\lim_{n\to\infty} \|f - f_n\|_V = 0.$$

*Hint* As we have seen in Exercise 6.6.19, $\{f_n\}$ converges pointwise to a function $f \in V$. Pick a subsequence $f_{n(k)}$ such that $\|f_{n(k)} - f_{n(k-1)}\|_V \leq 2^{-k}$. Then use Exercise 6.6.15 to prove $\|f - f_{n(k)}\|_V \leq 2^{-k}$. Then apply Exercise 6.6.15 again to show that $\lim_{n\to\infty} \|f - f_n\|_V = 0$. (Compare the hint in Exercise 6.6.12.)

## D. Differentiation

**6.6.21** Consider the series $\sum \frac{1}{n^2} e^{-n^2x^2}$.

(a) Prove that the corresponding series of the derivatives does not converge uniformly on $[-1, 1]$.
(b) Prove that the series converges everywhere to a function $f$ of locally bounded variation. Find a series representation for $f'$ a.e.

*Hint* Show that the total variation of $e^{-n^2x^2}$ is 2; use Theorem 6.5.3.

**6.6.22** Let $f$ be a function of locally bounded variation. Prove that $(Tf)' = |f'|$ a.e.

*Hint* Let $[a, b]$ be any bounded interval. For each $n$ select a sequence $a = a_0{}^n < \cdots < a^n_{s(n)} = b$ such that

$$\sum_{k=1}^{s(n)} |f(a_k) - f(a_{k-1})|$$

differs from $Tf(b) - Tf(a)$ at the most by $2^{-n}$. Define $f_n$ by induction on $k$ as follows: $f(x) = Tf(a)$ if $x = a_0{}^n$ and

$$f_n(x) = \begin{cases} f(x) - f(a^n_{k-1}) + f_n(a^n_{k-1}) & \text{if } f(a_k{}^n) \geq f(a^n_{k-1}) \\ -f(x) + f(a^n_{k-1}) + f_n(a^n_{k-1}) & \text{if } f(a_k{}^n) < f(a^n_{k-1}) \end{cases} \quad \text{for } a^n_{k-1} \leq x \leq a_k{}^n$$

that is, on $[a^n_{k-1}, a_k{}^n]$, $f_n(x) = f(x) + \text{constant}$ if $f(a_k{}^n) \geq f(a^n_{k-1})$ and $f_n(x) = -f(x) + \text{constant}$ if $f(a_k{}^n) < f(a^n_{k-1})$, the constants being chosen in such a way that $f_n$ is well defined at the points $a_k{}^n$, and $f_n(a) = Tf(a)$. Notice that $f_n'(x) = \pm f'(x)$ a.e. on $[a, b]$ and

$$f_n(a_k{}^n) - f_n(a^n_{k-1}) = |f(a_k{}^n) - f(a^n_{k-1})|,$$

$$Tf(b) - f_n(b) = Tf(b) - Tf(a) - \sum_{k=1}^{s(n)} [f_n(a_k{}^n) - f_n(a^n_{k-1})] \leq 2^{-n}.$$

Show that $Tf - f_n$ is monotone nondecreasing on $[a, b]$. Notice that

$$Tf(x) - Tf(x') \geq |f(x) - f(x')| \geq f_n(x) - f_n(x')$$

if $x > x'$ belongs to the same interval $[a^n_{k-1}, a_k{}^n]$. Thus

$$0 \leq \sum_{n=1}^{\infty} (Tf(x) - f_n(x)) \leq \sum_{n=1}^{\infty} (Tf(b) - f_n(b)) \leq \sum_{n=1}^{\infty} 2^{-n}$$

for $x \in [a, b]$. Now apply Fubini's differentiation theorem to prove $\lim [(Tf)'(x) - f_n'(x)] = 0$ for a.a. $x \in [a, b]$. Since $f_n'(x) = \pm f'(x)$ a.e. on $[a, b]$ and $(Tf)'(x) \geq 0$ for a.a. $x$, the assertion now follows easily.

**6.6.23** Let $f_1$ and $f_2$ be the parts of positive and negative variation of the function $f \in V_{\text{loc}}$. Use the previous exercise to prove that $f_1' = (f')^+$ and $f_2' = (f')^-$ a.e.

**6.6.24** Suppose $f, f_n \in V_{\text{loc}}$ and

$$\lim_{n \to \infty} T(f - f_n) = 0.$$

Prove that there is a subsequence $\{f_{n(k)}\}$ such that

$$f' = \lim_{k \to \infty} f'_{n(k)} \text{ a.e.}$$

*Hint* See the hint in Exercise 6.6.12. (Note that it is false in general that $f' = \lim_{n \to \infty} f_n'$ a.e.)

**6.6.25** Find a continuous function $f \in V_{\text{loc}}$ such that the derivative of $f$ does not exist at any rational point.

## E. The Density Theorem and the Theorem on Derivates

Let $E$ be a subset of the real line. A point $x$ on the real line, belonging to $E$ or not, is said to be a *density point* of $E$ if

$$\lim_{h,k \to 0} \frac{\sigma^*(E \cap (x-h, x+k))}{h+k} = 1 \qquad (h, k > 0),$$

where $\sigma^*$ denotes outer measure (see Definition 3.5.1).

**6.6.26** Show that almost all points of an arbitrary set $E$ of real numbers are density points of $E$.

*Hint* It suffices to show this for a set $E$, which is contained in a bounded interval $(a, b)$. Then $f(x) = \sigma^*(E \cap (-\infty, x))$ defines a bounded monotone nondecreasing function with the property that $f'(x) = 1$ if and only if $x$ is a density point of $E$. Let $E_n$ be an open set satisfying

$$E \subset E_n \subset (a, b), \qquad \sigma^*(E_n) \leq \sigma^*(E) + 2^{-n}, \qquad n \geq 1,$$

(see Proposition 3.5.6). Note that if $f_n(x) = \sigma(E_n \cap (-\infty, x))$, then $f_n'(x) = 1$ for all $n$ and $x$ in $E$. Now use Fubini's differentiation theorem on the series $\sum (f_n - f)$.

The following exercises concern the derivates of an arbitrary function of one variable. It is well known—examples are given in many calculus textbooks—that such functions, even if continuous, may be nondifferentiable at all points on the real line. Nevertheless, the behavior of the derivates is not quite irregular. The neatest statement of this kind is obtained by using two-sided derivates, the *upper derivate:*

$$\limsup_{t \to 0} \left\{\frac{1}{h+k}(f(x+h) - f(x-k)) : 0 < h, k \leq t, h + k \neq 0\right\} = f^r(x) \vee f^\ell(x).$$

and the *lower derivate:*

$$\liminf_{t \to 0} \left\{\frac{1}{h+k}(f(x+h) - f(x-k)) : 0 < h, k \leq t, h + k \neq 0\right\} = f_r(x) \wedge f^\ell(x).$$

*Theorem* *For any function $f$, the real line is the union of three sets, the first of which is a null set, the second consists of those points where the upper derivate is plus infinity and the lower derivate is minus infinity, and the third is the set of points where $f$ is differentiable.*

This theorem follows immediately from the result of Exercise 6.6.31. Thus, if the third set is empty, then the upper derivate of $f$ has to be plus infinity and the lower derivate minus infinity almost everywhere.

**6.6.27** Let $f$ be an arbitrary function on the real line and define $E$ to be the set of points $x > 0$ for which $f(x) - f(y) > 0$ for all $y \in (0, x)$. Show that

$$f_E'(x) = \lim_{h \to 0} \left\{ \frac{1}{h} (f(x+h) - f(x)) : x, x + h \in E \right\}$$

exists for a.a. $x \in E$.

*Hint* Apply Theorem 6.4.1 to the function $f_E$ defined on $(0, b)$, $b = \sup \{z : z \in E\}$, by

$$f_E(x) = \sup \{f(y) : 0 < y \leq x\}.$$

**6.6.28** Let $f_E'$ be defined as in the previous exercise. Show that $f_E'(x) = f^r(x)$ for a.a. $x$ in $E$.

*Hint* Let $x$ be a density point of $E$ as well as a point of existence of $f_E'(x)$. By definition, $f_E'(x) \leq f^r(x)$. To prove the converse inequality use the fact that if $x$ is a density point of $E$, then to each $\varepsilon > 0$ there is a $\delta > 0$ such that for each $h \in (0, \delta)$ there exists a $k \in (h, (1 + \varepsilon)h)$ with $x + k \in E$. Combine this with the inequality $f(x + h) < f(x + k)$ (valid by the hypothesis on $E$) to obtain $f^r(x) \leq f_E'(x)$.

**6.6.29** Show that $f_E'(x) = f_\ell(x)$ for a.a. $x$ in $E$.

**6.6.30** Show that $f_\ell(x) = f^r(x)$ for a.a. $x$ such that $f_\ell(x) > -\infty$.

*Hint* The set of all points $x$ such that $f_\ell(x) > -\infty$ is the union of the sets

$$E_{pq} = \left\{ x : x > p, \frac{f(x) - f(y)}{x - y} > q \text{ for } y \in (p, x) \right\}$$

as $p$ and $q$ range over all rational numbers. For each $E_{pq}$ separately one proves that $f_\ell(x) = f^r(x)$ a.e. by applying the results of the preceding two exercises to the function $g$ defined by

$$g(x) = f(x + p) - qx.$$

**6.6.31** Show that there is a null set $F$ such that, if $x$ is not in $F$, then all four of the following statements are true:

$$\begin{aligned}
f_\ell(x) &= f^r(x) \qquad \text{if } f_\ell(x) > -\infty, \\
f_r(x) &= f_\ell(x) \qquad \text{if } f_r(x) > -\infty, \\
f^\ell(x) &= f_r(x) \qquad \text{if } f^\ell(x) < \infty, \\
f^r(x) &= f^\ell(x) \qquad \text{if } f^r(x) < \infty.
\end{aligned}$$

*Hint* Apply Exercise 6.6.30 to $f(-x)$, $-f(x)$, and $-f(-x)$.

## 6.7 INTEGRATION AS INVERSE OF DIFFERENTIATION

One way of introducing the concept of integration in calculus is to define it as an inverse operation of differentiation. In a similar manner one can derive the theory of Lebesgue integration on the real line from the more subtle theory of differentiation discussed in the previous sections of this chapter. We will outline the method briefly in this section leaving some of the details to the student. In particular we assume that the student has solved Exercises 6.6.22 and 6.6.23, since these will be used in the following. Let us now forget the theory of Lebesgue integration for the remainder of this section.

We denote by $V^+$ the set of bounded monotone nondecreasing functions on the real line, and by $V$ the vector space of functions that can be written as the difference of two functions in $V^+$. The functions in $V$ are called functions of bounded variation. If $F \in V$, then the total variation function $TF$ and the parts $F_1$ and $F_2$ of positive and negative variation of $F$ belong to $V^+$. Namely, if $F = G_1 - G_2$ where $G_1, G_2 \in V^+$ and $G_2(0) = 0$, then $F_1$ and $F_2$ are bounded because $G_1$ and $G_2$ are bounded, and according to Theorem 6.1.10,

$$F_i(b) - F_i(a) \leq G_i(b) - G_i(a), \; i = 1, 2$$

for $b \geq a$. Consequently, $TF = F_1 + F_2$ is also bounded.

Notice that for a function $F$ in $V^+$ the limits

$$F(\infty) = \lim_{x\to\infty} F(x), \qquad F(-\infty) = \lim_{x\to-\infty} F(x)$$

exist. We can thus define the integral of a nonnegative function in the following way:

**6.7.1 Definition** *A nonnegative function $f$ on the real line is called integrable if and only if there is a bounded monotone nondecreasing function $F$ such that $F' = f$ a.e. The integral of $f$ is defined by the formula*

$$\int f\,dx = \inf\{F(\infty) - F(-\infty) : F \in V^+, F' = f \text{ a.e.}\}.$$

**6.7.2 Proposition** *Suppose $f$ is integrable. There is an $F \in V^+$ satisfying $F' = f$ a.e. and*

$$\int f\,dx = F(\infty) - F(-\infty),$$

*and if $F_0$ is any other function in $V^+$ with the same property, then $F - F_0$ is a constant.*

*Proof* We let

$$F(x) = \inf\{G(x) : G \in V^+, G(-\infty) = 0, G' = f \text{ a.e.}\}. \tag{6.7.3}$$

$F$ belongs to $V^+$ and $F(-\infty) = 0$. We have also

$$\int f\,dx = F(\infty) - F(-\infty) = F(\infty).$$

It remains to be shown that $F' = f$ a.e. To do this we need the following result.

*If $G \in V^+$ satisfies $G(-\infty) = 0$ and $G' = f$ a.e., then $G - F \in V^+$.* In fact, suppose $a \leq b$. We can find a function $H$ in $V^+$ for any $\varepsilon > 0$ satisfying $H' = f$ a.e., and such that

$$F(a) + \varepsilon \geq H(a) \geq F(a).$$

The function $K$ defined by

$$K(x) = \begin{cases} H(x) & \text{for } x \leq a \\ G(x) - G(a) + H(a) & \text{for } x > a \end{cases}$$

is monotone nondecreasing and satisfies $K(-\infty) = 0$ and $K' = f$ a.e. Thus $K(b) \geq F(b)$ by the definition of $F$; this can also be written as

$$G(b) - G(a) = K(b) - H(a) \geq F(b) - F(a) - \varepsilon.$$

This shows that $G(b) - G(a) \geq F(b) - F(a)$, since $\varepsilon$ was arbitrary.

Now we can complete the proof of Proposition 6.7.2. Since $F(\infty) = \inf\{G(\infty): G \in V^+, G(-\infty) = 0, G' = f \text{ a.e.}\}$, we can find a sequence $\{G_n\}$ of functions in $V^+$ satisfying $G_n(-\infty) = 0$, $G_n' = f$ a.e. and

$$0 \leq G_n(\infty) - F(\infty) \leq 2^{-n}.$$

$G_n - F$ is monotone nondecreasing, as we have observed above. Hence

$$0 \leq G_n(x) - F(x) \leq 2^{-n}$$

so that $\sum (G_n - F)$ is a convergent series monotone nondecreasing functions. Fubini's differentiation theorem (6.5.1) tells us now that $\sum (G_n - F)'$ converges. This proves $F' = f$ a.e.

Now suppose $F_0 \in V^+$ also satisfies $F_0' = f$ a.e. and

$$\int f\,dx = F_0(\infty) - F_0(-\infty).$$

Then

$$H = F_0 - F_0(-\infty) - F$$

is monotone nondecreasing by our above observation, and

$$H(-\infty) = F(-\infty) = 0,$$

$$H(\infty) = F_0(\infty) - F_0(-\infty) - F(\infty) = \int f\,dx - \int f\,dx = 0.$$

Consequently $F = F_0 - F_0(-\infty)$, and this completes the proof of Proposition 6.7.2.

In the following we need a lemma that generalizes the remark made in the proof of the last proposition.

**6.7.4 LEMMA** *Suppose $f$ is integrable and $F \in V^+$ is defined by Equation* (6.7.3). *If $G \in V^+$ satisfies $G' \geq f$ a.e. then*

$$G(b) - G(a) \geq F(b) - F(a)$$

*for $b \geq a$, that is, $G - F \in V^+$. In particular, $G(x) \geq F(x)$ if $G(-\infty) = 0$.*

*Proof* We have to show that the part $H$ of negative variation of $G - F$ is constant. According to Exercise 6.6.23,

$$H' = (G' - f)^- = 0.$$

$G_0 = F - H + H(-\infty)$ is monotone nondecreasing by Theorem 6.1.10. Furthermore, $G_0$ satisfies $G_0' = f$ a.e., $G_0(-\infty) = 0$ and $G_0 \leq F$. Hence $G_0 = F$ by the definition of $F$, which in turn implies $H = H(-\infty)$.

If $f$ is a nonnegative integrable function, and $F \in V^+$ satisfies $F' = f$ a.e. and

$$\int f\,dx = F(\infty) - F(-\infty),$$

then $F$ *is called a primitive function of* $f$. The primitive function is given by (6.7.3). Any two primitive functions of $f$ differ only by a constant. It is not difficult to show that $f\chi_{(a,b)}$ is again integrable and

$$\int f\chi_{(a,b)}\,dx = F(b) - F(a)$$

(Exercise 6.7.2). For the left-hand side we write also $\int_a^b f\,dx$.

In order to be able to extend our definition of integrable functions to functions of arbitrary sign, we have to show that integration is additive.

**6.7.5 LEMMA** *Suppose $f$ and $g$ are nonnegative integrable functions and $a \geq 0$. Then $af$ and $f + g$ are also integrable and*

$$\int af\,dx = a\int f\,dx, \qquad \int (f + g)\,dx = \int f\,dx + \int g\,dx.$$

*If $F$ and $G$ are primitives of $f$ and $g$, respectively, then $aF$ and $F + G$ are primitives of $af$ and $f + g$.*

*Proof* We leave the verification of the first equality to the reader. Now let $F$ and $G$ be primitives of $f$ and $g$, respectively. Then $f + g$ is integrable, since $(F + G)' = f + g$ a.e. Denote a primitive of $h = f + g$ by $H$. We may assume that

$$H(-\infty) = F(-\infty) = G(-\infty) = 0.$$

Then $H \leq F + G$ according to Equation (6.7.3). On the other hand, $H' \geq g$ so that $H - G \in V^+$ by Lemma 6.7.4. Since $(H - G)' = f$ a.e., we see from Equation (6.7.3) (or Lemma 6.7.4) that $H - G \geq F$, whence $H \geq F + G$. Together with the previous inequality this yields $H = F + G$, which implies the second equation of the lemma.

Suppose now that $f$ is a function on the real line that can be written in two different ways as the difference of nonnegative integrable functions:

$$f = f_1 - f_2 = g_1 - g_2.$$

Then $f_1 + g_2 = g_1 + f_2$, so that by the last lemma

$$\int f_1\,dx + \int g_2\,dx = \int g_1\,dx + \int f_2\,dx,$$

$$\int f_1\,dx - \int f_2\,dx = \int g_1\,dx - \int g_2\,dx.$$

Thus we may define the integral of $f$ as the quantity on either side of the last equality.

**6.7.6 DEFINITION** *A function $f$ on the real line is integrable if it can be written as the difference $f = f_1 - f_2$ of two nonnegative integrable functions and we let*

$$\int f\,dx = \int f_1\,dx - \int f_2\,dx.$$

*If $F_1$ and $F_2$ are primitives of $f_1$ and $f_2$, respectively, then $F = F_1 - F_2$ is called a primitive of $f$.*

The following propositions are now easily verified. We leave them as exercises to the reader (Exercises 6.7.3 and 6.7.4).

**6.7.7 PROPOSITION**

(a) *Any two primitives of an integrable function differ only by a constant.*
(b) *If $f$ is integrable, then so are $|f|$, $f^+$ and $f^-$.*
(c) *If $F$ is a primitive of the integrable function $f$, then $TF$, $F_1$, and $F_2$ are primitives of $|f|$, $f^+$, and $f^-$, respectively, $F_1$ and $F_2$ being the parts of positive and negative variation of $F$.*

**6.7.8 PROPOSITION**

(1) *If $f$ and $g$ are integrable, then so are $af + bg$, $f \vee g$, and $f \wedge g$ for any two real numbers $a$, $b$.*
(2) *If $f$ and $g$ are integrable and $a$, $b$ are real numbers, then*

$$\int (af + bg)\,dx = a\int f\,dx + b\int g\,dx.$$

*If $F$ and $G$ are primitives of $f$ and $g$, respectively, then $aF + bG$ is a primitive of $af + bg$.*

(3) $\int f\,dx \geq 0$ *if* $f \geq 0$.

These are the first three of our four basic properties of the Daniell integral. To verify the fourth we prove first Beppo Levi's theorem for our present setup.

### 6.7.9 THEOREM

**BEPPO LEVI'S THEOREM** *Suppose $\sum f_n$ is a series of integrable functions such that $\sum \int |f_n|\, dx$ converges. Then $\sum f_n$ converges almost everywhere, and if $f$ is any function that equals $\sum_{n=1}^{\infty} f_n$ a.e., then $f$ is integrable and*

$$\int f\, dx = \sum_{n=1}^{\infty} \int f_n\, dx.$$

*Proof* Since the hypothesis implies that $\sum \int f_n^+\, dx$ as well as $\sum \int f_n^-\, dx$ converges, we may assume that the $f_n$ are nonnegative. Let $F_n$ be the primitive of $f_n$ which satisfies $F_n(-\infty) = 0$. Then

$$0 \leq \sum_{n=1}^{\infty} F_n(x) \leq \sum_{n=1}^{\infty} F_n(\infty) = \sum_{n=1}^{\infty} \int f\, dx < \infty$$

for all $x$. Thus $\sum F_n$ converges to a function $F \in V^+$ and

$$F' = \sum_{n=1}^{\infty} F_n' = \sum_{n=1}^{\infty} f_n \qquad \text{a.e.}$$

by Fubini's differentiation theorem 6.5.1. This shows that $\sum f_n$ converges a.e. to the integrable function $f = F'$. We claim that $F$ is a primitive of $f$. To prove this, denote by $F_0$ the primitive of $f$ that satisfies $F_0(-\infty) = 0$. Furthermore, let $G_k$ be a primitive of the integrable function that equals $\sum_{n=k+1}^{\infty} f_n$ a.e.; we may assume $G_k(-\infty) = 0$. Then

$$0 \leq F_0 - \sum_{n=1}^{k} F_n = G_k$$

by (2) of Proposition 6.7.8. Since

$$G_k' = \sum_{n=k+1}^{\infty} f_n = \sum_{n=k+1}^{\infty} F_n' = \left(\sum_{n=k+1}^{\infty} F_n\right)',$$

we can apply Lemma 6.7.4, yielding

$$0 \leq F_0 - \sum_{n=1}^{k} F_n = G_k \leq \sum_{n=k+1}^{\infty} F_n,$$

$$0 \leq \int f\, dx - \sum_{n=1}^{k} \int f_n\, dx = F_0(\infty) - \sum_{n=1}^{k} F_n(\infty)$$

$$\leq \sum_{n=k+1}^{\infty} F_n(\infty).$$

The last term in each of these inequalities tends to zero as $k$ tends to infinity, whence

$$F_0 = \sum_{n=1}^{\infty} F_n = F,$$

$$\int f\,dx = \sum_{n=1}^{\infty} \int f_n\,dx.$$

This completes the proof of the theorem.

As a corollary we can now obtain the monotone convergence theorem and all the other convergence theorems in the same way as in Chapter 2.

The question naturally arises now whether Lebesgue integration is actually identical with the theory of integration outlined in this section. This is indeed the case. We will give a hint in Exercise 6.7.6 how to prove that a step function is integrable in the sense of Definition 6.7.6 and that the integral there defined is the Lebesgue integral. Theorem 6.7.9 implies then that the same holds for Lebesgue integrable functions. Conversely, every function that is integrable according to Definition 6.7.6 is also Lebesgue integrable. The proof of this latter assertion naturally makes use of the theory of Lebesgue integration. Therefore, we do not carry it out here. It is an immediate consequence of Corollary 7.1.7 in the following chapter.

## *EXERCISES*

*6.7.1* Show that the function $F$ defined in Equation (6.7.3) is continuous and conclude that the primitive of every integrable function is continuous.

*6.7.2* Suppose $f$ is integrable and $F$ is a primitive of $f$. Show that $f\chi_{(a,b)}$ is integrable for $a < b$ and

$$\int f\chi_{(a,b)}\,dx = F(b) - F(a).$$

*Hint* You may assume that $f$ is nonnegative. Show first that $f\chi_{(a,b)}$ is integrable. Then let $G$ be a primitive of $f\chi_{(a,b)}$ and observe that

$$\int f\chi_{(a,b)}\,dx = G(b) - G(a).$$

Lemma 6.7.4 applied to $F' \geq f\chi_{(a,b)}$ a.e. yields $G(b) - G(a) \leq F(b) - F(a)$. The converse inequality follows from Lemma 6.7.4 applied to $H' \geq f$ a.e., where $H$ is the function defined by

$$H(x) = \begin{cases} F(x) - F(a) + G(a) & \text{for } x \leq a \\ G(x) & \text{for } a \leq x \leq b \\ F(x) - F(b) + G(b) & \text{for } b \leq x \end{cases}$$

*6.7.3* Prove Proposition 6.6.7.

*Hint* Exercises 6.6.22 and 6.6.23 are useful for (b). In (c) let $G_1$ and $G_2$ be primitives of $f^+$ and $f^-$, respectively. $G_1 + G_2$ is a primitive of $|f| = f^+ + f^-$ (Lemma 6.7.5). $G_1 - G_2$ is a primitive of $f$, so you may assume $F = G_1 - G_2$. Use Theorem 6.1.10 to prove

$$G_i(\infty) - G_i(-\infty) \geq F_i(\infty) - F_i(-\infty), \qquad i = 1, 2.$$

Thus one has

$$G_1(\infty) + G_2(\infty) - (G_1(-\infty) + G_2(-\infty)) \geq TF(\infty) - TF(-\infty).$$

The converse inequality follows from Lemma 6.7.4 applied to $(TF)' = |f|$ a.e.

*6.7.4* Prove Proposition 6.7.8.

*Hint* To prove that $af + bg$ is integrable with primitive $aF + bG$, it suffices to show that $af$ is integrable with primitive $aF$ and $f + g$ is integrable with primitive $F + G$.

*6.7.5* For any function $f$ on the real line, $f_a$ denotes the function defined by the equation

$$f_a(x) = f(x + a).$$

Show that $f_a$ is integrable if $f$ is and

$$\int f_a \, dx = \int f \, dx.$$

*Hint* You may assume $f \geq 0$. Notice that the set of all $G \in V^+$ with $G' = f_a$ a.e. is identical with the set of all $F_a$ where $F \in V^+$ and $F' = f$ a.e. Furthermore, $F_a(-\infty) = F(-\infty)$ and $F_a(\infty) = F(\infty)$.

*6.7.6* Show that $\chi_{(a,b)}$ is integrable for every bounded open interval $(a, b)$ and

$$\int \chi_{(a,b)} \, dx = b - a.$$

Consequently, every step function is integrable and the integral defined in Definition 6.7.6 is identical with the Lebesgue integral.

*Hint* Let $\Phi$ be the function defined by

$$\Phi(x) = \begin{cases} 0 & \text{for } x \leq a \\ x - a & \text{for } a \leq x \leq b \\ b - a & \text{for } b \leq x. \end{cases}$$

Then $\Phi' = \chi_{(a,b)}$ a.e., so $\chi_{(b,a)}$ is integrable. It suffices now to show that $\Phi$ is a primitive of $\chi_{(a,b)}$. To do this let $\Psi$ be any primitive. There is a point $c \in (a, b)$

with $\Psi'(c) = 1$. Let $c'$ be any other point in $(a, b)$. Use the previous exercise and Exercise 6.7.2 to show

$$\frac{1}{h}[\Psi(c' + h) - \Psi(c')] = \frac{1}{h}[\Psi(c + h) - \Psi(c)]$$

for small $h$. Thus $\Psi'(c') = 1$ for all $c' \in (a, b)$. Use this information and the continuity of $\Psi$ (Exercise 6.7.1) to conclude that $\Psi$ and $\Phi$ differ only by a constant.

## SUMMARY

A function $f$ on the real line is of bounded variation on the closed bounded interval $[a, b]$ if its total variation on $[a, b]$,

$$T_{ab} = \sup\left\{\sum_{k=1}^{n} |f(x_k) - f(x_{k-1})| : a \leq x_0 \leq \cdots \leq x_n \leq b\right\},$$

is finite (Definition 6.1.2). The function $f$ is of locally bounded variation if it is of bounded variation on each bounded closed interval (Definition 6.1.8). The space $V_{\text{loc}}$ of functions of locally bounded variation is a linear space (Corollary 6.1.9).

The functions of locally bounded variation are exactly the functions that can be written as the difference of two monotone nondecreasing functions (Proposition 6.1.3 and Theorem 6.1.6).

If $f$ is of locally bounded variation, then the function $Tf$,

$$Tf(x) = \begin{cases} f(0) + T_{0x} & \text{for } x \geq 0 \\ f(0) - T_{x0} & \text{for } x \leq 0, \end{cases}$$

is the total variation function of $f$ (Definition 6.1.4). It has the property $Tf(b) - Tf(a) = T_{ab}$ for $a \leq b$ (Proposition 6.1.5). The parts of positive and negative variation of $f$,

$$f_1 = \tfrac{1}{2}(Tf + f), \qquad f_2 = \tfrac{1}{2}(Tf - f),$$

are both monotone nondecreasing and the following relations hold for them (Theorem 6.1.6):

$$f = f_1 - f_2, \qquad Tf = f_1 + f_2,$$
$$f_1(0) = f(0) = Tf(0), \qquad f_2(0) = 0.$$

Among all the pairs $(g_1, g_2)$ of monotone nondecreasing functions satisfying

$$f = g_1 - g_2, \qquad g_2(0) = 0$$

they are distinguished by the property

$$0 \leq f_i(b) - f_i(a) \leq g_i(b) - g_i(a), \qquad i = 1, 2$$

for $a \leq b$ (Theorem 6.1.10).

The set of points of discontinuity of a monotone nondecreasing function (and more generally, of a function of locally bounded variation) $f$ is countable (Proposition 6.2.3); say $\{x_n : n \geq 1\}$ are the discontinuities of $f$. To each $x_n$, one can attach an elementary jump function $s_n$, describing the discontinuity (see Equation (6.2.4)) such that $\sum s_n$ converges uniformly on each bounded interval to a monotone nondecreasing jump function $s$ with the property that $g = f - s$ is monotone nondecreasing and continuous (Lemma 6.2.6 and Corollary 6.2.8).

Every monotone nondecreasing function possesses a derivative almost everywhere (Theorem 6.4.1), and the same holds for a function of locally bounded variation (Theorem 6.4.12).

If the series $\sum f_n$ of monotone nondecreasing functions converges to the (monotone nondecreasing) function $f$, then

$$f' = \sum_{n=1}^{\infty} f_n' \qquad \text{a.e.}$$

This is Fubini's differentiation theorem (Theorem 6.5.1). Similarly, if $\sum f_n$ is a series of functions of locally bounded variation such that $\sum Tf_n$ converges everywhere, then $\sum f_n$ converges everywhere to a function $f$ of locally bounded variation and

$$f' = \sum_{n=1}^{\infty} f_n' \qquad \text{a.e.}$$

(Theorem 6.5.3).

# 7

# Absolutely Continuous Functions

While the discussion in the previous chapter has been independent of earlier parts of the book, we are now going to make use of the theory of Lebesgue integration to explore the relationship between a function of locally bounded variation and its derivative. One would like to prove a theorem similar to the fundamental theorem of calculus which says that the indefinite integral of the derivative of a continuously differentiable function differs from that function at most by a constant. Unfortunately, such a theorem does not hold for functions of locally bounded variation; for instance the derivative of a jump function is zero almost everywhere (Exercise 6.6.5) so that there is no hope of recovering the jump function from its derivative. But even a strictly increasing continuous function may have a derivative equal to zero almost everywhere as is attested by the example in the first section of this chapter. But if we restrict our attention to a smaller class of functions, the so-called absolutely continuous functions, then the fundamental theorem of calculus will hold. The absolutely continuous functions, a subclass of the class of functions of locally bounded variation, will therefore be in the center of our discussion in this chapter. These functions are introduced in Section 7.3 after a thorough investigation of the fundamental theorem of calculus in Section 7.2. Applications are discussed in Section 7.5. Section 7.4 is dispensable in the present context; it is used later, in Chapter 9, for the discussion of the Radon-Nikodym theorem.

## 7.1 INTEGRATION OF THE DERIVATIVE OF A FUNCTION IN $V_{loc}$

In the first part of this section we will prove that the indefinite integral of the derivative of a function $f$ of locally bounded variation exists, and then we will show by an example that even if we require $f$ to be continuous, the indefinite integral of $f'$ does not always represent $f$ up to a constant.

Recall that a function $f$ of locally bounded variation can be written as the difference

(7.1.1) $$f = g - s$$

of a continuous function $g$ of locally bounded variation and its jump part $s$ (Corollary 6.2.8) (see Figure 7.1). This decomposition has the following proposition as a consequence.

**7.1.2 PROPOSITION** *A function of locally bounded variation is measurable, and integrable on every bounded interval.*

*Proof* Let $f = g - s$, as in Equation (7.1.1). It suffices to prove that $g$ and $s$ are measurable. The function $g$ is measurable, since it is continuous (Corollary 3.1.5); $s$ is the difference $s_1 - s_2$ of the jump parts of two monotone nondecreasing functions, and $s_1$ and $s_2$ are each series of elementary jump functions described in Equation (6.2.4), which are clearly measurable. Thus $s$ is also measurable. The function $f$ is integrable on every bounded interval, since it is bounded on every bounded interval.

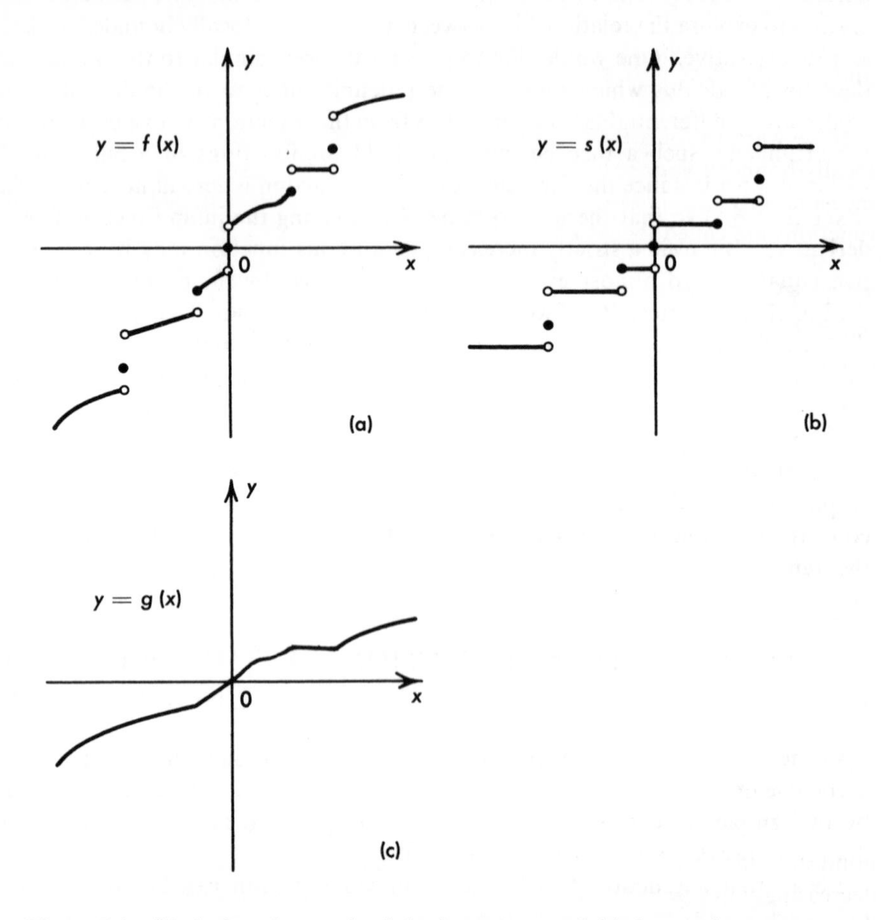


Figure 7.1 (b) depicts the graph of the jump part and (c) the continuous part of the monotone nondecreasing function $f$ whose graph is shown in (a).

7.1.3 COROLLARY *The derivative $f'$ of a function $f$ of locally bounded variation is measurable.*

*Proof* For each positive integer $n$ define the function $f_n$ by

$$f_n(x) = n\left(f\left(x + \frac{1}{n}\right) - f(x)\right). \tag{7.1.4}$$

The function $f_n$ is measurable, since $f$ and its translation $f(x + 1/n)$ are measurable (see Exercise 3.1.3). If $f$ is differentiable at $x$, then $\lim_{n\to\infty} f_n(x) = f'(x)$. Thus

$$f' = \lim_{n\to\infty} f_n \qquad \text{a.e.,}$$

and $f'$ is therefore measurable.

If we want to form the indefinite integral of the derivative $f'$ of a function $f$ of locally bounded variation, we have to know a little bit more about $f'$ than just its measurability. It should be at least integrable over each bounded interval. Such functions are called locally integrable.

**7.1.5 DEFINITION** *A measurable function $g$ on the real line is called locally integrable if, for each bounded interval $[a, b]$, $g\chi_{[a,b]}$ is integrable. The linear space of all locally integrable functions is denoted by $L^1_{\text{loc}}$.*

The functions $g \in L^1_{\text{loc}}$ are suitable for forming indefinite integrals $G$,

$$G(t) = \int_0^t g\,dx = \begin{cases} \int g\chi_{[0,t]}\,dx & \text{if } t \geq 0 \\ -\int g\chi_{[t,0]}\,dx & \text{if } t \leq 0. \end{cases}$$

**7.1.6 PROPOSITION** *Suppose $f \in V_{\text{loc}}$; then $f' \in L^1_{\text{loc}}$.*

*Proof* Since $f$ can be written as the difference of two monotone nondecreasing functions, we may as well assume that $f$ itself is monotone nondecreasing. Let $[a, b]$ be any bounded interval and define the monotone nondecreasing function $f_{ab}$ by

$$f_{ab}(x) = \begin{cases} f(b) & \text{for } b \leq x \\ f(x) & \text{for } a \leq x \leq b \\ f(a) & \text{for } x \leq a. \end{cases}$$

Then $f_{ab}' = f'\chi_{[a,b]}$ a.e. and the sequence $\{g_n\}$ of nonnegative functions $g_n$,

$$g_n(x) = n\left[f_{ab}\left(x + \frac{1}{n}\right) - f_{ab}(x)\right],$$

tends to $f'\chi_{[a,b]}$ a.e. The function $g_n$ vanishes off $[a - 1/n, b]$ and is bounded on this interval by $n[f(b) - f(a)]$. Hence $g_n$ is integrable and

$$\begin{aligned}\int g_n \, dx &= n\int_{a-1/n}^{b} f_{ab}\left(x + \frac{1}{n}\right) dx - n\int_{a-1/n}^{b} f_{ab} \, dx \\ &= n\int_{a}^{b+1/n} f_{ab} \, dx - n\int_{a-1/n}^{b} f_{ab} \, dx \\ &= n\int_{b}^{b+1/n} f_{ab} \, dx - n\int_{a-1/n}^{a} f_{ab} \, dx \\ &= f(b) - f(a).\end{aligned}$$

Thus

$$\liminf \int g_n \, dx \le f(b) - f(a),$$

and Fatou's lemma implies that

$$\liminf g_n = \lim_{n\to\infty} g_n = f'\chi_{[a,b]} \qquad \text{a.e.}$$

is integrable and

$$\int_a^b f' \, dx \le \liminf \int g_n \, dx \le f(a) - f(a).$$

The last inequality will be needed later, so we state it explicitly as a corollary.

**7.1.7 COROLLARY** *If $f$ is monotone nondecreasing, then $f'$ is locally integrable and*

$$\int_a^b f' \, dx \le f(b) - f(a)$$

*for all real numbers $a \le b$.*

The last proposition tells us that we may consider the primitive $F$,

$$F(t) = \int_0^t f' \, dx,$$

of the derivative $f'$ of a function $f$ in $V_{\text{loc}}$. Unfortunately, this primitive $F$ has in general no resemblance to $f$. For instance if $f$ equals its jump part $s$, then $f' = 0$ a.e. as is easily seen by Fubini's differentiation theorem (see Exercise 6.5.5); in this case $F$ would be zero though $f$ is not necessarily a constant. One might argue that a modification of the statement of the fundamental theorem of calculus might still be true; namely that perhaps $f$ equals $F$ plus a jump function. However, this attempt also fails as we will show by constructing a continuous, strictly increasing function $f$ with $f' = 0$ a.e. Then $F = 0$ and $f$, being continuous and not constant, does not equal any jump function (Exercise 6.2.1).

**7.1.8 EXAMPLE** *There is a strictly increasing continuous function $f$ with $f' = 0$ a.e.*

*Proof* Let us definitely fix a number $t$ in the open interval (0, 1); for instance $t = \frac{1}{2}$. By induction on $n$ we define monotone increasing functions $f_n$ in the following way (see Figure 7.2).

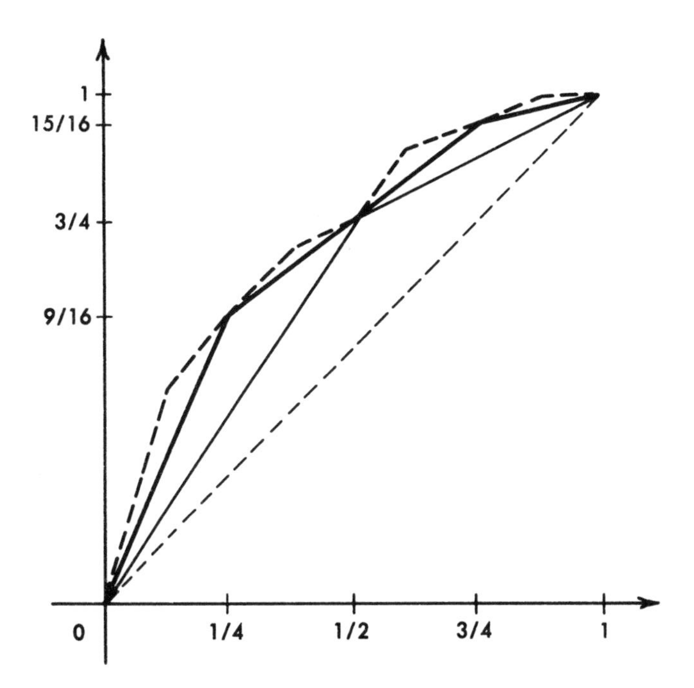


Figure 7.2 Construction of a monotone function with almost everywhere vanishing derivative.

(1) $f_0(x) = x$;
(2) $f_n$ shall be linear in each of the closed intervals

$$[(k-1)2^{-n}, k2^{-n}], \qquad k = 0, \pm 1, \cdots,$$

and for odd $k$ (that is, at those corners of $f_n$ that are not corners of $f_{n-1}$)

$$f_n(k2^{-n}) = \frac{1-t}{2} f_{n-1}((k-1)2^{-n}) + \frac{1+t}{2} f_{n-1}((k+1)2^{-n}),$$

while for even $k$

$$f_n(k2^{-n}) = f_{n-1}(k2^{-n}).$$

We assert that $f_n$ is monotone increasing. Let us prove this by induction on $n$. The function $f_0$ is clearly monotone increasing. Now suppose we have proved that $f_{n-1}$ is monotone increasing and let us show that $f_n$ has the same property. We have for odd $k$

$$\begin{aligned}
f_n(k2^{-n}) &= \frac{1-t}{2} f_{n-1}((k-1)2^{-n}) + \frac{1+t}{2} f_{n-1}((k+1)2^{-n}) \\
&> \frac{1-t}{2} f_{n-1}((k-1)2^{-n}) + \frac{1+t}{2} f_{n-1}((k-1)2^{-n}) \\
&= f_{n-1}((k-1)2^{-n}) = f_n((k-1)2^{-n}), \\
f_n(k2^{-n}) &< \frac{1-t}{2} f_{n-1}((k+1)2^{-n}) + \frac{1+t}{2} f_{n-1}((k+1)2^{-n}) \\
&= f_{n-1}((k+1)2^{-n}) = f_n((k+1)2^{-n}).
\end{aligned}$$

Since $f_n$ is linear over the intervals $[(k-1)2^{-n}, k2^{-n}]$ and $[k2^{-n}, (k+1)2^{-n}]$, it is thus monotone increasing.

Notice that $f_{n-1} \leq f_n$ and $f_n(m) = m$ for all integers $m$. Thus $f_n$ is an increasing sequence and, since $f_n(x) \leq f_n(m) \leq m$ is bounded for $x \leq m$, $\{f_n\}$ converges to a monotone nondecreasing function $f$. We will now show that $f$ is continuous, strictly increasing, and with a derivative equal to 0 a.e.

Let $x$ be any point on the real line and, for each $n$, define $\alpha_n$ to be the largest number $k2^{-n}$ satisfying $k2^{-n} < x$. Let $\beta_n = \alpha_n + 2^{-n}$, then

$$x \in (\alpha_n, \beta_n], \qquad \lim_{n\to\infty} \alpha_n = x = \lim_{n\to\infty} \beta_n.$$

We claim that

$$\begin{aligned}
f(\beta_n) - f(\alpha_n) &= \frac{1 \pm t}{2} (f(\beta_{n-1}) - f(\alpha_{n-1})) \qquad \text{for } n \geq 1, \\
f(\beta_0) - f(\alpha_0) &= 1.
\end{aligned} \tag{7.1.9}$$

First notice that for all integers $n, s \geq 0$,

$$\begin{aligned}
f_n(\alpha_n) &= f_{n+s}(\alpha_n) = f(\alpha_n), \\
f_n(\beta_n) &= f_{n+s}(\beta_n) = f(\beta_n).
\end{aligned}$$

From this it follows immediately that

$$f(\beta_0) - f(\alpha_0) = \beta_0 - \alpha_0 = 1.$$

Now let us check the first equation in (7.1.9) for the case that $\alpha_n = k2^{-n}$ and $k$ is odd; it can be derived similarly if $k$ is even. We have

$$\alpha_{n-1} = (k-1)2^{-n}, \qquad \beta_{n-1} = (k+1)2^{-n} = \beta_n$$

and thus

$$\begin{aligned} f(\beta_n) - f(\alpha_n) &= f_{n-1}(\beta_{n-1}) - f_n(\alpha_n) \\ &= f_{n-1}(\beta_{n-1}) - \frac{1-t}{2} f_{n-1}((k-1)2^{-n}) - \frac{1+t}{2} f_{n-1}((k+1)2^{-n}) \\ &= f_{n-1}(\beta_{n-1}) - \frac{1-t}{2} f_{n-1}(\alpha_{n-1}) - \frac{1+t}{2} f_{n-1}(\beta_{n-1}) \\ &= \frac{1-t}{2} (f(\beta_{n-1}) - f(\alpha_{n-1})). \end{aligned}$$

From Equation (7.1.9) we obtain for $n \geq 1$,

(7.1.10) $$f(\beta_n) - f(\alpha_n) = \prod_{i=1}^{n} \frac{1 + e_i t}{2} > 0$$

where $e_i = \pm 1$. We have

$$\prod_{i=1}^{n} \frac{1 + e_i t}{2} \leq \left(\frac{1+t}{2}\right)^n$$

and thus

$$f(x) - f(\alpha_n) \leq f(\beta_n) - f(\alpha_n) \leq \left(\frac{1+t}{2}\right)^n.$$

Since the right-hand side tends to zero as $n$ tends to infinity, we conclude

$$\lim_{n \to \infty} f(\alpha_n) = f(x).$$

This proves that $f$ is left continuous at $x$, because $f$ is monotone nondecreasing and $\alpha_n < x$ for all $n$. If we had chosen $\alpha_n$ to be the largest number $k2^{-n} \leq x$, then we would have $\beta_n > x$ for all $n$, and we could include

$$\lim_{n \to \infty} f(\beta_n) = f(x)$$

similarly as above. Thus $f$ is also right continuous at $x$. This proves that $f$ is in fact continuous at every point $x$.

The function $f$ is also strictly increasing. Let $(a, b)$ be any interval and pick $x \in (a, b)$, then we can find an integer $n$ with $(\alpha_n, \beta_n) \subset (a, b)$. The inequality (7.1.10) tells us now that $f$ cannot be constant on $(a, b)$.

Finally, $f$ has zero derivative almost everywhere. Let $x$ be a point at which the derivative of $f$ exists. We have $\beta_n - \alpha_n = 2^{-n}$ and therefore

$$f'(x) = \lim_{n \to \infty} \frac{f(\beta_n) - f(\alpha_n)}{\beta_n - \alpha_n} = \lim_{n \to \infty} \prod_{i=1}^{n} (1 + e_i t)$$

by Equation (7.1.10). The limit of the product

$$\prod_{i=1}^{n} (1 + e_i t)$$

cannot be different from zero since the logarithm of the product is the sum

$$\sum_{i=1}^{n} \log (1 + e_i t)$$

which does not converge, because its summands

$$\log (1 + e_i t) = \log (1 \pm t)$$

are bounded away from zero. Thus $f'(x) = 0$ as asserted.

## *EXERCISES*

*7.1.1* Suppose $f$ is a function of bounded variation; this means $f \in V_{\text{loc}}$ and $Tf$ is bounded (see Exercise 6.6.13). Prove that $f'$ is integrable.

*Hint* $f$ is the difference of two bounded monotone nondecreasing functions; apply Corollary 7.1.7 to prove that

$$\int_{-n}^{n} f' \, dx \leq [f(\infty) - f(-\infty)]$$

if $f$ is bounded and monotone nondecreasing.

*7.1.2* If $m \leq x < m + 1$, let $0 \cdot a_1 a_2 \cdots$ be a binary expansion of $x - m$ and define

$$f(x) = m + \sum_{n=1}^{\infty} a_n \left(\frac{1 - t}{2}\right)^{p(n)} \left(\frac{1 + t}{2}\right)^{n - p(n)}$$

where

$$p(n) = \sum_{k=1}^{n-1} a_k.$$

Prove that the series in the definition of $f(x)$ converges and is independent of the choice of the binary expansion of $x - m$. Then prove that the function $f$ is the same as the one constructed in Example 7.1.8.

## 7.2 THE PRIMITIVE OF A LOCALLY INTEGRABLE FUNCTION

We found out in the last section that we could form the primitive $h$,

$$h(t) = \int_{0}^{t} f' \, dx + c,$$

of the derivative $f'$ of a function $f$ of locally bounded variation, but we noticed also that the fundamental theorem of calculus does not hold; we cannot always choose the constant $c$ in the definition of $h$ in such a way that $h = f$ a.e. Thus the question arises, for which functions of locally bounded variation does the fundamental theorem of calculus hold? The answer is that the fundamental theorem holds exactly for the primitives $f$,

$$f(t) = \int_0^t g\, dx + c, \tag{7.2.1}$$

of functions $g$ in $L^1_{\text{loc}}$. To prove this we have to verify two facts. First we have to show that functions $f$ defined as in (7.2.1) are of locally bounded variation; then we have to prove that for such functions $f' = g$ a.e.

**7.2.2 PROPOSITION** *Suppose the function $g$ is locally integrable. Then the function $f$ defined by*

$$f(t) = \int_0^t g\, dx + c,$$

*where $c$ is a constant, is of locally bounded variation.*

*Proof* Since a constant is of locally bounded variation, we may as well assume that $c = 0$ in the definition of $f$. The functions $g^+$ and $g^-$ are nonnegative and locally integrable. Thus

$$f(t) = \int_0^t g^+\, dx - \int_0^t g^-\, dx$$

is a decomposition of $f$ into the difference of two monotone nondecreasing functions; $f$ is therefore of locally bounded variation.

Next we prove a proposition that is not actually needed, but which will complete the picture of the relationship between the functions $g$ and $f$ in Equation (7.2.1).

**7.2.3 PROPOSITION** *Suppose $g$ is locally integrable and let*

$$f(t) = \int_0^t g\, dx + c,$$

*where $c$ is a constant. The total variation of $f$ on the closed bounded interval $[a, b]$ equals*

$$T(f, a, b) = \int_a^b |g|\, dx.$$

*Proof* For any sequence $a \leq a_0 \leq \cdots \leq a_n \leq b$ we have

$$\begin{aligned}\sum_{k=1}^n |f(a_k) - f(a_{k-1})| &= \sum_{k=1}^n \left| \int_{a_{k-1}}^{a_k} g\, dx \right| \\ &\leq \sum_{k=1}^n \int_{a_{k-1}}^{a_k} |g|\, dx \\ &\leq \int_a^b |g|\, dx.\end{aligned}$$

Taking the supremum on the left-hand side, we find

$$T(f, a, b) \leq \int_a^b |g| \, dx.$$

To prove the opposite inequality, we make use of the fact that if $\eta$ is a step function vanishing off $[a, b]$ and assuming only the values $+1$, $-1$ and 0, then

$$\int_a^b \eta g \, dx \leq T(f, a, b).$$

Namely, if $(a_0, \cdots, a_n; e_1, \cdots, e_n)$ is a presentation of $\eta$ with $a \leq a_0 \leq \cdots \leq a_n \leq b$ and $e_k = +1, -1$, or 0 for $k = 1, \cdots, n$, then

$$\begin{aligned} \int_a^b \eta g \, dx &= \sum_{k=1}^{n} e_k \int_{a_{k-1}}^{a_k} g \, dx \\ &\leq \sum_{k=1}^{n} \left| \int_{a_{k-1}}^{a_k} g \right| dx \\ &= \sum_{k=1}^{n} |f(a_k) - f(a_{k-1})| \\ &\leq T(f, a, b)\,. \end{aligned}$$

Now suppose that $\{\varphi_n\}$ is a sequence of step functions that converges to $g\chi_{[a,b]}$ a.e. We may assume that all the $\varphi_n$ vanish off $[a, b]$. Let $\eta_n$ be the step function defined by

$$\eta_n(x) = \begin{cases} +1 & \text{if } \varphi_n(x) > 0 \\ 0 & \text{if } \varphi_n(x) = 0 \\ -1 & \text{if } \varphi_n(x) < 0. \end{cases}$$

Then, by the above remark,

$$\int_a^b \eta_n g \, dx \leq T(f, a, b).$$

On the other hand,

$$\lim_{n\to\infty} \eta_n g = |g|\chi_{[a,b]} \text{ a.e.},$$

$$|\eta_n g| \leq |g| \, \chi_{[a,b]}.$$

Thus, by Lebesgue's dominated convergence theorem,

$$\int_a^b |g| \, dx = \lim_{n\to\infty} \int_a^b \eta_n g \, dx \leq T(f, a, b),$$

and this establishes the proposition.

If we look at the definitions of the total variation function $Tf$ and the parts $f_1$ and $f_2$ of positive and negative variation (Definition 6.1.4 and Theorem 6.1.6), we can convince ourselves immediately of the following.

**7.2.4 COROLLARY** *Let f and g be as in Proposition 7.2.3. We have*

$$Tf(t) = \int_0^t |g| \, dx + c$$

$$f_1(t) = \int_0^t g^+ \, dx + c, \qquad f_2(t) = \int_0^t g^- \, dx.$$

Finally, we prove that the function $f$ in (7.2.1) is the primitive of its derivative.

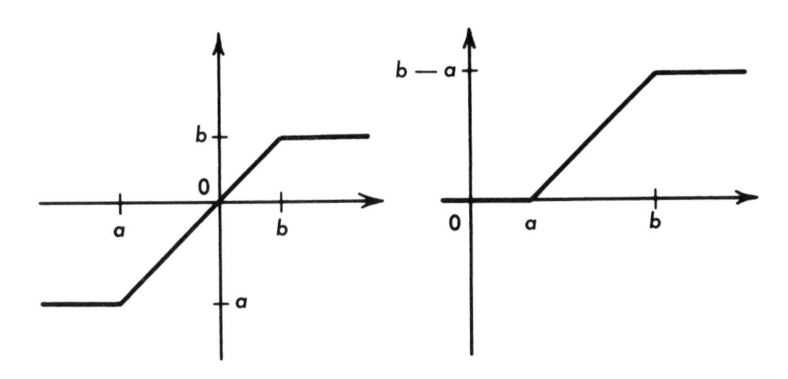


Figure 7.3 The primitive $\int_0^t \chi_{[a,b]} \, dx$ of the characteristic function of $[a, b]$. In (a) we have $a < 0 < b$; in (b) we have $0 < a < b$.

**7.2.5 THEOREM** *Suppose g is locally integrable and let*

$$f(t) = \int_0^t g \, dx + c$$

*where c is a constant. Then $f' = g$ a.e.*

*Proof* Since the derivative of the constant $c$ vanishes, we may assume that $c = 0$. We proceed now in two steps to prove $f' = g$ a.e.

First we assume $g$ is the characteristic function $\chi_{[a,b]}$ of a closed bounded interval $[a, b]$. Then (see Figure 7.3)

$$f(t) = \int_0^t g \, dx = \begin{cases} \displaystyle\int_0^a \chi_{[a,b]} \, dx & \text{for } t \le a \\ \displaystyle t - a + \int_0^a \chi_{[a,b]} \, dx & \text{for } a \le t \le b \\ \displaystyle\int_0^b \chi_{[a,b]} \, dx & \text{for } b \le t. \end{cases}$$

Clearly $f'(t) = g(t)$ for $t \neq a, b$. Since every step function is a linear combination of characteristic functions of closed intervals, it follows that $f' = g$ a.e. whenever $g$ is a step function.

Now let $N$ be any positive integer. Since the function $g \in L^1_{\text{loc}}$ is integrable on $(-N, N)$ we can find a series $\sum \varphi_n$ of step functions that converges almost everywhere to $g\chi_{(-N,N)}$ and satisfies

$$\sum_{n=1}^{\infty} \int |\varphi_n| \, dx < \infty.$$

Consequently,

$$\sum_{n=1}^{\infty} \int \varphi_n^+ \, dx < \infty \quad \text{and} \quad \sum_{n=1}^{\infty} \int \varphi_n^- \, dx < \infty.$$

Let $g_1$ and $g_2$ be two integrable functions such that

$$g_1 = \sum_{n=1}^{\infty} \varphi_n^+ \quad \text{a.e.,} \qquad g_2 = \sum_{n=1}^{\infty} \varphi_n^- \quad \text{a.e.}$$

Then $g\chi_{(-N,N)} = g_1 - g_2$ a.e. Furthermore,

$$f_1(t) = \int_0^t g_1 \, dx = \sum_{n=1}^{\infty} \int_0^t \varphi_n^+ \, dx$$

$$f_2(t) = \int_0^t g_2 \, dx = \sum_{n=1}^{\infty} \int_0^t \varphi_n^- \, dx$$

for all $t$ by the definition of the integral. These series are series of monotone nondecreasing functions. Thus we can apply Fubini's theorem on termwise differentiation of series of monotone nondecreasing functions (Theorem 6.5.1) which, together with the fact that the derivative of a primitive of $\varphi$ equals $\varphi$ a.e. if $\varphi$ is a step function, yields

$$f_1' = \sum_{n=1}^{\infty} \varphi_n^+ \quad \text{a.e.,} \qquad f_2' = \sum_{n=1}^{\infty} \varphi_n^- \quad \text{a.e.}$$

Thus for a.a. $t \in (-N, N)$,

$$\begin{aligned} f'(t) = f_1'(t) - f_2'(t) &= \sum_{n=1}^{\infty} \varphi_n^+(t) - \sum_{n=1}^{\infty} \varphi_n^-(t) \quad \text{a.e.} \\ &= \sum_{n=1}^{\infty} \varphi_n(t) \\ &= g(t). \end{aligned}$$

Actually, we could have simplified the last proof somewhat by using Corollary 7.2.4. This corollary tells us that $\int_0^t |\varphi_n| \, dx$ is the total variation function of $\int_0^t \varphi_n \, dx$. Since the series $\sum \int_0^t |\varphi_n| \, dx$ converges for all $t$, we can apply the differentiation theorem for series of functions of locally bounded variation (Theorem

6.5.3), which tells us that for a.a. $t \in (-N, N)$,

$$f'(t) = \left(\int_0^t g\,dx\right)' = \sum_{n=1}^{\infty}\left(\int_0^t \varphi_n\,dx\right)$$

$$= \sum_{n=1}^{\infty} \varphi_n(t) = g(t).$$

## *EXERCISES*

*7.2.1* Prove that every piecewise linear function (as defined in part D of the exercise section 1.6) is the indefinite integral $\int_{-\infty}^t \varphi\,dx$ of a step function $\varphi$.

*7.2.2* Prove that a step function is the derivative almost everywhere of a piecewise linear function if and only if $\int \varphi\,dx = 0$.

*7.2.3* Prove that the indefinite integral $\int_0^t g\,dx$ of a function $g \in L^1_{\text{loc}}$ is continuous.

*Hint* Lebesgue's dominated convergence theorem is useful here.

*7.2.4* Suppose $g \in L^1_{\text{loc}}$ is continuous at the point $c$. Prove that the indefinite integral $h$ of $g$,

$$h(t) = \int_0^t g\,dx$$

is differentiable at $c$ and that $h'(c) = g(c)$.

*Hint* Write $g(x) = g(c) + \eta(x)$ and estimate

$$\frac{1}{h}\int_c^{c+h} \eta\,dx = \frac{1}{h}\int_c^{c+h} g\,dx - g(c).$$

*7.2.5* Prove that if $g \in L^1_{\text{loc}}$, then the function $f$ defined by

$$f(t) = \int_0^t g\,dx + c$$

is of bounded variation if and only if $g$ is integrable.

# 7.3 THE FUNDAMENTAL THEOREM FOR ABSOLUTELY CONTINUOUS FUNCTIONS

In the previous section we have seen that the functions $f$ of locally bounded variation, for which the fundamental theorem of calculus holds, are exactly the primitives

(7.3.1)
$$f(t) = \int_0^t g\,dx + c$$

of locally integrable functions $g$. Unfortunately, it is not always easy to decide for a given function $f$ of locally bounded variation whether it is of the form (7.3.1). Thus another characterization of the functions defined in (7.3.1) is desirable. We will prove in this section that these functions are exactly the ones which are introduced in the following definition.

7.3.2 DEFINITION *A function $f$ on the real line is absolutely continuous if, for every bounded interval $[a, b]$ and every $\varepsilon > 0$, there is a $\delta > 0$ such that*

$$\sum_{k=1}^{n} |f(b_k) - f(a_k)| \leq \varepsilon$$

*for any sequence $a \leq a_1 \leq b_1 \leq \cdots \leq a_n \leq b_n \leq b$ with*

$$\sum_{k=1}^{n} (b_k - a_k) \leq \delta.$$

The definition implies immediately that an absolutely continuous function is continuous. It is also easily verified that the set of absolutely continuous functions is a linear space (Exercise 7.3.1). We will prove now that this set is contained in $V_{\text{loc}}$.

7.3.3 PROPOSITION *An absolutely continuous function is of locally bounded variation.*

*Proof* Suppose $f$ is absolutely continuous. Let $a < b$ and choose $\delta > 0$ to be the number that corresponds to $\varepsilon = 1$ in Definition 7.3.2. If $N$ is the smallest integer such that $N\delta \geq b - a$, then we can find a sequence $a = c_0 < c_1 < \cdots < c_N = b$ such that

$$c_k - c_{k-1} \leq \delta, \qquad k = 1, \cdots, N.$$

Now let $a \leq x_0 \leq \cdots \leq x_n \leq b$ be any sequence, and denote by $\{y_\ell : \ell = 0, \cdots, n + N + 1\}$ the points $\{x_j, c_k\}$ in increasing order,

$$a = y_0 \leq \cdots \leq y_{n+N+1} = b.$$

We have

$$\sum \{y_\ell - y_{\ell-1} : c_{k-1} < y_\ell \leq c_k\} = c_k - c_{k-1} \leq \delta$$

where the sum is taken over all $\ell$ such that $c_{k-1} < y_\ell \leq c_k$. Thus

$$\sum \{|f(y_\ell) - f(y_{\ell-1})| : c_{k-1} < y_\ell \leq c_k\} \leq 1$$

for $k = 0, \cdots, N$. Adding the last inequalities for all $k$, we get

$$\sum_{j=1}^{n} |f(x_j) - f(x_{j-1})| \leq \sum_{\ell=1}^{n+N+1} |f(y_\ell) - f(y_{\ell-1})| \leq N.$$

The total variation of $f$ on $[a, b]$ is therefore at most $N$.

7.3.4 PROPOSITION *Suppose $f$ is absolutely continuous. Then the total variation function $Tf$ and the parts of positive and negative variation, $f_1$ and $f_2$, are also absolutely continuous.*

*Proof* Let $[a, b]$ be a bounded interval and $\varepsilon > 0$. Choose $\delta > 0$ to be the number corresponding to $\varepsilon$ in Definition 7.3.2. If $a \leq a_1 \leq b_1 \leq \cdots \leq a_n \leq b_n \leq b$ is any sequence with

$$\sum_{k=1}^{n} (b_k - a_k) \leq \delta,$$

then for any subdivision $a_k \leq x_0^k \leq \cdots \leq x_{s(k)}^k \leq b_k$ we have

$$\sum_{k=1}^{n} \sum_{j=1}^{s(k)} (x_j^k - x_{j-1}^k) \leq \sum_{k=1}^{n} (b_k - a_k) \leq \delta$$

and therefore

$$\sum_{k=1}^{n} \left( \sum_{j=1}^{s(k)} |f(x_j^k) - f(x_{j-1}^k)| \right) \leq \varepsilon.$$

Taking the supremum over all possible subdivisions of $[a_k, b_k]$, $k = 1, \cdots, n$, we obtain

$$\sum_{k=1}^{n} [Tf(b_k) - Tf(a_k)] \leq \varepsilon,$$

which proves that $Tf$ is absolutely continuous. Since $Tf = f_1 + f_2$, we have

$$f_j(b_k) - f_j(a_k) \leq Tf(b_k) - Tf(a_k), \qquad j = 1, 2,$$

and hence

$$\sum_{k=1}^{n} [f_j(b_k) - f_j(a_k)] \leq \varepsilon, \qquad j = 1, 2.$$

Therefore $f_1$ and $f_2$ are also absolutely continuous.

After these preparations we are ready to show that the absolutely continuous functions are exactly the ones for which the fundamental theorem of calculus holds. But first we have to establish the absolute continuity of a primitive function (7.3.1).

7.3.5 LEMMA *Suppose $g$ is a locally integrable function and let*

$$f(t) = \int_0^t g\, dx + c.$$

*Then $f$ is absolutely continuous.*

*Proof* Let $a \leq b$. The sequence $\{|g| \wedge n\}$ of locally integrable functions increases to $|g|$. By the monotone convergence theorem (Theorem 2.3.1) we have

$$\lim_{n\to\infty} \int_a^b |g| \wedge n \, dx = \int_a^b |g| \, dx.$$

Now suppose $\varepsilon > 0$. We choose $n$ so large that

$$\int_a^b (|g| - |g| \wedge n) \, dx \leq \varepsilon.$$

With $\delta = \varepsilon/n$ we have for any sequence of intervals $a \leq a_1 \leq b_1 \leq \cdots \leq a_n \leq b_n \leq b$ of total length

$$\sum_{k=1}^{n} (b_k - a_k) \leq \delta,$$

the following estimate:

$$\begin{aligned}
\sum_{k=1}^{n} |f(b_k) - f(a_k)| &= \sum_{k=1}^{n} \left| \int_{a_k}^{b_k} g \, dx \right| \\
&\leq \sum_{k=1}^{n} \int_{a_k}^{b_k} |g| \, dx \\
&= \sum_{k=1}^{n} \int_{a_k}^{b_k} (|g| - |g| \wedge n) \, dx + \sum_{k=1}^{n} \int_{a_k}^{b_k} |g| \wedge n \, dx \\
&\leq \varepsilon + n \sum_{k=1}^{n} (b_k - a_k) \\
&\leq \varepsilon + n \frac{\varepsilon}{n} = 2\varepsilon.
\end{aligned}$$

This shows that $f$ is absolutely continuous.

In the proof of the fundamental theorem of calculus for absolutely continuous functions, we will make use of a topological theorem known as the Heine-Borel covering theorem. It states that, from any collection of open intervals that cover a closed bounded interval $[a, b]$, one can select a finite number of intervals that already cover $[a, b]$. Since this theorem is not always discussed in an elementary calculus course, we present a proof of it here.

## 7.3.6 LEMMA

HEINE-BOREL COVERING THEOREM *Let $[a, b]$ be a bounded closed interval and $\mathscr{I}$ a collection of open intervals that cover $[a, b]$,*

$$[a, b] \subset \bigcup \{I : I \in \mathscr{I}\}.$$

*Then one can find a finite number $I_1, \cdots, I_n$ of intervals in $\mathscr{I}$ that already cover $[a, b]$,*

$$[a, b] \subset I_1 \cup \cdots \cup I_n.$$

*Proof* Let us call a point $c \in [a, b]$ fine if $[a, c]$ can be covered by a finite number of intervals in $\mathscr{I}$. For instance, $a$ is fine. Let

$$c_0 = \sup \{c, c \in [a, b], c \text{ is fine}\}$$

There is an interval $I \in \mathscr{I}$ that contains $c_0$. We can find a fine $c_1 \in I$ such that $a \leq c_1 \leq c_0$, say

$$[a, c_1] \subset I_1 \cup \cdots \cup I_k, \qquad I_j \in \mathscr{I}.$$

But then

$$[a, c_0] \subset I_1 \cup \cdots \cup I_k \cup I$$

so that $c_0$ is fine.

In fact, $c_0 = b$. For if not, then there is a $c_2 \in I$ with $c_0 < c_2 \leq b$; $c_2$ is fine, since

$$[a, c_2] \subset I_1 \cup \cdots \cup I_k \cup I,$$

but this is a contradiction to the definition of $c_0$. Thus we must have $b = c_0$. This completes the proof.

**7.3.7 THEOREM** *If $f$ is absolutely continuous, then*

$$f(t) = \int_0^t f' dx + f(0)$$

*for all $t$ ("Fundamental Theorem of Calculus").*

*Proof* By Proposition 7.3.4, $f$ is the difference of two absolutely continuous monotone nondecreasing functions; namely, $f$ is the difference of its parts of positive and negative variation. Therefore we may assume for the proof that $f$ is monotone nondecreasing. All we have to show is that

$$g(t) = f(t) - \int_0^t f' \, dx$$

is constant, because we then have $g(t) = g(0) = f(0)$ for all $t$. The function $g$ is absolutely continuous, since $f$ and $\int_0^t f' \, dx$ are as was shown in Lemma 7.3.5. By Corollary 7.1.7,

$$g(b) - g(a) = f(b) - f(a) - \int_a^b f' \, dx \geq 0$$

for $a \leq b$. Thus $g$ is monotone nondecreasing. Furthermore,

$$g'(t) = f'(t) - f'(t) = 0$$

for a.a. $t$. Therefore the theorem will be proved once we have established the following lemma.

**7.3.8 Lemma** *Suppose g is a monotone nondecreasing, absolutely continuous function. If $g' = 0$ a.e., then g is a constant.*

*Proof* It suffices to show that $g$ is constant on every bounded interval $[a, b]$, $a < b$. Let $E$ be a null set in $[a, b]$ such that the derivative of $g$ exists and is zero at all points in $[a, b] - E$. Given $\varepsilon > 0$, we can find an open interval $I_x = (x_1, x_2)$ around every point $x \in [a, b] - E$ with

$$g(x_2) - g(x_1) \leq \frac{\varepsilon}{b - a}(x_2 - x_1), \tag{7.3.9}$$

this because

$$\begin{aligned} \frac{g(x_2) - g(x_1)}{x_2 - x_1} &= \frac{g(x_2) - g(x)}{x_2 - x_1} + \frac{g(x) - g(x_1)}{x_2 - x_1} \\ &\leq \frac{g(x_2) - g(x)}{x_2 - x} + \frac{g(x) - g(x_1)}{x - x_1} \end{aligned}$$

tends to zero as $x_2$ and $x_1$ tend to $x$. The collection of intervals $I_x$ covers the set $[a, b] - E$.

Now we cover the null set $E$ by a sequence $\{I_k\}$ of open intervals contained in $[a - 1, b + 1]$ and of total length less than or equal to $\delta$, where $\delta$ is the number corresponding to $\varepsilon$ and the interval $[a - 1, b + 1]$ in the definition of absolute continuity of $g$. The collection $\{I_x, I_k\}$ of open intervals covers the bounded closed interval $[a, b]$. Therefore we can find finitely many among them, say $J_1, \cdots, J_n$ among the $I_x$ and $J_1', \cdots, J_m'$ among the $I_k$, which cover $[a, b]$:

$$\bigcup_{j=1}^{n} J_j \cup \bigcup_{j=1}^{m} J_j' \supset [a, b].$$

We assume that none of the intervals $J_j$ or $J_j'$ is contained in the union of the rest of them, since such an interval $J_j$ or $J_j'$ would not be needed in covering $[a, b]$ and we could eliminate it. Furthermore, if we let

$$J_j = (a_j, b_j) \qquad \text{and} \qquad J_j' = (a_j', b_j'),$$

we may assume that we have enumerated the intervals in such a way that

$$a_1 \leq a_2 \leq \cdots \leq a_n \qquad \text{and} \qquad a_1' \leq a_2' \leq \cdots \leq a_m'.$$

Then also

$$b_1 \leq b_2 \leq \cdots \leq b_n \qquad \text{and} \qquad b_1' \leq b_2' \leq \cdots \leq b_m'$$

since, for instance, $b_{j+1} \leq b_j$ would imply $J_j \supset J_{j+1}$ and $J_{j+1}$ could therefore be eliminated. Under these circumstances, $J_{j+2}$ is disjoint from $J_j$, $j = 1, \cdots, n - 2$, and $J'_{j+2}$ is disjoint from $J_j'$, $j = 1, \cdots, m - 2$. If, for instance, $J_{j+2}$ and $J_j$ are not disjoint, then

$$(a_j, b_j) \cup (a_{j+2}, b_{j+2}) = (a_j, b_{j+2}) \supset (a_{j+1}, b_{j+1})$$

and $J_{j+1}$ could therefore be eliminated.

The intervals

$$[g(a_j), g(b_j)], \quad j = 1, \cdots, n \qquad \text{and} \qquad [g(a_j'), g(b_j')], \quad j = 1, \cdots, m$$

cover $[g(a), g(b)]$. Now we compute the total length of these intervals. We have by (7.3.9)

$$\begin{aligned}\sum \{(g(b_j) - g(a_j)) : 1 \le j \le n, j \text{ even}\} &\le \frac{\varepsilon}{b-a} \sum \{(b_j - a_j) : 1 \le j \le n, j \text{ even}\} \\ &\le \frac{\varepsilon}{b-a}(b-a) = \varepsilon,\end{aligned}$$

and similarly

$$\sum \{(g(b_j) - g(a_j)) : 1 \le j \le n, j \text{ odd}\} \le \varepsilon.$$

Since the total length of the sequence $\{I_k\}$ is less than, or equal to, $\delta$ and the $J_j'$ are taken from the $I_k$, we have

$$\sum \{(b_j' - a_j') : 1 \le j \le m, j \text{ even}\} \le \delta,$$
$$\sum \{(b_j' - a_j') : 1 \le j \le m, j \text{ odd}\} \le \delta,$$

and therefore by the definition of absolute continuity,

$$\sum \{(g(b_j') - g(a_j')) : 1 \le j \le m, j \text{ even}\} \le \varepsilon,$$
$$\sum \{(g(b_j') - g(a_j')) : 1 \le j \le m, j \text{ odd}\} \le \varepsilon.$$

This proves that the interval $[g(a), g(b)]$ can be covered by a finite number of intervals of total length less than, or equal to, $4\varepsilon$. Since $\varepsilon$ was arbitrary, $[g(a), g(b)]$ must reduce to a point, which means exactly that $g$ is constant on $[a, b]$.

7.3.10 COROLLARY *The following are equivalent for a function $f$ on the real line:*

(a) *$f$ is absolutely continuous;*
(b) *$f$ is of locally bounded variation and*

$$f(t) = \int_0^t f' \, dx + f(0);$$

(c) *there is a locally integrable function $g$ with*

$$f(t) = \int_0^t g \, dx + f(0).$$

*Proof* (a) implies (b) by Proposition 7.3.3 and Theorem 7.3.7. Statement (b) implies (c) by Proposition 7.1.6, and (c) implies (a) by Lemma 7.3.5.

## *EXERCISES*

*7.3.1* Prove that the set of absolutely continuous functions is a linear space, that is, if $f$ and $g$ are absolutely continuous, then so is $\alpha f + \beta g$ for any pair of real numbers $\alpha$, $\beta$.

*7.3.2* Prove that $f^+$ and $f^-$ are absolutely continuous if $f$ is.

*7.3.3* Prove that the product of two absolutely continuous functions is again absolutely continuous.

*7.3.4* Suppose $g \in L^1_{\text{loc}}$. Prove that there is $h \in L^1_{\text{loc}}$ with

$$\left(\int_0^t g\,dx\right)^2 = \int_0^t h\,dx.$$

*7.3.5* Suppose $f$ is differentiable at every point. If $f'$ is bounded on every bounded interval, then $f$ is absolutely continuous, and hence

$$f(t) = \int_0^t f'\,dx + f(0).$$

*Hint* Use the mean value theorem.

*Remark* In calculus courses this is usually proved only under the additional assumption that $f'$ is continuous to assure that the derivative of $\int_0^t f'\,dx$ equals $f'$ everywhere.

## 7.4 ANOTHER CHARACTERIZATION OF ABSOLUTELY CONTINUOUS FUNCTIONS

In this section we consider only monotone nondecreasing functions. For such functions, there is another definition of absolute continuity, equivalent to the old one, but more convenient for the discussion of integrals derived from monotone nondecreasing functions (see Chapter 9).

We say that an interval $I$ is an interval of constancy of a monotone nondecreasing function $f$ if $I$ contains more than one point and $f$ is constant on $I$, and if there is no larger interval containing $I$ on which $f$ is constant. Any two different intervals $I$ and $J$ of constancy of $f$ must be disjoint; if they were not, then $I \cup J$ would be an interval larger than $I$ on which $f$ is constant.

7.4.1 LEMMA *The set of intervals of constancy of a monotone nondecreasing function can be enumerated.*

*Proof* The proof is similar to the one of Proposition 6.2.3 where we have shown how to enumerate the points of discontinuity of a monotone nondecreasing function $f$. We first observe that there are at most two unbounded intervals of constancy for $f$, namely, the ones that have $-\infty$ or $+\infty$ as an end point. All other intervals of constancy are bounded and of positive length. There are only a finite number, namely $2n^2$, of such intervals of length greater than $1/n$ contained in $[-n, n]$. Thus if we enumerate these intervals first for $n = 1$, then for $n = 2$, and so on, we will list all intervals of constancy except the unbounded ones of which there are at most two.

7.4.2 THEOREM *A monotone nondecreasing function $f$ is absolutely continuous if and only if the following two conditions are satisfied.*

(a) *$f$ is continuous;*
(b) *$f$ maps null sets into null sets.*

*Proof* Suppose $f$ is absolutely continuous. We have already remarked earlier that $f$ is continuous, so we have to prove only statement (b). Let $E$ be a null set and $\varepsilon > 0$; choose $\delta$ to be the number that corresponds to $\varepsilon$ and a bounded interval $[a - 1, b + 1]$, $a < b$ in the definition of absolute continuity (Definition 7.3.2). We can cover $E \cap [a, b]$ by a countable number of open intervals $(a_k, b_k)$ contained in $[a - 1, b + 1]$ and of total length less than or equal to $\delta$. We may assume that these intervals are disjoint. Namely, $I = \bigcup (a_k, b_k)$ is an open set. Therefore $I$ is the union of a countable number of disjoint open intervals, $I = \bigcup (a_j', b_j')$ (see Lemma 3.3.6). The total length of the $(a_j', b_j')$ is the measure of $I$ which is less than, or equal to, the total length of $\{(a_k, b_k)\}$. We assume therefore right away that the intervals $(a_k, b_k)$ are disjoint. Thus by the definition of absolute continuity,

$$\sum_{k=1}^{n} [f(b_k) - f(a_k)] \leq \varepsilon$$

for any $n$. Therefore

$$f(E \cap [a, b]) = \{y : y = f(x) \text{ for some } x \in E \cap [a, b]\}$$

is covered by the system $\{[f(a_k), f(b_k)]\}$ of intervals of total length less than, or equal to, $\varepsilon$. This means that $f(E \cap [a, b])$ is a null set for every bounded interval $[a, b]$, and hence

$$f(E) = \bigcup_{n=1}^{\infty} f(E \cap [-n, n])$$

is a null set.

Conversely, suppose statements (a) and (b) are satisfied for the monotone nondecreasing function $f$. If $f$ were not absolutely continuous, then we could find a bounded interval $[a, b]$ and an $\varepsilon > 0$ such that for every integer $n$ there is a sequence $a \leq a_1{}^n \leq b_1{}^n \leq \cdots \leq a_{s(n)}^n \leq b_{s(n)}^n \leq b$ with

$$\sum_{k=1}^{s(n)} (b_k{}^n - a_k{}^n) \leq 2^{-n}$$

but

$$\sum_{k=1}^{s(n)} (f(b_k^n) - f(a_k^n)) > \varepsilon. \tag{7.4.3}$$

The set

$$E_n = \bigcup_{m \geq n} \bigcup_{k=1}^{s(m)} (a_k^m, b_k^m)$$

is measurable and has measure at most

$$\sum_{m=n}^{\infty} 2^{-m} = 2^{-n+1},$$

so that the measure of $E_n$ tends to zero as $n$ tends to infinity. Since $E_n \supset E_{n+1}$,

$$E = \bigcap_{n=1}^{\infty} E_n$$

has measure zero by Proposition 3.3.3. Consequently, $E$ and hence $f(E)$ is a null set. We would like to conclude that

$$F = \bigcap_{n=1}^{\infty} f(E_n)$$

is also a null set. Unfortunately, $F$ does not equal $f(E)$; but if $\{I_j : j = 1, \cdots\}$ are the intervals of constancy of $f$ and $c_j$ is the value of $f$ on $I_j$, then

$$F = \bigcap_{n=1}^{\infty} f(E_n) \subset f(E) \cup \bigcup_{j=1}^{\infty} \{c_j\}.$$

Namely, if $y \in F$, then, for each $n$, there is an $x_n \in E_n$ with

$$y = f(x_n),$$

so that in case $x_1 = x_n$ for all $n$, $x_1 \in E$ and thus $y = f(x_1) \in f(E)$; and in case $x_1 \neq x_n$ for some $n$, we have $x_1 \in I_j$ for some $j$ and then $y = f(x_1) = c_j$.

Hence $F$ is indeed a null set.

The image of $(a_k^n, b_k^n)$ is an interval $I_k^n$ with end points $f(a_k^n)$ and $f(b_k^n)$, since, by continuity, $f$ assumes all values between $f(a_k^n)$ and $f(b_k^n)$ on $(a_k^n, b_k^n)$. We have

$$f(E_n) = \bigcup_{m \geq n} \bigcup_{k=1}^{s(m)} I_k^m \subset [f(a), f(b)].$$

Thus $f(E_n)$ is measurable and of finite measure. Since $\{f(E_n)\}$ decreases to the null set $F$, the measure of $f(E_n)$ must tend to zero as $n$ tends to infinity. On the other hand,

$$f(a) \leq f(a_1) \leq f(b_1) \leq \cdots \leq f(a_{s(n)}^n) \leq f(b_{s(n)}^n) \leq f(b),$$

so that by Equation (7.4.3),

$$\bigcup_{k=1}^{s(n)} I_k^n$$

has measure greater than $\varepsilon$. Consequently, the measure of the larger set $f(E_n)$ is greater than $\varepsilon$ for all $n$, which is a contradiction.

## *EXERCISES*

*7.4.1* Let $E$ be a null set contained in $[0, \infty)$. Prove that

$$\sqrt{E} = \{y : y = \sqrt{x} \text{ for some } x \in E\}$$

is again a null set.

*Hint* Prove this first under the assumption that $E \subset [c, \infty)$ for some $c > 0$, using the inequality

$$\sqrt{b} - \sqrt{a} \leq \frac{1}{2\sqrt{c}}(b - a) \qquad \text{for } b \geq a \geq c$$

(which is also to be established).

*7.4.2* Use Exercise 7.4.1 and Theorem 7.4.2 to prove that the square root of a nonnegative monotone nondecreasing, absolutely continuous function is absolutely continuous.

*7.4.3* Suppose $g \in L^1$. Prove that there are $h_1, h_2 \in L^1$ with

$$\int_{-\infty}^{t} g\,dx = \left(\int_{-\infty}^{t} h_1\,dx\right) \cdot \left(\int_{-\infty}^{t} h_2\,dx\right)$$

*Answer* Let

$$f_1(t) = \int_{-\infty}^{t} g^+\,dx, \qquad f_2(t) = \int_{-\infty}^{t} g^-\,dx$$

and define

$$k_1 = \sqrt{f_1} + \sqrt{f_2}, \qquad k_2 = \sqrt{f_1} - \sqrt{f_2}, \qquad h_j = k_j', \qquad j = 1, 2.$$

*7.4.4* Prove that the function $g$ defined by

$$g(x) = \begin{cases} \left| x \right| \sin \dfrac{1}{x} \left|^{1/2} \right. & \text{for } x \neq 0 \\ 0 & \text{for } x = 0 \end{cases}$$

is continuous but not of locally bounded variation, and hence not absolutely continuous.

*7.4.5* Prove that the function $f$ defined by

$$f(x) = \begin{cases} x^2 \left| \sin \dfrac{1}{x} \right| & \text{for } x \neq 0 \\ 0 & \text{for } x = 0 \end{cases}$$

is absolutely continuous (and nonnegative), but $\sqrt{f}$ is not absolutely continuous.

## 7.5 APPLICATIONS

In this section we collect some of the results that follow from the fundamental theorem of calculus for absolutely continuous functions (Theorem 7.3.7). The first theorem is concerned with a decomposition of functions of locally bounded variation that has its counterpart in the decomposition of measures treated in Chapter 9.

Before stating the theorem we should like to recall some facts discussed in the previous chapter. We have seen in Corollary 6.2.8 that every function $f$ of locally bounded variation can be written as the sum

$$f = k + s$$

of a continuous function $k$ of locally bounded variation and a jump function $s$, the jump part of $f$. The derivative of the jump part $s$ of $f$ vanishes almost everywhere by Fubini's theorem (Theorem 6.5.1) on differentiation of series of monotone nondecreasing functions; $s$ is by definition the difference of two such series of elementary jump functions (see also Exercise 6.5.5).

**7.5.1 THEOREM** *A function $f$ of locally bounded variation can be decomposed into a sum*

$$f = g + h + s$$

*where $g$ is an absolutely continuous function satisfying $g(0) = f(0)$, $h$ is a continuous function of locally bounded variation with a vanishing derivative almost everywhere (a so-called singular function), and $s$ is the jump part of some function of locally bounded variation (namely $f$) satisfying $s(0) = 0$. This decomposition is unique. If $f$ is monotone nondecreasing, then so are $g$, $h$, and $s$.*

*Proof* To prove the existence of this decomposition, let $s$ be the jump part of $f$; then $s(0) = 0$. Define

$$g(t) = \int_0^t f'\,dx + f(0)$$

so that $g$ is absolutely continuous and $g(0) = f(0)$. Now let

$$h = (f - s) - g;$$

$h$ is continuous and of locally bounded variation, since both $f - s$ and $g$ are. Furthermore,

$$h' = f' - s' - g' = f' - f' = 0 \text{ a.e.}$$

To prove the uniqueness, suppose

$$f = g_1 + h_1 + s_1 = g_2 + h_2 + s_2$$

are two such decompositions. Then $g_1 - g_2 = h_1 - h_2 + s_1 - s_2$ is absolutely continuous and

$$g_1' - g_2' = h_1' - h_2' + s_1' - s_2' = 0 \text{ a.e.}$$

Thus $g_1 - g_2$ is constant and equal to $g_1(0) - g_2(0) = 0$, whence $g_1 = g_2$. Now, by Exercise 6.2.3, $s_1 - s_2$ is the jump part of a function of locally bounded variation, and since

$$s_1 - s_2 = h_2 - h_1 + g_2 - g_1 = h_2 - h_1$$

is continuous, $s_1 - s_2$ must vanish, because the function of which $s_1 - s_2$ is the jump part is continuous and thus does not have a jump part. This proves $s_1 = s_2$, and consequently $h_1 = h_2$ also.

We will conclude the present section by extending two of the most important manipulation tools of the theory of Riemann integration, namely, integration by parts and change of variables. In the proof of the theorem on integration by parts we need the following lemma.

7.5.2 LEMMA *The product of two absolutely continuous functions is again absolutely continuous.*

*Proof* Suppose $F$ and $G$ are absolutely continuous. Let $[a, b]$ be any bounded interval and $\varepsilon > 0$. Choose $\delta > 0$ such that for any sequence $a \leq a_1 \leq a_2 \leq \cdots \leq a_n \leq b_n \leq b$ satisfying

$$\sum_{k=1}^{n} (b_k - a_k) \leq \delta$$

we have

$$\sum_{k=1}^{n} |F(b_k) - F(a_k)| \leq \varepsilon,$$

$$\sum_{k=1}^{n} |G(b_k) - G(a_k)| \leq \varepsilon.$$

$F$ and $G$ are continuous on $[a, b]$; hence they are bounded in modulus by a constant $M$ on $[a, b]$. Now we have

$$\begin{aligned}
&\sum_{k=1}^{n} |F(b_k)G(b_k) - F(a_k)G(a_k)| \\
&\qquad = \sum_{k=1}^{n} |F(b_k)[G(b_k) - G(a_k)] + G(a_k)[F(b_k) - F(a_k)]| \\
&\qquad \leq M \sum_{k=1}^{n} |G(b_k) - G(a_k)| + M \sum_{k=1}^{n} |F(b_k) - F(a_k)| \\
&\qquad \leq 2M\varepsilon.
\end{aligned}$$

Thus $FG$ is absolutely continuous.

7.5.3 THEOREM *Suppose $f$ and $g$ are integrable functions on the bounded interval $[a, b]$. For $t \in [a, b]$ let*

$$F(t) = \int_a^t f\,dx + c_1, \qquad G(t) = \int_a^t g\,dx + c_2,$$

*where $c_1$ and $c_2$ are constants. Then $Fg$ and $Gf$ are integrable on $[a, b]$ and*

$$\int_a^b Fg\,dx + \int_a^b Gf\,dx = F(b)G(b) - F(a)G(a).$$

*Proof* We interpret $f$ and $g$ to be zero outside $[a, b]$ so that $F$ and $G$ are defined on the whole real line. $Fg$ is measurable, since it is a product of measurable functions. If $M$ is a bound for the modulus of the continuous function $F$ on the bounded interval $[a, b]$, then

$$|Fg| \leq M\,|g|$$

which proves that $Fg$ is integrable (Theorem 3.1.8). Similarly, $Gf$ is integrable. Now let $x$ be a point at which both $F$ and $G$ are differentiable. It is proved in calculus that then $FG$ is also differentiable at $x$ and

$$(FG)'(x) = F(x)G'(x) + G(x)F'(x). \tag{7.5.4}$$

We have therefore

$$(FG)' = Fg + Gf \text{ a.e.}$$

$FG$ is absolutely continuous, and thus by the fundamental theorem of calculus (Theorem 7.3.7),

$$\int_a^b (FG)'\,dx = F(b)G(b) - F(a)G(a).$$

Now we need only integrate (7.5.4) from $a$ to $b$ in order to prove the assertion of the theorem.

7.5.5 COROLLARY *If $f$ and $g$ are integrable and*

$$F(t) = \int_{-\infty}^t f\,dx, \qquad G(t) = \int_{-\infty}^t g\,dx$$

*then $Fg$ and $Gf$ are integrable and*

$$\int Fg\,dx + \int Gf\,dx = \int f\,dx \int g\,dx.$$

*Proof* The function $F$ is bounded, since

$$|F(t)| \leq \int_{-\infty}^t |f|\,dx \leq \int |f|\,dx.$$

Thus $|Fg|$ is bounded by a multiple of $|g|$ and $Fg$ is therefore integrable (Theorem 3.1.8). For the same reason, $Gf$ is integrable. Furthermore,

$$F(t) = \int_{-n}^{t} f\,dx + \int_{-\infty}^{-n} f\,dx, \qquad G(t) = \int_{-n}^{t} g\,dx + \int_{-\infty}^{-n} g\,dx$$

so that we can apply the previous theorem:

$$\int_{-n}^{n} Fg\,dx + \int_{-n}^{n} Gf\,dx = F(n)G(n) - F(-n)G(-n). \tag{7.5.6}$$

Notice that

$$\lim_{n\to\infty} F(-n) = 0 = \lim_{n\to\infty} G(-n)$$

while

$$\lim_{n\to\infty} F(n) = \int f\,dx, \qquad \lim_{n\to\infty} G(n) = \int g\,dx.$$

We obtain therefore the desired formula by passing to the limit in (7.5.6).

We will prove the theorem on the change of variables only for a substitution $t = t(x)$ where $t$ is a monotone nondecreasing, absolutely continuous function of $x$. Such a theorem holds also without the restrictive monotonicity requirement on $t$. However, we leave the discussion of this aspect to the exercises.

7.5.7 THEOREM *Let $t$ be a monotone nondecreasing, absolutely continuous function. Let $[a, b]$ be a bounded interval and suppose $f$ is an integrable function on $[t(a), t(b)]$. Then $(f \circ t)t'$ is an integrable function on $[a, b]$ and*

$$\int_{t(a)}^{t(b)} f\,dx = \int_{a}^{b} (f \circ t)t'\,dx. \tag{7.5.8}$$

*Proof* First suppose $f$ is the characteristic function of a closed bounded interval $[\alpha, \beta]$. We may assume that $f$ vanishes off $[t(a), t(b)]$, that is, that $[\alpha, \beta] \subset [t(a), t(b)]$, since only the behavior of $f$ on $[t(a), t(b)]$ matters in Equation (7.5.8). There are points in $[a, b]$ where $t$ has the values $\alpha$ and $\beta$ because $t$ is continuous and therefore takes on all values between $t(a)$ and $t(b)$ on $[a, b]$. Let

$$c = \inf\{x : x \in [a, b],\ t(x) = \alpha\},$$
$$d = \sup\{x : x \in [a, b],\ t(x) = \beta\}.$$

Then $t(c) = \alpha$ and $t(d) = \beta$ by the continuity of $t$ and $c \le d$, since $t$ is monotone nondecreasing. Since $f \circ t$ is the characteristic function of $[c, d]$,

$$\int_{a}^{b} (f \circ t)t'\,dx = \int_{c}^{d} t'\,dx = t(d) - t(c)$$
$$= \beta - \alpha = \int_{t(a)}^{t(b)} f\,dx.$$

Consequently, the theorem holds whenever $f$ is a step function.

Now suppose $f$ is an integrable function on $[t(a), t(b)]$. We interpret $f$ to be zero off $[t(a), t(b)]$. By Mikusiński's lemma (Lemma 2.1.10) we can find a series $\sum \varphi_n$ of step functions such that $\sum_{n=1}^{\infty} \int |\varphi_n| \, dx < \infty$ and

$$f(x) = \sum_{n=1}^{\infty} \varphi_n(x)$$

for all those $x$ for which $\sum |\varphi_n(x)|$ converges. But then

$$\text{(7.5.9)} \qquad \begin{aligned} f(t(x))t'(x) &= f(t(x))t'(x)\chi_{[a,b]}(x) \\ &= \sum_{n=1}^{\infty} \varphi_n(t(x))t'(x)\chi_{[a,b]}(x) \end{aligned}$$

whenever the right-hand side converges absolutely. We have

$$\begin{aligned} \sum_{n=1}^{\infty} \int_a^b |(\varphi_n \circ t)t'| \, dx &= \sum_{n=1}^{\infty} \int_a^b (|\varphi_n| \circ t)t' \, dx \\ &= \sum_{n=1}^{\infty} \int_{t(a)}^{t(b)} |\varphi_n| \, dx \leq \sum_{n=1}^{\infty} \int |\varphi_n| \, dx < \infty. \end{aligned}$$

Thus (7.5.9) holds for a.a. $x$ by Beppo Levi's theorem and

$$\begin{aligned} \int_a^b (f \circ t)t' \, dx &= \sum_{n=1}^{\infty} \int_a^b (\varphi_n \circ t)t' \, dx \\ &= \sum_{n=1}^{\infty} \int_{t(a)}^{t(b)} \varphi_n \, dx = \int_{t(a)}^{t(b)} f \, dx. \end{aligned}$$

7.5.10 COROLLARY *Let $t$ be a monotone nondecreasing absolutely continuous function. Define*

$$\alpha = \lim_{x \to -\infty} t(x), \qquad \beta = \lim_{x \to \infty} t(x),$$

*(these limits may be $-\infty$ or $\infty$). If $f$ is integrable, then $(f \circ t)t'$ is integrable and*

$$\int_\alpha^\beta f \, dx = \int (f \circ t)t' \, dx.$$

*(Actually, $f$ need only be integrable on $(\alpha, \beta)$.)*

*Proof* We know by the last theorem that $(f \circ t)t'\chi_{[-n,n]}$ is integrable for all $n$. Therefore $(f \circ t)t'$ is measurable. On the other hand,

$$\int_{-n}^{n} |(f \circ t)t'| \, dx = \int_{t(-n)}^{t(n)} |f| \, dx \leq \int_\alpha^\beta |f| \, dx$$

converges as $n$ tends to infinity, whence $|(f \circ t)t'|$ is integrable; and so $(f \circ t)t'$ is also integrable. Now we have

$$\int_{t(-n)}^{t(n)} f\,dx = \int_{-n}^{n} (f \circ t)t'\,dx,$$

and passing to the limit as $n$ tends to infinity we obtain the desired formula.

Theorem 7.5.7 can be generalized in the following way:

**7.5.11 THEOREM** *Let $t$ be an absolutely continuous function and $f$ a bounded integrable function. Then $(f \circ t)t'$ is locally integrable and for $a \leq b$,*

$$\int_{t(a)}^{t(b)} f\,dx = \int_{a}^{b} (f \circ t)t'\,dx.$$

An outline of the proof of this theorem is discussed in part F of the exercise section 7.6 where a complete description of the generality and limitations of the theorem is also given. Some special cases of Theorem 7.5.11 that can be derived from Theorem 7.5.7 are presented in Exercises 7.5.4 and 7.5.5.

Notice that, in contrast with Theorem 7.5.7, it is important in Theorem 7.5.11 that we have some information about the behavior of the function $f$ outside the closed interval with end points $t(a)$ and $t(b)$ in order tc define $f \circ t$ on $[a, b]$; actually it would suffice to know $f$ on the interval $[\alpha_0, \beta_0]$ whose end points are the minimum $\alpha_0$ and the maximum $\beta_0$ of $t$ on $[a, b]$, and to require that $f$ is integrable on $[\alpha_0, \beta_0]$. Also, the requirement that $f$ be bounded is necessary, unless one wants to put some restriction on $t$ (see Exercise 7.5.3). We should point out also that $(f \circ t)t'$ is not always integrable even if $f$ is bounded and integrable (Exercise 7.5.2); thus Corollary 7.5.10 cannot be generalized to the situation of Theorem 7.5.11 (see, however, Exercise 7.6.28).

## *EXERCISES*

*7.5.1* Prove the following theorem of calculus:
If the functions $F$ and $G$ on the real line are differentiable at the point $x$, then $FG$ is also differentiable at $x$ and

$$(FG)'(x) = F'(x)G(x) + F(x)G'(x).$$

*7.5.2* Let $f$ be the characteristic function of $[-1, 1]$ and $t(x) = \sin x$. By Exercise 7.3.5 $t$ is an absolutely continuous function. Calculate $(f \circ t)t'$ and prove that this function is not integrable.

*7.5.3* Let $f$ and $t$ be the functions defined by

$$f(x) = \begin{cases} |x|^{-1/2} & \text{for } x \neq 0 \\ 0 & \text{for } x = 0 \end{cases} \qquad t(x) = \begin{cases} x^2 \sin^2 \dfrac{1}{x} & \text{for } x \neq 0 \\ 0 & \text{for } x = 0 \end{cases}$$

Prove that $f$ is integrable on $[t(0), t(\pi/2)]$ and $t$ is absolutely continuous, but $(f \circ t)t'$ fails to be integrable on $[0, 2/\pi]$. Thus Theorem 7.5.11 does not hold for this choice of functions.

*Hint* Prove that the derivative of $t$ equals zero at the origin and calculate the derivative of $t$ at points $x \neq 0$ to show that $t'$ exists everywhere and is locally bounded. Thus $t$ is absolutely continuous by Exercise 7.3.5. Now prove that for $x \neq 0$,

$$(f \circ t)t'(x) = \eta_1(x)\left|2 \sin \frac{1}{x}\right| - \eta_2(x)\frac{2}{|x|}\cos\frac{1}{x}$$

where $\eta_1(x)$ and $\eta_2(x)$ are functions that assume only the values $+1$ and $-1$. Show that $(1/x)\cos(1/x)$ is not integrable on $(0, 2/\pi]$ and then conclude that $(f \circ t)t'$ cannot be integrable on $[0, 2/\pi]$.

*7.5.4* Prove that Theorem 7.5.11 is true even without the restriction that $f$ is bounded if $t$ is an absolutely continuous function with the following property. There is a sequence $a_k$ of points indexed on the set of all integers such that

(a) $\cdots < a_{k-1} < a_k < a_{k+1} < \cdots$;

(b) $\lim_{k\to-\infty} a_k = -\infty$, $\lim_{k\to\infty} a_k = \infty$;

(c) either $t$ or $-t$ is monotone nondecreasing on $[a_{k-1}, a_k]$, $k = 0, \pm 1, \cdots$.

*7.5.5* Prove that Theorem 7.5.11 holds if the absolutely continuous function $t$ is continuously differentiable and the set $E = \{x : t'(x) = 0\}$ is countable.

*Hint* Since $E$ and $t(E)$ are null sets, you have only to establish that $(f \circ t)t'$ is integrable on $[a, b] - E$ for any bounded closed interval $[a, b]$ and

$$\int_{[t(a),t(b)]-E} f\,dx = \int_{[a,b]-E} (f \circ t)t'\,dx$$

(where we assume for the moment that $t(a) \leq t(b)$; if $t(a) > t(b)$, you have to interchange $t(a)$ and $t(b)$ in this formula and put a minus sign on the left, since $\int_{t(a)}^{t(b)} f\,dx = -\int_{t(b)}^{t(a)} f\,dx$). Now notice that $R - E = \{x : t'(x) \neq 0\}$ is an open set and thus the disjoint union of a sequence of open intervals $(a_k, b_k)$ (Lemma 3.3.6). Since $t'$ does not change sign on $(a_k, b_k)$, either $t$ or $-t$ is monotone nondecreasing on $[a_k, b_k]$; therefore you can apply Theorem 7.5.7.

## 7.6 EXERCISES

### A. The Indefinite Integral

**7.6.1** Suppose $f \in L^1_{\text{loc}}$ and $\int_a^b f\,dx = 0$ for all $a \leq b$. Prove that $f = 0$ a.e.

*Hint* Consider $F(t) = \int_0 f\,dx$.

7.6.2 For any function $F$, we let

$$D_r F(t) = \lim_{h\to 0, h>0} \frac{1}{h}[F(t+h) - F(t)],$$

$$D_\ell F(t) = \lim_{h\to 0, h>0} \frac{1}{h}[F(t) - F(t-h)],$$

$$SDF(t) = \lim_{h\to 0, h>0} \frac{1}{2h}[F(t+h) - F(t-h)],$$

if these limits exist. Now establish the following:

(a) $D_r \int_0^t f\,dx = f(t+0)$ if $f$ is monotone nondecreasing.

(b) $D_\ell \int_0^t f\,dx = f(t-0)$ if $f$ is monotone nondecreasing.

(c) $SD \int_0^t f\,dx = \frac{1}{2}[f(t+0) + f(t-0)]$ if $f$ is monotone nondecreasing.

(d) Prove that the equations in (a) to (c) hold also if $f$ is of locally bounded variation.

(e) Give an example of a function $f \in L^1_{\text{loc}}$ for which $SD \int_0^t f\,dx$ does not exist everywhere.

7.6.3 Similarly as $L^1_{\text{loc}}$ we can define a space $L^p_{\text{loc}}$ for $p \geq 1$. Here $L^p_{\text{loc}}$ is the linear space of all functions $f$ with the property that $f\chi_{[a,b]}$ belongs to $L^p$ for every bounded interval $[a, b]$. We say that a function $F$ is Hölder-continuous of order $s > 0$ if, for each interval $[a, b]$, there is a constant $M$ such that

$$|F(t) - F(t')| \leq M\,|t - t'|^s \qquad \text{for } t, t' \in [a, b].$$

Prove the following:

(a) $L^p_{\text{loc}} \subset L^1_{\text{loc}}$ for $p \geq 1$;

(b) If $f \in L^2_{\text{loc}}$, then $F(t) = \int_0^t f\,dx$ is Hölder-continuous of order $\frac{1}{2}$.

*Hint* Use the Schwarz inequality (Proposition 5.1.8).

(c) If $f \in L^p_{\text{loc}}$, then $F(t) = \int_0^t f\,dx$ is Hölder-continuous of order $1/q$ where $q$ is the conjugate exponent to $p$.

*Hint* Use Hölder's inequality (Proposition 5.4.6).

(d) If $F$ is Hölder continuous of order $s > 1$, then $f$ is a constant.

*Hint* Prove that $\lim_{h\to 0} 1/h[F(x+h) - F(x)] = 0$ for all $x$.

**7.6.4** We say that $F$ is locally Lipschitz if, for every bounded interval $[a, b]$, there is a constant $M$ with

$$|F(t) - F(t')| \leq M|t - t'| \qquad \text{for } t, t' \in [a, b].$$

Prove that an absolutely continuous function $F$ is locally Lipschitz if and only if $F'$ is locally bounded. (Recall that we agreed to let $F'(x) = 0$ if the derivative of $F$ does not exist at $x$.)

**7.6.5** Suppose $F$ is absolutely continuous and $F' \geq 0$ a.e. Show that $F$ is monotone nondecreasing. Why is a similar statement false for a function $F$ of locally bounded variation?

## B. Examples of Absolutely Continuous Functions

**7.6.6** Suppose the function $f$ is Hölder-continuous of order $s > 0$, that is, there is a constant $M > 0$ for each bounded interval $[a, b]$ such that

$$|f(x) - f(x')| \leq M\,|x - x'|^s \qquad \text{for } x, x' \in [a, b].$$

Prove that $f$ is absolutely continuous. In particular, a function satisfying a Lipschitz condition (as in Exercise 7.6.4) on each bounded interval is absolutely continuous.

**7.6.7** If $f$ is continuously differentiable, then $f$ is absolutely continuous.

*Hint* Use the mean value theorem to prove that $f$ is Hölder-continuous of order $s = 1$ (locally Lipschitz). Then apply Exercise 7.6.6.

**7.6.8** If $f$ is absolutely continuous, then $|f|^p$ is absolutely continuous for $p \geq 1$.

**7.6.9** Suppose the function $f$ on the real line $R$ is absolutely continuous on $R - \{0\}$; this means that the condition in Definition 7.3.2 is satisfied for every closed bounded interval $[a, b]$ that does not contain 0.

(a) Suppose $f$ is of locally bounded variation. Prove that

$$f(0+0) = \lim_{x\to 0,\, x>0} f(x)$$

exists.

*Hint* If this limit does not exist, then there is a monotone decreasing sequence $\{x_n\}$ converging to zero such that $\{f(x_n)\}$ is not a Cauchy sequence. Show that there is $\varepsilon > 0$ and subsequences $\{x_{n(k)}\}$ and $\{x_{m(k)}\}$ of $\{x_n\}$ such that $x_{m(k+1)} \leq x_{n(k)} < x_{m(k)}$ and

$$|f(x_{m(k)}) - f(x_{n(k)})| \geq \varepsilon.$$

(b) Suppose $f$ is of locally bounded variation and continuous at 0. Prove that $f$ is absolutely continuous.

*Hint* It suffices to prove that $f$ is absolutely continuous on each bounded interval of the form $[0, b]$ and $[a, 0]$. For $\varepsilon > 0$ choose $c \in [0, b]$ such that the total variation of $f$ on $[0, c]$ is less than $\varepsilon/2$. Then choose $\delta > 0$ corresponding to $\varepsilon/2$ and the interval $[c, b]$ according to Definition 7.3.2. Prove that for any sequence

$$0 \leq a_1 \leq b_1 \leq \cdots \leq a_n \leq b_n \leq b,$$

the following inequality holds:

$$\sum_{k=1}^{n} |f(b_k) - f(a_k)| \leq \varepsilon.$$

(c) Show that $f$ need not be absolutely continuous if we require only that $f$ be continuous at 0.

**7.6.10** Show that the following functions are absolutely continuous.

(a) $f(x) = |x|^p$ if $p > 0$

(b) $g(x) = \begin{cases} x^\alpha \sin x^{-\beta} & \text{for } x \neq 0 \\ 0 & \text{for } x = 0 \end{cases}$ if $\alpha > \beta > 0$.

## C. Convergence of Absolutely Continuous Functions

**7.6.11** We say that a sequence $\{g_n\}$ of functions in $L^1_{\text{loc}}$ converges in $L^1_{\text{loc}}$ to the locally integrable function $g$ if, for each bounded interval $[a, b]$, $\{g_n \chi_{[a,b]}\}$ converges to $g\chi_{[a,b]}$ in $L^1$, that is, if

$$\lim_{n \to \infty} \int_a^b |g - g_n| \, dx = 0$$

for $a \leq b$. Suppose $f$ and $f_n$ are absolutely continuous. Prove that $\{T(f - f_n)\}$ tends to zero if and only if $\{f_n'\}$ tends to $f'$ in $L^1_{\text{loc}}$ and $\{f_n(0)\}$ tends to $f(0)$. Recall that $Th$ denotes the total variation function of $h$ (Definition 6.1.4). It has the property that $Th(b) - Th(a)$ is equal to the total variation of $h$ on $[a, b]$ (Proposition 6.1.5).

*Hint* Proposition 7.2.3 is useful here.

**7.6.12** Suppose $\{f_n\}$ is a sequence of absolutely continuous functions such that

$$\lim_{n,m \to \infty} T(f_n - f_m) = 0.$$

Prove that there is an absolutely continuous function $f$ with $\lim_{n \to \infty} T(f - f_n) = 0$.

*Hint* Use Exercise 7.6.11 and Exercise 2.7.27 (or Theorem 5.3.9).

**7.6.13** Suppose $\{f_n\}$ is a sequence of absolutely continuous functions such that

$$f_n(b) - f_n(a) \geq f_{n-1}(b) - f_{n-1}(a)$$

for $a \leq b$. If $f$ is a function of locally bounded variation to which the sequence $\{f_n\}$ converges everywhere, then $f$ is actually absolutely continuous and $\lim_{n\to\infty} f_n' = f'$ a.e.

*Hint* Show $f_n' \leq f_{n+1}' \leq f'$ and apply the monotone convergence theorem.

## D. Mapping Properties of Absolutely Continuous Functions

**7.6.14** Recall that a subset $A$ of the real line $R$ is closed if and only if $R - A$ is open, which means that every point $x \notin A$ is contained in an open interval $(a, b)$ that does not meet $A$. Prove the following topological lemmas.

(a) A subset $A$ of the real line is closed if and only if the limit of every convergent sequence in $A$ belongs to $A$.

*Hint* If $A$ is not closed, then there is a point $x \notin A$ such that $A \cap (x - 1/n, x + 1/n) \neq 0$ for all $n$. If $x_n$ is a point in this set, then $\lim_{n\to\infty} x_n = x$.

(b) If $A$ is a closed bounded set and $f$ a continuous function on the real line, then $f(A)$ is also closed and bounded.

*Hint* Let $\{y_n\}$ be a sequence in $f(A)$ that converges to $y$ and say $y_n = f(x_n)$, $x_n \in A$. The sequence $\{x_n\}$ is a bounded sequence, so there is a convergent subsequence $\{x_{n(k)}\}$. Show

$$\lim_{k\to\infty} x_{n(k)} = x \in A \qquad \text{and} \qquad f(x) = y \in f(A).$$

**7.6.15** Suppose $f$ is a monotone nondecreasing, absolutely continuous function. Prove that $f(M)$ is measurable for every measurable set $M$.

*Hint* Assume first that $M$ is integrable. For each $n$ choose a closed bounded set $A_n \subset M$ such that $M - A_n$ has measure less than $1/n$ (Corollary 3.5.8).

$$E = M - \bigcup_{n=1}^{\infty} A_n$$

has measure zero and

$$f(M) = f(E) \cup \bigcup_{n=1}^{\infty} f(A_n)$$

(see Exercise 7.6.14).

**7.6.16** Prove that an absolutely continuous function maps null sets into null sets.

*Hint* The proof is similar to the first part of the proof of Theorem 7.4.2. If $E$ is a null set, $[a, b]$ a bounded interval and $\varepsilon > 0$, one may choose a sequence $(a_k, b_k)$ of pairwise disjoint open intervals of total length less than, or equal to, $\delta$ covering $E \cap [a, b]$, where $\delta$ is the number that corresponds to $\varepsilon$ and $[a - 1, b + 1]$ in the definition of absolute continuity of $f$. One may assume $[a_k, b_k] \subset [a - 1, b + 1]$. If $f$ attains its maximum $M_k$ on $[a_k, b_k]$ at $b_k'$ and its minimum $m_k$ at $a_k'$, then $b_k' - a_k' \leq b_k - a_k$ and $f(E \cap [a, b])$ is covered by the sequence $[m_k, M_k]$ of intervals the total length of which is easily estimated.

**7.6.17** An absolutely continuous function maps measurable sets into measurable sets (see the hint for Exercise 7.6.15).

## E. Composition of Absolutely Continuous Functions

**7.6.18** Let $F(x) = x^{1/3}$ and

$$t(x) = \begin{cases} x^3 \sin^3 \dfrac{1}{x} & \text{for } x \neq 0 \\ 0 & \text{for } x = 0. \end{cases}$$

Then $F$ and $t$ are absolutely continuous; in fact, $t$ is continuously differentiable. But $F \circ t$ is not absolutely continuous (it is even not of locally bounded variation).

**7.6.19** If $F$ and $t$ are absolutely continuous and $t$ is monotone nondecreasing, then $F \circ t$ is absolutely continuous.

**7.6.20** If the absolutely continuous function $F$ is locally Lipschitz and $t$ is absolutely continuous, then $F \circ t$ is absolutely continuous. (For the definition of locally Lipschitz see Exercise 7.6.4.)

**7.6.21** In calculus it is shown that if the function $t$ is differentiable at $x$ and the function $F$ is differentiable at the point $t(x)$, then $F \circ t$ is differentiable at $x$ and

$$(F \circ t)'(x) = F'(t(x)) \cdot t'(x).$$

(a) Suppose $F$ and $t$ are absolutely continuous functions and $t$ is monotone nondecreasing, so that $F \circ t$ is absolutely continuous by Exercise 7.6.19. If $t$ has the property that $\{x : t(x) \in E\}$ is a null set whenever $E$ is a null set, then

$$(F \circ t)' = (F' \circ t)t' \qquad \text{a.e.}$$

(b) Suppose $t$ is a strictly increasing and continuously differentiable function Show that $t$ has the property required in (a).

*Hint* Prove that the range of $t$ is an open interval $(a, b)$ and that $t^{-1}$ exists as a function on $(a, b)$. Then observe that $t^{-1}$ is continuously differentiable on $(a, b)$; the rule

$$(t^{-1})'(y) = \frac{1}{t'(x)}, \qquad y = t(x)$$

is usually shown in calculus. Now apply Theorem 7.4.2.

(c) Integrate the equation in (a) to give another proof of Theorem 7.5.7 for the special situation described in (a).

## F. Discussion of Theorem 7.5.11

**7.6.22** We have seen in Exercise 7.6.20 that $F \circ t$ is absolutely continuous if $F$ is locally Lipschitz (and hence absolutely continuous by Exercise 7.6.6) and $t$ is absolutely continuous. Prove that under these hypotheses

$$(F \circ t)' = (F' \circ t)t' \qquad \text{a.e.}$$

*Hint* If $t$ and $F \circ t$ are differentiable at $x$ and $t'(x) \neq 0$, say $t'(x) > 0$, then there is an interval $(a, b)$ containing $x$ with $t(a) < t(x) < t(b)$ and $t(x) \neq t(x')$ for $x' \in [a, b]$, $x' \neq x$. Now show that $F$ is differentiable at $t(x)$ and

$$F'(t(x)) = \frac{(F \circ t)'(x)}{t'(x)}$$

in the following way. If $\{y_n\}$, $y_n \neq t(x)$ is a sequence in $(t(a), t(b))$ tending to $t(x)$, then there are $x_n \in (a, b)$ with $t(x_n) = y_n$, and we have necessarily

$$\lim_{n \to \infty} x_n = x;$$

for $\{x_n\}$ cannot have a cluster point $x' \neq x$, since then there would be a subsequence $\{x_{n(k)}\}$ converging to $x'$ and thus

$$t(x') = \lim_{k \to \infty} t(x_{n(k)}) = \lim_{k \to \infty} y_{n(k)} = t(x),$$

a contradiction to the choice of $[a, b]$. Now show

$$\lim_{n \to \infty} \frac{F(t(x)) - F(y_n)}{t(x) - y_n} = \frac{(F \circ t)'(x)}{t'(x)}.$$

If $t$ is differentiable at $x$ and $t'(x) = 0$, then $F'(t(x))t'(x) = 0$ and $F \circ t$ is also differentiable at $x$ with derivative equal to zero; this follows easily from the Lipschitz condition

$$\left| \frac{f(t(x)) - F(t(x'))}{x - x'} \right| \leq M \left| \frac{t(x) - t(x')}{x - x'} \right|$$

for $x'$ in a bounded interval around $x$.

**7.6.23** If $f$ is a bounded locally integrable function and $t$ is absolutely continuous, then $(f \circ t)t'$ is locally integrable and

$$\int_{t(a)}^{t(b)} f\,dx = \int_a^b (f \circ t)t'\,dx.$$

This proves Theorem 7.5.11.

*Hint* Let $F$ be the indefinite integral of $f$; then $F$ is locally Lipschitz by Exercise 7.6.4. The formula in Exercise 7.6.22 shows now that $(f \circ t)t'$ is locally integrable, and by integrating this formula one obtains the desired result.

The following exercises deal with the problem of how to find the most general kind of hypotheses that will ensure the validity of the conclusion of Theorem 7.5.11.

**7.6.24** Suppose $f$ is locally integrable and $t$ is absolutely continuous. If $(f \circ t)t'$ is locally integrable, then

$$\int_{t(a)}^{t(b)} f\,dx = \int_a^b (f \circ t)t'\,dx.$$

*Hint* Apply Exercise 7.6.23 to the functions

$$f_n = \operatorname{mid}(-n, f, n) = (-n) \vee f \wedge n,$$

and then use Lebesgue's dominated convergence theorem.

**7.6.25** If $f$ is locally integrable and $t$ is absolutely continuous, and if the conclusion of Theorem 7.5.11 holds, then $F \circ t$ is absolutely continuous where $F$ is the primitive of $f$. Furthermore,

$$(F \circ t)' = (F' \circ t)t' \qquad \text{a.e.}$$

**7.6.26** Suppose $f$ is locally integrable and $t$ is absolutely continuous. Let $F$ be the primitive of $f$. We have seen in Exercise 7.6.25 that a necessary condition for the conclusion of Theorem 7.5.11 to hold is that $F \circ t$ be absolutely continuous. Prove that this condition is also sufficient.

*Hint* Let $G$ be the primitive of $|f|$ and show that $G \circ t$ is also absolutely continuous. This can be done in the following way. Let $\varepsilon > 0$; then we can find for each bounded interval $[a, b]$ a $\delta > 0$ such that

$$\sum_{k=1}^{m} \left| \int_{t(x_k)}^{t(y_k)} f\,dx \right| = \sum_{k=1}^{m} |F(t(y_k)) - F(t(x_k))| \leq \frac{\varepsilon}{2}$$

whenever $a \leq x_1 \leq y_1 \leq \cdots \leq x_m \leq y_m \leq b$ is a sequence of numbers with $\sum_{k=1}^{m}(y_k - x_k) \leq \delta$. Now let $a \leq a_1 \leq b_1 \leq \cdots \leq a_n \leq b_n \leq b$ be any sequence with $\sum_{k=1}^{n}(b_k - a_k) \leq \delta$.

$$\left| \int_{t(a_k)}^{t(b_k)} |f|\,dx \right| = |G(t(b_k)) - G(t(a_k))|$$

is the total variation of $F$ on the interval with end points $t(a_k)$ and $t(b_k)$ (Proposition 7.2.3). Therefore, if $t(a_k) \leq t(b_k)$, we can find a sequence $t(a_k) \leq y_0^k \leq \cdots \leq y_{s(k)}^k \leq t(b_k)$ of points such that

$$\sum_{j=1}^{s(k)} \left| \int_{y_{j-1}^k}^{y_j^k} f\,dx \right| = \sum_{j=1}^{s(k)} |F(y_j^k) - F(y_{j-1}^k)|$$

differs from

$$\int_{t(a_k)}^{t(b_k)} |f|\,dx = \sum_{j=1}^{s(k)} \int_{y_{j-1}^k}^{y_j^k} |f|\,dx$$

by less than $\varepsilon/2n$. Show that there is a sequence $a_k = x_0^k \leq \cdots \leq x_{s(k)}^k = b_k$ with $t(x_j^k) = y_j^k$ for $j = 0, \cdots, s(k)$. Similarly we treat the case $t(b_k) \leq t(a_k)$. Now show

$$\sum_{k=1}^{n} |G(t(b_k)) - G(t(a_k))| = \sum_{k=1}^{n} \left| \int_{t(a_k)}^{t(b_k)} |f|\,dx \right| \leq \varepsilon.$$

This proves that $G \circ t$ is also absolutely continuous. By Exercise 7.6.24 it suffices now to show that $(f \circ t)t'$ is locally integrable in order to prove that the conclusion of Theorem 7.5.11 holds. Let

$$f_n = \operatorname{mid}(-n, f, n) = (-n) \vee f \wedge n.$$

$(f_n \circ t)t'$ is locally integrable (Exercise 7.6.23). Show

$$\left| \int_a^b (f_n \circ t)t'\,dx \right| \leq |G(t(b)) - G(t(a))|$$

whence $|(f_n \circ t)t'| \leq |(G \circ t)'|$ for all $n$ so that one can apply Lebesgue's dominated convergence theorem.

**7.6.27** Suppose $F$, $t$, and $F \circ t$ are absolutely continuous. Derive from Exercise 7.6.26 that

$$(F \circ t)' = (F' \circ t)t' \qquad \text{a.e.}$$

**7.6.28** Suppose $t$ is an absolutely continuous function such that

$$t(\infty) = \lim_{x\to\infty} t(x), \qquad t(-\infty) = \lim_{x\to-\infty} t(x)$$

exist or are $+\infty$ or $-\infty$. If $f$ is an integrable function with the property that $(f \circ t)t'$ is also integrable, then

$$\int_{t(-\infty)}^{t(\infty)} f\,dx = \int_{-\infty}^{\infty} (f \circ t)t'\,dx.$$

(Notice that $t(\infty)$ and $t(-\infty)$ do not exist for every absolutely continuous function $t$; they do not exist for instance for $t = \sin x$).

*Hint* Apply the result of Exercise 7.6.24.

# SUMMARY

A function $f$ on the real line is called locally integrable if, for every bounded closed interval $[a, b]$, $f\chi_{[a,b]}$ is integrable. The linear space of locally integrable functions is denoted by $L^1_{\text{loc}}$ (Definition 7.1.5). For instance, the derivative $f'$ of a function $f$ of locally bounded variation is locally integrable (Proposition 7.1.6).

The functions $g \in L^1_{\text{loc}}$ are suitable for the formation of primitives $f$,

$$f(t) = \int_0^t g\, dx + c,$$

where $c$ is constant. Such a primitive is of locally bounded variation (Proposition 7.2.2). However, it is not true in general that even a continuous monotone increasing function is a primitive of its derivative (Example 7.1.8). But a primitive $f$ of a function $g \in L^1_{\text{loc}}$ is always a primitive of its derivative, that is, $f' = g$ a.e. (Theorem 7.2.5).

There are some interesting formulas for the total variation function $Tf$ and the parts $f_1$ and $f_2$ of positive and negative variation of a primitive $f$,

$$f(t) = \int_0^t g\, dx + c,$$

of a function $g \in L^1_{\text{loc}}$; these are (Corollary 7.2.4)

$$Tf(t) = \int_0^t |g|\, dx + c$$

$$f_1(t) = \int_0^t g^+\, dx + c, \qquad f_2(t) = \int_0^t g^-\, dx.$$

A function $f$ on the real line is absolutely continuous if for every pair $a < b$ of real numbers and $\varepsilon > 0$ there is a $\delta > 0$ such that

$$\sum_{k=1}^{n} |f(b_k) - f(a_k)| \le \varepsilon$$

for every sequence $a \le a_1 \le b_1 \le \cdots \le a_n \le b_n \le b$ satisfying

$$\sum_{k=1}^{n} (b_k - a_k) \le \delta$$

(Definition 7.3.2). Absolutely continuous functions are of locally bounded variation (Proposition 7.3.3). They are exactly those functions $f \in V_{\text{loc}}$ for which the fundamental theorem of calculus holds:

$$f(t) = \int_0^t f'\, dx + f(0)$$

(Theorem 7.3.7, Corollary 7.3.10).

A monotone nondecreasing function $f$ on the real line is absolutely continuous if and only if the following two conditions are satisfied (Theorem 7.4.2):

(a) $f$ is continuous;
(b) $f$ maps null sets into null sets.

If $f$ and $g$ are locally integrable and $F$ and $G$ are primitives of $f$ and $g$, respectively, then $Fg$ and $Gf$ are also locally integrable and

$$\int_a^b Fg\,dx + \int_a^b Gf\,dx = F(b)G(b) - F(a)G(a)$$

(Theorem 7.5.3). If $f$ and $g$ are integrable, then so are $Fg$ and $Gf$ and

$$\int Fg\,dx + \int Gf\,dx = \int f\,dx \int g\,dx$$

(Corollary 7.5.5).

Suppose $t$ is a monotone nondecreasing, absolutely continuous function and $[a, b]$ a bounded interval. If $f$ is an integrable function on $[t(a), t(b)]$, then $(f \circ t)t'$ is an integrable function on $[a, b]$ and

$$\int_{t(a)}^{t(b)} f\,dx = \int_a^b (f \circ t)t'\,dx$$

(Theorem 7.5.7). If $f$ is an integrable function on the real line, then so is $(f \circ t)t'$ and

$$\int_\alpha^\beta f\,dx = \int (f \circ t)t'\,dx$$

where

$$\alpha = \lim_{x \to -\infty} t(x), \qquad \beta = \lim_{x \to \infty} t(x)$$

(Corollary 7.5.10). Theorem 7.5.7 holds also without the restriction that $t$ be monotone nondecreasing if $f$ is a bounded integrable function on the real line (Theorem 7.5.11, Exercise 7.6.23).

# 8

# Stieltjes Integrals

This chapter on (Lebesgue-) Stieltjes integrals is essentially independent of Chapters 4 to 7. In addition to the material in Chapters 1 to 3 we will use only the results of Sections 6.1 and 6.2 on the space $V_{\text{loc}}$ of functions of locally bounded variation.

In the present chapter we present two important lines of thought. First, we give an example of a reasonably wide class of integrals for functions on the real line, which includes the Lebesgue integral as defined in Chapters 1 and 2 as a special case. These are the Lebesgue-Stieltjes integrals. In fact, they are the only integrals on the real line that can be defined using step functions as elementary functions. Second, we will investigate the concept of continuous linear functionals on the linear space $\mathscr{C}$ of continuous functions which vanish off some interval. These continuous linear functionals turn out to be closely related with Stieltjes integrals. The Riesz representation theorem tells us that they can be written as the difference of two Stieltjes integrals.

## 8.1 DEFINITION OF THE STIELTJES INTEGRAL

Recall that we denote the linear space of functions of locally bounded variation by $V_{\text{loc}}$. This space contains as a subset the set $V_{\text{loc}}^+$ of monotone nondecreasing functions. $V_{\text{loc}}^+$ is not a linear space but a cone, that is, if $\alpha, \beta \in V_{\text{loc}}^+$ and $a, b \geq 0$, then $a\alpha + b\beta \in V_{\text{loc}}^+$. It is not true in general that the product of two functions in $V_{\text{loc}}^+$ belongs to $V_{\text{loc}}^+$; however, a similar statement holds for the composition product;

$$\alpha \circ \beta \in V_{\text{loc}}^+ \qquad \text{if} \quad \alpha, \beta \in V_{\text{loc}}^+,$$

where

$$(\alpha \circ \beta)(x) = \alpha(\beta(x)).$$

The identity function $\sigma \in V_{\text{loc}}^+$ defined by

$$\sigma(x) = x$$

for all real numbers $x$ serves as an identity for the composition operation:

$$\sigma \circ \alpha = \alpha \circ \sigma = \alpha \qquad \text{for} \quad \alpha \in V_{\text{loc}}^+.$$

This fact makes it natural to ask whether $V_{\text{loc}}^+$ is actually a group under composition, that is, whether each $\alpha \in V_{\text{loc}}^+$ has a uniquely defined inverse $\alpha^{-1}$ satisfying

$$\alpha \circ \alpha^{-1} = \alpha^{-1} \circ \alpha = \sigma.$$

However, it is not as nice as all that, and in general the best we can do is to construct a kind of "pseudo-inverse" $\alpha_1$, which is neither uniquely determined by $\alpha$ nor does it satisfy the reciprocity relations exactly.

**8.1.1 DEFINITION** *If $\alpha \in V_{\text{loc}}^{+}$, then $J_\alpha$ will denote the smallest interval containing all the values of $\alpha$, that is, the interval with end points*

$$\alpha(-\infty) = \lim_{x \to -\infty} \alpha(x), \qquad \alpha(\infty) = \lim_{x \to \infty} \alpha(x),$$

*where the first end point is included in the interval if and only if there is a real number $y$ such that $\alpha(y) = \alpha(-\infty)$, and correspondingly for the second end point.*

As an example, let $\alpha$ be the function arc tan; then $\alpha$ is defined by the conditions

$$\tan \alpha(x) = x, \qquad |\alpha(x)| < \frac{\pi}{2}.$$

In this case $J_\alpha = (-\pi/2, \pi/2)$ is a bounded open interval. On the other hand, if $\alpha(x) = x^+$, then $J_\alpha = [0, \infty)$, which is closed and half infinite.

We want to construct now an inverse $\alpha_1$ to $\alpha \in V_{\text{loc}}^{+}$ as a function on $J_\alpha$. Intuitively, the graph of $\alpha$ in the $xy$ plane,

$$\{(x, y) : y = \alpha(x)\},$$

should (approximately) coincide with the graph

$$\{(x, y) : x = \alpha_1(y), y \in J_\alpha\}$$

of $\alpha_1$ considered over $J_\alpha$ on the $y$-axis. However, this poses some problem. If $c$ is any value of $\alpha$, let $I_c$ be the interval on which $\alpha$ adopts the value $c$; this may be just one point or a nondegenerate interval. In any case, the endpoints of $I_c$ are

$$a_c = \sup \{x : \alpha(x) < c\}, \qquad b_c = \inf \{x : c < \alpha(x)\}.$$

Only one point in $I_c$ can be the value of $\alpha_1$ at $c$; thus if $I_c$ contains more than one point we have to make a choice for $\alpha_1(c)$,

$$a_c \le \alpha_1(c) \le b_c$$

(see Figure 8.1). On the other hand, there may be a $c' \in J_\alpha$ which is not a value of $\alpha$, namely, if there is a point $x_0$ at which $\alpha$ has a jump such that

$$\alpha(x_0 - 0) \le c' \le \alpha(x_0 + 0), \qquad \alpha(x_0) \ne c'.$$

Notice that

$$x_0 = \sup \{x : \alpha(x) < c'\} = \inf \{x : \alpha(x) > c'\}.$$

In this case we would, of course, define

$$\alpha_1(c') = x_0 = \sup \{x : \alpha(x) < c'\} = \inf \{x : \alpha(x) > c'\}$$

(see Figure 8.1). We introduce our construction now in a formal definition.

**8.1.2 DEFINITION** *If $\alpha \in V_{\text{loc}}^{+}$, then any function $\alpha_1$ defined on $J_\alpha$ and satisfying*

$$\sup \{y : \alpha(y) < x\} \le \alpha_1(x) \le \inf \{y : x < \alpha(y)\}, \qquad x \in J_\alpha,$$

*is called an inverse of $\alpha$.*

In this definition the sup is to be interpreted as $-\infty$ if no $y$ with $\alpha(y) < x$ exists; this is the case when $x$ is the left end point of $J_\alpha$. Similarly, the inf is to be interpreted as $+\infty$ if no $y$ with $\alpha(y) > x$ exists, which happens when $x$ is the right end point of $J_\alpha$.

The function $\alpha$ can have more than one inverse only if there is a point $c \in J_\alpha$ with

$$\sup \{y : \alpha(y) < c\} < \inf \{y : c > \alpha(y)\},$$

that is, if for some $c \in J_\alpha$, $\alpha$ assumes the value $c$ at more than one point.

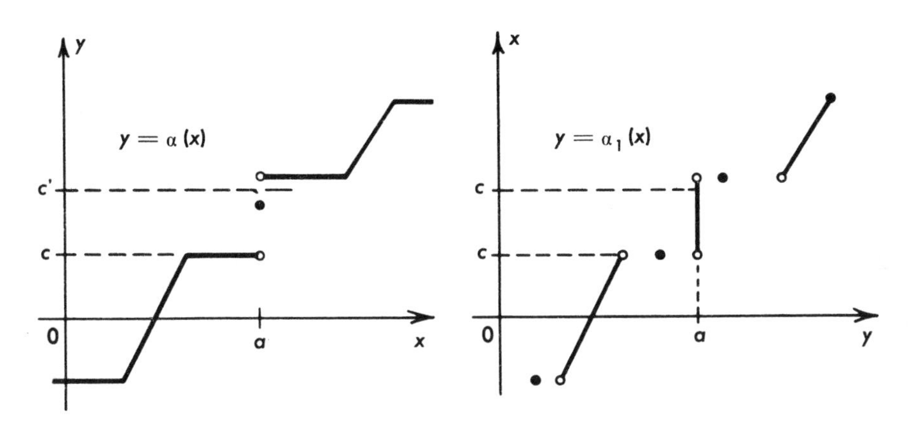


Figure 8.1 Illustration of an inverse $\alpha_1$ to a monotone nondecreasing function $\alpha$.

For instance, if $\alpha = \text{arc tan}$, then $\alpha_1$ is the restriction to $(-\pi/2, \pi/2)$ of the tangent function. On the other hand, if

$$\alpha(x) = [x] = \sup \{n : n \text{ integer}, n \leq x\},$$

then $\alpha_1$ defined by

$$\alpha_1(x) = [x] + 1$$

is one possible inverse, but one can also take $\alpha_1$ defined by

$$\alpha_1(x) = [x]' = \inf \{n : n \text{ integer}, n \geq x\}.$$

Though inverses defined by Definition 8.1.2 are not unique, they all have such reciprocity properties as are required for our purposes.

8.1.3 LEMMA *If $\alpha_1$ is an inverse of a function $\alpha \in V^+_{\text{loc}}$, then $\alpha_1$ is monotone nondecreasing on $J_\alpha$ and for any $\varepsilon > 0$,*

$$\begin{aligned}
\alpha_1(\alpha(a-0) - \varepsilon) &< a \qquad \text{if } \alpha(a-0) - \varepsilon \in J_\alpha, \\
\alpha_1(\alpha(a-0) + \varepsilon) &\geq a \qquad \text{if } \alpha(a-0) + \varepsilon \in J_\alpha, \\
\alpha_1(\alpha(a+0) - \varepsilon) &\leq a \qquad \text{if } \alpha(a+0) - \varepsilon \in J_\alpha, \\
\alpha_1(\alpha(a+0) + \varepsilon) &> a \qquad \text{if } \alpha(a+0) + \varepsilon \in J_\alpha.
\end{aligned}$$

*Proof* Suppose that $x, y \in J_\alpha$, $x < y$ and $\alpha_1(x) \neq \alpha_1(y)$. Then

$$\alpha_1(x) \leq \inf\{z : \alpha(z) > x\} \leq \sup\{z : \alpha(z) < y\} \leq \alpha_1(y),$$

so that $\alpha_1$ is monotone nondecreasing. To prove the third of the four relations above, we note that $\alpha(y) > \alpha(a + 0) - \varepsilon$ if $y > a$. Thus

$$\alpha_1(\alpha(a + 0) - \varepsilon) \leq \inf\{y : \alpha(y) > \alpha(a + 0) - \varepsilon\} \leq a$$

as claimed. On the other hand, there is $y_0 < a$ such that

$$\alpha(a - 0) - \varepsilon < \alpha(y_0) \leq \alpha(a - 0);$$

hence

$$\alpha_1(\alpha(a - 0) - \varepsilon) \leq \inf\{y : \alpha(y) > \alpha(a - 0) - \varepsilon\} \leq y_0 < a$$

proving the first relation in Lemma 8.1.3. The second and fourth relations have proofs symmetric to the third and first respectively, so we omit them.

8.1.4 COROLLARY *If $\chi$ is the characteristic function of the closed bounded interval $[a, b]$, then $\chi \circ \alpha_1$ is the characteristic function, defined on $J_\alpha$, of a bounded interval with end points $\alpha(a - 0)$ and $\alpha(b + 0)$ so that*

$$\int_{J_\alpha} \chi \circ \alpha_1 \, dx = \alpha(b + 0) - \alpha(a - 0).$$

This last result is really what we have been aiming at. It shows us that the increase of $\alpha$ over an interval—with the increments at the end points included as should be natural, since the interval was assumed to be closed—can be obtained by an integration process involving the characteristic function of that interval. An inverse $\alpha_1$ to the function $\alpha$ was used, but the result does not depend on the special choice of $\alpha_1$. We will rewrite this result using $a_0$ instead of $a$ and $a_1$ instead of $b$; thus

$$\chi(a_0 - 0) = 0, \qquad \chi(a_0) = 1, \qquad \chi(a_0 + 0) = 1,$$

$$\chi(a_1 - 0) = 1, \qquad \chi(a_1) = 1, \qquad \chi(a_1 + 0) = 0.$$

We have with this notation

$$\int_{J_\alpha} \chi \circ \alpha_1 \, dx = -\sum_{k=0}^{1} [\chi(a_k) - \chi(a_k - 0)]\alpha(a_k - 0)$$

$$- \sum_{k=0}^{1} [\chi(a_k + 0) - \chi(a_k)]\alpha(a_k + 0).$$

Since $\chi$ is continuous at all points except $a_0$ and $a_1$, we could in the above formula sum over any finite number of points $a_0, a_1, \cdots, a_n$ containing the two discontinuities of $\chi$. Recall now that by Corollary 1.1.4 every step function $\varphi$ is a linear combination of characteristic functions of closed intervals; hence $\varphi \circ \alpha_1$ is a step function restricted to $J_\alpha$ and

$$\int_{J_\alpha} \varphi \circ \alpha_1 \, dx = -\sum_{k=0}^{n} [\varphi(a_k) - \varphi(a_k - 0)]\alpha(a_k - 0)$$
$$-\sum_{k=0}^{n} [\varphi(a_k + 0) - \varphi(a_k)]\alpha(a_k + 0)$$

for a step function $\varphi$ with all its discontinuities contained among $\{a_k, k = 0, \cdots, n\}$. Thus we can state the following definition.

**8.1.5 DEFINITION** *The Lebesgue-Stieltjes integral $\int \varphi \, d\alpha$ of a step function $\varphi \in L$ with respect to a function $\alpha \in V_{\text{loc}}^+$ is defined by*

$$\int \varphi \, d\alpha = \int_{J_\alpha} \varphi \circ \alpha_1 \, dx$$

*where $\alpha_1$ is any inverse to $\alpha$.*

**8.1.6 PROPOSITION** *For any $\alpha \in V_{\text{loc}}^+$, the integral $\int \varphi \, d\alpha$ defined on $L$ satisfies Properties* (1) *to* (5) *of the abstract integration theory.*

*Proof* Properties (1), (2), and (3) are immediate from Definition 8.1.5. Property (5) is not concerned with the integral and is, of course, satisfied for the set $L$ of all step functions on the real line. To verify (4), let $\{\varphi_n\}$ be a sequence of nonnegative step functions decreasing to zero. The sequence $\{\psi_n\}$ of step functions defined by

$$\psi_n(x) = \begin{cases} \varphi_n(\alpha_1(x)) & \text{if } x \in J_\alpha \\ 0 & \text{otherwise} \end{cases}$$

decreases to zero everywhere; thus

$$\lim_{n\to\infty} \int \varphi_n \, d\alpha = \lim_{n\to\infty} \int \psi_n \, dx = 0$$

by Property (4) for the Lebesgue integral (Theorem 1.2.8).

We will also write down two formulas giving alternative definitions of $\int \varphi \, d\alpha$. If the step function $\varphi$ has presentation $(a_0, \cdots, a_n; c_1, \cdots, c_n)$, then

$$\int \varphi \, d\alpha = \sum_{k=0}^{n} [\varphi(a_k - 0) - \varphi(a_k)]\alpha(a_k - 0) + \sum_{k=1}^{n} [\varphi(a_k) - \varphi(a_k + 0)]\alpha(a_k + 0), \tag{8.1.7}$$

$$\int \varphi \, d\alpha = \sum_{k=1}^{n} c_k[\alpha(a_k - 0) - \alpha(a_{k-1} + 0)] + \sum_{k=0}^{n} \varphi(a_k)[\alpha(a_k + 0) - \alpha(a_k - 0)]. \tag{8.1.8}$$

The first equation is the one that we derived earlier from Corollary 8.1.4, while the second one is obtained from the first by resummation using the relations

$$\varphi(a_0 - 0) = \varphi(a_n + 0) = 0$$
$$c_k = \varphi(a_{k-1} + 0) = \varphi(a_k - 0), \qquad k = 1, \cdots, n.$$

If $\alpha$ is a continuous function, then the second term in (8.1.8) drops out and we have

$$\int \varphi \, d\alpha = \sum_{k=1}^{n} c_k[\alpha(a_k) - \alpha(a_{k-1})].$$

Notice the great similarity between this formula and the one in the definition of the Lebesgue integral for step functions (Definition 1.1.5).

In addition to Equation (8.1.8) it will prove useful to memorize the following special cases:

$$\int \chi_{[a,b]} \, d\alpha = \alpha(b + 0) - \alpha(a - 0) \qquad \text{for } a \leq b,$$

$$\int \chi_{(a,b]} \, d\alpha = \alpha(b + 0) - \alpha(a + 0) \qquad \text{for } a \leq b,$$

$$\int \chi_{[a,b)} \, d\alpha = \alpha(b - 0) - \alpha(a - 0) \qquad \text{for } a \leq b,$$

$$\int \chi_{(a,b)} \, d\alpha = \alpha(b - 0) - \alpha(a + 0) \qquad \text{for } a \leq b.$$

The relation used in Definition 8.1.5 carries over to integrable functions as well:

**8.1.9 PROPOSITION** *If $f$ is a $d\alpha$-integrable function on the real line and $\alpha_1$ is any inverse to $\alpha$, then $f \circ \alpha_1$ is dx-integrable on $J_\alpha$ and*

$$\int f \, d\alpha = \int_{J_\alpha} f \circ \alpha_1 \, dx.$$

*Conversely, if $f$ is a function on the real line such that $f \circ \alpha_1$ is dx-integrable on $J_\alpha$ for some inverse $\alpha_1$ of $\alpha$, then $f$ is $d\alpha$-integrable.*

*Proof* Let $f$ be a $d\alpha$-integrable function on the real line. By Mikusiński's lemma (Lemma 2.1.8), there is a series $\sum \varphi_n$ of step functions satisfying

$$\sum_{n=1}^{\infty} \int |\varphi_n| \, d\alpha < \infty \qquad \text{and} \qquad f(x) = \sum_{n=1}^{\infty} \varphi_n(x)$$

whenever the last series converges absolutely. Then $\sum \varphi_n \circ \alpha_1$ is a series of step functions on $J_\alpha$ that satisfies

$$\sum_{n=1}^{\infty} \int_{J_\alpha} |\varphi_n \circ \alpha_1| \, dx = \sum_{n=1}^{\infty} \int |\varphi_n| \, d\alpha < \infty,$$

$$f(\alpha_1(y)) = \sum_{n=1}^{\infty} \varphi_n(\alpha_1(y))$$

for all $y \in J_\alpha$ for which the last series converges absolutely. Thus by Mikusiński's lemma, $f \circ \alpha_1$ is $dx$-integrable on $J_\alpha$ and

$$\int_{J_\alpha} f \circ \alpha_1 \, dx = \sum_{n=1}^{\infty} \int_{J_\alpha} \varphi_n \circ \alpha_1 \, dx = \sum_{n=1}^{\infty} \int \varphi_n \, d\alpha = \int f \, d\alpha.$$

The proof of the converse statement is somewhat technical, and we have to make some preparations. It is apparent from Definition 8.1.2 and from Equations (8.1.7) and (8.1.8) that the values of $\alpha$ at its points of discontinuity do not influence the choice of $\alpha_1$ or the value of the integral. Also, if $f \circ \alpha_1$ is integrable on $J_\alpha$ for some inverse $\alpha_1$, then $f \circ \alpha_1$ is integrable for any inverse $\alpha_1$, since two such inverses differ only at a denumerable number of points, corresponding to the intervals of constancy of $\alpha$ (compare Lemma 7.4.1). Accordingly, we may arrange for this proof so that the values of both $\alpha$ and $\alpha_1$ at their respective points of discontinuity lie in the interior of the gaps of these discontinuities, that is, if $\alpha(x - 0) < \alpha(x + 0)$ for some $x$, then

$$\alpha(x - 0) < \alpha(x) < \alpha(x + 0)$$

and if $\sup\{y : \alpha(y) < x\} < \inf\{y : \alpha(y) > x\}$, then

$$\sup\{y : \alpha(y) < x\} < \alpha_1(x) < \inf\{y : \alpha(y) > x\}.$$

Having taken these precautions, we suppose that $f \circ \alpha_1$ is $dx$-integrable and that $\sum \varphi_n$ is a series of step functions, vanishing off $J_\alpha$ and satisfying

$$\sum_{n=1}^{\infty} \int |\varphi_n| \, dx < \infty, \qquad f(\alpha_1(x)) = \sum_{n=1}^{\infty} \varphi_n(x)$$

at all $x \in J_\alpha$ for which the last series converges absolutely. Let $\{J_k\}$ be an enumeration of the intervals of constancy of $\alpha_1$. If $\varphi_n$ is not constant on $J_k$, then we replace $\varphi_n$ on $J_k$ by its mean value

$$|J_k|^{-1} \int_{J_k} \varphi_n \, dx \qquad \left( |J_k| = \int_{J_k} dx \right)$$

on that interval. This either diminishes or leaves unchanged the value of $\int |\varphi_n| \, dx$. If we do this for all $n$, then the relation

$$f(\alpha_1(x)) = \sum_{n=1}^{\infty} \varphi_n(x)$$

will still hold for $x \in J_k$, since both sides equal their mean values over $J_k$. Hence we may suppose that all $\varphi_n$ are constant on each $J_k$.

Now consider the function $\alpha \circ \alpha_1$ on $J_\alpha$. Because of the condition on $\alpha$, it maps each interval of constancy of $\alpha_1$ into itself, whereas by the condition on $\alpha_1$ it equals the identity on the range of values $\alpha(R)$ of $\alpha$. Since this range of values and the intervals of constancy of $\alpha_1$ together cover $J_\alpha$, it follows that $\varphi_n \circ \alpha \circ \alpha_1 = \varphi_n$ on

$J_\alpha$ for all $n$. Hence, if we put $\psi_n = \varphi_n \circ \alpha$, we have

$$\sum_{n=1}^{\infty} \int |\psi_n| \, d\alpha = \sum_{n=1}^{\infty} \int_{J_\alpha} |\varphi_n \circ \alpha \circ \alpha_1| \, dx$$

$$= \sum_{n=1}^{\infty} \int |\varphi_n| \, dx < \infty,$$

$$f(x) = \sum_{n=1}^{\infty} \psi_n(x)$$

for all $x$ in the range of values $\alpha_1(J_\alpha)$ of $\alpha_1$ for which the last series converges absolutely, that is, $d\alpha$ a.e. on $\alpha_1(J_\alpha)$. But $R - \alpha_1(J_\alpha)$ is a $d\alpha$-null set, since it is covered by the $d\alpha$-null intervals $I_k$ on which $\alpha$ is constant. Namely, suppose $I_k$ has end points $a_k < b_k$, say for instance, $I_k = (a_k, b_k]$. Then $\alpha(b_k) = \alpha(b_k - 0)$ so that $\alpha$ must be continuous at $b_k$ by our assumption on $\alpha$; thus $\alpha(b_k + 0) = \alpha(b_k - 0)$ in this case, and the $d\alpha$-measure of $I_k$ is

$$\alpha(b_k + 0) - \alpha(a_k + 0) = \alpha(b_k - 0) - \alpha(a_k + 0) = 0.$$

Hence $f = \sum_{n=1}^{\infty} \psi_n \; d\alpha$ a.e., and consequently $f$ is $d\alpha$-integrable as claimed.

## *EXERCISES*

*8.1.1* Show that if $\alpha$ is continuous and strictly increasing everywhere (that is, $\alpha(x) < \alpha(y)$ if $x < y$), and furthermore $J_\alpha = R$, then $\alpha_1$ is uniquely determined and

$$\alpha \circ \alpha_1 = \alpha_1 \circ \alpha = \sigma.$$

*8.1.2* Let $\alpha$ and $\alpha_1$ be defined by $\alpha(x) = [x]$ and $\alpha_1(x) = [x] + 1$ and let $\chi$ be the characteristic function of a bounded closed interval of length greater than one. Show that $\chi \circ \alpha_1$ is not the characteristic function of a *closed* interval.

*8.1.3* Find what simplifications can be made in Equation (8.1.7) if $\varphi$ is right-continuous.

*8.1.4* Show that if $\alpha, \beta \in V_{\text{loc}}^{+}$ satisfy

$$\alpha(x) = \tfrac{1}{2}(\alpha(x + 0) + \alpha(x - 0)), \qquad \beta(x) = \tfrac{1}{2}(\beta(x + 0) + \beta(x - 0))$$

for all real $x$ and $\alpha(0) = \beta(0) = 0$ ($\alpha$ and $\beta$ are "normalized"), then $\int \varphi \, d\alpha = \int \varphi \, d\beta$ for all $\varphi \in L$ if and only if $\alpha(x) = \beta(x)$ for all $x$.

*8.1.5* Rewrite the second part of the proof of Proposition 8.1.9 assuming that $\alpha$ is continuous and strictly increasing.

## 8.2 PROPERTIES OF STIELTJES INTEGRALS

We have found that every monotone nondecreasing function $\alpha$ on the real line gives rise to an integral on $L$, the (Lebesgue-) Stieltjes integral with respect to $\alpha$, which satisfies Properties (1) to (5). We see from Equations (8.1.7) and (8.1.8) that the values of $\alpha$ at the points of discontinuity (which are denumerable, by Proposition 6.2.3) do not influence the integral. Also, by (8.1.8), a constant may be added to $\alpha$ without changing the integral. We will prove now that the converse holds also.

8.2.1 PROPOSITION *If $\int \varphi \, d\alpha = \int \varphi \, d\beta$ for all $\varphi \in L$, then the two functions $\alpha, \beta \in V_{\text{loc}}^{+}$ differ by a fixed constant at all their points of continuity.*

*Proof* The set of points in $R$ where both $\alpha$ and $\beta$ are continuous is the complement of a denumerable set. Let $\xi$ be such a point and let $x$ be any other point of continuity for both $\alpha$ and $\beta$. Suppose $x < \xi$ and let $\chi$ be the characteristic function of $[x, \xi]$. Then

$$\int \chi \, d\alpha = \alpha(\xi) - \alpha(x) = \int \chi \, d\beta = \beta(\xi) - \beta(x)$$

so that

$$\alpha(x) - \beta(x) = \alpha(\xi) - \beta(\xi)$$

and the same result is obtained when $\xi < x$. This proves Proposition 8.2.1, because $\alpha(\xi) - \beta(\xi)$ is a fixed constant.

8.2.2 COROLLARY *If $\int \varphi \, d\alpha = \int \varphi \, d\beta$ for all $\varphi \in L$, then $\alpha$ and $\beta$ have the same discontinuities.*

*Proof* Let $a$ be a point of discontinuity for $\alpha$. Since the set of points where both $\alpha$ and $\beta$ are continuous is a dense set, we may choose a sequence $\{x_n\}$, $x_n > a$, of such points which tends to $a$. Then

$$\alpha(a + 0) - \beta(a + 0) = \lim_{n \to \infty} (\alpha(x_n) - \beta(x_n)) = \alpha(\xi) - \beta(\xi)$$

and likewise we can show that

$$\alpha(a - 0) - \beta(a - 0) = \alpha(\xi) - \beta(\xi).$$

Thus

$$\alpha(a + 0) - \alpha(a - 0) = \beta(a + 0) - \beta(a - 0)$$

so that $\beta$ is discontinuous at all points of discontinuity of $\alpha$, and the converse statement is also true, by symmetry.

So far we have considered only Stieltjes integrals on the linear space $L$ of step functions. Actually, there are no other integrals on $L$. This is the heart of the Riesz representation theorem which, in its full generality, will be discussed in Section 8.5.

### 8.2.3 THEOREM

RIESZ REPRESENTATION THEOREM *Every integral $\int \varphi \, d\mu$ on the linear space $L$ of step functions on the real line can be written as the Stieltjes integral with respect to some function $\mu \in V_{\text{loc}}^{+}$.*

*Proof* For each real number $x$, let $\psi_x$ be the step function

$$\psi_x = \begin{cases} \chi_{(0,x]} & \text{if } x > 0 \\ 0 & \text{if } x = 0 \\ -\chi_{(x,0]} & \text{if } x < 0. \end{cases}$$

Define the function $\mu$ by

$$\mu(x) = \int \psi_x \, d\mu.$$

By Property (3) the function $\mu$ is monotone nondecreasing. It is also right-continuous:

$$\mu(x+0) = \lim_{y_n \to x, y_n > x} \int \psi_{y_n} \, d\mu = \int \psi_x \, d\mu = \mu(x)$$

by the monotone convergence theorem. Note that we have here, in each case, convergence everywhere. Let $x$ and $b$ be two real numbers, $x < b$. Then $\psi_b - \psi_x$ is simply the characteristic function of the half-closed interval $(x, b]$. Let $\psi$ be the characteristic function of a closed bounded interval $[a, b]$, then

$$\chi = \psi_b - \lim_{x \to a, x < a} \psi_x$$

everywhere, so that

$$\int \chi \, d\mu = \int \psi_b \, d\mu - \lim_{x \to a \; x < a} \int \psi_x \, d\mu$$

$$= \mu(b) - \mu(a-0) = \mu(b+0) - \mu(a-0);$$

thus $\int \chi \, d\mu$ is the Stieltjes integral of $\chi$ with respect to $\mu$. Since every function in $L$ is a linear combination of characteristic functions of closed bounded intervals, it follows that the integral $\int \varphi \, d\mu$ on $L$ is really the Stieltjes integral with respect to the function $\mu$ defined above.

We have now a very satisfactory theory for integrals on the linear space $L$ of step functions on the real line and we cannot in fact hope for many more results in this direction. We turn now to the class of all continuous functions and to certain classes derived from it, like the ones defined in part C of the exercise Section 3.6. Each Stieltjes integral on $L$ gives rise to a class of integrable and measurable functions on $R$, and it is natural to ask for some reasonably wide class of functions that are, say, measurable for all Stieltjes integrals. We will find such a class in the class of Baire functions, which generalizes the aforementioned classes discussed in part C of Section 3.6.

**8.2.4 DEFINITION** *The smallest vector space of functions on the real line which contains all continuous functions and is closed under pointwise everywhere limits is called the space of Baire functions and is denoted by* $\mathscr{B}$.

If $\{f_n\}$ is a sequence belonging to a vector space which is closed under pointwise everywhere limits, and

$$f(x) = \lim_{n\to\infty} f_n(x)$$

for all real $x$, then $f$ is also in this vector space. We remark that the family of all vector spaces that have this property and contain all continuous functions is not empty, since the space of all real-valued functions of one real variable is one such space. The space of Baire functions is the intersection of all the vector spaces in this family. The space of (Lebesgue) measurable functions is also a vector space of functions containing the continuous functions and closed under pointwise everywhere limits. Since $\mathscr{B}$ is the smallest such space, *every Baire function is measurable with respect to Lebesgue measure.*

**8.2.5 DEFINITION** *If $a < b$, the linear space of all continuous functions $f$ such that $f(x) = 0$ if $x \leq a$ or $x \geq b$ is denoted by $\mathscr{C}_{ab}$. The union of all sets $\mathscr{C}_{ab}$ is a linear space denoted by $\mathscr{C}$ and referred to as the space of continuous functions vanishing off some bounded interval.*

**8.2.6 LEMMA** *If $K$ is a vector space of functions on the real line that contains either the space $L$ of step functions or the set $\mathscr{C}$, and if $\int \varphi\, d\mu$ is any integral on $K$ satisfying Properties* (1) *to* (5), *then all Baire functions are measurable with respect to $d\mu$.*

*Proof* In either case, all functions in $\mathscr{C}$ are measurable, because if $f \in \mathscr{C}$, then $\{f_n\}$ defined by

$$f_n(x) = f([nx]/n)$$

is a sequence of step functions tending everywhere to $f$ so that even in the first case the functions in $\mathscr{C}$ are measurable. Now, if $g$ is any continuous function, then

$$\text{mid}\,(-(n - |x|)^+, g, (n - |x|)^+)$$

is a sequence of functions in $\mathscr{C}$ that converges everywhere to $g$; thus $g$ is also measurable. The space of all $d\mu$-measurable functions is closed under pointwise-everywhere convergence by Proposition 3.1.4, and it contains the continuous functions, as we have just proved. By Definition 8.2.4 it therefore contains the space of Baire functions, proving the lemma.

**8.2.7 COROLLARY** *If $f$ is a Baire function vanishing outside a $d\mu$-integrable set $E$ and bounded in absolute value by a constant $M$, then $f$ is integrable with respect to $d\mu$ and*

$$\left|\int f\, d\mu\right| \leq M\mu(E).$$

*Proof* Since $M\chi_E$ is a $d\mu$-integrable function and $|f| \leq M\chi_E$, $f$ is integrable and

$$\left|\int f\,d\mu\right| \leq \int |f|\,d\mu \leq M\mu(E).$$

**8.2.8 COROLLARY** *If $\alpha$ is a monotone nondecreasing function, then every Baire function is $d\alpha$-measurable and every function in $\mathscr{C}$ is $d\alpha$-integrable.*

We shall now see that in the case where $f$ is a function in $\mathscr{C}_{ab}$, we can define its Stieltjes integral with respect to a function $\alpha \in V_{\text{loc}}^{+}$ in another way, analogous to the Riemann integral discussed in Section 2.0. As in Proposition 2.0.4 we choose a sequence $\{\Delta_n\}$,

$$\Delta_n : a = a_0{}^n < a_1{}^n < \cdots < a_{m(n)}^n = b,$$

of subdivisions of $[a, b]$ satisfying

$$\lim_{n\to\infty} \ell(\Delta_n) = 0,$$

where $\ell(\Delta_n)$ is the maximum length of the intervals $[a_{i-1}^n, a_i{}^n]$, $i = 1, \cdots, m(n)$. However, we do not construct $\varphi_n$ exactly as in (2.0.3), but we use the device of defining $\varphi_n$ by

$$\varphi_n(x) = \begin{cases} f(x_i{}^n) & \text{for } x \in (a_{i-1}^n, a_i{}^n), \quad i = 1, \cdots m(n) \\ c_i{}^n & \text{for } x = a_i{}^n, \quad i = 0, \cdots, m(n) \\ 0 & \text{for } x \notin [a, b] \end{cases}$$

where $x_i{}^n$ is any point in $[a_{i-1}^n, a_i{}^n]$ and $c_i{}^n$ is chosen in the following way:

$$c_i{}^n = \begin{cases} f(x_i{}^n) & \text{if } \alpha(a_i{}^n + 0) - \alpha(a_i{}^n - 0) = 0 \\ (\alpha(a_i^n + 0) - \alpha(a_i^n - 0))^{-1}[f(x_{i+1}^n)(\alpha(a_i^n + 0) - \alpha(a_i^n)) & \\ \quad + f(x_i{}^n)(\alpha(a_i^n) - \alpha(a_i{}^n - 0))] & \text{if } \alpha(a_i{}^n + 0) - \alpha(a_i{}^n - 0) \neq 0. \end{cases}$$

Here we have set $x_0{}^n = a$ and $x_{m(n)+1}^n = b$, which implies

$$f(x_0{}^n) = f(a) = 0, \qquad f(x_{m(n)+1}^n) = f(b) = 0.$$

We claim that $\{\varphi_n\}$ tends to $f$ everywhere. In fact, if $\varepsilon > 0$ and $x \in [a, b]$, then we can choose a $\delta > 0$ so that

$$|f(x) - f(x')| \leq \varepsilon \qquad \text{if } |x - x'| \leq \delta.$$

Let $N$ be an integer such that $\ell(\Delta_n) \leq \delta$ for $n \geq N$. With this choice of $N$ we have

$$|f(x) - \varphi_n(x)| \leq \varepsilon \qquad \text{for } n \geq N;$$

this is clear if $x \in (a_{i-1}^n, a_i)$ or $x = a_i{}^n$ and $c_i{}^n$ is defined by the first equation, because $\varphi_n(x) = f(x_i{}^n)$ and $|x - x_i{}^n| \leq \delta$ in this case. If $x = a_i{}^n$ and $c_i{}^n$ is defined by the second equation, we compute

$$\begin{aligned}|f(x) - \varphi_n(x)| &= |f(a_i^n) - c_i^n| \\ &= (\alpha(a_i^n + 0) - \alpha(a_i^n - 0))^{-1} |(f(a_i^n) - f(x_{i+1}^n))(\alpha(a_i^n + 0) \\ &\qquad - \alpha(a_i^n)) + (f(a_i^n) - f(x_i^n))(\alpha(a_i^n) - \alpha(a_i^n - 0))| \\ &\leq (\alpha(a_i^n + 0) - \alpha(a_i^n - 0))^{-1}\varepsilon \cdot [(\alpha(a_i^n + 0) - \alpha(a_i^n)) \\ &\qquad + (\alpha(a_i^n) - \alpha(a_i^n - 0)) \\ &= \varepsilon.\end{aligned}$$

Thus $\{\varphi_n\}$ tends to $f$, and since $|\varphi_n| \leq M\chi_{[a,b]}$ where $M$ is the maximum of $|f|$, we can apply Lebesgue's dominated convergence theorem which yields

$$\lim_{n\to\infty} \int \varphi_n \, d\alpha = \int f \, d\alpha.$$

We will now use Equation (8.1.8) to evaluate $\int \varphi_n \, d\alpha$. First notice that

$$\begin{aligned}&c_i^n(\alpha(a_i^n + 0) - \alpha(a_i^n - 0)) \\ &\qquad = f(x_{i+1}^n)(\alpha(a_i^n + 0) - \alpha(a_i^n)) + f(x_i^n)(\alpha(a_i^n) - \alpha(a_i^n - 0))\end{aligned}$$

holds also if $\alpha$ is continuous at $a_i^n$. Using our assumption $f(x_0^n) = f(x_{m(n)+1}^n) = 0$, we now obtain

$$\begin{aligned}\int \varphi_n \, d\alpha &= \sum_{i=1}^{m(n)} f(x_i^n)(\alpha(a_i^n - 0) - \alpha(a_{i-1}^n + 0)) \\ &\quad + \sum_{i=0}^{m(n)} c_i^n(\alpha(a_i^n + 0) - \alpha(a_i^n - 0)) \\ &= \sum_{i=1}^{m(n)} f(x_i^n)(\alpha(a_i^n - 0) - \alpha(a_{i-1}^n + 0)) \\ &\quad + \sum_{i=1}^{m(n)} f(x_i^n)(\alpha(a_{i-1}^n + 0) - \alpha(a_{i-1}^n)) \\ &\quad + \sum_{i=1}^{m(n)} f(x_i^n)(\alpha(a_i^n) - \alpha(a_i^n - 0)) \\ &= \sum_{i=1}^{m(n)} f(x_i^n)(\alpha(a_i^n) - \alpha(a_{i-1}^n)).\end{aligned}$$

Thus we have proved the following proposition.

**8.2.9 PROPOSITION** *Suppose $f \in \mathscr{C}_{ab}$ and $\alpha \in V_{\text{loc}}^+$. For any sequence*

$$\Delta_n : a = a_0^n < a_1^n < \cdots < a_{m(n)}^n = b$$

*of subdivisions of* $[a, b]$ *satisfying* $\lim_{n\to\infty} \ell(\Delta_n) = 0$, *we have*

$$\int f\,d\alpha = \lim_{n\to\infty} \sum_{i=1}^{m(n)} f(x_i^n)(\alpha(a_i^n) - \alpha(a_{i-1}^n)), \tag{8.2.10}$$

*where* $x_i^n \in [a_{i-1}^n, a_i^n]$ *is chosen arbitrarily.*

The sums on the right of (8.2.10) are sometimes referred to as the Riemann sums associated with $f$ and the subdivisions $\Delta_n$. When these sums are used to define the integral $\int f\,d\alpha$ as in (8.2.10), $\int f\,d\alpha$ is sometimes called the Riemann-Stieltjes integral of $f$ with respect to $\alpha$.

In proving Proposition 8.2.9 we used the fact that $f(a) = f(b) = 0$. If $f$ is supposed only to be continuous on $[a, b]$ and, say, zero outside $[a, b]$, then the Riemann-Stieltjes integral of $f$ over $[a, b]$ as defined by the limit on the right of (8.2.10) may well be different from the Stieltjes integral of $f$ (see Exercise 8.2.5 in this regard).

## *EXERCISES*

*8.2.1* Which is the Stieltjes integral representing the integral

$$\int \varphi\,d\mu = \varphi(0), \qquad \varphi \in L?$$

*8.2.2* Which is the Stieltjes integral representing the integral

$$\int \varphi\,d\mu = \int \varphi x^2\,dx, \qquad \varphi \in L?$$

*8.2.3* Let $\alpha \in V_{\mathrm{loc}}^+$. Show that a degenerate interval $[a, a] = \{a\}$ has $d\alpha$-measure zero if and only if $\alpha$ is continuous at $a$.

*8.2.4* Prove that the product of two Baire functions is again a Baire function.

*Hint* Suppose $f$ and $g$ are Baire functions. Suppose first that $g$ is continuous. Show that

$$\mathscr{B}_g = \{h : hg \in \mathscr{B}\}$$

is a vector space which contains the continuous functions and is closed under pointwise-everywhere limits, and conclude $f \in \mathscr{B} \subset \mathscr{B}_g$. Then prove $g \in \mathscr{B} \subset \mathscr{B}_f$ for arbitrary $f, g \in \mathscr{B}$.

*8.2.5* Let $\alpha \in V_{\mathrm{loc}}^+$. A function $f$ on a closed bounded interval $[a, b]$ is said to be Riemann-Stieltjes integrable on $[a, b]$ (with respect to $\alpha$) if there is a number $I$ such that

$$I = \lim_{n\to\infty} \sum_{i=1}^{m(n)} f(x_i^n)(\alpha(a_i^n) - \alpha(a_{i-1}^n))$$

for any sequence $\{\Delta_n\}$,

$$\Delta_n : a = a_0{}^n < \cdots < a^n_{m(n)} = b$$

of subdivisions of $[a, b]$ satisfying

$$\lim_{n\to\infty} \ell(\Delta_n) = 0$$

and any choice $x_i{}^n \in [a^n_{i-1}, a_i{}^n]$. This number $I$ is also denoted by $\int_a^b f\,d\alpha$. Suppose $f$ is continuous on $[a, b]$. We interpret $f$ to be zero outside $[a, b]$. Prove that $f$ is $d\alpha$-integrable and Riemann-Stieltjes integrable, and establish the identity

$$\int f\chi_{[a,b]}\,d\alpha = \int_a^b f\,d\alpha + f(a)(\alpha(a) - \alpha(a - 0)) + f(b)(\alpha(b + 0) - \alpha(b)).$$

Which are the conditions that

$$\int f\chi_{[a,b]}\,d\alpha = \int_a^b f\,d\alpha?$$

*Hint* Re-examine the proof of Proposition 8.2.9. You cannot conclude anymore that $f(x_0{}^n) = f(a)$ and $f(x^n_{m(n)+1}) = f(b)$ equal zero.

## 8.3 CONTINUOUS LINEAR FUNCTIONALS ON $\mathscr{C}$

Let $\mathscr{C}$ be the linear space of continuous functions on the real line that vanish off some bounded interval (Definition 8.2.5). For the functions $f \in \mathscr{C}$ we introduce a norm $\|f\|$ which is the maximum value of $|f|$,

$$\|f\| = \sup\{f(x) : x \in R\}.$$

The rules

$$\|\lambda f\| = |\lambda| \cdot \|f\|, \quad \lambda \in R, f \in \mathscr{C},$$
$$\|f + g\| \leq \|f\| + \|g\|, \quad f, g \in \mathscr{C}$$

are easily verified.

8.3.1 DEFINITION *A bounded linear functional $A$ on $\mathscr{C}$ assigns to each function $f$ in $\mathscr{C}$ a real number $A(f)$, subject to the following conditions:*

(a) *If $\lambda$ and $\mu$ are real numbers and $f, g \in \mathscr{C}$, then*

$$A(\lambda f + \mu g) = \lambda A(f) + \mu A(g)$$

*so that, in particular, $A(0) = 0$.*

(b) *For each bounded closed interval $[a, b]$, there is a constant $M_{ab}$ such that*

$$|A(f)| \leq M_{ab}\|f\| \quad \text{for} \quad f \in \mathscr{C}_{ab}.$$

*The smallest possible bound $M_{ab}$ that can be used in Condition* (b) *is called the norm of $A$ on $[a, b]$ and is denoted by $\|A\|_{ab}$. If $A$ satisfies only Condition* (a) *then $A$ is called a linear functional on $\mathscr{C}$.*

The constant $M_{ab}$ satisfies the inequality in Condition (b) if and only if

$$M_{ab} \geq \frac{|A(f)|}{\|f\|}$$

for $f \in \mathscr{C}_{ab}$ with $\|f\| \neq 0$. Thus the smallest such constant $\|A\|_{ab}$ is given by the formula

$$\|A\|_{ab} = \sup \{\|f\|^{-1} |A(f)| : f \in \mathscr{C}_{ab}, f \neq 0\}.$$

8.3.2 PROPOSITION *A linear functional $A$ on $\mathscr{C}$ is bounded if and only if it satisfies the following continuity condition:*

(c) *If the sequence $\{f_n\}$ in $\mathscr{C}_{ab}$ converges uniformly to $f \in \mathscr{C}_{ab}$ in the sense that $\lim_{n\to\infty} \|f - f_n\| = 0$, then*

$$\lim_{n\to\infty} A(f_n) = f.$$

*Therefore a bounded linear functional is also called a continuous linear functional.*

*Proof* (Compare Proposition 5.3.2) Suppose $A$ is bounded and let $\{f_n\}$ be a sequence in $\mathscr{C}_{ab}$ that converges uniformly to $f \in \mathscr{C}_{ab}$. Then $\{A(f_n)\}$ converges to $A(f)$, because

$$|A(f) - A(f_n)| = |A(f - f_n)| \leq \|A\|_{ab} \|f - f_n\|.$$

Conversely, suppose $A$ satisfies the continuity condition (c). If $A$ were not bounded, we could find a closed bounded interval $[a, b]$ and, for each integer $n$, a function $f_n$ in $\mathscr{C}_{ab}$ such that

$$|A(f_n)| > n \|f_n\|.$$

We have $A(f_n) \neq 0$, whence $f_n \neq 0$. Let

$$g_n = \frac{1}{n} \|f_n\|^{-1} f_n.$$

The sequence $\{g_n\}$ of functions in $\mathscr{C}_{ab}$ converges uniformly to zero since $\|g_n\| = 1/n$. But $\{A(g_n)\}$ does not converge to zero, because

$$|A(g_n)| = \frac{1}{n} \|f_n\|^{-1} |A(f_n)| > 1$$

for all $n$. This contradicts Condition (c).

Examples for continuous linear functionals on $\mathscr{C}$ are the Stieltjes integrals. Suppose $\alpha$ is a monotone nondecreasing function on the real line. We have seen in Corollary 8.2.6 that the functions in $\mathscr{C}$ are $d\alpha$-integrable. Thus

$$\int f \, d\alpha, \quad f \in \mathscr{C}$$

defines a linear functional on $\mathscr{C}$. This functional is bounded, because we have $|f| \leq \|f\| \, \chi_{(a,b)}$ for $f \in \mathscr{C}_{ab}$, and therefore

$$\left| \int f \, d\alpha \right| \leq \int |f| \, d\alpha \leq \int \chi_{(a,b)} \, d\alpha \, \|f\|$$
$$= (\alpha(b - 0) - \alpha(a + 0)) \, \|f\|.$$

We leave it as an exercise to verify that $\alpha(b - 0) - \alpha(a + 0)$ is actually equal to the norm on $[a, b]$ of the bounded linear functional defined by $\int f \, d\alpha$ (Exercise 8.3.2).

Since $\mathscr{C}$ is a space of elementary functions satisfying Property (1) of Section 2.5, one naturally asks oneself if, maybe, a continuous linear functional can be regarded as an integral on $\mathscr{C}$. One condition in Section 2.5 is conspicuously absent, namely the positivity condition (3). We introduce it here as a definition.

**8.3.3 DEFINITION** *The set of all nonnegative functions in $\mathscr{C}$ is denoted by $\mathscr{C}^+$. A linear functional $A$ on $\mathscr{C}$ is called positive if*

$$A(f) \geq 0 \qquad \textit{for all} \quad f \in \mathscr{C}^+.$$

We can now show that a positive continuous linear functional is in fact an integral on $\mathscr{C}$.

**8.3.4 PROPOSITION** *Each positive continuous linear functional on $\mathscr{C}$ is an integral on $\mathscr{C}$, regarded as a class of elementary functions on the real line, satisfying Conditions* (1) *to* (4) *of Section 2.5.* (*$\mathscr{C}$ also satisfies Property* (5) *of Section 3.1.*)

*Proof* We need only check the continuity condition (4). Let $\{\varphi_n\}$ be a decreasing sequence of nonnegative functions in $\mathscr{C}$, $\varphi_n \geq \varphi_{n+1} \geq 0$, such that

$$\lim_{n \to \infty} \varphi_n(x) = 0$$

for all $x$. Suppose $\varphi_1 \in \mathscr{C}_{ab}$ so that each $\varphi_n$ vanishes off $(a, b)$. Since

$$|A(\varphi_n)| \leq \|A\|_{ab} \, \|\varphi_n\|$$

for all $n$, we need only show that the decreasing sequence $\{\|\varphi_n\|\}$ tends to zero. If this were not the case, we could find a $\delta > 0$ with $\|\varphi_n\| \geq \delta$ for all $n$. Let

$$x_n = \inf \{x : \varphi_n(x) \geq \delta\}.$$

We have $\varphi_n(x_n) \geq \delta$, since $\varphi_n$ is continuous. Then $\{x_n\}$ is an increasing sequence in $(a, b)$; it converges therefore to a point $x_0$. Since

$$\varphi_k(x_n) \geq \varphi_n(x_n) \geq \delta$$

for $n \geq k$, we obtain

$$\varphi_k(x_0) = \lim_{n \geq k, n \to \infty} \varphi_k(x_n) \geq \delta > 0$$

which contradicts the hypothesis $\lim_{n \to \infty} \varphi_n(x_0) = 0$.

In the previous section we have discussed integrals on the set $L$ of step functions on the real line and in this section we are considering integrals on $\mathscr{C}$. One has a strong intuitive feeling that these two things are really "the same," and we shall make a precise statement of this.

8.3.5 DEFINITION *An integral on the set L of all step functions and an integral on $\mathscr{C}$ are called equivalent if their sets of integrable functions are the same and the values of the integrals coincide throughout that set.*

8.3.6 PROPOSITION *Each integral on L is equivalent to one and only one integral on $\mathscr{C}$, and vice versa.*

*Proof* It follows from Definition 8.3.5 that an integral on one of the two spaces $L$ or $\mathscr{C}$ cannot be equivalent to two distinct integrals. This proves the uniqueness. Corollary 8.2.6 shows that every integral on $\mathscr{C}$ defines an integral on $L$, because every step function is a Baire function; and the comparison theorem (Theorem 2.5.9) implies that these two integrals are equivalent. Similarly, Corollary 8.2.6 and the comparison theorem prove that every integral on $L$ is equivalent to an integral on $\mathscr{C}$.

Since, according to Proposition 8.2.3, the only integrals on $L$ are the Stieltjes integrals, we can conclude the same for $\mathscr{C}$.

8.3.7 COROLLARY

RIESZ REPRESENTATION THEOREM *For every positive continuous linear functional A on $\mathscr{C}$, there is a monotone nondecreasing function $\alpha$ such that*

$$A(f) = \int f\,d\alpha, \qquad f \in \mathscr{C}.$$

In the remainder of this chapter our effort will be directed toward proving a similar theorem for continuous linear functionals that are not necessarily positive. To achieve this aim we have to look closer into the space of continuous linear functionals.

The set of all continuous linear functionals on $\mathscr{C}$ is a vector space with the definition of the linear combination $\lambda A + \mu B$; $\lambda, \mu \in R$ of two continuous linear functionals $A$, $B$ on $\mathscr{C}$ by

$$(\lambda A + \mu B)(f) = \lambda[A(f)] + \mu[B(f)] \qquad \text{for } f \in \mathscr{C}.$$

Property (a) of Definition 8.3.1 is evidently fulfilled for $\lambda A + \mu B$, and Property (b) is satisfied with

$$M_{ab} = |\lambda|\, \|A\|_{ab} + |\mu|\, \|B\|_{ab}.$$

The verification of this is left to Proposition 8.3.9. We denote the origin of this vector space by 0, an ordinary zero, that is $0(f) = 0$ for all $f \in \mathscr{C}$. The ambiguity inherent in this notation will not be troublesome.

The values of a linear functional on $\mathscr{C}^+$ determines it completely, as is shown by the following proposition

**8.3.8 Proposition** *A rule that assigns the real number $A(f)$ to each function $f \in \mathscr{C}^+$ so that $A(\lambda f + \mu g) = \lambda A(f) + \mu A(g)$ if $\lambda$ and $\mu$ are nonnegative numbers and $f, g \in \mathscr{C}^+$ can be extended in one and only one way to a linear functional on $\mathscr{C}$.*

*Proof* If $f = f^+ - f^-$ is in $\mathscr{C}$, then $A(f)$ has to be defined by

$$A(f) = A(f^+) - A(f^-).$$

This proves the uniqueness of the assumed extension. To prove that the above definition satisfies the linearity condition (a) of Definition 8.3.1, we remark first that if

$$f = f_1 - f_2, \quad f_1, f_2 \in \mathscr{C}^+,$$

then $f^+ + f_2 = f^- + f_1$ is a function in $\mathscr{C}^+$, so that

$$A(f^+) + A(f_2) = A(f^+ + f_2) = A(f^- + f_1) = A(f^-) + A(f_1)$$

or, equivalently,

$$A(f) = A(f^+) - A(f^-) = A(f_1) - A(f_2).$$

Hence

$$\begin{aligned} A(\lambda f + \mu g) &= A(\lambda^+ f^+ + \lambda^- f^- + \mu^+ g^+ + \mu^- g^- - \lambda^- f^+ - \lambda^+ f^- - \mu^+ g^- - \mu^- g^+) \\ &= (\lambda^+ - \lambda^-)[A(f^+) - A(f^-)] + (\mu^+ - \mu^-)[A(g^+) - A(g^-)] \\ &= \lambda A(f) + \mu A(g) \end{aligned}$$

as claimed.

We conclude this section by proving an inequality for the norm, analogous to the Minkowski inequality for $L^p$ spaces.

**8.3.9 Proposition** *If $a, b, \lambda$ are real numbers, $a < b$, and $A$, $B$ are continuous linear functionals on $\mathscr{C}$, then*

$$\|\lambda A\|_{ab} = |\lambda| \, \|A\|_{ab}$$

*and*

$$\big| \|A\|_{ab} - \|B\|_{ab} \big| \le \|A + B\|_{ab} \le \|A\|_{ab} + \|B\|_{ab}.$$

*Proof* The inequality

$$|\lambda A(f)| = |A(\lambda f)| \le \|A\|_{ab} \, \|\lambda f\| = |\lambda| \, \|A\|_{ab} \, \|f\|$$

shows that

$$\|\lambda A\|_{ab} \le |\lambda| \, \|A\|_{ab},$$

and conversely, if $\lambda \ne 0$,

$$\|A\|_{ab} = \|\lambda^{-1} \lambda A\|_{ab} \le |\lambda^{-1}| \, \|\lambda A\|_{ab}$$

so that

$$|\lambda| \, \|A\|_{ab} \le \|\lambda A\|_{ab} \le |\lambda| \, \|A\|_{ab}$$

and the conclusion $\|\lambda A\|_{ab} = |\lambda|\,\|A\|_{ab}$ follows for $\lambda \neq 0$; it holds trivially for $\lambda = 0$. Next, we have for any $f \in \mathscr{C}_{ab}$

$$|(A + B)(f)| \leq |A(f)| + |B(f)| \leq (\|A\|_{ab} + \|B\|_{ab})\,\|f\|;$$

hence $\|A + B\|_{ab} \leq \|A\|_{ab} + \|B\|_{ab}$, proving the second inequality. Now rewrite this inequality twice:

$$\|A\|_{ab} = \|(A + B) - B\|_{ab} \leq \|A + B\|_{ab} + \|-B\|_{ab}$$
$$\|B\|_{ab} = \|-A + (A + B)\|_{ab} \leq \|-A\|_{ab} + \|A + B\|_{ab}$$

or, since $\|-A\|_{ab} = \|A\|_{ab}$, $\|-B\|_{ab} = \|B\|_{ab}$,

$$\big|\,\|A\|_{ab} - \|B\|_{ab}\big| = (\|A\|_{ab} - \|B\|_{ab}) \vee (\|B\|_{ab} - \|A\|_{ab}) \leq \|A + B\|_{ab}$$

which is the first inequality.

## *EXERCISES*

*8.3.1* Show that if $A$ is a linear functional on $\mathscr{C}$ which is not a priori assumed to satisfy Condition (b) of Definition 8.3.1, and if moreover $A$ is positive in the sense of Definition 8.3.3, then $A$ also satisfies Condition (b), that is, a positive linear functional is automatically continuous.

*Hint* Show that

$$|A(f)| \leq A(\varphi_{ab})\,\|f\| \qquad \text{for} \quad f \in \mathscr{C}_{ab}$$

if $\varphi_{ab} = (x - a + 1)^+ \wedge 1 \wedge (b + 1 - x)^+$.

*8.3.2* Let $\alpha \in V^+_{\text{loc}}$. Show that the norm on $[a, b]$, $a < b$, of the continuous linear functional $\int f\,d\alpha$, $f \in \mathscr{C}$ is equal to

$$\int \chi_{(a,b)}\,d\alpha = \alpha(b - 0) - \alpha(a + 0).$$

*8.3.3* Show that if $f$ is any continuous function on $R$ and $A$ is a continuous linear functional on $\mathscr{C}$, then $fA$ defined by

$$fA(g) = A(fg) \qquad \text{for all} \quad g \in \mathscr{C}$$

is a continuous linear functional on $\mathscr{C}$, and that, if $\|f\|_{ab} = \sup\{|f(x)| : a \leq x \leq b\}$, then

$$\|fA\|_{ab} \leq \|f\|_{ab}\,\|A\|_{ab}.$$

*8.3.4* Show that

$$(\lambda f + \mu g)A = \lambda fA + \mu gA, \qquad f(\lambda A + \mu B) = \lambda fA + \mu fB$$

if $\lambda$, $\mu$ are real numbers, and $f$, $g$ continuous functions, and $A$, $B$ continuous linear functionals on $\mathscr{C}$.

*8.3.5* Show that $\delta_a$ defined by

$$\delta_a(f) = f(a) \qquad \text{for all} \quad f \in \mathscr{C}$$

is a continuous linear functional on $\mathscr{C}$ and

$$(x - a)\delta_a = 0.$$

## 8.4 OPERATIONS ON FUNCTIONALS

We shall now develop some functional calculus dealing mainly with lattice operations on the space of continuous linear functionals on $\mathscr{C}$.

**8.4.1 DEFINITION** *If $A$ and $B$ are continuous linear functionals on $\mathscr{C}$, then we define the real number $A \vee B(f)$ for each $f \in \mathscr{C}^+$ by*

$$A \vee B(f) = \sup \{A(u) + B(v): u, v \in \mathscr{C}^+, u + v = f\}.$$

The supremum in this definition is finite. Namely, suppose $f \in \mathscr{C}_{ab}{}^+$ and $f = u + v$ with $u, v \in \mathscr{C}^+$. Then $u, v \in \mathscr{C}_{ab}{}^+$ also and therefore

$$A(u) + B(v) \leq \|A\|_{ab} \|u\| + \|B\|_{ab} \|v\| \leq (\|A\|_{ab} + \|B\|_{ab}) \|f\|.$$

**8.4.2 LEMMA** *If $\lambda$ and $\mu$ are nonnegative numbers and $f, g \in \mathscr{C}^+$, then*

$$A \vee B(\lambda f + \mu g) = \lambda(A \vee B)(f) + \mu(A \vee B)(g)$$

*Proof* Since it is obvious that

$$A \vee B(\lambda f) = \lambda(A \vee B)(f) \qquad \text{for} \quad \lambda \geq 0, f \in \mathscr{C}^+$$

we have only to show that

$$A \vee B(f_1 + f_2) = A \vee B(f_1) + A \vee B(f_2)$$

for $f_1, f_2$ in $\mathscr{C}^+$. For a fixed, arbitrary $\varepsilon > 0$ choose $u$ and $v$ in $\mathscr{C}^+$ such that $u + v = f_1 + f_2$ and

$$A \vee B(f_1 + f_2) \leq A(u) + B(v) + \varepsilon.$$

Then take

$$u_1 = u \wedge f_1, \qquad u_2 = (u_1 - f_1)^+ = (f_2 - v)^+,$$
$$v_1 = (f_1 - u)^+ = (v - f_2)^+, \qquad v_2 = v \wedge f_2.$$

Obviously $u_1, u_2, v_1, v_2 \in \mathscr{C}^+$ and

$$u_1 + u_2 = u, \qquad u_1 + v_1 = f_1,$$
$$v_1 + v_2 = v, \qquad u_2 + v_2 = f_2.$$

Hence

$$A \vee B(f_1 + f_2) - \varepsilon \leq A(u) + B(v) = A(u_1) + B(v_1) + A(u_2) + B(v_2)$$
$$\leq A \vee B(f_1) + A \vee B(f_2)$$

so that

$$A \vee B(f_1 + f_2) \leq A \vee B(f_1) + A \vee B(f_2),$$

since $\varepsilon$ was arbitrary. To prove the converse inequality, take any $\varepsilon > 0$ and choose $u_1, u_2, v_1$, and $v_2$ in $\mathscr{C}^+$ so that $u_1 + v_1 = f_1$, $u_2 + v_2 = f_2$, and

$$A \vee B(f_1) \leq A(u_1) + B(v_1) + \varepsilon, \qquad A \vee B(f_2) \leq A(u_2) + B(v_2) + \varepsilon.$$

Then $(u_1 + u_2) + (v_1 + v_2) = f_1 + f_2$ and therefore we have, by the definition of $A \vee B(f_1 + f_2)$,

$$A \vee B(f_1 + f_2) \geq A(u_1 + u_2) + B(v_1 + v_2) \geq A \vee B(f_1) + A \vee B(f_2) - 2\varepsilon,$$

or, since $\varepsilon$ was arbitrary,

$$A \vee B(f_1 + f_2) \geq A \vee B(f_1) + A \vee B(f_2).$$

This proves Lemma 8.4.2.

According to Proposition 8.3.8 we can extend $A \vee B$ to a functional on all of $\mathscr{C}$:

**8.4.3 DEFINITION** *$A \vee B(f) = A \vee B(f^+) - A \vee B(f^-)$ for $f \in \mathscr{C}$.*

**8.4.4 PROPOSITION** *$A \vee B$ is a continuous linear functional on $\mathscr{C}$ and $\|A \vee B\|_{ab} \leq \|A\|_{ab} + \|B\|_{ab}$.*

*Proof* Choose $f \in \mathscr{C}_{ab}$ such that $|f| \leq 1$ and take, for an arbitrary $\varepsilon > 0$, $u_1, u_2, v_1, v_2 \in \mathscr{C}^+$ such that $u_1 + v_1 = f^+$, $u_2 + v_2 = f^-$, and

$$|A \vee B(f^+) - A(u_1) - B(v_1)| \leq \varepsilon$$
$$|A \vee B(f^-) - A(u_2) - B(v_2)| \leq \varepsilon.$$

Then

$$\begin{aligned}
&|A \vee B(f^+) - A \vee B(f^-)| - |A(u_1) - A(u_2) + B(v_1) - B(v_2)| \\
&\qquad \leq |A \vee B(f^+) - A \vee B(f^-) - [A(u_1) - A(u_2) + B(v_1) - B(v_2)]| \\
&\qquad \leq |A \vee B(f^+) - A(u_1) - B(v_1)| + |A \vee B(f^-) - A(u_2) - B(v_2)| \leq 2\varepsilon, \\
&|A \vee B(f)| = |A \vee B(f^+) - A \vee B(f^-)| \leq |A(u_1 - u_2)| + |B(v_1 - v_2)| + 2\varepsilon.
\end{aligned}$$

Now, since $0 \leq u_1, v_1 \leq f^+$ and $0 \leq u_2, v_2 \leq f^-$, it follows that

$$|u_1 - u_2|, |v_1 - v_2| \leq |f| \leq 1,$$

whence

$$|A \vee B(f)| \leq \|A\|_{ab} + \|B\|_{ab} + 2\varepsilon,$$

thereby proving Proposition 8.4.4, since $\varepsilon$ was arbitrary.

As we have now defined the one lattice operation $A \vee B$, we can define all the others from this one, and, conversely, we could have taken any one of the other lattice operations in Definition 8.4.5 to begin with. The choice of $A \vee B$ as our starting point is a matter of judgment; it appears, however, that the crucial first half of Lemma 8.4.2 is more transparent for this operation.

**8.4.5 DEFINITION** *If $A$ and $B$ are continuous linear functionals on $\mathscr{C}$, then we define the continuous linear functionals $A \wedge B$, $A^+$, $A^-$ and $|A|$* by

$$A \wedge B = -(-A \vee -B),$$
$$A^+ = A \vee 0,\ A^- = (-A) \vee 0,$$
$$|A| = A^+ + A^-.$$

So far, the relation of these operations to the lattice operations on the real line is mainly formal, but we shall see that by introducing a natural order relation among the linear functionals we get quite a far-reaching analogy.

**8.4.6 DEFINITION** *If $A$ and $B$ are linear functionals on $\mathscr{C}$, we say that $A$ is greater than $B$ and write*

$$A \geq B,$$

*or that $B$ is smaller than $A$, $B \leq A$, if the functional $A - B = (-B) - (-A)$ is positive. Consequently $A \geq B$ and $-B \geq -A$ are equivalent statements.*

**8.4.7 PROPOSITION** *If $A \geq B$ and $B \geq A$, then $A = B$.*

*Proof* $A(f) = B(f)$ for all $f \in \mathscr{C}^+$ by Definition 8.3.3 and hence, by Proposition 8.3.8, for all $f$ in $\mathscr{C}$.

The following proposition characterizes $A \vee B$ as the lowest upper bound of $A$ and $B$, which is quite similar to the definition of the sup of two (or more) real numbers.

**8.4.8 PROPOSITION** *$A \vee B$ is the unique smallest linear functional that is greater than both $A$ and $B$.*

*Proof* $A \vee B(f) \geq A(f), B(f)$ for $f \in \mathscr{C}^+$ follows by putting $u = f$, $v = 0$ and $u = 0$, $v = f$ in Definition 8.4.1. Thus $A \vee B$ is greater than both $A$ and $B$. Now let $D$ be any linear functional such that $D \geq A$ and $D \geq B$. Then

$$D(f) = D(u) + D(v) \geq A(u) + B(v) \qquad \text{if} \quad u, v \in \mathscr{C}^+, u + v = f,$$

from which it follows that $D \geq A \vee B$, so that $A \vee B$ is indeed the smallest linear functional that is greater than both $A$ and $B$. If $D$ has the same property, then one would have also $A \vee B \geq D$ so that $D = A \vee B$ by Proposition 8.4.7, as claimed.

**8.4.9 COROLLARY** *$A \wedge B$ is the unique greatest continuous linear functional that is smaller than both $A$ and $B$.*

**8.4.10 COROLLARY** *$A^+$, $A^-$, and $|A|$ are positive functionals.*

We list below some elementary computation rules that further elaborate the above-mentioned analogy. The list is not complete; some very simple rules like

"$A \vee B = B \vee A$" and "$A \vee D \geq B \vee D$ if $A \geq B$," that can be verified at a glance from the definitions are not mentioned and others are found in the exercises.

**8.4.11 PROPOSITION** *If $A$ and $B$ denote continuous linear functionals on $\mathscr{C}$ and $\lambda$ a real number, then*

(a) $(\lambda A) \vee (\lambda B) = \lambda(A \vee B)$ if $\lambda \geq 0$,
(b) $|\lambda A| = |\lambda|\,|A|$,
(c) $A \vee B = A + (B - A) \vee 0 = A + (B - A)^+ = A + (A - B)^-$,
(d) $A \wedge B = A - (A - B) \vee 0 = A - (A - B)^+ = A - (B - A)^-$,
(e) $A = A^+ - A^-$,
(f) $A^+ \wedge A^- = 0$,
(g) $A \vee B = \frac{1}{2}(A + B) + \frac{1}{2}|A - B|$, $A \wedge B = \frac{1}{2}(A + B) - \frac{1}{2}|A - B|$.

*Proof* Statement (a) follows directly from Definition 8.4.1. To prove (b), suppose first that $\lambda \geq 0$. Then, using Statement (a),

$$|\lambda A| = (\lambda A) \vee 0 + (-\lambda A) \vee 0 = \lambda(A \vee 0 + (-A) \vee 0) = \lambda\,|A|.$$

If $\lambda < 0$, then Statement (a) and Definition 8.4.5 yield

$$|\lambda A| = (\lambda A) \vee 0 + (-\lambda A) \vee 0 = -\lambda((-A) \vee 0 + A \vee 0) = -\lambda\,|A|$$

completing the proof of (b). If $f$ is a function in $\mathscr{C}^+$ and $u \in \mathscr{C}^+$ is such that $u \leq f$ and

$$(B - A) \vee 0\,(f) \leq B(u) - A(u) + \varepsilon$$

where $\varepsilon > 0$ is a preassigned number, then

$$(A + (B - A) \vee 0)(f) - \varepsilon \leq A(f - u) + B(u) \leq A \vee B(f);$$

hence $A + (B - A) \vee 0 \leq A \vee B$, since $\varepsilon$ was arbitrary. On the other hand,

$$A \leq A + (B - A) \vee 0, \qquad B = A + (B - A) \leq A + (B - A) \vee 0$$

so that $A \vee B \leq A + (B - A) \vee 0$ by Proposition 8.4.8. This proves (c) according to Proposition 8.4.7. Statement (d) is merely a reformulation of (c) using Definition 8.4.5, and the last statement, (g), follows by linear combination of (c) and (d). Incidentally, (g) shows how to define $A \vee B$ and $A \wedge B$ if the operation $|A|$ were defined first, which is often the case in other presentations. Finally, Statement (e) is obtained by putting $B = 0$ in (c) and (f) by applying (d) to $A^+$ and $A^-$ instead of $A$ and $B$.

We shall now derive some properties of the norm.

**8.4.12 LEMMA** *If $A$ is a positive continuous linear functional on $\mathscr{C}$, then*

$$\|A\|_{ab} = A(\chi_{(a,b)})$$

*for all $a < b$. Here $\chi_{(a,b)}$ denotes the characteristic function of the open interval $(a, b)$.*

*Proof* $A$ is an integral by Proposition 8.3.4 and

$$|A(f)| \leq \|f\|\, A(\chi_{(a,b)}) \qquad \text{for} \quad f \in \mathscr{C}_{ab}$$

since $|f| \leq \|f\|\, \chi_{(a,b)}$. Thus $\|A\|_{ab} \leq A(\chi_{(a,b)})$. The sequence

$$f_n = (nx - na)^+ \wedge 1 \wedge (nb - nx)^+ \in \mathscr{C}_{ab}$$

increases to $\chi_{(a,b)}$ whence by the monotone convergence theorem

$$\|A\|_{ab} \leq A(\chi_{(a,b)}) = \lim_{n\to\infty} A(f_n) \leq \|A\|_{ab}$$

from which the lemma follows immediately.

8.4.13 COROLLARY *If $A, B \geq 0$ then*

$$\|A + B\|_{ab} = \|A\|_{ab} + \|B\|_{ab}.$$

Thus the norm is additive for positive continuous linear functionals. The norm is also additive, in another important case, when $A$ and $B$ are what we will call mutually singular.

8.4.14 DEFINITION *The two continuous linear functionals $A$ and $B$ are called mutually singular if $|A| \wedge |B| = 0$.*

8.4.15 LEMMA *If $A$ and $B$ are positive, then they are mutually singular if and only if*

$$\|A - B\|_{ab} = \|A\|_{ab} + \|B\|_{ab} \qquad \text{for} \quad \text{all } a < b.$$

8.4.16 COROLLARY $\|A\|_{ab} = \|A^+\|_{ab} + \|A^-\|_{ab} = \|\,|A|\,\|_{ab} = |A|\,(\chi_{(a,b)})$.

*Proof* By Proposition 8.4.11 (g), $A + B = A \vee B$ if $A \wedge B = 0$. Then, by Definition 8.4.1, for $f \in \mathscr{C}_{ab}{}^+$ and $\varepsilon > 0$ functions $u, v \in \mathscr{C}^+$ exist such that $u + v = f$ and

$$2(A + B)(f) = 2(A \vee B)(f) \leq 2A(u) + 2B(v) + \varepsilon.$$

Hence, subtracting $(A + B)(f) = A(u) + A(v) + B(u) + B(v)$ from the above and observing that $|u - v| \leq f$, we obtain

$$\begin{aligned}(A + B)(f) &\leq A(u) - A(v) - B(u) + B(v) + \varepsilon \\ &= (A - B)(u - v) + \varepsilon \leq \|A - B\|_{ab}\|u - v\| + \varepsilon \\ &\leq \|A - B\|_{ab}\, \|f\| + \varepsilon.\end{aligned}$$

Thus for any $f \in \mathscr{C}_{ab}$,

$$|(A + B)(f)| \leq (A + B)(|f|) \leq \|A - B\|_{ab}\, \|f\|,$$

from which it follows that $\|A + B\|_{ab} \leq \|A - B\|_{ab}$. Furthermore, from Proposition 8.3.9 and Corollary 8.4.13 we get

$$\|A\|_{ab} + \|B\|_{ab} = \|A + B\|_{ab} \leq \|A - B\|_{ab} \leq \|A\|_{ab} + \|B\|_{ab}$$

so that indeed $\|A - B\|_{ab} = \|A\|_{ab} + \|B\|_{ab}$.

Corollary 8.4.16 now follows easily from Proposition 8.4.11, (e) and (f), and Lemma 8.4.12.

To prove the sufficiency of Lemma 8.4.15, we use Proposition 8.4.11 (d), Corollary 8.4.13, and Corollary 8.4.16:

$$\begin{aligned}\|A - B\|_{ab} &= \|A\|_{ab} + \|B\|_{ab} \\ &= \|A \wedge B + (A - B)^{+}\|_{ab} + \|A \wedge B + (A - B)^{-}\|_{ab} \\ &= 2\,\|A \wedge B\|_{ab} + \|(A - B)^{+}\|_{ab} + \|(A - B)^{-}\|_{ab} \\ &= 2\,\|A \wedge B\|_{ab} + \|A - B\|_{ab}.\end{aligned}$$

Consequently $\|A \wedge B\|_{ab} = 0$ for all $a < b$, which implies $A \wedge B = 0$ as claimed.

Thus we have proved a special case of the proposition that $\|A + B\|_{ab} = \|A\|_{ab} + \|B\|_{ab}$ if $A$ and $B$ are mutually singular. The general result will not be used in the sequel, so that we have only outlined its proof in the exercise section of this chapter (Exercise 8.6.16).

## *EXERCISES*

In these exercises, $A$, $B$, and $D$ denote continuous linear functionals on $\mathscr{C}$.

*8.4.1* Show that $(A \vee B) \vee D = A \vee (B \vee D)$

*Hint* Show that the value of both these functionals on $f \in \mathscr{C}^{+}$ is given by

$$\sup\,\{A(u) + B(v) + D(w) : u, v, w \in \mathscr{C}^{+}, u + v + w = f\}.$$

*8.4.2* Show that $A \vee (B \wedge D) \leq (A \vee B) \wedge (A \vee D)$.

*8.4.3* Show that $\delta_a$ and $\delta_b$ are mutually singular if $a \neq b$ ($\delta_a$ is defined in Exercise 8.3.5).

*8.4.4* Show that $A \vee (A \wedge B) = A \wedge (A \vee B) = A$.

*8.4.5* Show that $A \wedge (B + D) \leq A \wedge B + A \wedge D$ if $A, B, D \geq 0$ and give an example where there is strict inequality.

*Hint* Show first that $A \wedge (B + D) \leq A \wedge B + D$.

## 8.5 THE RIESZ REPRESENTATION THEOREM

By Corollary 8.3.7 each positive continuous linear functional on $\mathscr{C}$ is a Stieltjes integral. Furthermore, Proposition 8.4.11 (e) has shown that every continuous linear functional on $\mathscr{C}$ can be written as the difference of two integrals on $\mathscr{C}$. This strongly suggests that one should define and study the concept that consists in the difference of two Stieltjes integrals.

**8.5.1 DEFINITION** *The (signed) Lebesgue-Stieltjes integral* $\int \varphi \, d\alpha$ *of a step function* $\varphi \in L$ *with respect to a function* $\alpha \in V_{loc}$ *is defined by*

$$\int \varphi \, d\alpha = \int \varphi \, d\alpha_1 - \int \varphi \, d\alpha_2$$

*where* $\alpha_1$ *and* $\alpha_2$ *are, respectively, the parts of positive and negative variation of* $\alpha$, *in the sense of Definition 6.1.7.*

Since the functions in $\mathscr{C}$ are integrable for $d\alpha_1$ and $d\alpha_2$, we may regard this also as a definition of $\int \varphi \, d\alpha$ on $\mathscr{C}$ for a function $\alpha$ of bounded variation. The rule $A$ that assigns to each function $f \in \mathscr{C}$ the real number $\int f \, d\alpha$ is a continuous linear functional on $\mathscr{C}$. The linear operations among such continuous linear functionals are closely related to those in $V_{loc}$.

**8.5.2 PROPOSITION** *If* $\alpha, \beta \in V_{loc}$ *and* $a, b$ *are real numbers, then*

$$\int \varphi \, d(a\alpha + b\beta) = a \int \varphi \, d\alpha + b \int \varphi \, d\beta$$

*for* $\varphi \in L$ *or* $\varphi \in \mathscr{C}$.

*Proof* Suppose first $\varphi \in L$ and let $\alpha = \gamma_1 - \gamma_2$ be any decomposition of $\alpha$ into the difference of two monotone nondecreasing functions. Then $\alpha_1 + \gamma_2 = \alpha_2 + \gamma_1$, where $\alpha_1$ and $\alpha_2$ are the parts of positive and negative variation of $\alpha$. It follows immediately from Equation (8.1.8) that

$$\int \varphi \, d(\alpha_1 + \gamma_2) = \int \varphi \, d\alpha_1 + \int \varphi \, d\gamma_2$$
$$= \int \varphi \, d(\alpha_2 + \gamma_1) = \int \varphi \, d\alpha_2 + \int \varphi \, d\gamma_1.$$

By a passage to the limit, this formula can also be established for $\varphi \in \mathscr{C}$; if $\varphi \in \mathscr{C}_{ab}$, one just has to apply Lebesgue's dominated convergence theorem to a bounded sequence $\{\varphi_n\}$ of step functions vanishing off $[a, b]$ and tending to $\varphi$ everywhere. Thus

$$\int \varphi \, d\alpha = \int \varphi \, d\alpha_1 - \int \varphi \, d\alpha_2 = \int \varphi \, d\gamma_1 - \int \varphi \, d\gamma_2,$$

that is, the formula in Definition 8.4.1 is valid for any decomposition of $\alpha$ into the difference of two monotone nondecreasing functions. Let $\beta_1$ and $\beta_2$ be the parts of positive and negative variation of $\beta$, and suppose $a \geq 0, b \leq 0$. The other possible cases are treated similarly.

$$\gamma_1 = a\alpha_1 - b\beta_2, \qquad \gamma_2 = a\alpha_2 - b\beta_1$$

are monotone nondecreasing and

$$a\alpha + b\beta = \gamma_1 - \gamma_2.$$

Hence

$$\int \varphi \, d(a\alpha + b\beta) = \int \varphi \, d\gamma_1 - \int \varphi \, d\gamma_2$$

$$= \int \varphi \, d(a\alpha_1) + \int \varphi \, d(-b\beta_2) - \int \varphi \, d(a\alpha_2) - \int \varphi \, d(-b\beta_1).$$

The rule

$$\int \varphi \, d(c\gamma) = c \int \varphi \, d\gamma$$

follows easily for $\gamma \in V_{loc}^+$ and $c \geq 0$ from Equation (8.1.8) if $\varphi$ is a step function, and by passing to the limit is easily derived also for $\varphi \in \mathscr{C}$. Therefore we have

$$\int \varphi \, d(a\alpha + b\beta) = a \int \varphi \, d\alpha_1 + (-b) \int \varphi \, d\beta_2 - a \int \varphi \, d\alpha_2 - (-b) \int \varphi \, d\beta_1$$

$$= a \int \varphi \, d\alpha + b \int \varphi \, d\beta$$

for $\varphi \in L$ or $\varphi \in \mathscr{C}$.

We will now show that these signed Stieltjes integrals furnish all the continuous linear functionals on $\mathscr{C}$.

### 8.5.3 THEOREM

RIESZ REPRESENTATION THEOREM *Each continuous linear functional $A$ on $\mathscr{C}$ can be written in the form*

$$A(f) = \int f \, d\alpha, \qquad f \in \mathscr{C},$$

*with some function $\alpha$ in $V_{loc}$ ,which is uniquely determined up to a constant at all but a denumerable number of points. Furthermore, for any such representation,*

$$\|A\|_{ab} \leq T\alpha(b - 0) - T\alpha(a + 0)$$

*where $T\alpha$ is the total variation function of $\alpha$ (Definition 6.1.4), and $\alpha$ can be chosen so that equality holds for all $a$ and $b$, $a < b$.*

*Proof* Let $A$ be a continuous linear functional on $\mathscr{C}$ then $A^+$ and $A^-$ are positive continuous linear functionals and hence, by Corollary 8.3.7, representable in the form

$$A^+(f) = \int f \, d\beta_1, \quad A^-(f) = \int f \, d\beta_2 \qquad \text{for } f \in \mathscr{C}$$

with $\beta_1, \beta_2 \in V_{loc}^+$. Put $\beta_1 - \beta_2 = \alpha$. Thus we can construct our representation:

$$A(f) = A^+(f) - A^-(f) = \int f \, d\beta_1 - \int f \, d\beta_2 = \int f \, d\alpha$$

for $f \in \mathscr{C}$. For this representation of $A$ we can also estimate $T\alpha(b-0) - T\alpha(a+0)$ by Theorem 6.1.10:

$$T\alpha(b-0) - T\alpha(a+0) \leq \beta_1(b-0) - \beta_1(a+0) + \beta_2(b-0) - \beta_2(a+0)$$
$$= A^+(\chi_{(a,b)}) + A^-(\chi_{(a,b)}) = \|A^+\|_{ab} + \|A^-\|_{ab} = \|A\|_{ab}.$$

Here we have also used Lemma 8.4.12 and Corollary 8.4.16. Now let $\gamma$ be any function in $V_{\text{loc}}$ such that

$$A(f) = \int f\,d\gamma \qquad \text{for all } f \in \mathscr{C}.$$

If we fix the real number $\xi$ and let $a$ be an arbitrary number less than $\xi$, put $\varphi$ equal to the characteristic function of $[a, \xi]$ and use Equation (8.1.7) on $\int \varphi\,d\alpha_1$, $\int \varphi\,d\alpha_2$, $\int \varphi\,d\gamma_1$ and $\int \varphi\,d\gamma_2$, then we get

$$\gamma(a-0) = \alpha(a-0) + (\gamma(\xi+0) - \alpha(\xi+0)).$$

The same relation remains valid for $a > \xi$, as can be seen by considering the characteristic function of $(\xi, a)$ instead. Thus $\alpha$ and $\gamma$ differ by the constant $\gamma(\xi+0) - \alpha(\xi+0)$ at all their common points of continuity, that is, at all except a denumerable number of points (compare with the proof of Proposition 8.2.1). However, $\alpha$ and $\gamma$ do not have to have the same discontinuities altogether, since $\gamma$ may have a removable discontinuity at a point of continuity of $\alpha$. The two positive continuous linear functionals $D_1$ and $D_2$ defined on $\mathscr{C}$ by

$$D_1(f) = \int f\,d\gamma_1, \quad D_2(f) = \int f\,d\gamma_2$$

satisfy the relation $A = D_1 - D_2$; but $D_1$ and $D_2$ are not necessarily mutually singular, as was the case with $A^+$ and $A^-$. We get, however, the following identity from the general inequality $\|\lambda A + \mu B\|_{ab} \leq |\lambda|\,\|A\|_{ab} + |\mu|\,\|B\|_{ab}$ (see Proposition 8.3.9),

$$T\gamma(b-0) - T\gamma(a+0) = \gamma_1(b-0) - \gamma_1(a+0) + \gamma_2(b-0) - \gamma_2(a+0)$$
$$= D_1(\chi_{(a,b)}) + D_2(\chi_{(a,b)}) = \|D_1\|_{ab} + \|D_2\|_{ab} \geq \|A\|_{ab}.$$

This together with the converse inequality valid for $\gamma = \alpha$ completes the proof of Theorem 8.5.3.

8.5.4 COROLLARY *If*

$$A(f) = \int f\,d\alpha \qquad \text{for } f \in \mathscr{C}$$

*is any representation of the continuous linear functional $A$ on $\mathscr{C}$ as an integral with respect to a function $\alpha$ in $V_{\text{loc}}$ of minimal total variation:*

$$\|A\|_{ab} = T\alpha(b-0) - T\alpha(a+0) \qquad \textit{for all } a < b,$$

*and $\alpha_1$, $\alpha_2$ are the parts of the positive and negative variation of $\alpha$, then for $f \in \mathscr{C}$,*

$$|A|(f) = \int f\,d\alpha_1 + \int f\,d\alpha_2,$$

$$A^+(f) = \int f\,d\alpha_1, \quad A^-(f) = \int f\,d\alpha_2.$$

*Proof* By Corollary 8.4.16,

$$|A|(\chi_{(a,b)}) = \|A\|_{ab} = \alpha_1(b-0) - \alpha_1(a+0) + \alpha_2(b-0) - \alpha_2(a+0)$$
$$= \int \chi_{(a,b)}\,d\alpha_1 + \int \chi_{(a,b)}\,d\alpha_2.$$

Thus, since every step function is a linear combination of characteristic functions of open intervals, the relation

$$|A|(f) = \int f\,d\alpha_1 + \int f\,d\alpha_2$$

holds for all step functions and hence also for all $f \in \mathscr{C}$. Then, using Proposition 8.4.11 (g) and the relation $A(f) = \int f\,d\alpha_1 - \int f\,d\alpha_2$, we obtain

$$A^+(f) = \tfrac{1}{2}(A(f) + |A|(f)) = \int f\,d\alpha_1,$$

$$A^-(f) = \tfrac{1}{2}(-A(f) + |A|(f)) = \int f\,d\alpha_2$$

as claimed.

The Riesz representation theorem is one of the most important theorems in analysis. By contrast, the remainder of this section is devoted to a topic that is more of a curiosity, but which does illustrate the techniques that we possess at this stage.

It is easy to see that every function in $V_{\text{loc}}$ is locally integrable with respect to each Stieltjes integral, because each such function is a locally bounded Baire function. Now let $\alpha$ and $\beta$ be two functions in $V_{\text{loc}}$ and let $(a, b)$ be a bounded open interval. We can then form the two integrals $\int_{(a,b)}\alpha\,d\beta$ and $\int_{(a,b)}\beta\,d\alpha$ and we may ask ourselves whether some relation like the classical rule for integration by parts holds between these two integrals. Note that the inclusion or exclusion of an end-point in the interval of integration may affect the value of the integrals if $\alpha$ or $\beta$, or both, have discontinuities at these points. Thus we cannot use the notation $\int_a^b$.

**8.5.5 Proposition** *If $(a, b)$ is a bounded open interval and $\alpha$, $\beta$ are functions in $V_{\text{loc}}$, then*

$$\int_{(a,b)} \alpha\,d\beta + \int_{(a,b)} \beta\,d\alpha = \alpha(b-0)\beta(b-0) - \alpha(a+0)\beta(a+0) + \sum (\alpha^L\beta^L - \alpha^R\beta^R).$$

*Here $\alpha^L$ and $\alpha^R$ are functions defined by*

$$\alpha^L(x) = \alpha(x) - \alpha(x - 0), \qquad \alpha^R(x) = \alpha(x + 0) - \alpha(x)$$

*and the summation sign denotes a sum over the values at all discontinuities of $\alpha$ and $\beta$ in $(a, b)$.*

*Proof* Suppose first that $\alpha, \beta \in V_{\text{loc}}^{+}$ and construct the integral $\int \varphi\, d\mu$ on the set $L$ of step functions on $R^2$ defined by Definition 4.2.1 by putting

$$\int \xi\, d\mu_1 = \int \xi\, d\alpha, \qquad \int \eta\, d\mu_2 = \int \eta\, d\beta$$

in Definition 4.1.5. Let $\chi$ be the characteristic function of the open triangle $D \subset R^2$ defined by

$$D = \{(x, y) : a < y < x < b\}.$$

The triangle $D$ is measurable with respect to $d\mu$, since it is a union of the countable family of rectangles

$$P_k = \{(x, z) : a < z < r_k, r_\kappa < x < b\}$$

where the sequence $\{r_k\}$ enumerates all rational numbers in the open interval $(a, b)$. It is also contained in the square $\{(x, y) : a < x, y < b\}$, so that $D$ is a $d\mu$-integrable set and hence $\chi$ is a $d\mu$-integrable function. Now evaluate $\int \chi\, d\mu$ in two ways by Fubini's theorem (Theorem 4.1.8):

$$\begin{aligned}
\int \chi\, d\mu &= \int_{(a,b)} \left\{ \int_{(y,b)} d\alpha(x) \right\} d\beta(y) = \int_{(a,b)} (\alpha(b - 0) - \alpha(y + 0))\, d\beta(y) \\
&= \alpha(b - 0)(\beta(b - 0) - \beta(a + 0)) - \int_{(a,b)} \alpha(y + 0)\, d\beta(y) \\
&= \int_{(a,b)} \left\{ \int_{(a,x)} d\beta(y) \right\} d\alpha(x) = \int_{(a,b)} (\beta(x - 0) - \beta(a + 0))\, d\alpha(x) \\
&= -\beta(a + 0)(\alpha(b - 0) - \alpha(a + 0)) + \int_{(a,b)} \beta(x - 0)\, d\alpha(x).
\end{aligned}$$

We note that $\beta(x - 0) = \beta(x) - \beta^L(x)$, $\alpha(y + 0) = \alpha(y) + \alpha^R(y)$ and get

$$\begin{aligned}
\int_{(a,b)} \alpha\, d\beta + \int_{(a,b)} \beta\, d\alpha &= \alpha(b - 0)\beta(b - 0) - \alpha(a + 0)\beta(a + 0) \\
&\quad + \int_{(a,b)} \beta^L\, d\alpha - \int_{(a,b)} \alpha^R\, d\beta.
\end{aligned}$$

It remains to compute the last two integrals of the above expression. The functions $\beta^L$ and $\alpha^R$ are of bounded variation on $(a, b)$ and have nonzero values at only a denumerable set of points in $(a, b)$. If the sequence $\{x_k\}$ enumerates these points, we let $\beta_n{}^L$ and $\alpha_n{}^R$ be the functions that coincide with $\beta^L$ and $\alpha^R$ at $x_1, \cdots, x_n$

and vanish everywhere else. Then $\lim \beta_n{}^L = \beta^L$ and $\lim \alpha_n{}^R = \alpha^R$ everywhere on $(a, b)$, whereas $|\beta_n{}^L| \leq |\beta^L|$ and $|\alpha_n{}^R| \leq |\alpha^R|$, so that Lebesgue's dominated convergence theorem applies. If we then use Equation (8.1.8) to evaluate the integrals of the step functions $\beta_n{}^L$ and $\alpha_n{}^R$, we get

$$\int_{(a,b)} \beta^L \, d\alpha - \int_{(a,b)} \alpha^R \, d\beta$$
$$= \lim_{n\to\infty} \sum_{k=1}^{n} [\beta^L(x_k)(\alpha^L(x_k) + \alpha^R(x_k)) - \alpha^R(x_k)(\beta^L(x_k) + \beta^R(x_k))]$$
$$= \sum (\beta^L\alpha^L - \alpha^R\beta^R)$$

as required, the last sum being taken over all discontinuities of $\alpha$ and $\beta$ in $(a, b)$.

We have now proved Proposition 8.5.5 for the special case where $\alpha$ and $\beta$ are monotone nondecreasing functions. In the general case we decompose $\alpha$ and $\beta$ into their respective parts of positive and negative variation,

$$\alpha = \alpha_1 - \alpha_2, \qquad \beta = \beta_1 - \beta_2,$$

and add the expressions corresponding to each of the four pairs $(\alpha_i, \beta_j)$, $i, j = 1, 2$ with the appropriate sign, which is $(-1)^{i+j}$. This completes the proof of Proposition 8.5.5.

## *EXERCISES*

*8.5.1* Write the functional $\delta_a$ as a Stieltjes integral.

*8.5.2* Suppose $\alpha, \beta \in V_{\text{loc}}$ and define $\alpha \geq \beta$ to mean $\alpha - \beta \in V_{\text{loc}}^+$. Show that there exists a function $\gamma \in V_{\text{loc}}$ such that $\gamma \geq \alpha$, $\gamma \geq \beta$ and such that, if $\delta$ is another function in $V_{\text{loc}}$ that also satisfies $\delta \geq \alpha$, $\delta \geq \beta$, then $\delta \geq \gamma$. Show that $\gamma$ is uniquely determined up to an additive constant, at all points where both $\beta$ and $\alpha$ are continuous.

*8.5.3* Write the functional $(fA) \vee (gA)$ as a Stieltjes integral, if $f$ and $g$ are continuous functions and $A$ is represented by

$$A(\varphi) = \int \varphi \, d\alpha, \qquad \varphi \in \mathscr{C},$$

for some $\alpha \in V_{\text{loc}}$ (see Exercise 8.3.3).

*8.5.4* Show that if $\alpha$ and $\beta$ are functions in $V_{\text{loc}}$ that satisfy

$$\alpha(x) = \tfrac{1}{2}(\alpha(x - 0) + (x + 0)), \qquad \beta(x) = \tfrac{1}{2}(\beta(x - 0) + \beta(x + 0))$$

for all $x$, then

$$\int_{(a,b)} \alpha \, d\beta + \int_{(a,b)} \beta \, d\alpha = \alpha(b - 0)\beta(b - 0) - \alpha(a + 0)\beta(a + 0).$$

*8.5.5* Show that if $\alpha$ and $\beta$ are as above, then

$$\int \varphi\alpha \, d\beta + \int \varphi\beta \, d\alpha = \int \varphi \, d(\alpha\beta) \qquad \text{for } \varphi \in \mathscr{C}.$$

# 8.6 EXERCISES

## A. Examples of Stieltjes Integrals

**8.6.1** Let

$$\alpha(x) = \begin{cases} 0 & \text{for } x \le 0 \\ 2^{-n} & \text{for } 2^{-n} \le x < 2^{-n+1},\ n \ge 1 \\ 1 & \text{for } x \ge 1 \end{cases}$$

$$\beta(x) = \begin{cases} 0 & \text{for } x \le 0 \\ 2^{-n} & \text{for } 2^{-n} < x \le 2^{-n+1},\ n \ge 1 \\ 1 & \text{for } x > 1. \end{cases}$$

Compute $\int \alpha\, d\alpha$ and $\int \beta\, d\beta$.

**8.6.2** Prove that for $\varphi \in L$,

(a) $\displaystyle\int \varphi\, d(x^3) = 3 \int x^2 \varphi\, dx,$

(b) $\displaystyle\int \varphi\, d(\text{arc tan}) = \int 1/(1 + x^2)\varphi\, dx,$

(c) $\displaystyle\int \varphi\, d(e^x) = \int e^x \varphi\, dx,$

(d) $\displaystyle\int \varphi\, d(\sin) = \int \varphi \cos x\, dx.$

*Hint* Prove this first for the characteristic function of a closed interval.

**8.6.3** Prove that a function $f$ on the real line is $d(x^3)$-integrable if and only if $x^2 f$ is Lebesgue integrable, and show that

$$\int f\, d(x^3) = 3 \int x^2 f\, dx$$

if $f$ is $d(x^3)$-integrable.

*Hint* Use Mikusiński's lemma and Exercise 8.6.2(a).

## B. Stieltjes Integrals for Piecewise Linear Functions

For the definition of piecewise linear functions see part D of Section 1.6.

**8.6.4** To each monotone nondecreasing function $\alpha$ we let correspond a function $A$ according to the formula

$$A(t) = \int_0^t \alpha\, dx.$$

(a) Prove that $A$ is continuous, convex, and absolutely continuous, and show that $A$ has a derivative that equals $\alpha(x)$ at all points of continuity of $\alpha$.
(b) If $\beta$ is another monotone nondecreasing function such that $\int \varphi \, d\alpha = \int \varphi \, d\beta$ for all piecewise linear functions $\varphi$, then $A = B + cx$ for some constant $c$.

*Hint* Show that the hypothesis implies $\int \psi \, d\alpha = \int \psi \, d\beta$ for all step functions $\psi$.

(c) If $A$ is a continuous convex function on the real line that vanishes at 0, then

$$A(t) = \int_0^t \alpha \, dx$$

for some monotone nondecreasing function $\alpha$.

*Hint* Show that $A$ is absolutely continuous and let $\alpha = A'$.

**8.6.5** For a piecewise linear function $\varphi$ with presentation $(a_0, \cdots, a_n;\ c_1, \cdots, c_{n-1})$ define the changes of slope $\delta_k$ at the points $a_k$, $0 \leq k \leq n$, by

$$\delta_k = \lim_{0<h\to 0} \left[\frac{1}{h}(\varphi(a_k + h) - \varphi(a_k)) - \frac{1}{h}(\varphi(a_k) - \varphi(a_k - h))\right].$$

If $s_k$ denotes the slope of $\varphi$ on $(a_{k-1}, a_k)$,

$$s_k = \frac{c_k - c_{k-1}}{a_k - a_{k-1}}, \qquad c_0 = c_n = 0,\ 1 \leq k \leq n$$

then

$$\delta_k = s_{k+1} - s_k,\ 0 \leq k \leq n,$$

where we let $s_0 = 0 = s_{n+1}$.

(a) Show that

$$\sum_{k=0}^{n} \delta_k = \sum_{k=0}^{n} a_k \, \delta_k = 0,$$

and conversely, if $a_0 < \cdots < a_n$, $\delta_0, \cdots, \delta_n$ is a sequence of numbers such that the above relation holds, then there is a piecewise linear function $\varphi$ with presentation $(a_0, \cdots, a_n;\ c_1, \cdots, c_{n-1})$ and change of slope $\delta_k$ at $a_k$, $0 \leq k \leq n$.

*Hint* Let $\psi$ be a step function with presentation $(a_0, \cdots, a_n;\ d_1 \cdots, d_n)$ where

$$d_k = \sum_{j=1}^{k} \delta_{j-1}, \qquad 1 \leq k \leq n.$$

Show that $\varphi(t) = \int_{a_0}^{t} \psi \, dx$ defines the desired piecewise linear function $\varphi$.

(b) Let $\varphi$ be a piecewise linear function with presentation $(a_0, \cdots, a_n; c_1, \cdots, c_{n-1})$ and changes of slope $\delta_0, \cdots, \delta_n$. Show

$$\int \varphi \, d\alpha = \sum_{k=0}^{n} \delta_k A(a_k)$$

where $A(t) = \int_0^t \alpha \, dx$.

*Hint* Use Proposition 8.5.5 with $\beta = x$ to verify the formula

$$\int_{(a,b)} x \, d\alpha = b\alpha(b - 0) - a\alpha(a + 0) - (A(b) - A(a)),$$

which is useful in evaluating $\int \varphi \, d\alpha$.

**8.6.6** Suppose $\int \varphi \, d\mu$, $\varphi \in L_1$ is an integral on the linear space $L_1$ of piecewise linear functions. Show that there is a continuous convex function $A$ such that

$$\int \varphi \, d\mu = \sum_{k=0}^{n} \delta_k A(a_k), \qquad \varphi \in L_1,$$

where $(a_0, \cdots, a_n; c_1, \cdots, c_{n-1})$ is a presentation for $\varphi$ and $\delta_k$ is the change of slope of $\varphi$ at $a_k$, $0 \leq k \leq n$ (see the previous exercise). If $B$ is any other continuous convex function such that

$$\int \varphi \, d\mu = \sum_{k=0}^{n} \delta_k B(a_k), \qquad \varphi \in L_1,$$

then $A = B + cx + d$ where $c$ and $d$ are constants.

*Hint* Show that $\int \varphi \, d\mu$ is actually a Stieltjes integral and apply the previous exercise. For the second part of the assertion use Exercise 8.6.4.

## C. Baire Functions

**8.6.7** Suppose $F$ is a Baire function and $f$ is $d\alpha$-measurable where $\alpha \in V_{\text{loc}}^+$. Show that $F \circ f$ is $d\alpha$-measurable.

*Hint* Show that the set $\mathscr{A}$ of functions $F$ with the above property is a linear space containing the continuous functions and closed under pointwise-everywhere limits. Then apply Definition 8.2.4.

**8.6.8** Suppose $f_1, \cdots, f_k$ are Baire functions and $F$ is a continuous function of $k$ variables. Prove that $F(f_1, \cdots, f_k)$ is a Baire function.

*Hint* See Exercise 8.2.4 and Theorem 3.2.5.

**8.6.9** Similarly, as for functions of one variable, one can also define the concept of Baire functions for functions of several variables. The smallest vector space

$\mathscr{B}_k$ of functions of $k$ variables which contains all continuous functions and is closed under pointwise-everywhere limits, is called the space of Baire functions. Prove that if $F$ is a Baire function of $k$ variables and $f_1, \cdots, f_k$ are Baire functions of one variable, then $F(f_1, \cdots, f_k)$ is a Baire function of one variable.

*Hint* Use the previous exercise to show that the set $\mathscr{A}$ of all functions $F$ is a linear space containing the continuous functions, and that $\mathscr{A}$ is closed under pointwise-everywhere limits.

**8.6.10** Suppose $F$ is a Baire function of $k$ variables and $f_1, \cdots, f_k$ are $d\alpha$-measurable, where $\alpha \in V_{\text{loc}}^+$. Prove that $F(f_1, \cdots, f_k)$ is $d\alpha$-measurable.

## D. Limit Operations

**8.6.11** It is possible to approximate a function $\alpha \in V_{\text{loc}}^+$ by a sequence $\alpha_n$ of piecewise linear functions in $V_{\text{loc}}^+$ at all points of continuity of $\alpha$, for instance, by defining

$$\alpha_n(k2^{-n}) = \alpha(k2^{-n}),\ k = 0, \pm 1, \cdots$$

and prescribing that $\alpha_n$ be linear on each interval $[k2^{-n}, (k+1)2^{-n}]$. Show by an example that it is not necessarily true that

$$\lim_{n\to\infty} \int \varphi \, d\alpha_n = \int \varphi \, d\alpha$$

for all step functions $\varphi$.

**8.6.12** Let $\alpha_n$ and $\alpha$ be as in the previous exercise. Show that

$$\lim_{n\to\infty} \int \varphi \, d\alpha_n = \int \varphi \, d\alpha$$

holds if either $\varphi \in \mathscr{C}$ or $\varphi \in L$ and $\alpha$ does not have any discontinuities.

**8.6.13** Suppose $\{A_n\}$ is an increasing sequence of continuous linear functionals on $\mathscr{C}$, $A_{n+1} \geq A_n$. Show that if there is a continuous linear functional $B$ on $\mathscr{C}$, such that $A_n \leq B$ for all $n$, then $\{A_n(f)\}$ converges for each $f \in \mathscr{C}$ and the equation

$$\lim_{n\to\infty} A_n(f) = A(f)$$

defines a continuous linear functional $A$ on $\mathscr{C}$.

**8.6.14** Let $A$ and $B$ be two positive continuous linear functionals on $\mathscr{C}$ and let $\{\gamma_k\}$ be an enumeration of the rational numbers in the interval $(-1, 1)$. Show that if

$$D_n = \tfrac{1}{2}\sqrt{2}(\sqrt{1+\gamma_1}\,A + \sqrt{1-\gamma_1}\,B) \vee \cdots \vee (\sqrt{1+\gamma_n}\,A + \sqrt{1-\gamma_n}\,B),$$

then

$$\lim_{n\to\infty} D_n(f) = C(f), \qquad f \in \mathscr{C}$$

defines a continuous linear functional $C$ on $\mathscr{C}$.

*Hint* Use the previous exercise.

*Remark* For any two real numbers $a, b \geq 0$, the function

$$g(x) = \tfrac{1}{2}\sqrt{2}(\sqrt{1+x}\,a + \sqrt{1-x}\,b)$$

has a maximum on $[-1, 1]$ at $x_0 = (a^2 - b^2)/(a^2 + b^2)$ if $a^2 + b^2 \neq 0$ and at $x_0 = 0$ if $a = b = 0$. Furthermore,

$$g(x_0) = (a^2 + b^2)^{1/2}.$$

Thus

$$(a^2 + b^2)^{1/2} = \lim_{n\to\infty} \tfrac{1}{2}\sqrt{2}(\sqrt{1+\gamma_1}\,a + \sqrt{1-\gamma_1}\,b) \vee \cdots \vee (\sqrt{1+\gamma_n}\,a + \sqrt{1-\gamma_n}\,b).$$

For this reason one might define

$$C = (A^2 + B^2)^{1/2}$$

in the above exercise. However, one can find examples where

$$C(f) \neq [(A(f))^2 + (B(f))^2]^{1/2}$$

for certain $f \in \mathscr{C}^+$.

## E. Operations on Continuous Linear Functionals on $\mathscr{C}$

**8.6.15** Suppose $A$ is a positive continuous linear functional on $\mathscr{C}$ so that $A$ is actually an integral,

$$A(f) = \int f\,d\mu, \qquad f \in \mathscr{C}.$$

Let $g$ be a Baire function, which is bounded on every bounded interval. Show that it is possible to define a continuous linear functional $gA$ on $\mathscr{C}$ by

$$(gA)(f) = \int fg\,d\mu, \qquad f \in \mathscr{C}.$$

**8.6.16** Let $A$ and $B$ be continuous linear functionals on $\mathscr{C}$.

(a) Show that if $|A| \wedge |B| = 0$, then $(A^+ + B^+) \wedge (A^- + B^-) = 0$.

*Hint* Use the result of Exercise 8.4.5.

(b) Show that if $A$ and $B$ are mutually singular, then

$$\|A + B\|_{ab} = \|A\|_{ab} + \|B\|_{ab}.$$

**8.6.17** Let $A$ be a continuous linear functional. Prove that for $f \in \mathscr{C}^+$,

$$A^+(f) = \sup\{A(g) : 0 \leq g \leq f, g \in \mathscr{C}\},$$
$$A^-(f) = \sup\{-A(g) : 0 \leq g \leq f, g \in \mathscr{C}\}.$$

**8.6.18** For $f \in \mathscr{C}$ define $f_h$ by

$$f_h(x) = f(x + h).$$

Show that if $A$ is a positive continuous linear functional such that $A(f) = A(f_h)$ for all $f \in \mathscr{C}$ and all real numbers $h$, then there is a number $a \geq 0$ with

$$A(f) = a \int f\,dx, \qquad f \in \mathscr{C}.$$

*Hint* Let $\chi$ be the characteristic function of $[-1, 1]$. Consider $A$ as an integral and use Fubini's theorem on iterated integration to justify the following

$$\begin{aligned} 2A(f) &= \int_{-1}^{1} A(f)\,dh = \int_{-1}^{1} A(f_h)\,dh \\ &= A\left(\int_{-1}^{1} f(x+h)\,dh\right) = A\left(\int \chi(h) f(x+h)\,dh\right) \\ &= A\left(\int \chi(h-x) f(h)\,dh\right) = \int A(\chi_{-h}) f(h)\,dh \\ &= A(\chi) \int f(h)\,dh. \end{aligned}$$

**8.6.19** Let $A$ be a continuous linear functional such that $xA = 0$, where $xA$ is the functional $xA(f) = A(xf)$ defined in Exercise 8.3.3. Show that $A$ is a constant multiple of $\delta$ ($\delta(f) = f(0)$).

*Hint* Let $\alpha \in V_{\text{loc}}$ be a function such that $A(f) = \int f\,d\alpha$ for $f \in \mathscr{C}$. Use the formula in the hint to Exercise 8.6.5(b) to show that $\alpha$ is absolutely continuous on all open intervals not containing zero, and then, by differentiation, that $\alpha$ is constant on such intervals.

## F. A Theory of Integration for Signed Stieltjes Integrals

**8.6.20** Let $\alpha$ and $\beta$ be functions in $V_{\text{loc}}^{+}$ such that $\beta - \alpha \in V_{\text{loc}}^{+}$: Show that

(a) $\int \varphi\,d\alpha \leq \int \varphi\,d\beta$ for $\varphi \in L^{+}$.
(b) Each $d\beta$-null set is also $d\alpha$-null.
(c) Each $d\beta$-integrable function is also $d\alpha$-integrable.
(d) Each $d\beta$-measurable function is also $d\alpha$-measurable.
(e) Let $\alpha$ be a function of locally bounded variation and $\alpha = \alpha_1 - \alpha_2$ its decomposition into the parts of positive and negative variation. Use (c) and (d) to prove that a function $f$ which is integrable (measurable) for $|d\alpha| = d\alpha_1 + d\alpha_2$ is integrable (measurable) for both $d\alpha_1$ and $d\alpha_2$.

**8.6.21** Suppose $\alpha, \beta \in V_{\text{loc}}^{+}$ and $d\alpha \wedge d\beta = 0$. Prove that there are subsets $E$ and $F$ of the real line with the following properties:

(1) $E$ and $F$ are $d\gamma$-measurable for each $\gamma \in V_{\text{loc}}^{+}$;
(2) $E \cup F = R$;
(3) $E$ is $d\beta$-null and $F$ is $d\alpha$-null.

*Hint* Let $f_n$ be a function in $\mathscr{C}^{+}$ which is identically 1 on $[-n, n]$. Since $(-d\alpha) \vee (-d\beta) = 0$ there are, by Definition 8.4.1, functions $u_n, v_n \in \mathscr{C}^{+}$ such that $f_n = u_n + v_n$ and

$$0 \geq -\int u_n \, d\alpha - \int v_n \, d\beta \geq -2^{-n}.$$

Let $E$ be the set on which $\sum v_n$ diverges and $F$ the set on which $\sum u_n$ diverges. To prove (1) notice that

$$E = \bigcap_{k=1}^{\infty} \bigcup_{m=1}^{\infty} \left\{x : \sum_{n=1}^{m} v_n(x) \geq k\right\}.$$

**8.6.22** Let $\alpha \in V_{\text{loc}}$ and decompose $\alpha$ into its parts of positive and negative variation, $\alpha = \alpha_1 - \alpha_2$. Use the previous exercise to prove the following.

(a) A set that is both $d\alpha_1$-null and $d\alpha_2$-null is also $|d\alpha|$-null ($|d\alpha| = d\alpha_1 + d\alpha_2 = d(\alpha_1 + \alpha_2)$).
(b) A function that is both $d\alpha_1$- and $d\alpha_2$-integrable (measurable) is also $|d\alpha|$-integrable (measurable).

*Hint* Suppose $f$ is $d\alpha_1$- and $d\alpha_2$-integrable. Let $R = E \cup F$ as in the previous exercise, where $E$ is $d\alpha_2$-null, $F$ is $d\alpha_1$-null and both $E$ and $F$ are measurable for $d\alpha_1$, $d\alpha_2$ and $d(\alpha_1 + \alpha_2)$. By Mikusiński's theorem, there is a series $\sum \varphi_n$ of step functions such that $\sum \int |\varphi_n| \, d\alpha_1$ converges and

$$f(x) = \sum_{n=1}^{\infty} \varphi_n(x)$$

for all $x$ for which the series converges absolutely. Notice that

$$\sum_{n=1}^{\infty} \int |\varphi_n \chi_E| \, d(\alpha_1 + \alpha_2) = \sum_{n=1}^{\infty} \int |\varphi_n| \, d\alpha_1 < \infty$$

and conclude that $f\chi_E$ is $d(\alpha_1 + \alpha_2)$ integrable.

**8.6.23** Let $\alpha \in V_{\text{loc}}$, $\alpha = \alpha_1 - \alpha_2$ as in the last exercise. We say that $f$ is $d\alpha$-integrable if it is integrable for $d\alpha_1$ and $d\alpha_2$. According to Exercises 8.6.20(e) and 8.6.22 this is equivalent to saying that $f$ is $|d\alpha|$-integrable. Verify the inequality

$$\left| \int f \, d\alpha \right| \leq \int |f| \, |d\alpha|,$$

where $|d\alpha| = d(\alpha_1 + \alpha_2)$.

## G. Abstract Signed Integrals

In the following $L$ is a linear space of elementary functions on a set $S$ satisfying Properties (1) and (5). A rule that assigns a real number $\int \varphi \, d\mu$ to each $\varphi \in L$ is called a linear functional on $L$ if it satisfies Property (2):

$$\int (a\varphi + b\psi) \, d\mu = a \int \varphi \, d\mu + b \int \psi \, d\mu$$

where $\varphi, \psi \in L$ and $a, b$ are real numbers. Such a linear functional is an integral if it also satisfies Properties (3) and (4). A linear functional $\int \varphi \, d\mu$ on $L$ is a signed integral if integrals $\int \varphi \, d\mu_1$ and $\int \varphi \, d\mu_2$ exist on $L$ such that

$$\int \varphi \, d\mu = \int \varphi \, d\mu_1 - \int \varphi \, d\mu_2, \qquad \varphi \in L.$$

**8.6.24** Let $\int \varphi \, d\mu$ and $\int \varphi \, d\nu$ be signed integrals on $L$, say

$$\int \varphi \, d\mu = \int \varphi \, d\mu_1 - \int \varphi \, d\mu_2, \qquad \int \varphi \, d\nu = \int \varphi \, d\nu_1 - \int \varphi \, d\nu_2$$

where $\int \varphi \, d\mu_i$, $\int \varphi \, d\nu_i$, $i = 1, 2$, are integrals. Show that

$$\int \varphi \, d\mu \vee \nu = \sup \left\{ \int \xi \, d\mu + \int \eta \, d\nu : \xi, \eta \in L, \, 0 \le \xi, \eta \le \varphi, \, \xi + \eta = \varphi \right\}$$

exists for $\varphi \in L$, $\varphi \ge 0$. Show that, in fact,

$$\int \varphi \, d\mu \vee \nu \le \int \varphi \, d\mu_1 + \int \varphi \, d\mu_2 + \int \varphi \, d\nu_1 + \int \varphi \, d\nu_2.$$

As in Lemma 8.4.2 one can now show that

$$\int (a\varphi + b\psi) \, d\mu \vee \nu = a \int \varphi \, d\mu \vee \nu + b \int \varphi \, d\mu \vee \nu$$

if $\varphi$ and $\psi$ are nonnegative functions in $L$ and $a, b$ are nonnegative real numbers. According to Proposition 8.3.7 (which holds also for $L$ instead of $\mathscr{C}$) $\int \varphi \, d\mu \vee \nu$ extends to a linear functional on all of $L$ by the definition

$$\int \varphi \, d\mu \vee \nu = \int \varphi^+ \, d\mu \vee \nu - \int \varphi^- \, d\mu \vee \nu.$$

**8.6.25** Suppose $\int \varphi \, d\mu$ is a signed integral on $L$. Define

$$\int \varphi \, d(-\mu) = -\int \varphi \, d\mu, \qquad \int \varphi \, d0 = 0, \qquad \varphi \in L.$$

Show that

$$\int \varphi \, d\mu^+ = \int \varphi \, d\mu \vee 0, \qquad \int \varphi \, d\mu^- = \int \varphi \, d(-\mu) \vee 0$$

$$\int \varphi \, d\,|\mu| = \int \varphi \, d\mu^+ + \int \varphi \, d\mu^-$$

are integrals on $L$. Furthermore, verify

$$\int \varphi \, d\mu = \int \varphi \, d\mu^+ - \int \varphi \, d\mu^-, \qquad \varphi \in L.$$

*Hint* Suppose $\int \varphi \, d\mu = \int \varphi \, d\mu_1 - \int \varphi \, d\mu_2$, $\varphi \in L$, where $\int \varphi \, d\mu_1$ and $\int \varphi \, d\mu_2$ are integrals on $L$. To prove Properties (3) and (4) for $\int \varphi \, d\mu^+$ and $\int \varphi \, d\nu^-$, verify

$$0 \leq \int \varphi \, d\mu^+ \leq \int \varphi \, d\mu_1, \qquad 0 \leq \int \varphi \, d\mu^- \leq \int \varphi \, d\mu_2$$

for $\varphi \in L$, $\varphi \geq 0$ (see Exercise 8.6.24).

**8.6.26** Suppose $\int \varphi \, d\mu$ and $\int \varphi \, d\nu$ are signed integrals on $L$. Show that $\int \varphi \, d\mu \vee \nu$ is a signed integral on $L$.

*Hint* Define $\int \varphi \, d(\mu - \nu) = \int \varphi \, d\mu - \int \varphi \, d\nu$ and verify $\int \varphi \, d\mu \vee \nu = \frac{1}{2}[\int \varphi \, d\mu + \int \varphi \, d\nu] + \frac{1}{2}\int \varphi \, d\,|\mu - \nu|$, $\varphi \in L$ (see Proposition 8.4.11).

## SUMMARY

For a monotone nondecreasing function $\alpha$, $J_\alpha$ is the smallest interval that contains all the values of $\alpha$. A function $\alpha_1$ on $J_\alpha$ is called an inverse to $\alpha$ if

$$\sup \{y : a(y) < x\} \leq \alpha_1(x) \leq \inf \{y : x < \alpha(y)\}, \; x \in J_\alpha$$

where the sup is interpreted to be $-\infty$ if no $y$ with $\alpha(y) < x$ exists, and similarly, the inf is $\infty$ if no $y$ with $\alpha(y) > x$ exists (Definitions 8.1.1 and 8.1.2).

For $\varphi \in L$, $\varphi \circ \alpha_1$ is a linear combination of characteristic functions of bounded intervals (Corollary 8.1.4), and

$$\int \varphi \, d\alpha = \int_{J_\alpha} \varphi \circ \alpha_1 \, dx, \qquad \varphi \in L$$

defines an integral on $L$ satisfying Properties (1) to (5) (Definition 8.1.5 and Proposition 8.1.6). This is the (Lebesgue-) Stieltjes integral with respect to $\alpha$. If $(a_0, \cdots, a_n; c_1, \cdots, c_n)$ is a presentation of the step function $\varphi$, then the following equations (8.1.7) and (8.1.8) hold:

$$\int \varphi \, d\alpha = \sum_{k=0}^{n} [\varphi(a_k - 0) - \varphi(a_k)]\alpha(a_k - 0) + \sum_{k=0}^{n} [\varphi(a_k) - \varphi(a_k + 0)]\alpha(a_k + 0),$$

$$\int \varphi \, d\alpha = \sum_{k=1}^{n} c_k[\alpha(a_k - 0) - \alpha(a_{k-1} + 0)] + \sum_{k=0}^{n} \varphi(a_k)[\alpha(a_k + 0) - \alpha(a_k - 0)].$$

A function $f$ on the real line is $d\alpha$-integrable if and only if $f \circ \alpha_1$ is (Lebesgue-) integrable on $J_\alpha$, and then

$$\int f\,d\alpha = \int_{J_\alpha} f \circ \alpha_1\,dx \qquad \text{(Proposition 8.1.9).}$$

The only integrals on the linear space $L$ of step functions are the Stieltjes integrals (Riesz representation theorem 8.2.3), and two monotone nondecreasing functions $\alpha$ and $\beta$ define the same Stieltjes integral if and only if they differ by a constant at their common points of continuity.

The set $\mathscr{B}$ of Baire functions is the smallest vector space of functions on the real line that contains the continuous functions and is closed under pointwise-everywhere limits (Definition 8.2.4). The Baire functions are $d\alpha$-measurable for each monotone nondecreasing function $\alpha$ (Corollary 8.2.8). The set of Baire functions contains the linear space $\mathscr{C}$ of continuous functions vanishing off some bounded interval. Every function in $\mathscr{C}$ is $d\alpha$-integrable (Corollary 8.2.8).

The subset of $\mathscr{C}$ of functions vanishing off a bounded closed interval $[a, b]$ is denoted by $\mathscr{C}_{ab}$. A bounded linear functional $A$ on $\mathscr{C}$ assigns to each $f \in \mathscr{C}$ a real number $A(f)$ subject to the conditions:

(a) if $\lambda$, $\mu$ are real numbers and $f, g \in \mathscr{C}$, then

$$A(\lambda f + \mu g) = \lambda A(f) + \mu A(g);$$

(b) for each bounded closed interval $[a, b]$, there is a constant $M_{ab}$ such that

$$|A(f)| \le M_{ab}\,\|f\| \qquad \text{for } f \in \mathscr{C}_{ab}$$

where $\|f\| = \sup\{|f(x)| : x \in R\}$. The smallest such $M_{ab}$ is called the norm $\|A\|_{ab}$ of $A$ on $[a, b]$ (Definition 8.3.1). A bounded linear functional is also called a continuous linear functional, because (b) is equivalent to the following continuity condition (Proposition 8.3.2):

(c) If the sequence $\{f_n\}$ in $\mathscr{C}_{ab}$ tends to $f \in \mathscr{C}_{ab}$ in norm, $\lim_{n\to\infty} \|f_n - f\| = 0$, then $\lim_{n\to\infty} A(f_n) = A(f)$.

For instance every Stieltjes integral defines a continuous linear functional on $\mathscr{C}$, in fact it defines a positive continuous linear functional in the sense that it assigns a nonnegative value to every nonnegative function. Conversely, every positive continuous linear functional $A$ on $\mathscr{C}$ is defined by a Stieltjes integral with respect to a monotone nondecreasing function $\alpha$,

$$A(f) = \int f\,d\alpha, \qquad f \in \mathscr{C}$$

(Riesz representation theorem, Corollary 8.3.7).

The set of continuous linear functionals on $\mathscr{C}$ is a linear space with the definition

$$(\lambda A + \mu B)(f) = \lambda A(f) + \mu B(f), \qquad f \in \mathscr{C}.$$

The norm on this linear space has the following properties (Proposition 8.3.9):

$$\|\lambda A\|_{ab} = |\lambda|\ \|A\|_{ab},$$
$$|\ \|A\|_{ab} - \|B\|_{ab}| \leq \|A + B\|_{ab} \leq \|A\|_{ab} + \|B\|_{ab}.$$

A continuous linear functional $A$ on $\mathscr{C}$ is greater than the continuous linear functional $B$, $A \geq B$, or $B$ is smaller than $A$, $B \leq A$, if $A - B$ is positive (Definition 8.4.6). Similarly as for real numbers, one can define lattice operations among continuous linear functionals $A$ and $B$ on $\mathscr{C}$. There is a continuous linear functional $A \vee B$ that is the unique smallest linear functional greater than both $A$ and $B$ (Propositions 8.4.4 and 8.4.8), and $A \wedge B = -(-A \vee -B)$ is the unique largest continuous linear functional smaller than both $A$ and $B$ (Corollary 8.4.9). The continuous linear functionals

$$A^+ = A \vee 0, \qquad A^- = (-A) \vee 0, \qquad |A| = A^+ + A^-$$

are positive (Corollary 8.4.10), and one has among others the following relations (Proposition 8.4.11):

$$A = A^+ - A^-, \qquad A^+ \wedge A^- = 0,$$
$$A \vee B = \tfrac{1}{2}(A + B) + \tfrac{1}{2}|A - B|,$$
$$A \wedge B = \tfrac{1}{2}(A + B) - \tfrac{1}{2}\,|A - B|.$$

Two continuous linear functionals $A$ and $B$ satisfying

$$|A| \wedge |B| = 0$$

are called mutually singular (Definition 8.4.14); for instance, $A^+$ and $A^-$ are mutually singular. One has the following relations for the norm:

$$\|A\|_{ab} = \|A^+\|_{ab} + \|A^-\|_{ab} = \|\ |A|\ \|_{ab} = |A|\,(\chi_{(a,b)}),$$

where $|A|(\chi_{(a,b)})$ is defined by considering the positive continuous linear functional $|A|$ as an integral (Corollary 8.4.16).

Every function $\alpha$ of locally bounded variation defines a continuous linear functional on $\mathscr{C}$ by the formula

$$\int f\, d\alpha = \int f\, d\alpha_1 - \int f\, d\alpha_2, \qquad f \in \mathscr{C}$$

where $\alpha_1$ and $\alpha_2$ are the parts of positive and negative variation of $\alpha$. This functional is called a signed Stieltjes integral (Definition 8.5.1). If $\alpha$ and $\beta$ are functions of locally bounded variation and $a$, $b$ are real numbers, then

$$\int f\, d(a\alpha + b\beta) = a\int f\, d\alpha + b\int f\, d\beta \qquad \text{(Proposition 8.5.2).}$$

We then have the following theorem.

## RIESZ REPRESENTATION THEOREM

According to Theorem 8.5.3 and Corollary 8.5.4, each continuous linear functional $A$ on $\mathscr{C}$ can be written in the form

$$A(f) = \int f\,d\alpha, \qquad f \in \mathscr{C},$$

with some function $\alpha$ of locally bounded variation, and any two functions $\alpha$ and $\alpha_0$ representing $A$ differ by only a constant at all common points of continuity. For any such representation,

$$\|A\|_{ab} \leq T\alpha(b-0) - T\alpha(a+0),$$

where $T\alpha$ is the total variation function of $\alpha$, and $\alpha$ can be chosen such that equality holds for all $a < b$. If equality holds, then

$$|A|(f) = \int f\,d\alpha_1 + \int f\,d\alpha_2$$

$$A^+(f) = \int f\,d\alpha_1, \qquad A^-(f) = \int f\,d\alpha_2,$$

where $\alpha_1$ and $\alpha_2$ are the parts of positive and negative variation of $\alpha$.

# 9

# The Radon-Nikodym Theorem

The Radon-Nikodym theorem says that under certain circumstances two Stieltjes integrals $\int \varphi \, d\alpha$ and $\int \varphi \, d\beta$ are related by an equation

$$\int \varphi \, d\alpha = \int \varphi h \, d\beta$$

where $h$ is a locally $d\beta$-integrable function called the Radon-Nikodym derivative of $d\alpha$ with respect to $d\beta$. The first two sections of this chapter are devoted to a proof of the Radon-Nikodym theorem, which yields an explicit formula for the Radon-Nikodym derivative $h$ in terms of $\alpha$ and $\beta$.

In the third section we present another proof of the Radon-Nikodym theorem which is valid also for abstract integrals, but which does not yield an explicit formula for the Radon-Nikodym derivative. Moreover, this proof is less elementary in that it uses the results of Chapter 5 on $L^2$-spaces. Section 9.4 discusses some applications, mainly the characterization of continuous linear functionals on $L^p$-spaces.

## 9.1 ABSOLUTE CONTINUITY

We will now adopt the widely used convention that the functional that assigns the number $\int f \, d\mu$ to the function $f$ is called "the measure $d\mu$." Until further mention these "measures" will be positive continuous linear functionals on $\mathscr{C}$, so that they are in fact Stieltjes integrals with respect to monotone nondecreasing functions.

We begin our study of the relation of two measures to each other by considering the case where one of them is the Lebesgue measure $dx$ on $R$ and the other is a measure $d\alpha$ arising from a function $\alpha \in V_{\text{loc}}^{+}$. This case has been almost completely settled in Chapter 7, as can be seen from the proof of the following special case of the Radon-Nikodym theorem.

**9.1.1 THEOREM** *If $\alpha$ is a monotone nondecreasing, absolutely continuous function, then*

$$\int \varphi \, d\alpha = \int \varphi \alpha' \, dx$$

*for each step function $\varphi$ in $L$.*

*Proof* It suffices to verify the statement for the case when $\varphi$ is the characteristic function of a closed bounded interval $[a, b]$. Then we have to prove

$$\alpha(b) - \alpha(a) = \int_a^b \alpha' \, dx$$

This, however, is nothing but Theorem 7.3.7.

We could, in fact, easily prove that $f\alpha'$ is $dx$-integrable for each $d\alpha$-integrable function $f$ and that $\int f \, d\alpha = \int f\alpha' \, dx$; however, we will obtain this as a special case of the main result of this chapter. For the moment, we need to derive an equivalent definition of absolute continuity, which we shall subsequently generalize.

**9.1.2 PROPOSITION** *The function $\alpha \in V_{\text{loc}}^+$ is absolutely continuous if and only if every dx-null set is also $d\alpha$-null.*

*Proof* The idea of the proof of Proposition 9.1.2 is to use the characterization of absolute continuity given in Theorem 7.4.2. In both cases of the proposition the function $\alpha$ is continuous to begin with, in the "if" case because each single point is a $d\alpha$-null set (Exercise 8.2.3). Hence we want to show that $\alpha$ maps $dx$-null sets into $dx$-null sets if and only if every $dx$-null set is also $d\alpha$-null. This is an immediate consequence of the following lemma, whose proof therefore implies Proposition 9.1.2.

**9.1.3 LEMMA** *Let $\alpha$ be a continuous function in $V_{\text{loc}}^+$. Then $E$ is a $d\alpha$-null set if and only if the set $\alpha(E)$ is dx-null.*

*Proof* Let $\overline{E}$ be the "saturation" of $E$ defined by

$$\overline{E} = \{y : \alpha(y) = \alpha(x) \text{ for some } x \in E\},$$

the set $\overline{E}$ is larger than $E$ by parts of the intervals of constancy $\{I_k\}$ of $\alpha$, that is,

$$E \subset \overline{E} \subset E \cup \bigcup_{k \geq 1} I_k.$$

As $\alpha$ is continuous, $\bigcup_{k\geq 1} I_k$ is a $d\alpha$-null set, so that $E$ is $d\alpha$-null if and only if $\overline{E}$ is. Now if $\chi$ is the characteristic function of $\bar{E}$, then $\chi \circ \alpha_1$ is that of $\alpha(E)$, so that Lemma 9.1.3 follows from Proposition 8.1.9.

Hence we can generalize the concept of absolute continuity as follows.

**9.1.4 DEFINITION** *If $\alpha$ and $\beta$ are functions in $V_{\text{loc}}^+$ and every $d\beta$-null set is also $d\alpha$-null, then $d\alpha$ is said to be absolutely continuous with respect to $d\beta$.*

*Remark* This is sometimes denoted $d\alpha \ll d\beta$, which emphasizes the transitivity: $d\alpha \ll d\gamma$ if $d\alpha \ll d\beta$ and $d\beta \ll d\gamma$, and also the fact that $d\alpha \ll d\beta$ if $d\alpha \leq d\beta$ in the sense of Definition 8.4.6.

Absolute continuity and mutual singularity, defined by Definition 8.4.14, are antithetical concepts, as shown in the following proposition.

**9.1.5 PROPOSITION** *If $d\alpha$ and $d\beta$ are mutually singular and $d\alpha$ is absolutely continuous with respect to $d\beta$, then $d\alpha = 0$.*

*Proof* Let $f$ be an arbitrary function in $\mathscr{C}^+$. Since $d\alpha \wedge d\beta = 0$ or, equivalently, $(-d\alpha) \vee (-d\beta) = 0$ we can, by Definition 8.4.1, find functions

$u_n, v_n \in \mathscr{C}^+$ such that $u_n + v_n = f$ and

$$0 \geq -\int v_n \, d\alpha - \int u_n \, d\beta \geq -2^{-n}.$$

Then $\sum u_n$ diverges on a $d\beta$-null set $E$ and $\sum v_n$ diverges on a $d\alpha$-null set $F$. By hypothesis, $E$ is also $d\alpha$-null and hence so is $E \cup F$. But $E \cup F$ covers the whole set $\{x : f(x) \neq 0\}$, hence $f$ is $d\alpha$-equivalent to the zero function and $\int f \, d\alpha = 0$. Proposition 8.3.8 then shows that $d\alpha = 0$.

It is possible to extract more information from the above proof by using the fact that the real line is a denumerable union of bounded intervals.

9.1.6 PROPOSITION *Two measures $d\alpha$ and $d\beta$ are mutually singular if and only if there exists a $d\alpha$-null set whose complement is $d\beta$-null.*

*Proof* Let $f_m \in \mathscr{C}^+$ be a function that does not vanish anywhere on the interval $(-m, m)$, for instance the function defined by

$$f_m(x) = (m - |x|)^+.$$

Construct corresponding sets $E_m$ and $F_m$ according to the proof of Proposition 9.1.5. Then $E = \bigcup_{m=1}^{\infty} E_m$ is a $d\beta$-null set, $F = \bigcup_{m=1}^{\infty} F_m$ is $d\alpha$-null and $E \cup F$ is the whole real line. Hence the complement of $F$ is $d\beta$-null.

Conversely, for a fixed arbitrary $\varepsilon > 0$, choose $f, g \in \mathscr{C}_{ab}$, $0 \leq f, g \leq \chi_{(a,b)}$ such that

$$\|d\alpha\|_{ab} - \varepsilon \leq \int f \, d\alpha, \qquad \|d\beta\|_{ab} - \varepsilon \leq \int g \, d\beta$$

and let $\chi$ be the characteristic function of a $d\alpha$-null set whose complement is $d\beta$-null. Then

$$\|d\alpha\|_{ab} + \|d\beta\|_{ab} - 2\varepsilon \leq \int (f(1 - \chi) - g\chi)(d\alpha - d\beta) \leq \|d\alpha - d\beta\|_{ab}$$

because $|f(1 - \chi) - g\chi| \leq \chi_{[a,b]}$. Since $\varepsilon$ was arbitrary, it follows that $\|d\alpha - d\beta\|_{ab} = \|d\alpha\|_{ab} + \|d\beta\|_{ab}$, thus $d\alpha$ and $d\beta$ are mutually singular, by Lemma 8.4.15.

The next definition contains a simple example of mutually singular measures.

9.1.7 DEFINITION *A measure $d\alpha_0$ is called diffuse if every point—and hence every denumerable set—is $d\alpha_0$-null. A measure $d\alpha_a$ is called atomic if there exists a denumerable set whose complement is $d\alpha_a$-null.*

9.1.8 COROLLARY *A diffuse and an atomic measure are always mutually singular.*

In Corollary 6.2.8 we have seen that every monotone nondecreasing function $\alpha$ can be decomposed into the sum

$$\alpha = \alpha_0 + \alpha_a$$

of a continuous monotone nondecreasing function $\alpha_0$ and the jump part of $\alpha$. Then $d\alpha_0$ is diffuse, and $d\alpha_a$ is atomic. In fact, if $\{x_n\}$ is an enumeration of the points of discontinuity of $\alpha$, then

$$\int \varphi \, d\alpha_a = \sum_{n \geq 1} \varphi(x_n)(\alpha(x_n + 0) - \alpha(x_n - 0))$$

for every step function $\varphi$.

**9.1.9 PROPOSITION** *If $\alpha$ is a monotone nondecreasing function and $\alpha = \alpha_0 + \alpha_a$ is its decomposition into a continuous part $\alpha_0$ and a jump part $\alpha_a$, then $d\alpha = d\alpha_0 + d\alpha_a$ where $d\alpha_0$ is diffuse and $d\alpha_a$ is atomic.*

Whenever we use the notation $d\alpha = d\alpha_0 + d\alpha_a$, we shall mean this decomposition into a diffuse and an atomic measure. The decomposition is unique, since

$$d\alpha_a = \chi \, d\alpha, \qquad d\alpha_0 = (1 - \chi) \, d\alpha$$

where $\chi$ is the characteristic function of the denumerable set of points with nonzero $d\alpha$-measure. Moreover, it behaves in a very satisfactory way in relation to absolute continuity.

**9.1.10 PROPOSITION** *If $d\alpha = d\alpha_0 + d\alpha_a$ is absolutely continuous with respect to $d\beta = d\beta_0 + d\beta_a$, then $d\alpha_0$ is absolutely continuous with respect to $d\beta_0$ and $d\alpha_a$ is absolutely continuous with respect to $d\beta_a$.*

*Proof* Let $E$ denote the set of all discontinuities of $\beta$, that is, the smallest set whose complement is $d\beta_a$-null. If the set $F$ is $d\beta_0$-null, then $F - E$ is a $d\beta$-null set; hence it is $d\alpha$-null, hence $d\alpha_0$-null. But then $F$ is $d\alpha_0$-null since $E$ is denumerable, so that $d\alpha_0$ is indeed absolutely continuous with respect to $d\beta_0$. For the atomic measures, it is important to observe that a set is a null set for such a measure if and only if all its points are null sets. Hence it suffices to show that each $d\beta_a$-null point is also $d\alpha_a$-null. But if a point is $d\beta_a$-null, then it is also $d\beta$-null; hence $d\alpha_a$-null, as desired.

Our aim is to prove Theorem 9.1.1 with a suitable function $\alpha'$ when $dx$ is replaced by a measure $d\beta$ and where we assume that $d\alpha$ is absolutely continuous with respect to $d\beta$. This is known as the Radon-Nikodym theorem. Because of the last proposition, the following case of the Radon-Nikodym theorem, though simple, nevertheless reduces the general case to that of considering diffuse measures.

**9.1.11 PROPOSITION**

**RADON-NIKODYM THEOREM FOR ATOMIC MEASURES** *Let $d\alpha$ and $d\beta$ be atomic measures and suppose $d\alpha$ is absolutely continuous with respect to $d\beta$. Then* *the function h defined by*

$$h(x) = \begin{cases} \dfrac{\alpha(x+0) - \alpha(x-0)}{\beta(x+0) - \beta(x-0)} & \text{if } \beta \text{ is discontinuous at } x \\ 0 & \text{if } \beta \text{ is continuous at } x \end{cases}$$

*is locally $d\beta$-integrable, and if $f$ is any $d\alpha$-integrable function, then $fh$ is $d\beta$-integrable and satisfies the relation*

$$\int f\, d\alpha = \int fh\, d\beta.$$

*If $h_0$ is any other locally $d\beta$-integrable function satisfying the above relation, then the function $h - h_0$ is $d\beta$-null.*

*Proof* Let $\{x_k\}$ be a sequence enumerating all discontinuities of $\beta$, that is, $\beta$ is continuous at $x$ if and only if $x \neq x_k$ for all natural numbers $k$. Then the set

$$E = \{x : x \neq x_k \text{ for all } k\}$$

is $d\beta$-null, hence $d\alpha$-null. Thus a $d\alpha$-integrable function $f$ can have arbitrary values on $E$, but on the points $x_k$ its values must be such that the series

$$\sum_{k=1}^{\infty} f(x_k)(\alpha(x_k + 0) - \alpha(x_k - 0))$$

converges absolutely, in which case its sum defines $\int f\, d\alpha$ (see Example 2.5.5). Then the same series defines $\int fh\, d\beta$, so that $fh$ is indeed $d\beta$-integrable and $\int f\, d\alpha = \int fh\, d\beta$. If $\chi$ is the characteristic function of a bounded interval, then $\chi$ is $d\alpha$-integrable. Hence $\chi h$ is $d\beta$-integrable, that is $h$ is locally $d\beta$-integrable. Finally, if $h_0$ is another locally $d\beta$-integrable function such that $fh_0$ is $d\beta$-integrable for any $d\alpha$-integrable function $f$, and

$$\int f\, d\alpha = \int fh_0\, d\beta,$$

then take $f$ to be the characteristic function of the point $x_k$. It follows that $h_0(x_k) = h(x_k)$, or that $h - h_0$ vanishes off $E$; hence the function $h - h_0$ is $d\beta$-null, as claimed.

*Remark* The function $h$ is sometimes called the Radon-Nikodym derivative of $\alpha$ with respect to $\beta$ and denoted by

$$h = \frac{d\alpha}{d\beta}.$$

The difficulty in establishing the Radon-Nikodym theorem for diffuse measures lies in pinpointing the Radon-Nikodym derivative $h$, as we have been able to do in the present elementary case. However, the spadework for this has been done in Chapters 6 and 7, culminating in Theorem 7.3.7. We shall proceed from that standpoint in the next section.

## *EXERCISES*

*9.1.1* Show that if $f$ is $d\alpha$-integrable, where $\alpha$ is an absolutely continuous function in $V_{\text{loc}}^+$, then $f\alpha'$ is $dx$-integrable.

*Hint* Use Lemma 2.1.9.

*9.1.2* For any $\alpha \in V_{\text{loc}}^+$, show that the set

$$E = \{x : \alpha'(x) = 0\}$$

is a $d\alpha$-null set.

*Hint* Use Lemma 6.4.8, with $f = \alpha$. Show that if $\chi_n$ is the characteristic function of $H_{\exp(-n)}$, then $\sum \chi_n$ is a series of $d\alpha$-integrable functions that diverges $d\alpha$ a.e. on $E \cap (a, b)$ but satisfies

$$\sum_{n=1}^{\infty} \int \chi_n \, d\alpha < \infty.$$

*9.1.3* If $\alpha \in V_{\text{loc}}^+$ satisfies $\alpha(x - 0) < \alpha(x) < \alpha(x + 0)$ at all points of discontinuity, show that $E$ is a $d\alpha$-null set if and only if $\alpha(E)$ is $dx$-null.

*9.1.4* Let $\alpha$ be a monotone nondecreasing jump function (Definition 6.2.7). Show that $d\alpha$ is an atomic measure.

*9.1.5* With $\alpha \geq 0$ as above, show that $d(\alpha^2)$ is absolutely continuous with respect to $d\alpha$ and compute $d(\alpha^2)/d\alpha$.

## 9.2 THE RADON-NIKODYM THEOREM

In Definition 8.1.2 we introduced an inverse $\alpha_1$ to a monotone nondecreasing function $\alpha$ as a function on the interval $J_\alpha$ satisfying

$$a_x = \sup\{y : \alpha(y) < x\} \leq \alpha_1(x) \leq \inf\{y : \alpha(y) > x\} = b_x$$

for $x \in J_\alpha$, where $a_x = -\infty$ if $x$ equals the left end point of $J_\alpha$ and $b_x = \infty$ if $x$ equals the right end point of $J_\alpha$.

Suppose now $\alpha$ is continuous. Then $\alpha$ assumes all values in $J_\alpha$, since it does not have any jumps. We have in this case

$$\alpha(a_x) = x = \alpha(b_x),$$

and thus the above condition on $\alpha_1$ can also be written

$$\alpha(\alpha_1(x)) = x, \qquad x \in J_\alpha,$$

provided $\alpha$ is continuous.

**9.2.1 LEMMA** *Suppose $\alpha$ and $\beta$ are continuous monotone nondecreasing functions and $d\alpha$ is absolutely continuous with respect to $d\beta$. Then*

(a) *$\alpha$ is constant on every interval of constancy of $\beta$;*
(b) *$\alpha \circ \beta_1 \circ \beta \circ \alpha_1(x) = x$ for $x \in J_\alpha$*
(c) *$\alpha \circ \beta_1$ is continuous on $J_\beta$.*

*Proof* Since $\beta$ is continuous, an interval of constancy of $\beta$ is a $d\beta$-null set, and hence a $d\alpha$-null set; therefore $\alpha$ cannot increase on it. This proves Statement (a).

To establish (b), let $z = \alpha_1(x)$. We have

$$\beta(\beta_1(\beta(z))) = \beta(z)$$

because $\beta$ is continuous. Thus either $z = \beta_1(\beta(z))$ or $z$ and $\beta_1(\beta(z))$ belong to the same interval of constancy of $\beta$. In any event we may conclude according to (a) that

$$\alpha \circ \beta_1 \circ \beta \circ \alpha_1(x) = \alpha(\beta_1(\beta(z))) = \alpha(z) = \alpha(\alpha_1(x)) = x.$$

In (c) we prove first that $\alpha \circ \beta_1$ is right continuous at every point $x \in J_\beta$ different from the right end point of $J_\beta$. Since $\beta$ is continuous,

$$\begin{aligned}\beta(\beta_1(x+0)) &= \beta(\lim_{y\to x, y>x} \beta_1(y)) = \lim_{y\to x, y>x} \beta(\beta_1(y)) \\ &= \lim_{y\to x, y>x} y = x = \beta(\beta_1(x)).\end{aligned}$$

Thus $\beta_1(x)$ and $\beta_1(x+0)$ are either equal, or belong, to the same interval of constancy of $\beta$. Statement (a) therefore implies that

$$\alpha(\beta_1(x)) = \alpha(\beta_1(x+0)).$$

Using the continuity of $\alpha$, we now obtain

$$\alpha(\beta_1(x)) = \alpha(\beta_1(x+0)) = \lim_{y\to x, y>x} \alpha(\beta_1(y)) = \alpha \circ \beta_1(x+0)$$

which proves that $\alpha \circ \beta_1$ is right continuous at $x$. Similarly we can show that $\alpha \circ \beta_1$ is left continuous at every point of $J_\beta$ different from the left end point. This completes the proof of the lemma.

With these preliminaries settled we are ready for the Radon-Nikodym theorem.

**9.2.2 THEOREM**

**RADON-NIKODYM THEOREM** *If the measure $d\alpha$ is absolutely continuous with respect to the measure $d\beta$, then a locally $d\beta$-integrable function $h \geq 0$ exists such that*

$$\int \varphi \, d\alpha = \int \varphi h \, d\beta$$

*for all step functions $\varphi$. Conversely, if some locally $d\beta$-integrable function g satisfies $\int \varphi \, d\alpha = \int \varphi g \, d\beta$ for every step function $\varphi$, then the function $h - g$ is $d\beta$-null.*

*Proof* Suppose first that $d\alpha$ and $d\beta$ are diffuse. Then $\alpha$ and $\beta$ are both continuous and we can make use of Lemma 9.2.1. The function $\alpha \circ \beta_1$ is continuous on $J_\beta$. It is, moreover, absolutely continuous on each bounded closed subinterval $[a, b]$ of $J_\beta$, which means that the function $(\alpha \circ \beta_1)_{ab}$ defined by

$$(\alpha \circ \beta_1)_{ab}(x) = \begin{cases} \alpha(\beta_1(a)) & \text{if } x \leq a \\ \alpha(\beta_1(x)) & \text{if } a \leq x \leq b \\ \alpha(\beta_1(b)) & \text{if } b \leq x \end{cases}$$

is absolutely continuous. To see this, we apply Theorem 7.4.2. We want to show that the function $(\alpha \circ \beta_1)_{ab}$ maps an arbitrary ($dx$-) null set $E$ into a null set. Obviously, we may suppose that $E$ is contained in $[a, b]$, since what may be outside is mapped into the two point set $\{\alpha(\beta_1(a)), \alpha(\beta_1(b))\}$. Then $\beta(\beta_1(E)) = E$, so that by Lemma 9.1.3, $\beta_1(E)$ is $d\beta$-null, hence by hypothesis, $d\alpha$-null. Again by Lemma 9.1.3 it follows that the set $\alpha(\beta_1(E))$ is $dx$-null. Thus $\alpha \circ \beta_1$ is absolutely continuous on each closed bounded subinterval of $J_\beta$, as claimed, and if $a, b \in J_\beta$, $a \leq b$, then an application of Theorem 7.3.7 for $f = (\alpha \circ \beta_1)_{ab}$ shows that

$$\alpha \circ \beta_1(b) - \alpha \circ \beta_1(a) = \int_a^b (\alpha \circ \beta_1)'_{ab}\, dx = \int_a^b (\alpha \circ \beta_1)'\, dx.$$

Hence, if $\psi$ is the characteristic function of a bounded interval whose end points $a$ and $b$ belong to $J_\beta$, then

$$\int_{J_\beta} \psi\, d(\alpha \circ \beta_1)_{ab} = \int_{J_\beta} \psi(\alpha \circ \beta_1)'\, dx. \tag{9.2.3}$$

Now let $\chi$ be the characteristic function of a closed bounded interval $[a', b']$. Statement (b) of Lemma 9.2.1 shows that $\beta_1 \circ \beta \circ \alpha_1$ is an inverse for $\alpha$ whence, by Definition 8.1.5,

$$\int \chi\, d\alpha = \int_{J_\alpha} \chi \circ \beta_1 \circ \beta \circ \alpha_1\, dx.$$

Then $\chi \circ \beta_1$ is the characteristic function of an interval with end points $a, b$ contained in $[\beta(a' - 0), \beta(b' + 0)] \subset J_\beta$. The restriction of $\beta \circ \alpha_1$ to $[\alpha(\beta_1(a)), \alpha(\beta_1(b)]$ is an inverse to $(\alpha \circ \beta_1)_{ab}$ by (b) of Lemma 9.2.1; therefore

$$\int_{J_\alpha} \chi \circ \beta_1 \circ \beta \circ \alpha_1\, dx = \int_{J_\beta} \chi \circ \beta_1\, d(\alpha \circ \beta_1)_{ab}.$$

Applying (9.2.3), we conclude

$$\begin{aligned} \int \chi\, d\alpha &= \int_{J_\beta} \chi \circ \beta_1\, d(\alpha \circ \beta_1)_{ab} \\ &= \int_{J_\beta} \chi \circ \beta_1 (\alpha \circ \beta_1)'\, dx \\ &= \int_{J_\alpha} \chi \circ \beta_1 \cdot [(\alpha \circ \beta_1)' \circ \beta \circ \beta_1]\, dx \\ &= \int \chi[(\alpha \circ \beta_1)' \circ \beta]\, d\beta. \end{aligned}$$

The last step follows from Proposition 8.1.9. The function

$$h = (\alpha \circ \beta_1)' \circ \beta \tag{9.2.4}$$

is thus $d\beta$-integrable on every bounded interval and

$$\int \varphi \, d\alpha = \int \varphi h \, d\beta$$

for every step function $\varphi$.

We proceed now to consider general measures $d\alpha$ and $d\beta$, $d\alpha$ absolutely continuous with respect to $d\beta$. If $d\alpha = d\alpha_0 + d\alpha_a$ and $d\beta = d\beta_0 + d\beta_a$ are their respective decompositions into diffuse and atomic parts, then by Proposition 9.1.10, $d\alpha_0 \ll d\beta_0$ and $d\alpha_a \ll d\beta_a$. By the above, there exists a locally $d\beta_0$-integrable function $h_0$ such that

$$\int \varphi \, d\alpha_0 = \int \varphi h_0 \, d\beta_0$$

and by Proposition 9.1.11 a function $h_a$ vanishing off the denumerable set $E$ of discontinuities of $\beta$, which is also locally $d\beta_a$-integrable, such that

$$\int \varphi \, d\alpha_a = \int \varphi h_a \, d\beta_a$$

for all step functions $\varphi$. We may assume that $h_0$ vanishes on $E$, which is denumerable, and hence a null set for the diffuse measure $d\beta_0$. Thus

$$\int \varphi h_0 \, d\beta_a = 0, \qquad \int \varphi h_a \, d\beta_0 = 0$$

for all step functions $\varphi$. Consequently, $h = h_0 + h_a$ is locally $d\beta$-integrable and

$$\begin{aligned} \int \varphi \, d\alpha &= \int \varphi \, d\alpha_0 + \int \varphi \, d\alpha_a \\ &= \int \varphi(h_0 + h_a) \, d\beta_0 + \int \varphi(h_0 + h_a) \, d\beta_a = \int \varphi h \, d\beta \end{aligned}$$

for all step functions $\varphi$.

Suppose now that $h - g$ is a locally $d\beta$-integrable function such that

$$\int \varphi(h - g) \, d\beta = \int \varphi h \, d\beta - \int \varphi g \, d\beta = 0$$

for all step functions $\varphi$. Let $\chi$ be the characteristic function of some bounded interval $I$ and $\{\varphi_n\}$ a sequence of step functions satisfying $|\varphi_n| \le \chi$ and

$$\lim_{n \to \infty} \varphi_n = \text{mid}\,(-\chi, h - g, \chi) \qquad d\beta \text{ a.e.}$$

Then Lebesgue's dominated convergence theorem shows that

$$\int_I |h - g| \wedge (h - g)^2 \, d\beta = \lim_{n \to \infty} \int \varphi_n(h - g) \, d\beta = 0.$$

Thus $h - g$ is a $d\beta$-null function (see Corollary 2.2.6). This completes the proof of Theorem 9.2.2.

**9.2.5 DEFINITION** *The function $h$ in Theorem 9.2.2 is called the Radon-Nikodym derivative of the measure $d\alpha$ with respect to the measure $d\beta$ and is denoted*

$$h = \frac{d\alpha}{d\beta}.$$

Actually, one should say $h$ is a Radon-Nikodym derivative of $d\alpha$ with respect to $d\beta$. However, the last theorem tells us also that any two Radon-Nikodym derivatives are essentially equal; they can differ only on a $d\beta$-null set.

If $h$ is any nonnegative locally $d\beta$-integrable function, then the rule that assigns the number $\int \varphi h \, d\beta$ to a step function $\varphi$ is an integral on $L$. The corresponding measure is also referred to as the "measure $h\, d\beta$." The theorem that we have just proved says that a measure $d\alpha$ is absolutely continuous with respect to a measure $d\beta$ only if it can be written $h\, d\beta$ for some locally $d\beta$-integrable function $h$. The converse of this is also true.

**9.2.6 THEOREM** *A measure $d\alpha$ is absolutely continuous with respect to a measure $d\beta$ if and only if it can be written*

$$\alpha = h\, d\beta$$

*for some locally $d\beta$-integrable function $h \geq 0$.*

*Proof* We have to show that $h\, d\beta$ is absolutely continuous with respect to $d\beta$, that is, that any $d\beta$-null set $E$ is also $h\, d\beta$-null. Because the real line is a denumerable union of bounded intervals, it suffices to consider the case when $E$ is contained in such an interval, which we denote by $I$. Furthermore, it is clear that we are through if we succeed to show that $E$ is $g\, d\beta$-null for some $d\beta$-integrable function $g$ that is larger than $\chi_I h\, d\beta$ almost everywhere, since if $\sum \varphi_n$ diverges on $E \subset I$ and satisfies

$$\sum_{n=1}^{\infty} \int_I |\varphi_n| \, g \, d\beta < \infty$$

then surely

$$\sum_{n=1}^{\infty} \int \chi_I \, |\varphi_n| \, h \, d\beta < \infty.$$

Let $\sum \psi_n$ be a series of step functions such that

$$\chi_I h = \sum_{n=1}^{\infty} \psi_n \qquad d\beta \text{ a.e.}, \qquad \sum_{n=1}^{\infty} \int |\psi_n| \, d\beta < \infty.$$

Then define $g$ by

$$g(x) = \begin{cases} \chi_I(x) + \displaystyle\sum_{n=1}^{\infty} |\psi_n(x)| & \text{if } \displaystyle\sum_{n=1}^{\infty} |\psi(x)| < \infty \\ \chi_I(x) & \text{otherwise.} \end{cases}$$

Obviously, $g$ is $d\beta$-integrable and $g \geq \chi_I h \, d\beta$ a.e. Now suppose that $\sum \varphi_n$ is a series of nonnegative step functions such that $\{\sum \varphi_n(x)\}$ diverges for $x \in E$, while $\{\sum \int \varphi_n \, d\beta\}$ converges. Let

$$\omega_n = \chi_I + \sum_{k=1}^{n} |\varphi_k|.$$

Since $\{(\varphi_n/\omega_m)g\}$ decreases to $\varphi_n$ on $I$ as $m$ tends to infinity, we can find an $m(n)$ by the monotone convergence theorem such that

$$\int_I \left(\frac{\varphi_n}{\omega_{m(n)}}\right) g \, d\beta < \int \varphi_n \, d\beta + 2^{-n}$$

thus assuring that $\sum \int_I (\varphi_n/\omega_{m(n)}) g \, d\beta$ converges. The series $\sum \varphi_n/\omega_{m(n)}$ diverges on $E$ except possibly at those points belonging to the set $F$ where $\{\omega_n\}$ diverges. Thus $E - F$ is a $g \, d\beta$-null set. It remains therefore to be shown that $F$ is $g \, d\beta$-null.

The increasing sequence $\{\omega_n\}$ of step functions converges to $g$ off $F$ and diverges to infinity on $F$. Since $g$ is $d\beta$-integrable, we may choose an increasing sequence $y_1 < y_2 < \cdots$ of positive numbers, such that

$$\int_{\{x \, : \, g(x) \geq y_n\}} g \, d\beta \leq 2^{-n}.$$

Define the function $f$ by

$$f(y) = \begin{cases} n & \text{if } y_n \leq y < y_{n+1} \quad \text{for } n \geq 1 \\ 0 & \text{if } y < y_1. \end{cases}$$

Then

$$\int (f \circ g) g \, d\beta = \sum_{n=1}^{\infty} \int_{\{x \, : \, y_n \leq g(x) < y_{n+1}\}} (f \circ g) g \, d\beta \leq \sum_{n=1}^{\infty} n 2^{-n} = 2$$

so that, because of the monotonicity of $f$,

$$\int (f \circ \omega_n) g \, d\beta \leq \int (f \circ g) g \, d\beta \leq 2$$

for all $n$. But the increasing sequence $\{f \circ \omega_n\}$ diverges on $F$ so that this set is indeed $g \, d\beta$-null.

We conclude this section with a proof of the Radon-Nikodym theorem for integrable functions.

**9.2.7 THEOREM** *Suppose $h$ is a nonnegative locally $d\beta$-integrable function. Let $d\alpha = h \, d\beta$. A function $f$ is $d\alpha$-integrable if and only if $fh$ is $d\beta$ integrable and then*

$$\int f \, d\alpha = \int fh \, d\beta.$$

*Proof* First suppose that $f$ is $d\alpha$-integrable. By Mikusiński's lemma there is a series $\sum \varphi_n$ of step functions satisfying

$$\sum_{n=1}^{\infty} \int |\varphi_n| \, d\alpha < \infty \qquad \text{and} \qquad f(x) = \sum_{n=1}^{\infty} \varphi_n(x)$$

for all $x$ for which the last series converges absolutely. Then

$$\sum_{n=1}^{\infty} \int |\varphi_n h| \, d\beta = \sum_{n=1}^{\infty} \int |\varphi_n| \, d\alpha < \infty,$$

$$f(x)h(x) = \sum_{n=1}^{\infty} \varphi_n(x)h(x)$$

for all $x$ for which this last series converges absolutely. Hence $fh$ is $d\beta$-integrable and

$$\int fh \, d\beta = \sum_{n=1}^{\infty} \int \varphi_n h \, d\beta = \sum_{n=1}^{\infty} \int \varphi_n \, d\alpha = \int f \, d\alpha.$$

To prove the converse we observe first that every $d\beta$-measurable function, and hence in particular $h$, is also $d\alpha$-measurable. For let $f$ be a $d\beta$-measurable function and $\varphi$ a nonnegative step function. Choose a sequence $\{\varphi_n\}$ of step functions tending $d\beta$ a.e. to the $d\beta$-integrable function mid $(-\varphi, f, \varphi)$. We may as well assume that $|\varphi_n| \leq \varphi$ for all $n$, replacing the sequence $\{\varphi_n\}$ by $\{\text{mid}\,(-\varphi, \varphi_n, \varphi)\}$ if necessary. Since, by Theorem 9.2.6, every $d\beta$-null set is also $d\alpha$-null, $\{\varphi_n\}$ tends also $d\alpha$ a.e. to mid $(-\varphi, f, \varphi)$ which therefore is $d\alpha$-integrable according to Lebesgue's dominated convergence theorem. This proves that $f$ is $d\alpha$-measurable.

Suppose now that $fh$ is $d\beta$-integrable. By Mikusiński's lemma we can find a series $\sum \varphi_n$ of step functions satisfying

$$\sum_{n=1}^{\infty} \int |\varphi_n| \, d\beta < \infty \qquad \text{and} \qquad f(x)h(x) = \sum_{n=1}^{\infty} \varphi_n(x)$$

for all $x$ for which the last series converges absolutely. For a fixed $\varepsilon > 0$, the functions $\varphi_n h(h^2 + \varepsilon)^{-1}$ are $d\alpha$-integrable since they are $d\alpha$-measurable and

$$|\varphi_n| \, h(h^2 + \varepsilon)^{-1} \leq \frac{|\varphi_n|}{2\sqrt{\varepsilon}}.$$

The latter inequality holds because the function $\lambda(\lambda^2 + \varepsilon)^{-1}$ attains its maximum $\frac{1}{2}\sqrt{\varepsilon}$ at $\lambda = \sqrt{\varepsilon}$. Hence, by the first part of the proof,

$$\sum_{n=1}^{\infty} \int \frac{|\varphi_n| \, h}{h^2 + \varepsilon} \, d\alpha = \sum_{n=1}^{\infty} \int \frac{|\varphi_n| \, h^2}{h^2 + \varepsilon} \, d\beta \leq \sum_{n=1}^{\infty} \int |\varphi_n| \, d\beta < \infty,$$

$$\frac{fh^2}{h^2 + \varepsilon} = \sum_{n=1}^{\infty} \frac{\varphi_n h}{h^2 + \varepsilon} \qquad d\alpha \text{ a.e.}$$

so that the functions

$$f_k = fh^2\left(h^2 + \frac{1}{k}\right)^{-1}$$

are $d\alpha$-integrable for all integers $k \geq 1$. The monotone convergence theorem shows that the function $f_0$ defined by

$$f_0(x) = \begin{cases} f(x) & \text{if } h(x) > 0 \\ 0 & \text{if } h(x) = 0 \end{cases}$$

is $d\alpha$-integrable, for

$$f_0^+ = \lim_{k\to\infty} f_k^+, \qquad f_0^- = \lim_{k\to\infty} f_k^-$$

monotone and everywhere, and

$$\int f_k^+ \, d\alpha \leq \int \frac{|f|\, h^2}{h^2 + 1/k} \, d\alpha \leq \sum_{n=1}^{\infty} \int \frac{|\varphi_n|\, h}{h^2 + 1/k} \, d\alpha$$

$$= \sum_{n=1}^{\infty} \int \frac{|\varphi_n|\, h^2}{h^2 + 1/k} \, d\beta \leq \sum_{n=1}^{\infty} \int |\varphi_n| \, d\beta < \infty,$$

$$\int f_k^- \, d\alpha \leq \sum_{n=1}^{\infty} \int |\varphi_n| \, d\beta < \infty$$

for all $k$. But $f$ and $f_0$ differ only on the set $E$ where $h$ vanishes, which is a $d\alpha$-null set, namely, if $I$ is any bounded interval and $\chi$ is the characteristic function of $I \cap E$, then $\chi$ is $d\alpha$-integrable because $h$ is $d\alpha$-measurable, and by the first part of the proof

$$\int \chi \, d\alpha = \int \chi h \, d\beta = 0$$

Hence $f = f_0 \; d\alpha$ a.e. so that $f$ is $d\alpha$-integrable. This concludes the proof of Theorem 9.2.7.

## *EXERCISES*

*9.2.1* Suppose that $\alpha, \beta \in V_{\text{loc}}^+$ and $d\alpha$ is absolutely continuous with respect to $d\beta$. Let $\gamma$ be the continuous function on $J_\beta$ that coincides with $\alpha \circ \beta_1$ outside the intervals of constancy of $\beta_1$ and is linear on the intervals of constancy of $\beta_1$. Prove that $\gamma$ is absolutely continuous on each bounded closed interval in $J_\beta$ and that

$$\int \varphi \, d\alpha = \int \varphi h \, d\beta, \qquad \varphi \in L$$

where

$$h = \gamma' \circ \beta.$$

*9.2.2* Show that if $d\alpha \leq d\beta$, then $d\alpha$ is absolutely continuous with respect to $d\beta$ and $0 \leq d\alpha/d\beta \leq 1 \; d\beta$ a.e.

*9.2.3* Suppose $d\alpha \leq d\beta$ and let $h = d\alpha/d\beta$. Show that if $d\alpha$ is absolutely continuous with respect to $d\gamma = d\beta - d\alpha$, then the set $\{x : h(x) = 1\}$ is $d\beta$-null.

*Hint* Notice

$$\int \varphi \, d\alpha = \int \varphi\left(\frac{d\alpha}{d\gamma}\right) d\gamma$$
$$= \int \varphi\left(\frac{d\alpha}{d\gamma}\right) d\beta - \int \varphi\left(\frac{d\alpha}{d\gamma}\right) h \, d\beta$$

and conclude that

$$(1 - h)\frac{d\alpha}{d\gamma} = h \qquad d\beta \text{ a.e.}$$

*9.2.4* Suppose that $d\alpha_n$ and $d\beta$ are measures satisfying

$$\sum_{n=1}^{\infty} \int \varphi \, d\alpha_n = \int \varphi \, d\beta, \qquad \varphi \in L^+$$

where $L^+$ is the set of all nonnegative step functions. Show that there are locally $d\beta$-integrable functions $h_n$ such that $d\alpha_n = h_n \, d\beta$ and $\sum_{n=1}^{\infty} h_n = 1$ $d\beta$ a.e.

*9.2.5* Show that if $d\alpha \ll d\gamma$ and $d\beta \ll d\gamma$, then $d\alpha + d\beta \ll d\gamma$ and

$$\frac{d\alpha + d\beta}{d\gamma} = \frac{d\alpha}{d\gamma} + \frac{d\beta}{d\gamma}$$

## 9.3 THE ABSTRACT RADON-NIKODYM THEOREM

In this section we return again to the abstract setting with a set $S$ on which a space $L$ of real-valued elementary functions is given which satisfies Properties (1) and (5)(Section 2.5). But we will now consider several integrals $\int \varphi \, d\mu$, $\int \varphi \, d\nu$ defined on $L$, each subject to Conditions (2), (3), and (4). Moreover, we will restrict the generality of the setting by another condition on $L$:

(6) There is a sequence $\{\eta_n\}$ of nonnegative functions in $L$ such that

$$S = \bigcup_{n=1}^{\infty} \{x : \eta_n(x) > 0\}.$$

The sets $\{x : \eta_n(x) \geq 1/m\}$ are $d\mu$-integrable for any integral $\int \varphi \, d\mu$ on $L$, and $S$ is thus the union of a denumerable number of $d\mu$-integrable sets. *An integral with this property is called σ-finite.* Condition (6) therefore implies that every integral on $L$ is $\sigma$-finite. Conversely, one can show that if merely one integral on $L$ is known to be $\sigma$-finite, then Condition (6) holds. We leave the verification of this assertion to the reader (Exercise 9.3.1).

In order to establish an abstract Radon-Nikodym theorem, an additional condition like (6) is needed. There are, however, alternate conditions less restrictive than (6) but more complicated to state, that will also ensure the validity of the

Radon-Nikodym theorem. We have chosen (6), because in most situations one can reduce the problem easily to a setup in which it holds.

We define absolute continuity formally as in Definition 9.1.4; suppose $\int \varphi \, d\mu$ and $\int \varphi \, d\nu$ are integrals on $L$, then $d\mu$ is absolutely continuous with respect to $d\nu$ if every $d\nu$-null set is also $d\mu$-null. For the Radon-Nikodym theorem we also need to know what our locally $d\nu$-integrable functions shall be.

**9.3.1 DEFINITION** *Suppose $\int \varphi \, d\nu$ is an integral on $L$. A function $h$ on $S$ is called locally $d\nu$-integrable if $h\varphi$ is $d\nu$-integrable for each $\varphi \in L$.*

**9.3.2 LEMMA** *A locally $d\nu$-integrable function is $d\nu$-measurable.*

*Proof* Suppose $h$ is locally $d\nu$-integrable. Then $h(\eta_n \wedge 1)$ is $d\nu$-integrable where $\{\eta_n\}$ is the sequence of functions in Condition (6).

$$g = \sum_{n=1}^{\infty} 2^{-n}(\eta_n \wedge 1)$$

is a positive $d\nu$-measurable function. Hence

$$h = g^{-1} \sum_{n=1}^{\infty} 2^{-n} h(\eta_n \wedge 1)$$

is $d\nu$-measurable.

For a nonnegative locally $d\nu$-integrable function $h$,

$$\int \varphi \, d\mu = \int \varphi h \, d\nu, \qquad \varphi \in L$$

defines an integral on $L$. As in Theorem 9.2.6, $d\mu$ is absolutely continuous with respect to $d\nu$. To prove that every $d\nu$-null set $E$ is also $d\mu$-null we observe first that $E$ is $d\nu$-null if and only if there is a series $\sum \psi_n$ of bounded nonnegative functions in $L$ that diverges on $E$ and satisfies $\sum_{n=1}^{\infty} \int \psi_n \, d\nu < \infty$. In fact, let $\sum \varphi_n$ be any series of nonnegative functions in $L$ with these properties; then we can take $\psi_n = \varphi_n \wedge 1$. Thus, in order to prove that $E$ is also $d\mu$-null, we may assume that all the functions in $L$ are bounded. With this assumption the proof of Theorem 9.2.6 will work if we replace $I$ by $\{x : \eta_k(x) > 0\}$ and $\chi_I$ by $\eta_k \wedge 1$ where $\eta_k$ is any of the functions occurring in Condition (6).

The proof of Theorem 9.2.7 can also be taken over word for word; we have only to interpret the arbitrary bounded interval $I$ to be an arbitrary $d\mu$-integrable set. Since $S$ can be covered by a sequence of $d\mu$-integrable sets if Condition (6) holds, a set $E \subset S$ is $d\mu$-null if and only if $E \cap I$ is $d\mu$-null for any $d\mu$-integrable set $I$.

Thus Theorem 9.2.7 is also valid for our present setting; a function $g$ is $d\mu$-integrable if and only if $fh$ is $d\nu$-integrable and then

$$\int f \, d\mu = \int fh \, d\nu.$$

We will make repeated use of this property in the proof of the following abstract version of the Radon-Nikodym theorem.

### 9.3.3 THEOREM

RADON-NIKODYM THEOREM *Suppose $\int \varphi \, d\mu$ and $\int \varphi \, d\nu$ are two integrals on the linear space L of functions on S. If Condition* (6) *holds, then the following two statements are equivalent:*

(a) *there is a nonnegative locally dν-integrable function h such that*

$$\int \varphi \, d\mu = \int \varphi h \, d\nu \qquad \text{for } \varphi \in L,$$

(b) *dμ is absolutely continuous with respect to dν.*

*The function h in Statement (a) is unique up to the addition of a dν-null function.*

*Proof* We have already remarked above that (a) implies (b) as in Theorem 9.2.6.

To establish the converse, let us first assume that 1 is integrable for $d\mu$ and $d\nu$. We define a new integral on $L$ by

$$\int \varphi \, d\lambda = \int \varphi \, d\mu + \int \varphi \, d\nu.$$

Then

$$\int \varphi \, d\mu \leq \int \varphi \, d\lambda, \qquad \int \varphi \, d\nu \leq \int \varphi \, d\lambda$$

for nonnegative $\varphi \in L$, which implies immediately that every $d\lambda$-integrable function $f$ is also $d\mu$-integrable as well as $d\nu$-integrable and

$$\int f \, d\lambda = \int f \, d\mu + \int f \, d\nu.$$

Let $L^2$ be the space of $d\lambda$-measurable functions with a $d\lambda$-integrable square (Definition 5.1.1). Each function $f$ in $L^2$ is $d\lambda$-integrable because $1 \in L^2$, and therefore it is $d\mu$-integrable also. Thus

$$A(f) = \int f \, d\mu, \qquad f \in L^2$$

defines a continuous linear functional on $L^2$, because we have by the Schwarz inequality

$$|A(f)| \leq \int |f| \, d\mu \leq \int |f| \, d\lambda$$
$$\leq \|f\| \, \|1\|.$$

Therefore, by Theorem 5.3.6, there is a $g \in L^2$ such that

$$A(f) = \int f \, d\mu = \int fg \, d\lambda \qquad \text{for } f \in L^2.$$

If we choose $f$ to be the characteristic function of the set $E = \{x : g(x) < 0\}$, then

$$0 \leq \int f\, d\mu = \int_E g\, d\lambda \leq 0$$

whence $\int_E g\, d\lambda = 0$, that is, $E$ is a $d\lambda$-null set and thus $g \geq 0$ $d\lambda$ a.e. We may therefore assume $g \geq 0$ everywhere, altering $g$ on the $d\lambda$-null set $E$, if necessary. Now let us take $f$ to be the characteristic function of the set $F = \{x : g(x) \geq 1\}$, then

$$\int f\, d\mu = \int fg\, d\lambda = \int fg\, d\mu + \int fg\, d\nu,$$

$$0 \geq \int_F (1 - g)\, d\mu = \int_F g\, d\nu \geq 0.$$

Consequently,

$$\int_F (1 - g)\, d\mu = 0 = \int_F g\, d\nu.$$

From this we can conclude two things. The vanishing of the first of these two integrals proves that $g = 1$ $d\mu$ a.e. on $F$, whence $g \leq 1$ $d\mu$ a.e. The vanishing of the second integral shows that $F$ is a $d\nu$-null set and, in particular, $g < 1$ $d\nu$ a.e. Thus

$$\int_F (1 - g)\, d\lambda = \int_F (1 - g)\, d\mu + \int_F (1 - g)\, d\nu = 0$$

so that $g \leq 1$ $d\lambda$ a.e. We may thus as well assume that $g \leq 1$ everywhere.

The relation

$$\int f\, d\mu = \int fg\, d\lambda \tag{9.3.4}$$

can now be shown to hold also for $d\lambda$-integrable functions $f$. Namely, the bounded functions $f_n = \operatorname{mid}(-n, f, n)$ belong to $L^2$ by Proposition 5.1.2, whence

$$\int f_n\, d\mu = \int f_n g\, d\lambda.$$

$\{f_n\}$ tends to $f$ everywhere. Since $|f_n| \leq |f|$ and $|f_n g| \leq |f|$ $d\lambda$ a.e., we can apply Lebesgue's dominated convergence theorem to the last equation, thus obtaining (9.3.4). If $f$ is $d\lambda$-integrable, then so is $fg^n$ for all integers $n \geq 1$. Equation (9.3.4) applied repeatedly therefore yields

$$\begin{aligned}\int f\, d\mu &= \int fg\, d\lambda = \int fg\, d\nu + \int fg\, d\mu \\ &= \int fg\, d\nu + \int fg^2\, d\nu + \int fg^2\, d\mu \\ &= \int f \sum_{k=1}^{n} g^k\, d\nu + \int fg^n\, d\mu\end{aligned} \tag{9.3.5}$$

for all $d\lambda$-integrable functions $f$. The sequence $\{\sum_{k=1}^{n} g^k\}$ converges off the $d\nu$-null set $F = \{x : g(x) = 1\}$ to the nonnegative $d\nu$-measurable function $h$ defined by

$$h(x) = \begin{cases} \sum_{k=1}^{\infty} [g(x)]^k & \text{if } x \notin F \\ 0 & \text{if } x \in F, \end{cases}$$

and the decreasing sequence $\{g^n\}$ tends to the characteristic function of $F$. For a nonnegative $d\lambda$-integrable function $f$ we can apply the monotone convergence theorem to (9.3.5) and obtain

$$\int f\,d\mu = \int fh\,d\nu + \int_F f\,d\mu, \tag{9.3.6}$$

which, of course, holds then, by linearity, for all $d\lambda$-integrable functions. Until now we have not used the fact that $d\mu$ is absolutely continuous with respect to $d\nu$. If we do, we find that the $d\nu$-null set $F$ is also $d\mu$-null, and hence by the last equation

$$\int f\,d\mu = \int fh\,d\nu$$

for every $d\lambda$-integrable function $f$. In particular,

$$\int \varphi\,d\mu = \int \varphi h\,d\nu \qquad \text{for } \varphi \in L.$$

This proves our assertion in the event that 1 is integrable for $d\mu$ and $d\nu$.

Let us forget now about this restrictive condition. We assume only that $d\mu$ is absolutely continuous with respect to $d\nu$. Using the sequence $\{\eta_n\}$ of functions in Condition (6), we define an everywhere-positive function $p$ by

$$p = \sum_{n=1}^{\infty} 2^{-n}\left(1 + \int \eta_n\,d\lambda\right)^{-1}(\eta_n \wedge 1)$$

where $\int \varphi\,d\lambda$ is the integral

$$\int \varphi\,d\lambda = \int \varphi\,d\mu + \int \varphi\,d\nu, \qquad \varphi \in L.$$

We have $0 < p(x) \leq 1$ for all $x$. Also, $p$ is $d\lambda$-integrable, and hence integrable for both $d\mu$ and $d\nu$. Since $p \leq 1$, $p$ is locally integrable for $d\mu$, $d\nu$, and $d\lambda$. Now we introduce new integrals

$$\int \varphi\,d\mu' = \int \varphi p\,d\mu, \qquad \int \varphi\,d\nu' = \int \varphi p\,d\nu,$$

$$\int \varphi\,d\lambda' = \int \varphi p\,d\lambda = \int \varphi\,d\mu' + \int \varphi\,d\nu'.$$

The function 1 is integrable for each of these integrals. We know already that $d\mu'$ is absolutely continuous with respect to $d\mu$. Moreover, $d\nu$ is absolutely continuous with respect to $d\nu'$; namely, if $E$ is $d\nu'$-null set, then $p\chi_E$ is a $d\nu$-null function which implies that $E$ is $d\nu$-null because $p$ is everywhere positive. Thus $d\mu'$ is absolutely continuous with respect to $d\nu'$. As we have shown above, there is a nonnegative locally $d\nu'$-integrable function $h$ such that

$$\int fp\, d\mu = \int f\, d\mu' = \int fh\, d\nu' = \int fph\, d\nu$$

for all $d\lambda'$-integrable functions $f$. In particular, if $\varphi \in L$, then $\varphi/p$ is $d\lambda'$-integrable because $(\varphi/p)p = \varphi$ is $d\lambda$-integrable. Hence, taking $f = \varphi/p$ in the above equality,

$$\int \varphi\, d\mu = \int \varphi h\, d\nu \qquad \text{for } \varphi \in L.$$

This equation shows also that $h$ is locally $d\nu$-integrable.

It remains to be proved that the function $h$ in the last equation is unique up to the addition of a $d\nu$-null function. Suppose there is another locally $d\nu$-integrable function $h_0$ such that

$$\int \varphi\, d\mu = \int \varphi h_0\, d\nu \qquad \text{for } \varphi \in L.$$

Let $\chi$ be the characteristic function of the $d\nu$-measurable set $E = \{x : h(x) - h_0(x) > 0\}$. Then $\varphi\chi$ is $d\nu$-integrable for any nonnegative function $\varphi$ in $L$, and we can find a sequence $\{\varphi_n\}$ of nonnegative functions in $L$ tending to $\varphi\chi$ $d\nu$ a.e. We may also assume that $\varphi_n \leq \varphi$, replacing $\varphi_n$ by $\varphi_n \wedge \varphi$ if necessary. By hypothesis,

$$\int \varphi_n(h - h_0)\, d\nu = 0$$

for all $n$. Since $|\varphi_n(h - h_0)| \leq \varphi\, |h - h_0|$, we can apply Lebesgue's dominated convergence theorem,

$$\begin{aligned}\int_E \varphi(h - h_0)\, d\nu &= \int \varphi\chi(h - h_0)\, d\nu \\ &= \lim_{n\to\infty} \int \varphi_n(h - h_0)\, d\nu = 0.\end{aligned}$$

Thus $\varphi(h - h_0)$ vanishes $d\nu$ a.e. on $E$, and since $h - h_0$ is positive on $E$, $\varphi$ must vanish $d\nu$ a.e. on $E$. In particular, each of the functions $\eta_k$ in Postulate (6) vanishes on $E$ $d\nu$ a.e., which shows that $E$ is a $d\nu$-null set, or $h - h_0 \leq 0$ $d\nu$ a.e. Similarly, $h - h_0 \geq 0$ $d\nu$ a.e. and therefore $h - h_0 = 0$ $d\nu$ a.e. This completes the proof of Theorem 9.3.3.

## *EXERCISES*

*9.3.1* Show that if there is a $\sigma$-finite integral $\int \varphi\, d\mu$ on the vector space $L$ of functions on $S$, then $L$ satisfies Condition (6).

*Hint* Notice that if $E$ is a $d\mu$-null set and $\sum \varphi_n$, $\varphi_n \in L$ is a series of nonnegative functions that diverges on $E$, then

$$E \subset \bigcup_{n=1}^{\infty} \{x : \varphi_n(x) > 0\}.$$

*9.3.2* Give another proof of the uniqueness part of Theorem 9.3.3 modeled after the corresponding part of Theorem 9.2.2.

*Hint* For each of the functions $\eta_k$ in Postulate (6) choose a sequence $\{\varphi_n\}$ of functions in $L$ satisfying

$$\lim_{n\to\infty} \varphi_n = \text{mid}\,(-\eta_k, h - h_0, \eta_k) \qquad d\nu \text{ a.e.}$$

## 9.4 APPLICATIONS

We have actually obtained much more in the proof of Theorem 9.3.3 than just the Radon-Nikodym theorem. In deriving Equation (9.3.6), we have not used any hypothesis other than that 1 be integrable for $d\mu$ and $d\nu$. But even this restriction is unnecessary, as can be shown by introducing the integrals

$$\int \varphi\, d\mu' = \int \varphi p\, d\mu, \qquad \int \varphi\, d\nu' = \int \varphi p\, d\nu$$

$$\int \varphi\, d\lambda' = \int \varphi p\, d\lambda,$$

as in the proof of Theorem 9.3.3. The function 1 is integrable for $d\mu'$ and $d\nu'$, whence by Equation (9.3.6),

$$\int f\, d\mu' = \int fh\, d\nu' + \int_F f\, d\mu',$$

for all $d\lambda'$-integrable functions $f$. In this equation $h$ is a $d\nu'$-measurable function and $F$ is a $d\mu'$-integrable set which is a null set for $d\nu'$. Taking $f = \varphi/p$, $\varphi \in L$ in the last equation, we obtain

$$\int \varphi\, d\mu = \int \varphi h\, d\nu + \int \chi_F \varphi\, d\mu, \qquad \varphi \in L$$

This shows in particular that $h$ is locally $d\nu$-integrable and $\chi_F$ is locally $d\mu$-integrable, hence $d\mu$-measurable. $F$ is a null set for $d\nu$, because $d\nu$ is absolutely continuous with respect to $d\nu'$. Let

$$\int \varphi\, d\mu_s = \int_F \varphi\, d\mu, \qquad \varphi \in L,$$

where $d\mu_s$ is "concentrated" on the $d\nu$-null set $F$ in the sense that

$$\int \varphi\, d\mu_s = \int_F \varphi\, d\mu_s, \qquad \varphi \in L.$$

This is also expressed by saying that $d\mu_s$ is singular with respect to $d\nu$. Thus we obtain the following theorem.

### 9.4.1 THEOREM

LEBESGUE'S DECOMPOSITION THEOREM *Suppose* $\int \varphi \, d\mu$ *and* $\int \varphi \, d\nu$ *are two integrals on the linear space L of functions on a set S. If Condition* (6) *holds, then there is a nonnegative, locally* $d\nu$*-integrable function h and an integral* $\int \varphi \, d\mu_s$ *singular with respect to* $\int \varphi h \, d\nu$ *such that*

$$\int \varphi \, d\mu = \int \varphi h \, d\nu + \int \varphi \, d\mu_s, \qquad \varphi \in L.$$

We close our discussion with an application of the Radon-Nikodym theorem to the determination of the continuous linear functionals on $L^p$-spaces associated with an integral $\int \varphi \, d\mu$ on a space $L$ of elementary functions defined on a set $S$. These $L^p$-spaces were introduced in Definitions 5.4.1 and 5.4.4 for the Lebesgue integral, but they can, of course, be defined for any integral. At the end of Chapter 5 we already foresaw such an application; we observe, however, that because of the restrictive condition (6) made on $L$ in the last section, the result we get here will not be as general as the one described in part E of the exercise section 5.5 of Chapter 5. There a geometric proof based on inequalities of Beurling and Clarkson was indicated, but this difference is unimportant for most practical purposes.

Recall that a bounded linear functional $F$ on $L^p$ assigns a real number $F(f)$ to each $f \in L^p$ subject to the conditions:

(a) $F(af + bg) = aF(f) + bF(g)$ for $f, g \in L^p$ and $a, b$ real numbers;
(b) there is a constant $M \geq 0$ such that

$$|F(f)| \leq M \, \|f\|_p \qquad \text{for } f \in L^p.$$

$F$ is called a linear functional if only Condition (a) is satisfied. A bounded linear functional $F$ is also called a continuous linear functional, because

$$\lim_{n \to \infty} F(f_n) = F(f)$$

if $f_n$ tends to $f$ in the sense that

$$\lim_{n \to \infty} \|f - f_n\|_p = 0$$

(see Proposition 5.3.2).

A linear functional $F$ on $L^p$ is called positive if

$$F(f) \geq 0 \qquad \text{for } f \in L^p, f \geq 0.$$

For such a functional we have the inequality

$$|F(f)| \leq F(|f|), \qquad f \in L^p$$

as follows immediately from

$$F(|f|) - F(f) = F(|f| - f) \geq 0,$$
$$F(|f|) + F(f) = F(|f| + f) \geq 0.$$

**9.4.2 LEMMA** *Every continuous linear functional on $L^p$ is the difference of two positive continuous linear functionals on $L^p$.*

*Proof* Suppose $F$ is a continuous linear functional on $L^p$. For nonnegative $f \in L^p$ we define $F^+(f)$ by

$$F^+(f) = (F \vee 0)(f) = \sup \{F(u) : 0 \leq u \leq f, u \in L^p\}.$$

This is just Definition 8.4.1 applied to $L^p$ instead of $\mathscr{C}$ with $A = F$ and $B = 0$. Notice that the sup is finite; in fact,

$$\begin{aligned} F^+(f) &= \sup \{F(u) : 0 \leq u \leq f, u \in L^p\} \\ &\leq \sup \{M \|u\|_p : 0 \leq u \leq f, u \in L_p\} = M \|f\|_p, \end{aligned}$$

where $M$ is a constant such that $|F(f)| \leq M \|f\|_p$ for $f \in L_p$. As in Lemma 8.4.2 we can extend $F^+$ to a linear functional on all of $L_p$. By definition $F^+$ is positive and it is continuous, since

$$|F^+(f)| \leq F^+(|f|) \leq M \| \, |f| \, \|_p = M \|f\|_p, \qquad f \in L^p.$$

Now let $F^-$ be the linear functional defined by

$$F^-(f) = F^+(f) - F(f), \qquad f \in L^p.$$

It follows immediately from the definition of $F^+$ that $F^-$ is positive; $F^-$ is also continuous:

$$|F^-(f)| \leq |F(f)| + |F^+(f)| \leq 2M \|f\|_p.$$

Thus we have decomposed $F$ into a difference $F = F^+ - F^-$ of two positive continuous linear functionals.

Recall that $p$ and $q$ are conjugate exponents if

$$p = \infty \text{ and } q = 1, \quad \text{or} \quad p = 1 \text{ and } q = \infty,$$
$$\text{or } 1 < p, q < \infty \text{ and } \frac{1}{p} + \frac{1}{q} = 1.$$

The continuous linear functionals on $L^p$, $1 \leq p < \infty$, can now be characterized as follows.

**9.4.3 THEOREM** *Let $\int \varphi \, d\mu$ be an integral on a space L of elementary functions for which Condition* (6) *of the last section holds. For every continuous linear functional F on $L^p$, $1 \leq p < \infty$, there is $g \in L^q$ such that*

$$F(f) = \int fg \, d\mu, \qquad f \in L^p,$$

*p and q being conjugate exponents. The function g is uniquely determined by F up to the addition of a null function.*

*Proof* According to Lemma 9.4.2 we need prove the theorem only for a positive continuous linear functional $F$. Let $L_0$ be the linear space of bounded

$d\mu$-integrable functions. It follows from the general comparison theorem (Theorem 2.5.7) that we can as well take $L_0$ as our space of elementary functions. Condition (6) is also satisfied for $L_0$; for if $\{\eta_n\}$ is the sequence of nonnegative functions in $L$ such that

$$S = \bigcup_{n=1}^{\infty} \{x : \eta_n(x) > 0\}$$

then $\{\eta_n \wedge 1\}$ has the same property and $\eta_n \wedge 1 \in L_0$. By Proposition 5.4.2, $L_0 \subset L^p$. Thus $F$ defines a positive linear functional on $L_0$. We claim that

$$\int f\, d\nu = F(f), \qquad f \in L_0,$$

is an integral. We have only to verify Property (4). Let $\{f_n\}$ be a decreasing sequence of nonnegative functions in $L_0$ such that $\lim_{n\to\infty} f_n(x) = 0$ for all $x$. Then by the monotone convergence theorem,

$$\lim_{n\to\infty} \|f_n\|_p = \lim_{n\to\infty} \left\{ \int f_n{}^p\, d\mu \right\}^{1/p} = 0,$$

whence

$$\lim_{n\to\infty} \int f_n\, d\nu = \lim_{n\to\infty} F(f_n) = 0$$

because $F$ is continuous.

The characteristic function $\chi_E$ of any $d\mu$-null set belongs to $L_0$ and

$$\int \chi_E\, d\nu = F(\chi_E) \leq M\, \|\chi_E\|_p = 0$$

so that $E$ is also $d\nu$-null. Therefore $d\nu$ is absolutely continuous with respect to $d\mu$. By the Radon-Nikodym theorem (Theorem 9.3.3) there is a nonnegative locally $d\mu$-integrable function $g$ such that

$$F(f) = \int fg\, d\mu \qquad \text{for } f \in L_0.$$

Actually, $g$ belongs to $L^q$. To prove this, we consider first the case $p > 1$. Let $E_n$ be an increasing sequence of $d\mu$-integrable sets whose union is $S$; for instance

$$E_n = \left\{ x : \eta_1 \vee \cdots \vee \eta_n(x) > \frac{1}{n} \right\}$$

where $\{\eta_n\}$ is the sequence of functions postulated in Condition (6). We denote the characteristic function of $E_n$ by $\chi_n$.

$$g_n = \chi_n(g \wedge n)$$

defines an increasing sequence of functions in $L_0$ that tends everywhere to $g$. Moreover, $g_n{}^r \in L_0$ for any $r \geq 0$, because $g_n{}^r \leq n^r \chi_n$. Thus

$$\int g_n{}^q\, d\mu \leq \int g_n^{q-1} g\, d\mu = F(g_n^{q-1})$$

$$\leq M\, \|g_n^{q-1}\|_p = M \left\{ \int g_n{}^q\, d\mu \right\}^{1/p}$$

whence

$$\left\{\int g_n{}^q \, d\mu\right\}^{1/q} \leq M.$$

The monotone convergence theorem implies now that $g^q = \lim g_n{}^q$ is $d\mu$-integrable. This proves $g \in L^q$ if $p > 1$. The case $p = 1$ is even easier to settle. We have

$$\left|\int fg \, d\mu\right| = |F(f)| \leq M \int |f| \, d\mu, \qquad f \in L_0$$

in this case. Let $E = \{x : g(x) > M + 1\}$; then

$$(M + 1) \int \chi_E \chi_n \, d\mu \leq \int \chi_E \chi_n g \, d\mu \leq M \int \chi_E \chi_n \, d\mu$$

whence $\int \chi_E \chi_n \, d\mu = 0$ for each of the characteristic functions $\chi_n$ defined above. Thus $E$ is a $d\mu$-null set and $g \leq M + 1 \; d\mu$ a.e. This shows $g \in L^\infty$ as claimed.

We have therefore established the existence of a function $g \in L^q$ such that

$$F(f) = \int fg \, d\mu \qquad \text{for } f \in L_0.$$

By Hölder's inequality, $\int fg \, d\mu$ defines a continuous linear functional on $L^p$. If $f \in L^p$ then, according to Theorem 5.4.10, there is a sequence $\{f_n\}$ of functions in $L_0$ such that

$$\lim_{n \to \infty} \|f - f_n\|_p = 0.$$

The continuity of $F$ implies now

$$F(f) = \lim_{n \to \infty} F(f_n) = \lim_{n \to \infty} \int f_n g \, d\mu = \int fg \, d\mu.$$

This completes the proof of the existence of $g$.

Suppose there is another function $g_0 \in L^q$ such that

$$F(f) = \int fg_0 \, d\mu, \qquad f \in L^p.$$

Let $\chi$ be the characteristic function of the set $E$ where $g - g_0$ is strictly positive. Then $\chi\chi_n \in L^p$ for each of the characteristic functions of the integrable sets $E_n$ constructed above. Hence

$$\int \chi\chi_n(g - g_0) \, d\mu = 0,$$

whence $g - g_0$ vanishes $d\mu$ a.e. on $E \cap E_n$ for all $n$, or $g - g_0 \leq 0 \; d\mu$ a.e. By symmetry, $g - g_0 \geq 0 \; d\mu$ a.e., so that $g$ and $g_0$ differ only by a null function.

## 9.5 EXERCISES

In the following, $\alpha$, $\beta$, and $\gamma$ denote functions in $V^+_{\text{loc}}$.

### A. Absolute Continuity

**9.5.1**

(a) Suppose $\alpha$ is continuous. Prove that $d\alpha$ is absolutely continuous with respect to $d\beta$ if and only if $\alpha$ maps $d\beta$-null sets into $d\alpha$-null sets.
(b) Prove that the continuity hypothesis in (a) can be replaced by the condition, "if $\alpha$ is discontinuous at a point, then so is $\beta$."
(c) Prove that the condition in (b) cannot be relaxed.

**9.5.2** Suppose $\alpha, \beta \geq 0$. Show that $d(\alpha\beta) \ll d\alpha + d\beta$.

*Hint* Show that for a nonnegative step function $\varphi$ vanishing off a bounded interval $[a, b]$,

$$\int \varphi\, d(\alpha\beta) \leq \beta(b+0)\int \varphi\, d\alpha + \alpha(b+0)\int \varphi\, d\beta.$$

**9.5.3** Suppose $d\alpha$ and $d\beta$ are both absolutely continuous with respect to $d\gamma$, say $d\alpha = h\, d\gamma$ and $d\beta = g\, d\gamma$. Show that $d\alpha \leq d\beta$ if and only if $h \leq g\, d\gamma$ a.e.

**9.5.4** Let $L$ be a linear space of elementary functions on a set $S$ satisfying Properties (1) and (5). $\int \varphi\, d\mu$, $\int \varphi\, d\nu$, and $\int \varphi\, d\lambda$ denote integrals on $L$.

(a) If $a, b \geq 0$, then

$$\int \varphi\, d(a\mu + b\nu) = a\int \varphi\, d\mu + b\int \varphi\, d\nu, \qquad \varphi \in L,$$

is an integral on $L$.
(b) Prove that for $\varphi \in L^+$, $\int \varphi\, d\mu \wedge (\nu + \lambda) \leq \int \varphi\, d\mu \wedge \lambda + \varphi\, d\mu \wedge \lambda$. (See part E of the exercise section 8.6, and in particular Exercise 8.6.25.)
(c) Show that for $n > 0$,

$$\int \varphi\, d\mu_n = \int \varphi\, d\mu \wedge n\nu - \int \varphi\, d\mu \wedge (n-1)\nu$$

is an integral on $L$.

*Hint* Use (b) to show that for $\varphi \in L$, $\varphi \geq 0$,

$$\int \varphi\, d\mu \wedge n\nu \leq \int \varphi\, d\mu \wedge (n-1)\nu + \int \varphi\, d\nu,$$

$$0 \leq \int \varphi\, d\mu_n \leq \int \varphi\, d\nu.$$

(d) Suppose $L$ also satisfies Condition (6). Prove that

$$(\alpha) \qquad \int \varphi\, d\mu = \int \varphi\, h\, d\nu, \qquad \varphi \in L,$$

for some nonnegative locally $d\nu$-integrable function $h$ if and only if

$$(\beta) \qquad \int \varphi\, d\mu = \lim_{n\to\infty} \int \varphi\, d\mu \wedge n\nu, \qquad \varphi \in L.$$

*Hint* Suppose ($\alpha$) holds. Observe that for $\varphi \in L$, $\varphi \geq 0$,

$$\int \varphi(h \wedge n)\, d\nu \leq \int \varphi\, d\mu \wedge n\nu \leq \int \varphi\, d\mu$$

and then conclude ($\beta$). Conversely, if ($\beta$) holds, then

$$\int \varphi\, d\mu = \sum_{n=1}^{\infty} \int \varphi\, d\mu_n$$

where $\int \varphi\, d\mu_n$ are the integrals defined in (c). Notice that $\int \varphi\, d\mu_n \leq \int \varphi\, d\nu$ for $\varphi \in L$, $\varphi \geq 0$. Thus, by the Radon-Nikodym theorem,

$$\int \varphi\, d\mu_n = \int \varphi g_n\, d\nu$$

for some nonnegative locally $d\nu$-integrable function $g_n$ and

$$\int \varphi\, d\mu = \sum_{n=1}^{\infty} \int \varphi g_n\, d\nu.$$

Use Condition (6) to conclude that $\sum_{n=1}^{\infty} g_n$ converges $d\nu$ a.e. to a function $h$ satisfying ($\alpha$).

## B. Relations between Radon-Nikodym Derivatives

**9.5.5** Show that if $h$ and $g$ are nonnegative and locally $d\beta$-integrable, and if $d\alpha = (h\, d\beta) \vee (g\, d\beta)$, then $d\alpha$ is absolutely continuous with respect to $d\beta$ and $d\alpha/d\beta = h \vee g\, d\beta$ a.e.

**9.5.6** Suppose $h$ and $g$ are nonnegative and locally $d\beta$-integrable. Let

$$d\alpha = ((h\, d\beta)^2 + (g\, d\beta)^2)^{1/2}$$

be defined as in Exercise 8.6.14. Use the previous exercise and the remark to Exercise 8.6.14 to show that $d\alpha$ is absolutely continuous with respect to $d\beta$ and $d\alpha/d\beta = (h^2 + g^2)^{1/2}\, d\beta$ a.e.

**9.5.7** Define the function $H_a$ by

$$H_a(x) = \begin{cases} 1 & \text{if } x \geq a \\ 0 & \text{if } x < a. \end{cases}$$

For each of the following pairs of functions $\alpha$, $\beta$ decide whether $d\alpha$ is absolutely continuous with respect to $d\beta$ and, if so, compute $d\alpha/d\beta$.

(a) $\alpha = \sum_{n=1}^{\infty} H_{2n}$, $\beta = \sum_{n=1}^{\infty} H_n$
(b) $\alpha = \text{arc tan}$, $\beta = x^3$
(c) $\alpha = x^3$, $\beta = \text{arc tan}$
(d) $\alpha = \text{arc tan} + H_0$, $\beta = x + H_1$
(e) $\alpha = f$, the function defined in Example 7.1.8, $\beta = \text{arc tan}$.
(f) $a = e^x + \sum_{n=1}^{\infty} 2^{-n} H_{2/n}$, $\beta = x^5 + \sum_{n=1}^{\infty} 3^{-n} H_{1/n}$.

**9.5.8** Show that if $d\alpha \ll d\beta \ll d\gamma$, then

$$\frac{d\alpha}{d\gamma} = \left(\frac{d\alpha}{d\beta}\right)\left(\frac{d\beta}{d\gamma}\right) \qquad d\gamma \text{ a.e.}$$

**9.5.9** Show that if $d\alpha \ll d\beta$ and $d\beta \ll d\alpha$, then

$$\frac{d\alpha}{d\beta} = \left(\frac{d\beta}{d\alpha}\right)^{-1} \qquad d\beta \text{ a.e.}$$

**9.5.10** Suppose that $d\alpha \ll d\gamma$ and $d\beta \ll d\gamma$. Prove that for $a, b \geq 0$, $d(a\alpha + b\beta) \ll d\gamma$ and

$$d(a\alpha + b\beta)/d\gamma = a(d\alpha/d\gamma) + b(d\beta/d\gamma) \qquad d\gamma \text{ a.e.}$$

**9.5.11** Suppose that $d\alpha \ll d\gamma$ and $d\beta \ll d\gamma$. Let $E$ be the set on which $d\beta/d\gamma$ vanishes and define

$$h = \begin{cases} \left(\dfrac{d\alpha}{d\gamma}\right)\left(\dfrac{d\beta}{d\gamma}\right)^{-1} & \text{off } E \\ 0 & \text{on } E. \end{cases}$$

Show that $d\alpha \ll d\beta$ if and only if $h$ is locally $d\beta$-integrable and then $h = d\alpha/d\beta$ $d\beta$ a.e.

**9.5.12** Suppose $d\alpha \ll d\beta \ll d\gamma$.

(a) If $d\alpha$, $d\beta$, $d\gamma$ are atomic, then $d(\alpha \circ \beta)$ is atomic and absolutely continuous with respect to $d\gamma$ and

$$\frac{d(\alpha \circ \beta)}{d\gamma} = \left[\left(\frac{d\alpha}{d\beta}\right) \circ \beta\right]\left(\frac{d\beta}{d\gamma}\right).$$

*Hint* Use the formula in Proposition 9.1.11.

(b) Prove (a) under the hypothesis that $d\alpha$, $d\beta$, and $d\gamma$ are diffuse.

*Hint* Use Equation (9.2.4).

(c) Prove (a) for arbitrary $d\alpha$, $d\beta$, and $d\gamma$.

## C. Lebesgue Decomposition of Measures

**9.5.13** Prove that the Lebesgue decomposition of $d\alpha$ with respect to $d\beta$,

$$d\alpha = h\, d\beta + d\gamma, \qquad d\beta \wedge d\gamma = 0$$

is unique (see Theorem 9.4.1).

*Hint* Suppose that also

$$d\alpha = g\, d\beta + d\gamma', \qquad d\beta \wedge d\gamma' = 0.$$

Observe that $(d\gamma - d\gamma')^+ = (g - h)^+\, d\beta$ is absolutely continuous and mutually singular with respect to $d\beta$. Then apply Proposition 9.1.5.

**9.5.14** Let $d\alpha = h\, d\beta + d\gamma$ be the Lebesgue decomposition of $d\alpha$ with respect to $d\beta$. Suppose $d\alpha_1 \leq d\alpha$ and $d\alpha_1$ is absolutely continuous with respect to $d\beta$. Show that $d\alpha_1 \leq h\, d\beta$.

*Hint* Show that $d\beta$ and $(d\alpha_1 - h\, d\beta)^+$ are mutually singular and that the latter measure is absolutely continuous with respect to $d\beta$. Then apply Proposition 9.1.5.

**9.5.15** Suppose that

$$d\alpha_1 = h_1\, d\beta + d\gamma_1, \qquad d\alpha_2 = h_2\, d\beta + d\gamma_2$$

are the Lebesgue decompositions of $d\alpha_1$ and $d\alpha_2$ with respect to $d\beta$. Show that

$$d\alpha_1 + d\alpha_2 = (h_1 + h_2)\, d\beta + (d\gamma_1 + d\gamma_2)$$

is the Lebesgue decomposition of $d\alpha_1 + d\alpha_2$ with respect to $d\beta$.

## D. Absolute Continuity for Signed Measures

**9.5.16** For this exercise assume that $\alpha$, $\beta$ belong to $V_{\text{loc}}$. Also, $d\alpha$ is said to be absolutely continuous with respect to $d\beta$ if $|d\alpha|$ is absolutely continuous with respect to $|d\beta|$, that is, if every $|d\beta|$-null set is also $|d\alpha|$-null. Prove that if $d\alpha$ is absolutely continuous with respect to $d\beta$, then there is a locally $d\beta$-integrable function $h$ such that

$$\int \varphi\, d\alpha = \int \varphi h\, d\beta, \qquad \varphi \in L,$$

and that any other function $g$ with the same property differs from $h$ by only a $d\beta$-null function. One writes also in this case $d\alpha/d\beta = h$.

*Hint* If $d\beta \geq 0$, then $d\beta \gg (d\alpha)^+$ and $d\beta \gg (d\alpha)^-$, and the existence of $h$ is easily proved. In general, let $E$ be a $(d\beta)^+$-null set and $F$ a $(d\beta)^-$-null set such that $E \cup F = R$. Notice that $\chi_F\,|d\alpha| \ll \chi_F\,|d\beta| = (d\beta)^+$ and $\chi_E\,|d\alpha| \ll \chi_F\,|d\beta| = (d\beta)^-$ so that you can apply the above.

**9.5.17** Do Exercises 9.5.8 to 9.5.12 for $\alpha, \beta, \gamma \in V_{\text{loc}}$.

## SUMMARY

Let $\alpha$ and $\beta$ be monotone nondecreasing functions; $d\alpha$ is said to be absolutely continuous with respect to $d\beta$ if every $d\beta$-null set is also $d\alpha$-null (Definition 9.1.4). This is expressed in symbols by $d\alpha \ll d\beta$. The measure $d\alpha$ is absolutely continuous with respect to $dx$ if and only if the function $\alpha$ is absolutely continuous (Proposition 9.1.2).

The measure $d\alpha$ is said to be diffuse if every one point set is $d\alpha$-null and $d\alpha$ is called atomic if there is a denumerable set whose complement is $d\alpha$-null (Definition 9.1.7). Every measure $d\alpha$ has a decomposition $d\alpha = d\alpha_0 + d\alpha$ where $d\alpha_0$ is diffuse and $d\alpha_a$ is atomic (Proposition 9.1.9). If $d\alpha = d\alpha_0 + d\alpha_a$ is absolutely continuous with respect to $d\beta = d\beta_0 + d\beta_a$, then $d\alpha_0$ is absolutely continuous with respect to $d\beta_0$ and $d\alpha_a$ is absolutely continuous with respect to $d\beta_a$ (Proposition 9.1.10).

If $d\alpha$ is absolutely continuous with respect to $d\beta$, then there is a nonnegative, locally $d\beta$-integrable function $h$ such that

$$\int \varphi\, d\alpha = \int \varphi h\, d\beta$$

for all step functions $\varphi$, and any other locally $d\beta$-integrable function with the same property differs from $h$ only on a $d\beta$-null set (Radon-Nikodym theorem 9.2.2). If $d\alpha$ and $d\beta$ are diffuse, then

$$h = (\alpha \circ \beta_1)' \circ \beta,$$

where $\beta_1$ is an inverse to $\beta$ (Equation (9.2.4)). In particular, if $d\beta = dx$, then $h = \alpha'$ (Theorem 9.1.1). If $d\alpha$ and $d\beta$ are atomic, then (Proposition 9.1.11)

$$h(x) = \begin{cases} \dfrac{\alpha(x+0) - \alpha(x-0)}{\beta(x+0) - \beta(x-0)} & \text{if } \beta \text{ is discontinuous at } x \\ 0 & \text{if } \beta \text{ is continuous at } x. \end{cases}$$

The function $h$ is called the Radon-Nikodym derivative of $d\alpha$ with respect to $d\beta$ and is denoted $h = d\alpha/d\beta$ (Definition 9.2.5).

A measure $d\alpha$ is absolutely continuous with respect to a measure $d\beta$ if and only if there is a nonnegative, locally integrable function $h$ such that $d\alpha = h\, d\beta$ (Theorem 9.2.6); in either case, a function $f$ is $d\alpha$-integrable if and only if $fh$ is $d\beta$-integrable, and then (Theorem 9.2.7)

$$\int f\, d\alpha = \int fh\, d\beta.$$

The Radon-Nikodym theorem, under certain hypotheses, is also valid for an abstract theory of integration. Suppose $L$ is a linear space of elementary functions on a set $S$ satisfying Properties (1) and (5) and, in addition, the following condition:

(6) There is a sequence $\{\eta_n\}$ of nonnegative functions in $L$ such that

$$S = \bigcup_{n=1}^{\infty} \{x : \eta_n(x) > 0\}.$$

Now suppose $\int \varphi \, d\mu$ and $\int \varphi \, d\nu$ are integrals on $L$. The measure $d\mu$ is absolutely continuous with respect to $d\nu$ if and only if there is a nonnegative locally $d\nu$-integrable function $h$ such that

$$\int \varphi \, d\mu = \int \varphi h \, d\nu, \qquad \varphi \in L$$

(Theorem 9.3.3), where $h$ is said to be locally $d\nu$-integrable if $h\varphi$ is $d\nu$-integrable for each $\varphi \in L$ (Definition 9.3.1). In general, under the hypothesis that (6) holds, there is always a nonnegative locally $d\nu$-integrable function $h$ and a measure $d\mu_s$ concentrated on a $d\nu$-null set such that

$$\int \varphi \, d\mu = \int \varphi h \, d\nu + \int \varphi \, d\mu_s, \qquad \varphi \in L.$$

This is Lebesgue's decomposition theorem (Theorem 9.4.1). Another application of the abstract Radon-Nikodym theorem concerns the continuous linear functionals on the space $L^p$, $1 \le p < \infty$, of those $d\mu$-measurable functions $f$ such that $|f|^p$ is $d\mu$-integrable. If Condition (6) holds, then each continuous linear functional $F$ on $L^p$, $1 \le p < \infty$ is of the form

$$F(f) = \int fg \, d\mu$$

for some function $g$ in $L^q$, $p$ and $q$ being conjugate exponents (Theorem 9.4.3).

# 10

# Applications to the Theory of Fourier Series

In this last chapter we apply the knowledge that we have obtained so far to some basic problems in the theory of Fourier series. However, our selection of topics is very incomplete. For a more thorough and extensive treatment of the theory of Fourier series, we refer the reader to the vast literature on this subject, some of which is listed in the literature section at the end of this book.

The material of this chapter can be fitted in at various places in the book. The first section gives the definitions of Fourier series and trigonometric series and poses the problems. It depends only on Chapters 1 to 3.

Section 10.2 discusses the tests of Dini and Jordan for the convergence of a Fourier series, while Section 10.3 presents a method of recovering a function from its Fourier series by another method than ordinary summing of a series. These two sections are independent of each other. The first half of each of these sections can be read with only Chapters 1 to 3 as background, while the second half of Section 10.2 requires the knowledge of Sections 6.1 and 6.2 on functions of locally bounded variation, and the second half of Section 10.3 presupposes Sections 7.1 and 7.2 on the differentiation of indefinite integrals.

Section 10.4 covers Fourier series of square integrable functions on $[0, 2\pi)$ and depends only on Section 10.1. In order to read it, Sections 5.1 and 5.2 on $L^2$ spaces should be understood.

## 10.1 TRIGONOMETRIC SERIES AND FOURIER SERIES

A series of the form

$$\tfrac{1}{2}a_0 + \sum_n (a_n \cos nx + b_n \sin nx) \tag{10.1.1}$$

is called a *trigonometric series*. In this chapter we will investigate the problem of finding conditions on a function $f$ which ensure that it can be represented by a convergent trigonometric series. Suppose the trigonometric series (10.1.1) converges everywhere to the function $f$. Since $\cos nx$ and $\sin nx$ are periodic functions with period $2\pi$, we have

$$f(x) = f(x + 2k\pi), \qquad k = 0, \pm 1, \cdots$$

Thus we can at the most hope to represent periodic functions of period $2\pi$ by trigonometric series. Therefore we will consider in the following only functions $f$ on $[0, 2\pi)$ which we then extend to the whole real line by periodicity (see Figure 10.1):

$$f(x) = f(x - 2k\pi) \text{ for } x \in [2k\pi, 2(k+1)\pi), \qquad k = \pm 1, \pm 2, \cdots$$

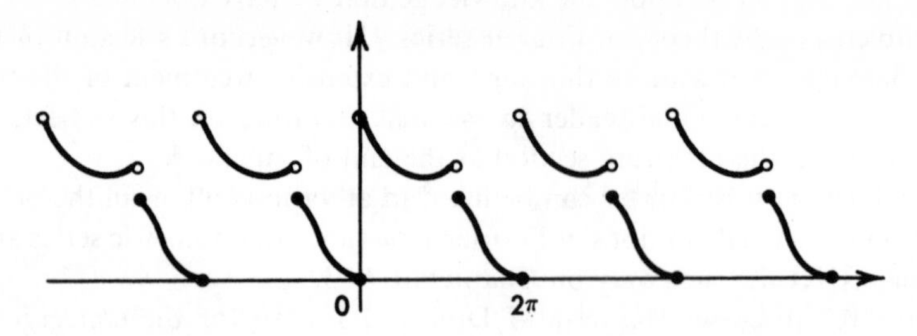


Figure 10.1 The function $f$ on $[0, 2\pi)$ is extended by periodicity to the whole real line.

**10.1.2 PROPOSITION** *Suppose the trigonometric series*

$$\tfrac{1}{2}a_0 + \sum_n (a_n \cos nx + b_n \sin nx)$$

*converges to the function $f$ a.e. and the partial sums $s_n$,*

$$s_n(x) = \tfrac{1}{2}a_0 + \sum_{m=1}^{n} (a_m \cos mx + b_m \sin mx),$$

*remain bounded, or bounded by an integrable function on $[0, 2\pi)$, then $f$ is integrable on $[0, 2\pi)$ and*

$$\begin{aligned} a_0 &= \frac{1}{\pi}\int_0^{2\pi} f(x)\,dx, \\ a_n &= \frac{1}{\pi}\int_0^{2\pi} f(x)\cos nx\,dx, \qquad n \geq 1, \\ b_n &= \frac{1}{\pi}\int_0^{2\pi} f(x)\sin nx\,dx, \qquad n \geq 1. \end{aligned} \tag{10.1.3}$$

*Proof* We need the following formulas which can be found in many a calculus text:

$$\int_0^{2\pi} \sin mx \sin nx\,dx = \int_0^{2\pi} \cos mx \cos nx\,dx = \begin{cases} 0 & \text{if } m \neq n \\ \pi & \text{if } m = n \geq 1 \end{cases}$$

$$\int_0^{2\pi} \cos mx \sin nx\,dx = 0, \qquad m, n \geq 0.$$

By hypothesis we may apply Lebesgue's dominated convergence theorem to the series

$$\tfrac{1}{2}a_0 \cos nx + \sum_{m=1}^{\infty} (a_m \cos mx \cos nx + b_m \sin mx \cos nx)$$

which converges to $f(x)\cos nx$ a.e. Integrating term by term and using the above formulas, we obtain

$$\int_0^{2\pi} f(x)\cos nx = \pi a_n, \qquad n \geq 1.$$

The same formula also holds for $a_0$, and the formula for $b_n$ is derived similarly.

**10.1.4 DEFINITION** *For any integrable function $f$ on $[0, 2\pi)$, the coefficients $a_n$ and $b_n$ given by Equation* (10.1.3) *are called the Fourier coefficients of $f$, and*

$$\tfrac{1}{2}a_0 + \sum_n (a_n \cos nx + b_n \sin nx)$$

*is the Fourier series of $f$.*

The last proposition gives sufficient conditions for a convergent trigonometric series to be the Fourier series of its limit. Actually, more is true; a trigonometric series that converges to an integrable function on $[0, 2\pi)$ must necessarily be the Fourier series of that function. This is a difficult theorem. For a proof we refer the reader to any of the books on Fourier series listed in the bibliography. However, there are convergent trigonometric series that are not Fourier series (see Exercise 10.5.7). Such series must necessarily converge to functions that are not integrable on $[0, 2\pi)$. In this connection the question of course arises of whether the Fourier series of an integrable function $f$ on $[0, 2\pi)$ must, if convergent, necessarily converge to $f$ a.e. We will obtain such a theorem in Exercise 10.3.3. In the meantime we will try to find conditions that will ensure that the Fourier series of an integrable function on $[0, 2\pi)$ converges. A vital tool will be the Riemann-Lebesgue theorem, which we have already encountered for the Fourier transform in Section 5.6.

**10.1.5 THEOREM**

**RIEMANN-LEBESGUE THEOREM** *Suppose $f$ is an integrable function. Then*

$$\lim_{t\to\infty} \int f(x)\cos tx\, dx = 0 = \lim_{t\to\infty} \int f(x)\sin tx\, dx.$$

*Proof* Let us prove the theorem first for a characteristic function $\chi$ of a bounded interval with end points $a \leq b$. We have

$$\int \chi \cos tx\, dx = \int_a^b \cos tx\, dx = \frac{1}{t}(\sin tb - \sin ta)$$

which tends to zero as $t$ increases to infinity, because the last term is bounded in absolute value by $2/t$. Similarly we show that the second limit is zero. Since every step function can be expressed as a linear combination of characteristic functions of bounded intervals, we conclude that the theorem holds for any step function. To prove the theorem for an integrable function $f$, let $\varepsilon > 0$ be given and choose a step function $\varphi$ according to Lemma 2.2.5. such that $\int |f - \varphi|\, dx < \varepsilon$. There is $t_0$.

such that

$$\int \varphi(x) \cos tx \, dx \leq \varepsilon$$

for $t \geq t_0$. Since $|\cos tx| \leq 1$, we obtain

$$\left| \int f(x) \cos tx \, dx \right| \leq \left| \int (f(x) - \varphi(x)) \cos tx \, dx \right| + \left| \int \varphi(x) \cos tx \, dx \right|$$
$$\leq \int |f - \varphi| \, dx + \varepsilon \leq 2\varepsilon$$

for $t \geq t_0$, thus proving that the integral on the left tends to zero. A similar argument proves the lemma for the sine integral.

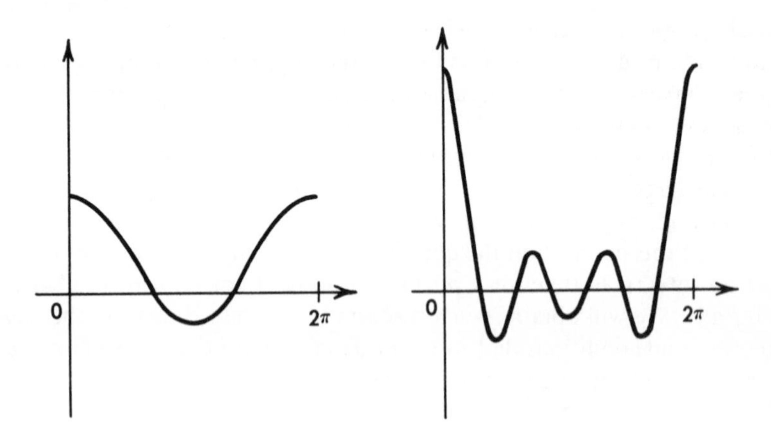


Figure 10.2 The graph of the Dirichlet kernel $D_n$ for $n = 1$ and $n = 3$.

An immediate consequence of the Riemann-Lebesgue theorem is the following corollary.

10.1.6 COROLLARY *The Fourier coefficients of an integrable function $f$ on $[0, 2\pi)$ tend to zero.*

The summation formula

$$D_n(x) = \tfrac{1}{2} + \sum_{m=1}^{n} \cos mx = \frac{\sin (n + \frac{1}{2})x}{2 \sin (\frac{1}{2}x)}, \tag{10.1.7}$$

valid when $x$ is not a multiple of $2\pi$, will be an essential tool in the discussion of the convergence problem for a Fourier series. The functions $D_n$ are called *Dirichlet kernels* (see Figure 10.2). They have the property

$$\frac{1}{\pi} \int_0^{2\pi} D_n \, dx = 1 = \frac{2}{\pi} \int_0^{\pi} D_n \, dx \tag{10.1.8}$$

as is easily seen from the definition of $D_n$. To prove the summation formula (10.1.7), we proceed by induction on $n$ using the formula

$$\sin(a \pm b) = \sin a \cos b \pm \cos a \sin b.$$

Equation (10.1.7) certainly holds for $n = 0$. For $n \geq 1$ we obtain

$$\begin{aligned}
\frac{\sin(n - \tfrac{1}{2})x}{2 \sin \tfrac{1}{2}x} + \cos nx &= \frac{1}{2 \sin \tfrac{1}{2}x}[\sin(n - \tfrac{1}{2})x + 2 \cos nx \sin \tfrac{1}{2}x] \\
&= \frac{1}{2 \sin \tfrac{1}{2}x}[\sin nx \cos \tfrac{1}{2}x - \cos nx \sin \tfrac{1}{2}x \\
&\qquad + 2 \cos nx \sin \tfrac{1}{2}x] \\
&= \frac{1}{2 \sin \tfrac{1}{2}x}[\sin nx \cos \tfrac{1}{2}x + \cos nx \sin \tfrac{1}{2}x] = D_n(x).
\end{aligned}$$

**10.1.9 PROPOSITION** *If $f$ is integrable over $[0, 2\pi)$, then the partial sums*

$$s_n(x) = \tfrac{1}{2}a_0 + \sum_{m=1}^{n} (a_m \cos mx + b_m \sin mx)$$

*of its Fourier series are given by the integral*

$$s_n(t) = \frac{1}{\pi}\int_0^{2\pi} f(x) D_n(t - x)\, dx.$$

*Proof* We have

$$\begin{aligned}
s_n(t) &= \frac{1}{2\pi}\int_0^{2\pi} f(x)\, dx + \frac{1}{\pi}\sum_{m=1}^{n}\int_0^{2\pi} f(x)(\cos mx \cos mt + \sin mx \sin mt)\, dx \\
&= \frac{1}{\pi}\int_0^{2\pi}\left[\frac{1}{2} + \sum_{m=1}^{n} \cos m(t - x)\right] f(x)\, dx \\
&= \frac{1}{\pi}\int_0^{2\pi} f(x) D_n(t - x)\, dx.
\end{aligned}$$

If we define the function $f$ on the whole real line by periodicity, then we can write the formula for $s_n(t)$ somewhat differently. Namely, since $D_n(x) = D_n(-x)$, we obtain

$$\begin{aligned}
s_n(t) = \frac{1}{\pi}\int_0^{2\pi} f(x) D_n(t - x)\, dx &= \frac{1}{\pi}\int_t^{t+2\pi} f(x + t) D_n(-x)\, dx \\
&= \frac{1}{\pi}\int_0^{2\pi} f(x + t) D_n(x)\, dx.
\end{aligned}$$

The latter equation holds because by periodicity

$$\int_0^t f(x+t)D_n(x)\,dx = \int_{2\pi}^{t+2\pi} f(x+t)D_n(x)\,dx.$$

Or, since

$$\int_\pi^{2\pi} f(x+t)D_n(x)\,dx = \int_{-2\pi}^{-\pi} f(-x+t)D_n(-x)\,dx$$
$$= \int_0^\pi f(t-x)D_n(x)\,dx,$$

we obtain

$$s_n(t) = \frac{1}{\pi}\int_0^\pi \{f(t+x)+f(t-x)\}D_n(x)\,dx.$$

10.1.10 COROLLARY *Suppose $f$ is a periodic function that is integrable on $[0, 2\pi)$. In order that, for a given $t$, $\{s_n(t)\}$ should converge to a limit $s(t)$, it is necessary and sufficient that*

$$\lim_{n\to\infty} \frac{1}{\pi}\int_0^\pi g(t,x)D_n(x)\,dx = 0$$

*where*

$$g(t,x) = f(t+x)+f(t-x)-2s(t).$$

*Proof* We have only to observe that by Equation (10.1.8),

$$\frac{1}{\pi}\int_0^\pi 2s(t)D_n(x)\,dx = s(t).$$

As an example let us consider the Fourier series of the characteristic function $\chi$ of an interval contained in $[0, 2\pi)$. For $x \in [2k\pi, 2(k+1)\pi)$ we define $\chi(x) = \chi(x - 2k\pi)$ so that $\chi$ is a periodic function. Let

$$\tfrac{1}{2}a_0 + \sum_n (a_n \cos nx + b_n \sin nx)$$

be the Fourier series of $\chi$.

10.1.11 PROPOSITION *The Fourier series of the characteristic function of an interval in $[0, 2\pi)$ converges for every $x \in [0, 2\pi)$ and its sum is*

$$\tfrac{1}{2}\{\chi(x+0)+\chi(x-0)\}$$

*if we extend $\chi$ periodically to the whole real line.*

*Proof* Let

$$g(t,x) = \chi(t+x)+\chi(t-x)-\chi(t+0)-\chi(t-0).$$

For each $t$, $g(t, x)$ vanishes (as a function of $x$) in an interval $(0, \delta)$, $\delta > 0$; in fact, for each $t$ we can find $\delta > 0$ such that $\chi(t+x)-\chi(t+0)$, as well as $\chi(t-x) - \chi(t-0)$, vanish for $0 < x < \delta$. Thus $g(t, x)/\sin x/2$ is integrable on $(0, \pi)$. We obtain therefore, according to the Riemann-Lebesgue theorem:

$$0 = \lim_{n\to\infty} \frac{1}{\pi} \int_0^\pi \frac{g(t, x)}{\sin x/2} \sin (n + \tfrac{1}{2})x \, dx$$
$$= \lim_{n\to\infty} \frac{1}{\pi} \int_0^\pi g(t, x) D_n(x) \, dx.$$

But this, by Corollary 10.1.10, just means that the Fourier series of $\chi$ converges to $\{\chi(t + 0) + \chi(t - 0)\}/2$ at every $t \in [0, 2\pi)$.

If $\chi$ is the characteristic function of an interval with end points $a$, $b$ in $[0, 2\pi)$, then its Fourier series converges to $\chi(x)$ for $x \neq a, b$ while it converges to $\tfrac{1}{2}$ if $x = a$ or $x = b$ if $\chi \neq \chi_{[0,2\pi)}$.

## *EXERCISES*

*10.1.1* Calculate the Fourier coefficients of the characteristic function $\chi$ of an interval $[0, x)$, $0 < x < 2\pi$ and use the fact that the Fourier series of $\chi$ converges to $\tfrac{1}{2}$ at $x$ to prove that

$$\frac{\pi - x}{2} = \sum_{n=1}^{\infty} \frac{\sin nx}{n}, \qquad x \in (0, 2\pi).$$

Then show that this is the Fourier series of $(\pi - x)/2$.

*10.1.2* Show that for $x \in (-\pi, \pi)$

$$\operatorname{sgn} x = \frac{4}{\pi} \sum_{n=1}^{\infty} \frac{\sin (2n - 1)x}{2n - 1} = \begin{cases} 1 & \text{if } x \in (0, \pi) \\ 0 & \text{if } x = 0 \\ -1 & \text{if } x \in (-\pi, 0). \end{cases}$$

*Hint* Apply Proposition 10.1.11.

*10.1.3* Suppose $f$ is an odd (even) periodic function that is integrable on $[0, 2\pi)$; that is, $f$ has the property

$$f(-x) = -f(x) \qquad (f(-x) = f(x)).$$

Show that the Fourier series of $f$ has the form $\sum b_n \sin nx$ $(a_0/2 + \sum a_n \cos nx)$.

*10.1.4*

(a) Show that if a Fourier series converges absolutely at a point $c$, then it converges also absolutely at $-c$. If a Fourier series converges absolutely at $c_1$ and $c_2$, then it converges absolutely at $c_1 + c_2$.
(b) Apply (a) to show that a Fourier series that converges absolutely for each $x$ in an interval $(a, b)$, $a < b$ converges absolutely everywhere.

*10.1.5* Prove that a Fourier series that converges absolutely for each $x$ in a closed bounded set of positive measure converges absolutely everywhere.

*Hint* Apply the previous exercise and the Steinhaus theorem.

*Remark* According to Corollary 3.5.8, one can relax the condition in the last exercise requiring only that the Fourier series should converge absolutely for each $x$ in a measurable set of positive measure.

## 10.2 CONVERGENCE TESTS

We apply now the Riemann-Lebesgue theorem in conjunction with Corollary 10.1.10 to derive some sufficient conditions for the convergence of a Fourier series. Our first step in this direction is the following result.

10.2.1 LEMMA *The Fourier series of an integrable function $f$ on $[0, 2\pi)$ converges for some $t \in [0, 2\pi)$ to $s(t)$ if and only if for some $\delta \in (0, \pi)$,*

$$\lim_{n\to\infty} \int_0^\delta \frac{\sin (n + \frac{1}{2})x}{x} g(t, x)\, dx = 0$$

*where we again let*

$$g(t, x) = f(t + x) + f(t - x) - 2\, s(t).$$

*Proof* By the Riemann-Lebesgue theorem

$$\lim_{n\to\infty} \int_\delta^\pi \sin (n + \tfrac{1}{2})x \frac{g(t, x)}{\sin \frac{1}{2}x}\, dx = 0$$

for any $\delta \in (0, \pi)$. By Corollary 10.1.10, the Fourier series of $f$ converges to $s(t)$ at $t$ if and only if

$$\lim_{n\to\infty} \int_0^\pi \sin (n + \tfrac{1}{2})x \frac{g(t, x)}{\sin \frac{1}{2}x}\, dx = 0.$$

Subtracting the previous equation, we obtain

$$\lim_{n\to\infty} \int_0^\delta \sin (n + \tfrac{1}{2})x \frac{g(t, x)}{\sin \frac{1}{2}x}\, dx = 0$$

as the necessary and sufficient condition for the Fourier series of $f$ to converge to $s(t)$ at $t$. Next we observe that the function

$$h(x) = \begin{cases} \dfrac{1}{\sin \frac{1}{2}x} - \dfrac{2}{x} & \text{if } x \in (0, \pi] \\ 0 & \text{if } x = 0 \end{cases}$$

is continuous on $[0, \pi]$. In fact, since $u/\sin u$ tends to 1 as $u = x/2$ approaches 0, we obtain

(10.2.2) $$\lim_{x\to 0}\left(\frac{1}{\sin \frac{1}{2}x} - \frac{1}{\frac{1}{2}x}\right) = \lim_{u\to 0}\frac{u}{\sin u}\left(\frac{u - \sin u}{u^2}\right) = 0,$$

the latter because the power series expansion of $(u - \sin u)/u^2$ starts with $u/6$. Thus $h$ is bounded on $[0, \pi]$ and $h(x)\,g(t, x)$ is integrable on $[0, \pi]$ so that, by the Riemann-Lebesgue theorem,

$$A_n = \int_0^\delta \sin(n + \tfrac{1}{2})x\left\{\frac{1}{\sin \frac{1}{2}x} - \frac{2}{x}\right\}g(t, x)\,dx$$

tends to zero as $n$ tends to infinity. Furthermore,

$$\int_0^\delta \sin(n + \tfrac{1}{2})x\,\frac{g(t, x)}{\sin \frac{1}{2}x}\,dx = 2\int_0^\delta \sin(n + \tfrac{1}{2})x\,\frac{g(t, x)}{x}\,dx + A_n.$$

Therefore the first integral tends to zero as $n$ tends to infinity if and only if the second one does. This completes the proof of the lemma.

As a corollary we obtain a condition for convergence of a Fourier series that is generally attributed to Dini.

### 10.2.3 PROPOSITION

**DINI'S TEST** *Suppose $f$ is an integrable function on $[0, 2\pi)$ and let*

$$g(t, x) = f(t + x) + f(t - x) - 2s(t).$$

*If $g(t, x)/x$ is integrable on $(0, \delta)$, for some $\delta \in (0, \pi)$, then the Fourier series of $f$ converges to $s(t)$ at $t$.*

*Proof* This is just an application of the Riemann-Lebesgue theorem and the last lemma.

**10.2.4 COROLLARY** *If the integrable function $f$ on $[0, 2\pi)$ is differentiable at $t$, then the Fourier series of $f$ converges to $f(t)$ at $t$.*

*Proof* Since $f$ is differentiable at $t$, we can find a $\delta$ such that

$$\left|\frac{1}{x}\{f(t \pm x) - f(t)\} - f'(t)\right| \leq 1$$

for $x \in (0, \delta)$. Hence, with $s(t) = f(t)$ and $g$ as in the last proposition,

$$\left|\frac{g(t, x)}{x}\right| \leq 2(1 + |f'(t)|)$$

for $x \in (0, \delta)$, that is, $g(t, x)/x$ is bounded and therefore integrable on $(0, \delta)$ so that Proposition 10.2.3 applies.

Before we can go on with the discussion of another test, we need to prove an auxiliary theorem known as the second mean value theorem. It is a generalization to integrals of Abel's lemma (Exercise 10.2.2).

### 10.2.5 THEOREM

SECOND MEAN VALUE THEOREM *Suppose $g$ is a nonnegative monotone nondecreasing function on the interval $[a, b]$, $a < b$, and $f$ is integrable on $[a, b]$. Then there is a $\delta \in [a, b]$ such that*

$$\int_a^b gf\,dx = g(b-0)\int_\delta^b f\,dx.$$

*Proof* We know by Corollary 6.2.8 that $g$ is measurable, and thus $gf$ is integrable because $g$ is bounded by $g(b)$. Let $M$ be the maximum and $m$ the minimum of the continuous function $F$ defined by

$$F(t) = \int_t^b f\,dx.$$

If $\varepsilon > 0$ is given, we can find an $a_1 > a_0 = a$ such that

$$g(a_1 - 0) - g(a_0 + 0) \leq \varepsilon, \qquad g(t) - g(a_0 + 0) > \varepsilon \qquad \text{for } t > a_1.$$

In fact, we have just to take

$$a_1 = \sup\{t : g(t) - g(a_0 + 0) \leq \varepsilon\}.$$

By induction on $n$ we can find $a_n > a_{n-1}$ with

$$g(a_n - 0) - g(a_{n-1} + 0) \leq \varepsilon, \qquad g(t) - g(a_{n-1} + 0) > \varepsilon \qquad \text{for } t > a_n$$

as long as $g(b) - g(a_{n-1} + 0) > \varepsilon$. If $g(b) - g(a_{n-1} + 0) \leq \varepsilon$, then let $a_n = b$. This happens for some

$$n \leq \frac{\{g(b) - g(a)\}}{\varepsilon}.$$

Define $\varphi$ to be a step function with presentation

$$(a_0, \cdots, a_n; g(a_1 - 0), \cdots, g(a_n - 0)).$$

Then $0 \leq \varphi - g \leq \varepsilon$ at all points different form $a_0, \cdots, a_n$. We have

$$\begin{aligned}\int_a^b \varphi f\,dx &= \sum_{k=1}^n g(a_k - 0)\int_{a_{k-1}}^{a_k} f\,dx \\ &= \sum_{k=1}^n [g(a_k - 0) - g(a_{k-1} - 0)]\int_{a_{k-1}}^b f\,dx \\ &= \sum_{k=1}^n [g(a_k - 0) - g(a_{k-1} - 0)]F(a_{k-1}),\end{aligned}$$

where we let $g(a_0 - 0) = 0$. Since $g(a_k - 0) - g(a_{k-1} - 0) \geq 0$, we conclude

$$\int_a^b \varphi f\,dx \leq \sum_{k=1}^n [g(a_k - 0) - g(a_{k-1} - 0)]M = g(b - 0)M,$$

$$\int_a^b \varphi f\,dx \geq \sum_{k=1}^n [g(a_k - 0) - g(a_{k-1} - 0)]m = g(b - 0)m.$$

On the other hand,

$$\left|\int_a^b \varphi f\,dx - \int_a^b gf\,dx\right| \leq \int_a^b |\varphi - g|\,|f|\,dx \leq \epsilon\int_a^b |f|\,dx.$$

Thus, since $\varepsilon$ was arbitrary,

$$mg(b - 0) \leq \int_a^b gf\,dx \leq Mg(b - 0).$$

The continuous function $g(b - 0)F$ takes every value between $mg(b - 0)$ and $Mg(b - 0)$. So we can find $\delta \in [a, b]$ with

$$\int_a^b gf\,dx = g(b - 0)F(\delta) = g(b - 0)\int_\delta^b f\,dx.$$

This completes the proof of the second mean value theorem.

Of course, we could also have proved the second mean value theorem with $g$, a nonnegative nonincreasing function (see Exercise 10.2.3). In this case there is a $\delta \in [a, b]$ such that

$$\int_a^b gf\,dx = g(a + 0)\int_a^\delta f\,dx.$$

As an application we have the following corollary.

**10.2.6 COROLLARY** *There is a constant $M > 0$ such that*

$$\left|\int_a^b \frac{\sin x}{x}\,dx\right| \leq M$$

*for all $a$, $b$.*

*Proof* The limit

$$\lim_{x\to 0} \frac{\sin x}{x} = 1$$

exists so that $(\sin x)/x$ can be defined to be continuous at 0. Since

$$\int_a^b \frac{\sin x}{x}\,dx = -\int_{-b}^{-a} \frac{\sin x}{x}\,dx,$$

it suffices to show that $\displaystyle\int_a^b \frac{\sin x}{x}\,dx$ is bounded for $b \geq a \geq 1$. But then, by the second mean value theorem, there is $\delta \in [a, b]$ with

$$\left| \int_a^b \frac{\sin x}{x}\, dx \right| = \left| 1 \cdot \int_a^\delta \sin x \, dx \right|$$
$$= |\cos a - \cos \delta| \le 2.$$

With these preparations we are ready to prove a convergence theorem for functions of bounded variation.

### 10.2.7 THEOREM

JORDAN'S TEST *Suppose the integrable function $f$ on $[0, 2\pi)$ is of bounded variation on the interval $[a, b]$. Then its Fourier series converges to*

$$s(t) = \tfrac{1}{2}\{f(t+0) + f(t-0)\}$$

*for each $t \in (a, b)$ and the partial sums $s_n(t)$ remain bounded on every closed interval contained in $(a, b)$.*

*Proof* We show first that the Fourier series of $f$ converges to $s(t)$ for each $t \in (a, b)$. Choose $\lambda \in (0, \pi)$ with $\lambda \le \min(t - a, b - t)$. There are monotone nondecreasing functions $g_1$ and $g_2$ on $[0, \lambda]$ such that for $x \in [0, \lambda]$,

$$g_1(x) - g_2(x) = g(x) = f(t + x) + f(t - x) - f(t + 0) - f(t - 0).$$

Since

$$0 = \lim_{\substack{x \to 0 \\ x > 0}} g(x) = g(0 + 0) = g_1(0 + 0) - g_2(0 + 0),$$

we may arrange that $g_i(0 + 0) = 0$, $i = 1, 2$, subtracting a constant from both $g_1$ and $g_2$ if necessary. Then $g_1$ and $g_2$ are nonnegative on $(0, \lambda]$. By Lemma 10.2.1 it suffices to show that

$$\lim_{n\to\infty} \int_0^\lambda \frac{\sin (n + \frac{1}{2})x}{x}\, g_i(x)\, dx = 0 \qquad i = 1, 2. \tag{10.2.8}$$

Let $\varepsilon > 0$ and choose $0 < \eta < \lambda$ such that $|g_i(x)| < \varepsilon$ for $x \in (0, \eta)$. By the second mean value theorem there is a $\delta \in [0, \eta]$ such that

$$\left| \int_0^\lambda \frac{\sin (n + \frac{1}{2})x}{x}\, g_i(x)\, dx \right|$$
$$\le \left| \int_0^\eta \frac{\sin (n + \frac{1}{2})x}{x}\, g_i(x)\, dx \right| + \left| \int_\eta^\lambda \frac{\sin (n + \frac{1}{2})x}{x}\, g_i(x)\, dx \right|$$
$$\le g_i(\eta - 0) \left| \int_\delta^\eta \frac{\sin (n + \frac{1}{2})x}{x}\, dx \right| + \left| \int_\eta^\lambda \frac{\sin (n + \frac{1}{2})x}{x}\, g_i(x)\, dx \right|$$
$$\le \varepsilon \left| \int_{(n+1/2)\delta}^{(n+1/2)\eta} \frac{\sin x}{x}\, dx \right| + \left| \int_\eta^\lambda \frac{\sin (n + \frac{1}{2})x}{x}\, g_i(x)\, dx \right|.$$

The first term is less than, or equal to, $\varepsilon M$ for some constant $M$ independent of $\eta$ and $\delta$ (Corollary 10.2.6) and the second term tends to zero as $n$ tends to infinity by the Riemann-Lebesgue theorem. This proves (10.2.8).

Now let us show that the Fourier series of $f$ converges boundedly on every closed interval $[c, d]$ contained in $(a, b)$. We may assume that $[c, d] \subset (a, b) \subset [0, 2\pi]$. We have for the partial sums

$$s_n(t) = \frac{1}{\pi}\int_a^{a+2\pi} f(x) D_n(t-x)\,dx$$

$$(10.2.9) \qquad = \frac{1}{\pi}\int_a^{a+2\pi} f(x)\frac{\sin(n+\tfrac{1}{2})(t-x)}{\tfrac{1}{2}(t-x)}\,dx$$

$$+ \frac{1}{\pi}\int_a^{a+2\pi} f(x)\left[\frac{1}{\sin\tfrac{1}{2}(t-x)} - \frac{2}{t-x}\right]\sin\left(n+\frac{1}{2}\right)(t-x)\,dx$$

(see Proposition 10.1.9). The function

$$\left|\frac{1}{\sin\tfrac{1}{2}(t-x)} - \frac{2}{t-x}\right|$$

is bounded for $t \in [c, d]$, $x \in [a, a+2\pi]$, say by $M$; namely, if we define this function to be zero for $t = x$, then it becomes continuous for $t \in [c, d]$, $x \in [a, a+2\pi]$ as we have seen in the proof of Lemma 10.2.1 (Equation (10.2.2). Thus we get

$$\left|\int_a^{a+2\pi} f(x)\left[\frac{1}{\sin\tfrac{1}{2}(t-x)} - \frac{2}{t-x}\right]\sin(n+\tfrac{1}{2})(t-x)\,dx\right| \le M\int_a^{a+2\pi}|f|\,dx$$

for $t \in [c, d]$. Hence it suffices to show that the first integral on the right of (10.2.9) is bounded on $[c, d]$ uniformly in $n$. Let $f_1$ and $f_2$ be two nonnegative monotone nondecreasing functions on $[a, b]$ such that $f = f_1 - f_2$. Then

$$\left|\int_a^{a+2\pi} f(x)\frac{\sin(n+\tfrac{1}{2})(t-x)}{\tfrac{1}{2}(t-x)}\,dx\right|$$

$$\le \sum_{i=1}^{2}\left|\int_a^b f_i(x)\frac{\sin(n+\tfrac{1}{2})(t-x)}{\tfrac{1}{2}(t-x)}\,dx\right| + \left|\int_b^{a+2\pi} f(x)\frac{\sin(n+\tfrac{1}{2})(t-x)}{\tfrac{1}{2}(t-x)}\,dx\right|$$

For the first term on the right we have, by the second mean value theorem,

$$\left|\int_a^b f_i(x)\frac{\sin(n+\tfrac{1}{2})(t-x)}{\tfrac{1}{2}(t-x)}\,dx\right| \le f_i(b-0)\left|\int_\delta^b \frac{\sin(n+\tfrac{1}{2})(t-x)}{\tfrac{1}{2}(t-x)}\,dx\right|$$

$$\le 2f_i(b-0)\left|\int_{(n+1/2)(t-\delta)}^{(n+1/2)(t-b)} \frac{\sin x}{x}\,dx\right|$$

which is bounded independently of $t$ and $n$ by Corollary 10.2.6. For the second term we obtain for $t \in [c, d]$

$$\left| \int_b^{a+2\pi} f(x) \frac{\sin (n + \frac{1}{2})(t - x)}{\frac{1}{2}(t - x)} \, dx \right| \leq \frac{2}{b - d} \int_b^{a+2\pi} |f| \, dx$$

since $|t - x| \geq b - d$ for $x \in [b, a + 2\pi]$. This completes the proof.

10.2.10 COROLLARY *If the (periodic) function $f$ is of locally bounded variation, then its Fourier series converges boundedly to $\{f(x + 0) + f(x - 0)\}/2$ everywhere, and to $f(x)$ at all points of continuity of $f$.*

As an application of Jordan's test we show that any Fourier series may be integrated term by term.

10.2.11 PROPOSITION *Suppose $f$ is an integrable function on $[0, 2\pi)$ and $g$ is a periodic function of locally bounded variation. Let*

$$\tfrac{1}{2}a_0 + \sum_n \{a_n \cos nx + b_n \sin nx\}$$

*be the Fourier series of $f$. Then*

$$\int_0^{2\pi} fg \, dx = \tfrac{1}{2}a_0 \int_0^{2\pi} g \, dx + \sum_{n=1}^{\infty} \int_0^{2\pi} \{a_n \cos nx + b_n \sin nx\} g(x) \, dx$$

*Proof* Let

$$\tfrac{1}{2}a_0' + \sum \{a_n' \cos nx + b_n' \sin nx\}$$

be the Fourier series of $g$ which converges boundedly to $g$ at all points of continuity of $g$, that is, almost everywhere (Corollary 10.2.10). Thus by Lebesgue's dominated convergence theorem,

$$\begin{aligned}
\int_0^{2\pi} fg \, dx &= \tfrac{1}{2}a_0' \int_0^{2\pi} f \, dx + \sum_{n=1}^{\infty} \left\{ a_n' \int_0^{2\pi} f(x) \cos nx \, dx + b' \int_0^{2\pi} f(x) \sin nx \, dx \right\} \\
&= \tfrac{1}{2}a_0' a_0 + \sum_{n=1}^{\infty} \{a_n' a_n + b_n' b_n\} \\
&= \tfrac{1}{2}a_0 \int g \, dx + \sum_{n=1}^{\infty} \int_0^{2\pi} \{a_n \cos nx + b_n \sin nx\} g(x) \, dx.
\end{aligned}$$

10.2.12 COROLLARY *The Fourier series of an integrable function on $[0, 2\pi)$ may be integrated term by term, that is,*

$$\int_a^b f \, dx = \tfrac{1}{2}a_0(b - a) + \sum_{n=1}^{\infty} \int_a^b \{a_n \cos nx + b_n \sin nx\} \, dx$$

*in the notation of the last proposition.*

*Proof* If $0 \le a \le b \le 2\pi$, this is just Proposition 10.2.11 with $g = \chi_{[a,b]}$.

## *EXERCISES*

*10.2.1* Show that Dini's test applies at 0 to the function $f$ defined by

$$f(x) = \begin{cases} x^{\alpha} \sin \dfrac{1}{x} & \text{for } x \in (0, \pi) \\ 0 & \text{for } x = 0 \text{ and } x \in [\pi, 2\pi). \end{cases}$$

Show that Jordan's test does not apply if $0 < \alpha < 1$ since $f$ is not of bounded variation in any interval containing 0.

*10.2.2* Prove *Abel's lemma*: If $\{a_1, \cdots, a_n\}$ and $\{b_1, \cdots, b_n\}$ are two sets of numbers such that for some constants $M \ge m \ge 0$,

$$m \le a_1 + \cdots + a_k \le M, \qquad k = 1, \cdots, n,$$
$$b_1 \ge b_2 \ge \cdots \ge b_n \ge 0,$$

then

$$mb_1 \le \sum_{k=1}^{n} b_k a_k \le b_1 M.$$

*Hint* Apply the second mean value theorem to the step functions $f$ and $g$ with presentations $(0, \cdots, n; a_1, \cdots, a_n)$ and $(0, \cdots, n; b_1, \cdots, b_n)$, respectively.

*10.2.3* Prove the second mean value theorem for a nonnegative nonincreasing function $g$.

*Hint* Apply the second mean value theorem to the functions $f$ and $g$ on $[-b, -a]$ defined by $f(x) = f(-x)$, $g(x) = g(-x)$.

*10.2.4* Show that for the Fourier series

$$\tfrac{1}{2}a_0 + \sum \{a_n \cos nx + b_n \sin nx\}$$

of any integrable function $f$ on $[0, 2\pi)$, the series $\sum b_n/n$ converges.

*Hint* Show that the function $F$ of bounded variation defined by

$$F(t) = \int_0^t \{f(x) - \tfrac{1}{2}a_0\}\, dx$$

has Fourier coefficients $A_n = -b_n/n$ and $B_n = a_n/n$. Then evaluate the convergent Fourier series of $F$ at 0.

*10.2.5* (*Localization principle*). Suppose $f$ and $h$ are periodic functions, both integrable on $[0, 2\pi)$, which coincide almost everywhere on some interval $(a, b)$. Use Lemma 10.2.1 to show that the Fourier series of $f$ converges at a point $t \in (a, b)$ if and only if the Fourier series of $h$ does.

## 10.3 SUMMATION BY ARITHMETIC MEANS

In the previous section we have discussed conditions which ensure that a Fourier series converges at a given point. Since even the Fourier series of a continuous function can diverge—we refer the reader again to the literature for such examples—the question arises whether it is possible to reconstruct a function from its Fourier series by some other means. This is indeed possible by the so-called method of summation by arithmetic means.

10.3.1 DEFINITION *A sequence $\{s_n : n \geq 0\}$ is said to converge to $s$ in the sense of Cesàro, or to be $(C, 1)$ convergent to $s$, if the sequence $\{\sigma_n\}$ of arithmetic means,*

$$\sigma_n = \frac{1}{n}\{s_0 + \cdots + s_{n-1}\},$$

*converges to $s$. A series is said to be summable by arithmetic means, or in the sense of Cesàro, or $(C, 1)$ summable, if the sequence of its partial sums is $(C, 1)$ convergent.*

The notation "$(C, 1)$ convergent" suggests that there are other concepts of "convergence"; but we will not discuss these here.

It is not true that a $(C, 1)$ convergent sequence converges. For instance the divergent sequence $\{1, 0, 1, 0 \cdots\}$ converges to $\frac{1}{2}$ in the sense of Cesàro. However, the converse is true.

10.3.2 PROPOSITION *If the sequence $\{s_n\}$ converges to $s$, then its arithmetic means converge to $s$.*

*Proof* For each $\varepsilon > 0$ we can find an integer $N$ such that

$$|s_n - s| \leq \varepsilon \qquad \text{for } n \geq N.$$

Now let $n > N$. We have

$$\begin{aligned} |\sigma_n - s| &= \frac{1}{n}\left|\sum_{k=0}^{n-1}(s_k - s)\right| \\ &\leq \frac{1}{n}\left|\sum_{k=0}^{N-1}(s_k - s)\right| + \frac{1}{n}\sum_{k=N}^{n-1}|s_k - s| \\ &\leq \frac{1}{n}A + \frac{n-N}{n}\varepsilon \leq 2\varepsilon \end{aligned}$$

if we choose $n \geq A/\varepsilon$. This proves the proposition.

We apply now the method of summation by arithmetic means to Fourier series. A vital tool will be the summation formula

$$\sum_{k=0}^{n-1} \sin (k + \tfrac{1}{2})x = \frac{1 - \cos nx}{2 \sin \frac{1}{2}x} \tag{10.3.3}$$

valid if $x$ is not a multiple of $2\pi$. To prove this, we recall the formulas

$$\cos (a - b) = \cos a \cos b + \sin a \sin b,$$
$$\cos (a + b) = \cos a \cos b - \sin a \sin b.$$

By subtracting the second equation from the first, we get

$$2 \sin a \sin b = \cos (a - b) - \cos (a + b). \tag{10.3.4}$$

We now prove Equation (10.3.3) by induction on $n$. It is true for $n = 1$, since the last equation yields $1 - \cos x = 2 \sin^2 x/2$ (with $a = b = x/2$). For $n \geq 1$ we have

$$\begin{aligned}\frac{1 - \cos nx}{2 \sin \frac{1}{2}x} + \sin (n + \tfrac{1}{2})x &= \frac{1}{2 \sin \frac{1}{2}x} \{1 - \cos nx + 2 \sin (n + \tfrac{1}{2})x \sin \tfrac{1}{2}x\} \\ &= \frac{1}{2 \sin \frac{1}{2}x} \{1 - \cos nx + \cos nx - \cos (n + 1)x\} \\ &= \frac{1 - \cos (n + 1)x}{2 \sin \frac{1}{2}x}.\end{aligned}$$

Using Equation (10.3.3), we find for the arithmetic means of the Dirichlet kernels (see Equation (10.1.7)):

$$F_n(x) = \frac{1}{n} \sum_{k=0}^{n-1} D_k(x) = \frac{1}{n} \sum_{k=0}^{n-1} \frac{\sin (k + \frac{1}{2})x}{2 \sin \frac{1}{2}x} = \frac{1 - \cos nx}{4n \sin^2 \frac{1}{2}x}. \tag{10.3.5}$$

The periodic functions $F_n$ are called Fejer kernels (Figure 10.3). The above formula is valid for $x$ not a multiple of $2\pi$. The Fejer kernels have the following

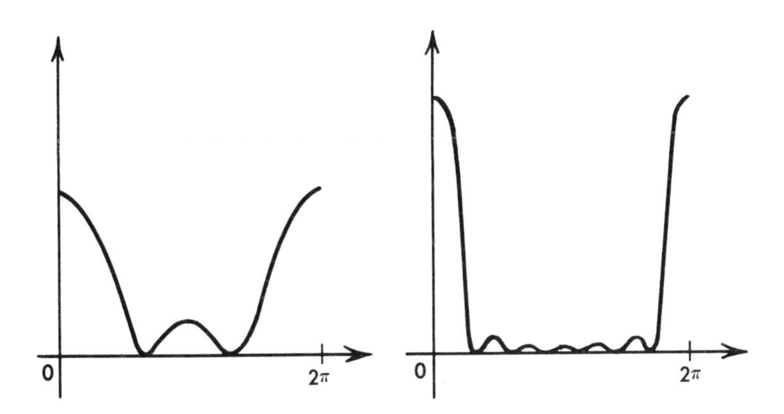


Figure 10.3 The graph of Fejer's kernel $F_n$ for $n = 1$ and $n = 3$.

important property

(10.3.6) $$\frac{1}{\pi}\int_0^{2\pi} F_n\,dx = 1 = \frac{2}{\pi}\int_0^{\pi} F_n\,dx$$

as is seen easily from the definition since the Dirichlet kernels have a similar property.

10.3.7 PROPOSITION *Suppose $f$ is a periodic function that is integrable on $[0, 2\pi)$. Then the arithmetic means $\sigma_n$ of its Fourier series are given by the formula*

$$\sigma_n(t) = \frac{1}{\pi}\int_0^{\pi} F_n(x)\{f(t+x) + f(t-x)\}\,dx.$$

*Proof* This follows immediately from the corresponding formula,

$$s_n(t) = \frac{1}{\pi}\int_0^{\pi} D_n(x)\{f(t+x) + f(t-x)\}\,dx$$

for the partial sums $s_n$ of the Fourier series of $f$, which we obtained in Proposition 10.1.9.

10.3.8 COROLLARY *The Fourier series of $f$ is summable with sum $s(t)$ by the method of arithmetic means if and only if*

$$\lim_{n\to\infty}\int_0^{\pi} g(t, x)F_n(x)\,dx = 0$$

*where*

$$g(x, t) = f(t+x) + f(t-x) - 2s(t).$$

*Proof* By Equation (10.3.6) we have

$$\frac{1}{\pi}\int_0^{\pi} 2s(t)\,dx = s(t),$$

so that the corollary follows indeed from the proposition.

As in Section 10.2 we can employ this corollary to find conditions under which a Fourier series is summable by the method of arithmetic means. But this time the result will be much stronger.

10.3.9 THEOREM

FEJER'S THEOREM *Suppose the periodic function $f$ is integrable on $[0, 2\pi)$. If the limits*

$$f(t+0) = \lim_{\substack{x\to 0\\ x>0}} f(t+x), \qquad f(t-0) = \lim_{\substack{x\to 0\\ x>0}} f(t-x)$$

*exist for a certain $t$, then the Fourier series of $f$ at $t$ is summable to $\{f(t+0) + f(t-0)\}/2$ by the method of arithmetic means. In particular, the Fourier series* *of $f$ at $t$ is summable to $f(t)$ by the method of arithmetic means whenever $f$ is continuous at $t$.*

*Proof* Notice that

$$\lim_{\substack{x\to 0\\ x>0}} g_t(x) = 0 \qquad \text{if } g_t(x) = f(x+t) + f(x-t) - f(t+0) - f(t-0).$$

Thus, for a given $\varepsilon > 0$, we can find a $\delta > 0$ such that

$$|g_t(x)| \le \varepsilon \qquad \text{for } x \in (0, \delta).$$

With this choice of $\delta$ we have

$$\left|\int_0^\pi g_t F_n\,dx\right| \le \left|\int_0^\delta g_t F_n\,dx\right| + \left|\int_\delta^\pi g_t F_n\,dx\right|$$

$$\le \varepsilon\int_0^\delta |F_n|\,dx + \frac{1}{4n}\int_\delta^\pi |g_t|\frac{1-\cos nx}{\sin^2 \frac{1}{2}x}\,dx.$$

Notice that the kernel $F_n$ is nonnegative whence, by Equation (10.3.6),

(10.3.10) $$\left|\int_0^\pi gF_n\,dx\right| \le \varepsilon\int_0^\pi F_n\,dx + \frac{1}{n}\frac{2}{4\sin^2\frac{1}{2}\delta}\int_\delta^\pi |g_t|\,dx$$

$$\le \varepsilon\frac{\pi}{2} + \frac{1}{n}A_t \le \pi\varepsilon$$

if we choose $n \ge 2A_t/\pi\varepsilon$. Thus

$$\lim_{n\to\infty}\int_0^\pi g_t F_n\,dx = 0,$$

and this completes the proof according to Corollary 10.3.8.

Let us remark that if $f$ is continuous at all points of a closed bounded interval $[a, b]$, then it is uniformly continuous there; thus we can choose the $\varepsilon$ in the last proof to be the same for all $t \in [a, b]$. The estimate (10.3.10) then holds for all $t \in [a, b]$, whence

$$\lim_{n\to\infty}\{\sigma_n(t) - f(t)\} = \frac{1}{\pi}\int_0^\pi g(x, t)F_n(x)\,dx = 0$$

uniformly in $t$.

**10.3.11 COROLLARY** *If the function $f$ is continuous at all points of a closed bounded interval $[a, b]$, then the sequence $\{\sigma_n\}$ of arithmetic means of the partial sums of its Fourier series converges uniformly to $f$ on $[a, b]$.*

**10.3.12 COROLLARY**

**WEIERSTRASS APPROXIMATION THEOREM** *Every continuous function $f$ on a closed bounded interval $[a, b]$ can be uniformly approximated on $[a, b]$ by polynomials.*

*Proof* We have to show that for every $\varepsilon > 0$ there is a polynomial $p$ such that

$$f(x) - p(x) \leq \varepsilon \qquad \text{for } x \in [a, b].$$

Let us assume for simplicity that $[a, b] = [0, \pi]$. Otherwise we would have to look at the function $f(\pi(x - a)/(b - a))$. We extend $f$ to $(\pi, 2\pi)$ by

$$f(x) = f(2\pi - x) \qquad \text{for } x \in (\pi, 2\pi)$$

and then by periodicity to all of the real line. Then $f$ becomes a continuous periodic function. By the last corollary, the sequence $\{\sigma_n\}$ of arithmetic means of the partial sums of the Fourier series of $f$ converges uniformly on $[0, \pi]$ to $f$. Each $\sigma_n$ in turn is a linear combination of the functions $\sin kx$ and $\cos kx$ so that it can be expanded into a power series; that is, each $\sigma_n$ can be uniformly approximated by polynomials on $[0, \pi]$, namely, by the partial sums of its power series.

Theorem 10.3.9 tells us that we can rediscover a continuous function if we know its Fourier series. But more is true. Every function with a known Fourier series can be reconstructed almost everywhere, as we will show now.

### 10.3.13 THEOREM

FEJER-LEBESGUE THEOREM *Let $f$ be a periodic function that is integrable on $[0, 2\pi)$. Then the sequence $\{\sigma_n(t)\}$ of arithmetic means of the partial sums of its Fourier series converges to $f(t)$ for each $t$ such that*

$$\lim_{h \to 0} \frac{1}{h} \int_0^h |f(t + x) - f(t)|\, dx = 0. \tag{10.3.14}$$

*Proof* Let

$$g_t(x) = f(t + x) + f(t - x) - 2f(t).$$

Note that

$$\left| \int_0^h |g_t(x)|\, dx \right| \leq \left| \int_0^h |f(t + x) - f(t)|\, dx \right| + \left| \int_0^h |f(t - x) - f(t)|\, dx \right|$$

so that we can find a $\delta$, $0 < \delta \leq 1$, for each $\varepsilon > 0$ such that

$$\int_0^h |g_t(x)|\, dx \leq h\varepsilon \qquad \text{for } h \in (0, \delta).$$

Furthermore, observe that $1 - \cos nx = 2 \sin^2 nx/2$ (setting $nx/2 = a = b$ in Equation (10.3.4)). Thus for $n \geq 1/\delta$,

$$\left| \int_0^\pi g_t F_n\, dx \right| \leq \int_0^{1/n} |g_t|\, F_n\, dx + \int_{1/n}^{\delta} |g_t|\, F_n\, dx + \int_{\delta}^{\pi} |g_t|\, F_n\, dx;$$

we now estimate the integrals on the right separately, using the inequalities

$$\sin a \leq a, \qquad \sin a \geq \frac{2}{\pi} a \qquad \text{for } a \in \left(0, \frac{\pi}{2}\right).$$

By our hypothesis on $n$ and $\delta$ we obtain

$$\int_0^{1/n} |g_t| \frac{2 \sin^2 \frac{1}{2}nx}{4n \sin^2 \frac{1}{2}x} dx \leq \frac{1}{2n} n^2 \frac{\pi^2}{4} \int_0^{1/n} |g_t| \, dx \leq \varepsilon \frac{\pi^2}{8}.$$

Using partial integration (Theorem 7.5.3), we get for the second integral

$$\begin{aligned}
\int_{1/n}^{\delta} |g_t| \frac{2 \sin^2 \frac{1}{2}nx}{4n \sin^2 \frac{1}{2}x} dx &\leq \frac{\pi^2}{2n} \int_{1/n}^{\delta} |g_t| \frac{1}{x^2} dx \\
&= \frac{\pi^2}{2n} \left\{ \frac{1}{\delta^2} G_t(\delta) - n^2 G_t\left(\frac{1}{n}\right) \right\} + \frac{\pi^2}{2n} \int_{1/n}^{\delta} \frac{2}{x^3} G_t(x) \, dx \\
&\leq \frac{\pi^2}{2n} \left\{ \frac{\varepsilon}{\delta} + 2\varepsilon \int_{1/n}^{1} \frac{1}{x^2} dx \right\} \leq \{\varepsilon/\delta + 2\varepsilon n\} \frac{\pi^2}{2n} \\
&\leq \frac{3}{2} \pi^2 \varepsilon,
\end{aligned}$$

where $G_t(h) = \int_0^h |g_t| \, dx$ is the primitive of $|g_t|$. The last integral to be estimated is

$$\int_{\delta}^{\pi} |g_t| \frac{2 \sin^2 \frac{1}{2}nx}{4n \sin^2 \frac{1}{2}x} dx \leq \frac{\pi^2}{n} \frac{1}{\delta^2} \int_0^{\pi} |g_t| \, dx$$

which can be made arbitrarily small by choosing $n$ large enough. Thus

$$\lim_{n \to \infty} \int_0^{\pi} g_t F_n \, dx = 0$$

which, according to Corollary 10.3.8, proves the theorem.

10.3.15 **Proposition** *The condition* (10.3.14) *of the last theorem holds for a.a.t. Thus* $\{\sigma_n(t)\}$ *converges to* $f(t)$ *for a.a.t.*

*Proof* For any real number $a$,

$$|f(t) - a| = \lim_{h \to 0} \frac{1}{h} \int_t^{t+h} |f(x) - a| \, dx = \lim_{h \to 0} \frac{1}{h} \int_0^h |f(t + x) - a| \, dx$$

holds for a.a. $t$ by Theorem 7.2.5. Let $E_a$ be the null set where this equation does not hold and set

$$E = \bigcup \{E_r : r \text{ is rational}\}.$$

Then $E$ is a null set. We claim that for any $t \notin E$,

$$\lim_{h \to 0} \frac{1}{h} \int_0^h |f(t + x) - f(t)| \, dx = 0$$

For, if $\varepsilon > 0$, let $r$ be a rational number with $|f(t) - r| \leq \varepsilon$. Then

$$\begin{aligned}\left| \frac{1}{h} \int_0^h |f(t + x) - f(t)| \, dx \right| &\leq \left| \frac{1}{h} \int_0^h |f(t + x) - r| \, dx \right| + \left| \frac{1}{h} \int_0^h |r - f(t)| \, dx \right| \\ &\leq \left| \frac{1}{h} \int_0^h |f(t + x) - r| \, dx \right| + \varepsilon \\ &\leq 3\varepsilon\end{aligned}$$

if we choose $\delta > 0$ such that

$$\left| \frac{1}{h} \int_0^h |f(t + x) - r| \, dx \right| \leq |f(t) - r| + \varepsilon \leq 2\varepsilon \qquad \text{for } |h| \leq \delta.$$

This completes the proof.

## *EXERCISES*

In the following exercises $f$ is a periodic function which is integrable on $[0, 2\pi)$ and $\sigma_n$ is the $n$th arithmetic mean of the partial sums $\{s_k\}$ of its Fourier series.

*10.3.1* If $f = \chi_{[0,\pi)}$, why does $\{\sigma_n\}$ not converge uniformly on $[0, \pi]$?

*10.3.2* Deduce Fejer's theorem from the Fejer-Lebesgue theorem.

*Hint* Show that the condition (10.3.14) is satisfied if $f$ is continuous at $t$. If $f$ is not continuous at $t$, but if $f(t + 0)$ and $f(t - 0)$ exist, modify $f$ so as to become continuous at $t$.

*10.3.3* If the sequence $\{s_n\}$ converges almost everywhere, it must necessarily converge to $f$ a.e.

## 10.4 FOURIER SERIES FOR FUNCTIONS IN $L^2(0, 2\pi)$

In this section we will apply the results of Sections 5.1 and 5.2 to Fourier series of square integrable functions on $[0, 2\pi)$. Let us denote by $L^2(0, 2\pi)$, or for short $L^2$, the set of all measurable functions $f$ on $[0, 2\pi)$ with an integrable square on $[0, 2\pi)$. Recall that $L^2$ is a linear space with norm

$$\|f\| = \left\{ \int_0^{2\pi} f^2 \, dx \right\}^{1/2}, \qquad f \in L^2$$

and scalar product

$$(f, g) = \int_0^{2\pi} fg\, dx, \qquad f, g \in L^2.$$

Since $\chi_{[0,2\pi)}$ belongs to $L^2, f = f\chi_{[0,2\pi)}$ is integrable for each $f \in L^2$. Thus a function $f$ in $L^2$ has a Fourier series,

$$\tfrac{1}{2}a_0 + \sum \{a_n \cos nx + b_n \sin nx\}.$$

Since $\cos nx$ and $\sin nx$ belong to $L^2$, it is natural to study the Fourier series of $f$ in $L^2$.

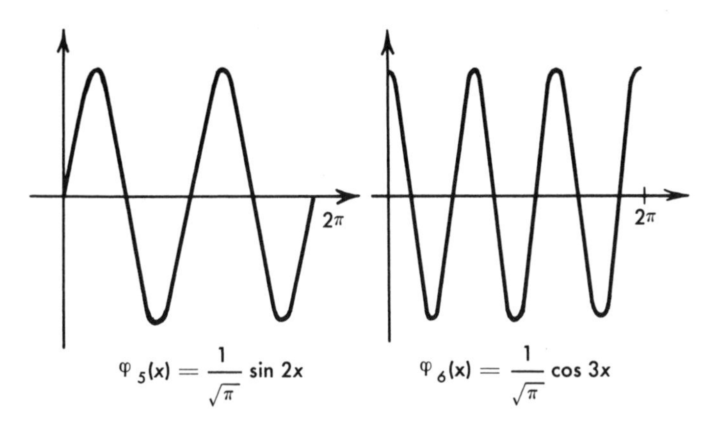


Figure 10.4 These are two typical functions of the trigonometric system (10.4.1).

If we let (Figure 10.4)

$$\varphi_1 = \frac{1}{\sqrt{2\pi}}\chi_{[0,2\pi)}, \quad \varphi_{2k} = \frac{1}{\sqrt{\pi}}\cos kx, \qquad k \geq 1 \tag{10.4.1}$$

$$\varphi_{2k+1} = \frac{1}{\sqrt{\pi}}\sin kx, \qquad k \geq 1$$

then we have according to the formulas in the proof of Proposition 10.1.2,

$$(\varphi_n, \varphi_m) = \begin{cases} 0 \text{ if } n \neq m \\ 1 \text{ if } n = m. \end{cases} \tag{10.4.2}$$

10.4.3 DEFINITION *A sequence $\{\varphi_n\}$ in $L^2$ is called an orthonormal system if it satisfies* (10.4.2). *The numbers*

$$c_n = (f, \varphi_n)$$

*are called the Fourier coefficients of the function $f \in L^2$ with respect to the orthonormal system $\{\varphi_n\}$.*

If we take for our $\varphi_n$ the functions in (10.4.1), then $c_n/\sqrt{\pi}$ are the ordinary Fourier coefficients of $f$ for $n \geq 2$ and $c_1/\sqrt{2\pi} = a_0/2$. Thus $\sum c_n\varphi_n$ is the Fourier series of $f$ in this case.

### 10.4.4 PROPOSITION

BESSEL'S INEQUALITY *If $\{\varphi_n\}$ is an orthonormal system for $L^2$, then we have for the Fourier coefficients (with respect to $\{\varphi_n\}$) of any function $f$ in $L^2$,*

$$\|s_n\|^2 = \sum_{k=1}^{n} c_k^2 \leq \|f\|^2, \qquad \text{where } s_n = \sum_{k=1}^{n} c_k\varphi_k.$$

*Proof* The function $g = f - s_n$ belongs to $L^2$ and we obtain for its norm

$$\begin{aligned} 0 \leq \|g\|^2 = (g, g) &= (f, f) - 2\sum_{k=1}^{n} c_k(f, \varphi_k) + \sum_{j=1}^{n}\sum_{k=1}^{n} c_j c_k(\varphi_j, \varphi_k) \\ &= \|f\|^2 - 2\sum_{k=1}^{n} c_k^2 + \sum_{k=1}^{n} c_k^2 \\ &= \|f\|^2 - \sum_{k=1}^{n} c_k^2 \end{aligned}$$

from which the assertion follows immediately.

### 10.4.5 COROLLARY *The series $\sum c_n^2$ converges and*

$$\sum_{n=1}^{\infty} c_n^2 \leq \|f\|^2.$$

For the ordinary Fourier coefficients of a function $f$ in $L^2$ we therefore have the relation

$$\tfrac{1}{2}a_0^2 + \sum_{n=1}^{\infty} (a_n^2 + b_n^2) \leq \frac{1}{\pi}\int_0^{2\pi} f^2\, dx.$$

A converse to Corollary 10.4.5 follows.

### 10.4.6 PROPOSITION *If $\{c_k\}$ is a sequence such that $\sum c_k^2$ converges and*

$$s_n = \sum_{k=1}^{n} c_k\varphi_k,$$

*then $\{s_n\}$ converges in $L^2$, that is, there is a function $g \in L^2$ such that*

$$\lim_{n\to\infty} \|s_n - g\| = 0.$$

*This function g has Fourier coefficients $c_k$ and*

$$\|g\|^2 = \sum_{k=1}^{\infty} c_k^2.$$

*Proof* $\{s_n\}$ is a Cauchy sequence in $L^2$, since for $m > n$

$$\|s_n - s_m\|^2 = \sum_{j=n+1}^{m} \sum_{k=n+1}^{m} c_j c_k (\varphi_j, \varphi_k) = \sum_{k=n+1}^{m} c_k^2$$

which tends to zero as $n$ and $m$ tend to infinity, because $\sum c_k^2$ converges. By the Riesz-Fischer theorem we therefore have a function $g$ in $L^2$ with

$$\lim_{n\to\infty} \|s_n - g\| = 0.$$

Then according to the Schwarz inequality

$$|(g, \varphi_k) - c_k| = |(g - s_n, \varphi_k)| \leq \|g - s_n\|, \qquad n \geq k,$$

so that necessarily $c_k = (g, \varphi_k)$. Finally,

$$\|s_n - g\|^2 = \left(\sum_{k=1}^{n} c_k\varphi_k - g, \sum_{k=1}^{n} c_k\varphi_k - g\right) = \|g\|^2 - \sum_{k=1}^{n} c_k^2$$

which tends to zero, whence $\|g\|^2 = \sum_{k=1}^{\infty} c_k^2$.

We are now interested in finding conditions on the $\varphi_k$ which will ensure that the function $g$ in the last proposition equals $f$ a.e. In particular, we want to prove that this is the case if the $\varphi_k$ are the trigonometric functions in (10.4.1).

Let us first consider a specific example.

10.4.7 LEMMA *If $\chi$ is the characteristic function of an interval in $[0, 2\pi)$, then the sequence $\{s_n\}$ of the partial sums*

$$s_n = \tfrac{1}{2}a_0 + \sum_{i=1}^{n} \{a_k \cos nx + b_k \sin nx\}$$

*of its Fourier series converges in $L^2$ to $\chi$ and*

$$\frac{1}{\pi}\int_0^{2\pi} \chi^2\, dx = \tfrac{1}{2}a_0^2 + \sum_{n=1}^{\infty} (a_n^2 + b_n^2).$$

*Proof* The sequence $\{s_n\}$ converges almost everywhere to $\chi$ by Proposition 10.1.11. If we choose a subsequence $\{s_{n(k)}\}$ such that $\|s_{n(k+1)} - s_{n(k)}\| \le 2^{-k}$, then

$$\|\chi\| + \|s_{n(1)}\| + \sum_{k=1}^{\infty} \|s_{n(k+1)} - s_{n(k)}\| < \infty$$

so that by Proposition 5.2.1,

$$\begin{aligned} 0 &= \lim_{m\to\infty} \left\| \chi - s_{n(1)} - \sum_{k=1}^{m} (s_{n(k+1)} - s_{n(k)}) \right\| \\ &= \lim_{m\to\infty} \|\chi - s_{n(m+1)}\|. \end{aligned}$$

Since $\{s_n\}$ is a Cauchy sequence according to the last proposition, we conclude

$$\lim_{n\to\infty} \|\chi - s_n\| = 0$$

(This is actually an immediate consequence of Theorem 10.2.7 which tells us that $s_n$ converges to $\chi$ boundedly almost everywhere, but we wanted to avoid any dependence on Section 10.2.) The lemma follows now from Proposition 10.4.6.

10.4.8 DEFINITION *An orthonormal system $\{\varphi_k\}$ is complete if for any $f$ in $L^2$*

$$s_n = \sum_{k=1}^{n} c_k\varphi_k, \qquad c_k = (f, \varphi_k)$$

*converges to $f$ in $L^2$.*

In order to show that the trigonometric system (10.4.1) is complete, we need the following characterization of complete orthonormal systems.

10.4.9 PROPOSITION *For an orthonormal system $\{\varphi_k\}$ the following are equivalent:*

(a) *$\{\varphi_k\}$ is complete,*
(b) *for every $f \in L^2$ and $\varepsilon > 0$ there is a finite linear combination*

$$g = \sum_{k=1}^{n} d_k\varphi_k$$

*such that $\|f - g\| \le \varepsilon$,*
(c) *if the Fourier coefficients of a function $f$ in $L^2$ vanish, then $f = 0$ a.e.*

*Proof* It is immediate from the definition that (a) implies (b). To prove that (b) implies (c), let $f$ be any function in $L^2$ with vanishing Fourier coefficients. For a given $\varepsilon > 0$ choose $g$ as in (b). Then

$$(f, f - g) = \|f\|^2 - \left(f, \sum_{k=1}^{n} d_k \varphi_k\right) = \|f\|^2$$
$$\leq \|f\| \, \|f - g\| \leq \varepsilon \, \|f\|$$

which implies $\|f\| \leq \varepsilon$. But $\varepsilon$ was arbitrary so that $f$ vanishes almost everywhere.
Finally, (c) implies (a). Let $f \in L^2$; then

$$s_n = \sum_{k=1}^{n} c_k \varphi_k$$

converges to a function $g$ in $L^2$ with the same Fourier coefficients as $f$ (Proposition 10.4.6), that is, $f - g$ has vanishing Fourier coefficients, whence $f = g$ a.e. by (c).

We can utilize Criterion (b) to prove that the trigonometric system (10.4.1) is complete.

10.4.10 THEOREM *The trigonometric system* (10.4.1) *is complete.*

*Proof* We prove that Condition (b) of the last proposition is verified. It is verified if $f$ is the characteristic function of an interval in $[0, 2\pi)$ (Lemma 10.4.7), and, since every step function vanishing off $[0, 2\pi)$ is a linear combination of such characteristic functions, Condition (b) is valid for all step functions in $L^2$. By Theorem 5.2.4 there is, for each $\varepsilon > 0$, a step function $\varphi$ with $\|f - \varphi\| < \varepsilon/2$. If we choose

$$g = \sum_{k=1}^{n} d_k \varphi_k$$

with $\|\varphi - g\| \leq \varepsilon/2$, then

$$\|f - g\| \leq \|f - \varphi\| + \|\varphi - g\| \leq \varepsilon$$

which proves our claim.

10.4.11 COROLLARY *Let $f$ be in $L^2$; then the sequence $\{s_n\}$ of partial sums*

$$s_n = \tfrac{1}{2}a_0 + \sum_{k=1}^{n} \{a_n \cos nx + b_n \sin nx\}$$

*of its Fourier series converges to $f$ in $L^2$.*

10.4.12 COROLLARY

PARSEVAL'S THEOREM *If $f$ and $g$ belong to $L^2$ and have Fourier series*

$$\tfrac{1}{2}a_0 + \sum \{a_n \cos nx + b_n \sin nx\}, \quad \tfrac{1}{2}a_0' + \sum \{a_n' \cos nx + b_n' \sin nx\},$$

*respectively, then*

$$\frac{1}{\pi}\|f\|^2 = \frac{1}{\pi}\int_0^{2\pi} f^2\,dx = \tfrac{1}{2}a_0^2 + \sum_{n=1}^{\infty}(a_n^2 + b_n^2),$$

$$\frac{1}{\pi}(f, g) = \frac{1}{\pi}\int_0^{2\pi} fg\,dx = \tfrac{1}{2}a_0a_0' + \sum_{n=1}^{\infty}(a_na_n' + b_nb_n').$$

*Proof* The expression for $\|f\|^2$ is just a restatement of Proposition 10.4.6. If $s_n$ and $s_n'$ denote the partial sums of the Fourier series of $f$ and $g$, respectively, then

$$\frac{1}{\pi}(f, s_n') + \frac{1}{\pi}(g, s_n) - \frac{1}{\pi}(s_n, s_n') = \tfrac{1}{2}a_0a_0' + \sum_{k=1}^{n}(a_ka_k' + b_kb_k')$$

as is easily verified. Thus

$$\frac{1}{\pi}(f - s_n, g - s_n') = \frac{1}{\pi}\{(f, g) - (f, s_n') - (g, s_n) + (s_n, s_n')\}$$

$$= (f, g) - \left\{\tfrac{1}{2}a_0a_0' + \sum_{k=1}^{n}(a_ka_k' + b_kb_k')\right\}.$$

The left-hand side tends to zero, since

$$|(f - s_n, g - s_n')| \leq \|f - s_n\|\,\|g - s_n'\|.$$

This proves the corollary.

The formula

$$(f, g) = \sum_{k=1}^{\infty} c_kc_k', \quad c_k = (f, \varphi_k), \quad c_k' = (g, \varphi_k)$$

is actually valid for any complete orthonormal system $\{\varphi_k\}$, the proof being identical to the one presented above.

## *EXERCISES*

*10.4.1* Use Parseval's theorem to evaluate $\sum 1/n^2$.

*Hint* Show that

$$\frac{\pi - x}{2} = \sum_{n=1}^{\infty}\frac{\sin nx}{n}.$$

*10.4.2* Using Parseval's theorem show that

$$\frac{1}{\pi}\int^{2\pi} xf(x)\,dx = \pi a_0 - 2\sum\frac{b_n}{n}$$

if $b_n$ are the Fourier sine coefficients of the function $f$ in $L^2$.

*10.4.3* Use Corollary 10.3.11 in conjunction with Criterion (b) of Proposition 10.4.9 to give another proof of the completeness of the trigonometric system (10.4.1).

*Hint* Note that Theorem 5.2.4 also holds with $\varphi$ a continuous function, since the continuous functions vanishing off an interval may be taken as elementary functions.

# 10.5 EXERCISES

## A. Examples of Fourier Series

**10.5.1** Expand the following functions into Fourier series and note where the Fourier series does not converge to the function in question:

(a) $x$
(b) $x^2$
(c) $e^x$
(d) $\cos ax$
(e) $\sin ax$
(f) $\sinh x$

**10.5.2** Let the function $f$ on $[0, 2\pi)$ be defined by

$$f(x) = \begin{cases} (x - \pi)^2 & \text{if } 0 \le x < \pi \\ \pi^2 & \text{if } \pi \le x < 2\pi. \end{cases}$$

Find the Fourier coefficients $\{a_n : n \ge 0\}$ of $f$ and deduce the formulas

$$\sum_{n=1}^{\infty} \frac{1}{n^2} = \frac{\pi^2}{6}, \qquad \sum_{n=1}^{\infty} \frac{(-1)^{n-1}}{n^2} = \frac{\pi^2}{12}.$$

**10.5.3** Show that

$$\tfrac{1}{8}x(\pi - x)(\pi - 2x) = \sum_{n=1}^{\infty} \frac{\sin 2nx}{n^3} \qquad \text{for } 0 \le x \le \pi$$

and deduce a formula for $\sum_{n=1}^{\infty} (-1)^{n-1}/(2n - 1)^3$.

**10.5.4** Show that $\sum (\cos nx)/n$ is the Fourier series of $-\log (2 \sin x/2)$.

**10.5.5** Suppose the integrable function $f$ on $[0, 2\pi)$ satisfies a Lipschitz condition at $t$, that is, there are constants $\delta$, $M > 0$ such that

$$|f(t + h) - f(t)| \le M\,|h| \qquad \text{for } |h| \le \delta.$$

Use Dini's test to prove that the Fourier series of $f$ converges to $f(t)$ at $t$.

## B. Trigonometric Series with Monotone-Decreasing Coefficients

**10.5.6** Suppose $\{b_n\}$ is a decreasing sequence of positive numbers tending to zero. Show that the series $\sum b_n \sin nx$ converges uniformly on any closed interval not containing a multiple of $2\pi$.

*Hint* Use Abel's lemma (Exercise 10.2.2) and the formula

$$\sum_{n=k}^{m} \sin nx = \frac{\cos (k - \frac{1}{2})x - \cos (m + \frac{1}{2})x}{2 \sin \frac{1}{2}x}.$$

**10.5.7** Observe that, by the previous exercise, $\sum_{n\geqq 2} \sin nx/\log n$ converges everywhere. Show that this series is not the Fourier series of any function.

*Hint* Apply the result of Exercise 10.2.4. Note

$$\sum_{n=2}^{k} \frac{1}{n \log n} \geq \int_2^k \frac{1}{x \log x}\, dx = \log \log k - \log \log 2$$

*Remark* The trigonometric series $\sum_{n\geq 2} \sin nx/\log n$ must converge to a function that is not integrable on $[0, 2\pi)$ (see Exercise 10.3.3).

**10.5.8** Let $\{b_n\}$ be as in Exercise 10.5.6 and assume in addition that the sequence $\{nb_n\}$ is bounded. Prove that the series $\sum b_n \sin nx$ converges boundedly on $(0, 2\pi)$ to a function of which it is the Fourier series.

*Hint* By the formula in Exercise 10.5.6,

$$\left|\sum_{n=k}^{m} \sin nx\right| \leq \frac{1}{\sin \frac{1}{2}x} \leq \frac{\pi}{x}, \qquad x \in (0, 2\pi).$$

Deduce that for $x \geq \pi/k$,

$$\left|\sum_{n=k}^{m} b_n \sin nx\right| \leq kb_k$$

(using Abel's lemma). If $x \leq \pi/m$, use $|\sin x| \leq |x|$ to show that

$$\left|\sum_{n=k}^{m} b_n \sin nx\right| \leq \pi \sup \{nb_n : k \leq n \leq m\}.$$

If $\pi/m \leq x \leq \pi/k$, say $x \in [\pi/(j+1), \pi/j]$, then use the above results to estimate

$$\left|\sum_{n=k}^{m} b_n \sin nx\right| \leq \left|\sum_{n=k}^{j}\right| + \left|\sum_{n=j+1}^{m}\right|$$

**10.5.9** Let $\{b_n\}$ be a sequence as in Exercise 10.5.6 and suppose that $\{nb_n\}$ tends to zero. Prove that $\sum b_n \sin nx$ converges uniformly to a continuous function of which it is the Fourier series.

*Hint* Reinvestigate the hint for the previous exercise.

## C. The Fourier Coefficients of Some Classes of Functions

**10.5.10** Suppose the periodic function $f$ satisfies a uniform Hölder condition of order $\alpha$, $0 < \alpha \leq 1$, that is, there is a constant $M$ such that

$$|f(x) - f(y)| \leq M\,|x - y|^\alpha.$$

Show that the Fourier coefficients of $f$ satisfy

$$|a_n| \leq \pi^\alpha M/n^\alpha, \qquad |b_n| \leq \pi^\alpha M/n^\alpha.$$

*Hint* Notice that

$$a_n = \frac{1}{2\pi}\int_0^{2\pi}\left\{f(x) - f\left(x + \frac{\pi}{n}\right)\right\}\cos nx\,dx,$$

and a similar formula holds for $b_n$.

**10.5.11** Suppose the periodic function $f$ is of locally bounded variation. Show that there is a constant $M$ such that

$$|a_n| \leq \frac{M}{n}, \quad |b_n| \leq \frac{M}{n},$$

where $a_n$ and $b_n$ are the Fourier coefficients of $f$.

*Hint* Let $f_1$ and $f_2$ be two nonnegative monotone nondecreasing functions on $[0, 2\pi)$ such that $f = f_1 - f_2$. Estimate the Fourier coefficients of $f_1$ and $f_2$ using the second mean value theorem.

**10.5.12** If the periodic function $f$ is absolutely continuous, then its Fourier coefficients satisfy

$$\lim_{n\to\infty} na_n = 0 = \lim_{n\to\infty} nb_n.$$

*Hint* Use integration by parts to estimate $a_n$ and $b_n$ (see Theorem 7.5.3).

## D. Summation by the Method of Arithmetic Means

In the following

$$S\colon\ \tfrac{1}{2}a_0 + \sum \{a_n \cos nx + b_n \sin nx\}$$

is any trigonometric series and $\sigma_n$ denotes the $n$th arithmetic mean of the sequence $\{s_k\}$ of partial sums of this series.

**10.5.13** Prove that the series $S$ is the Fourier series of a bounded function if and only if there is a constant $M$ such that $|\sigma_n| \leq M$ for all $n$.

*Hint* For the "only if" part use the positivity of Fejer's kernel. For the "if" part observe that for $0 < m \leq n$,

$$2M^2 \geq \frac{1}{\pi}\int_0^{2\pi} \sigma_n^2 \, dx \geq \tfrac{1}{2}a_0^2 + \sum_{k=1}^{m} (a_k^2 + b_k^2)\left(1 - \frac{k}{n}\right)^2$$

and let $n$ tend to infinity. Conclude that

$$\tfrac{1}{2}a_0^2 + \sum (a_k^2 + b_k^2)$$

converges. Then apply Proposition 10.4.6 and the Fejer-Lebesgue theorem.

**10.5.14** Show that $S$ is the Fourier series of a continuous function if and only if $\{\sigma_n\}$ converges uniformly.

*Hint* To show that $g = \lim_{n\to\infty} \sigma_n$ has Fourier coefficients $\{a_0, a_n, b_n : n \geq 1\}$, observe that

$$\frac{1}{\pi}\int_0^{2\pi} \sigma_n(x) \cos kx \, dx = \left(1 - \frac{k}{n}\right)a_k, \qquad k \leq n - 1,$$

and similarly for $b_k$.

**10.5.15** Suppose

$$\sum a_{2^n} \cos 2^n x$$

is a Fourier series. Show that the sequence $\{s_{2^n}\}$ of its partial sums converges almost everywhere.

*Hint* Prove that $\{\sigma_{2^n} - s_{2^n}\}$ converges to zero using an estimate of the form

$$|\sigma_{2^n} - s_{2^n}| = \left|\frac{1}{2^n}\sum_{k=1}^{n} 2^k a_{2^k} \cos 2^k x\right|$$
$$\leq \frac{1}{2^n}\left\{\left|\sum_{k=1}^{m-1}\right| + \left|\sum_{k=m}^{n}\right|\right\}.$$

## E. Fourier Series for Functions in $L^2$

**10.5.16** Suppose $f$ is an integrable function on $[0, 2\pi)$. If its Fourier coefficients are such that $a_0^2/2 + \sum (a_n^2 + b_n^2)$ converges, then $f$ belongs to $L^2(0, 2\pi)$.

*Hint* Observe that the sequence of partial sums $s_n$, and hence the sequence of their arithmetic means $\{\sigma_n\}$, converges in $L^2$ to a function $g$, and a subsequence of $\{\sigma_n\}$ converges to $g$ a.e.

10.5.17 Let $l^2$ be the family of sequences

$$\varphi = \{a_0, a_1, b_1, a_2, b_2, \cdots\}$$

such that

$$\|\varphi\|^2 = \tfrac{1}{2}a_0^2 + \sum_{n=1}^{\infty} (a_n^2 + b_n^2) < \infty.$$

The family $l^2$ can be considered as the space of square integrable functions $\varphi$ on the set of integers (with respect to some theory of integration as explained in Exercise 5.7.12),

$$\varphi(0) = \frac{a_0}{2}, \qquad \varphi(n) = a_n, \qquad \varphi(-n) = b_n, \qquad n \geq 1.$$

The scalar product is given by

$$(\varphi, \varphi') = \tfrac{1}{2}a_0a_0' + \sum_{n=1}^{\infty} (a_na_n' + b_nb_n').$$

For $f \in L^2(0, 2\pi)$ define

$$\mathscr{F}f = \{a_0, a_1, b_1, a_2, b_2, \cdots\},$$

the sequence of Fourier coefficients of $f$, and for $\varphi \in l^2$ let

$$\mathscr{F}^*\varphi = \tfrac{1}{2}a_0 + \sum_{n=1}^{\infty} (a_n \cos nx + b_n \sin nx)$$

(in the sense of $L^2$ convergence). Observe that $\mathscr{F}f \in l^2$ and $\mathscr{F}^*\varphi \in L^2(0, 2\pi)$ and verify the formulas

(1) $\mathscr{F}^*\mathscr{F}f = f$ a.e., $\qquad \mathscr{F}\mathscr{F}^*\varphi = \varphi$,
(2) $\|\mathscr{F}f\| = \|f\|$, $\qquad \|\mathscr{F}^*\varphi\| = \|\varphi\|$,
(3) $(\mathscr{F}f, \varphi) = (f, \mathscr{F}^*\varphi)$.

10.5.18 Let $f \in L^2(0, 2\pi)$ have Fourier coefficients $\{a_0, a_n, b_n : n \geq 1\}$. We say that $f$ has a weak derivative in $L^2(0, 2\pi)$ if there is a function $g$ in $L^2(0, 2\pi)$ with Fourier series

$$\sum (nb_n \cos nx + na_n \sin nx)$$

(which is the formal derivative of the Fourier series of $f$). In this case we write $f' = g$. Prove that $f$ is necessarily continuous (Sobolev's lemma).

*Hint* Observe that the function $\varphi$ defined on the integers by

$$\varphi(0) = 0, \qquad \varphi(\pm n) = \frac{1}{n}, \qquad n \geq 1,$$

belongs to $l^2$ as defined in the previous exercise. Conclude that the Fourier series of $f$ converges uniformly, because

$$\mathscr{F}\left(f - \frac{a_0}{2}\right) = (\mathscr{F}f')\varphi \in l^1.$$

**10.5.19** Show that $g \in L^2(0, 2\pi)$ is a weak derivative of $f \in L^2(0, 2\pi)$ (as defined in the previous exercise) if

$$\lim_{h \to 0} \left\| \frac{f_h - f}{h} - g \right\| = 0,$$

where $f_h(x) = f(x + h)$.

*Hint* Show first that $f_h$ has Fourier coefficients

$$A_0 = a_0, \qquad A_n = a_n \cos nh + b_n \sin nh,$$
$$B_n = b_n \cos nh - a_n \sin nh.$$

Then compute

$$\lim_{h \to 0} \left(\frac{1}{h}(f_h - f) - g, \cos nx\right), \quad \lim_{h \to 0} \left(\frac{1}{h}(f_h - f) - g, \sin nx\right)$$

to obtain the Fourier coefficients of $g$.

**10.5.20** Let $L_c^2(0, 2\pi)$, or simply $L_c^2$, be the space of complex-valued measurable functions $f$ on $[0, 2\pi)$ for which $|f|^2$ is integrable (see Section 5.5). Show that

$$\frac{1}{\sqrt{2\pi}} e^{inx}, \qquad n = 0, \pm 1, \pm 2, \cdots$$

is a complete orthonormal system for $L_c^2$. For $f \in L_c^2$,

$$c_n = \frac{1}{2\pi} \int_0^{2\pi} f(x) e^{inx}\, dx, \qquad n = 0, \pm 1, \pm 2, \cdots,$$

are called the (complex) Fourier coefficients of $f$, and

$$c_0 + \sum (c_n e^{inx} + c_{-n} e^{-inx})$$

is called the (complex) Fourier series of $f$. (This definition makes sense also for $f \in L_c^1(0, 2\pi)$.)

**10.5.21** In the notation of the last exercise let $f, g \in L_c^2$. We extend $f$ and $g$ to the whole real line by periodicity. Prove that $f(x)g(t - x)$ is integrable for a.a $t$. Then define the convolution product $f * g$ of $f$ with $g$ by

$$(f * g)(t) = \begin{cases} -\dfrac{1}{2\pi} \displaystyle\int_0^{2\pi} f(x) g(t - x)\, dx & \text{if the integral exists} \\ 0 & \text{if not.} \end{cases}$$

Prove that $f * g \in L_c^2$ and $f * g = g * f$.

*Hint* See the hint to Exercise 5.7.29, or proceed as follows. If $\{c_n\}$ and $\{c_n'\}$ are the (complex) Fourier coefficients of $f$ and $g$ respectively, then $\{c_n c_n'\}$ are the Fourier coefficients of $f * g$ (which is integrable, as is easily seen by Fubini's theorem). Then observe that $|c_0 c_0'| + \sum(|c_n c_n'| + |c_{-n} c_{-n}'|)$ converges so that the Fourier series of $f * g$ converges uniformly. Thus $f * g$ is in fact equal almost everywhere to a continuous function.

10.5.22 Show that

$$\left\{\frac{1}{\sqrt{\pi}}\chi_{[0,\pi)}, \frac{\sqrt{2}}{\sqrt{\pi}}\cos nx : n \geq 1\right\}, \quad \left\{\frac{\sqrt{2}}{\sqrt{\pi}}\sin nx : n \geq 1\right\}$$

each is a complete orthonormal system for $L^2(0, \pi)$.

## SUMMARY

The Fourier coefficients of an integrable function $f$ on $[0, 2\pi)$ are defined by

$$a_0 = \frac{1}{\pi}\int_0^{2\pi} f\,dx$$

$$a_n = \frac{1}{\pi}\int_0^{2\pi} f(x)\cos nx\,dx, \quad b_n = \frac{1}{\pi}\int_0^{2\pi} f(x)\sin nx\,dx$$

$n \geq 1$, and the series

$$\frac{a_0}{2} + \sum (a_n \cos nx + b_n \sin nx)$$

is called the Fourier series of $f$ (Definition 10.1.4). The sequences $\{a_n\}$ and $\{b_n\}$ tend to zero (Corollary 10.1.6), or more generally, the Riemann-Lebesgue theorem (Theorem 10.1.5) states that

$$\lim_{t\to\infty}\int_0^{2\pi} f(x)\cos tx\,dx = 0 = \lim_{t\to\infty}\int_0^{2\pi} f(x)\sin tx\,dx.$$

In the study of the convergence of the Fourier series of $f$ it is convenient to extend the definition of $f$ to the whole real line by periodicity,

$$f(x) = f(x - 2k\pi) \qquad \text{if } x \in [2k\pi, 2(k+1)\pi).$$

If $s_n$ is the $n$th partial sum of the Fourier series of $f$,

$$s_n = \frac{a_0}{2} + \sum_{k=1}^{n} (a_k \cos kx + b_k \sin kx),$$

then

$$s_n(t) = \frac{1}{\pi}\int_0^{2\pi} f(x) D_n(t - x)\,dx$$

(Proposition 10.1.9), where

$$D_n(x) = \tfrac{1}{2} + \sum_{m=1}^{n} \cos mx = \frac{\sin (n + \tfrac{1}{2})x}{2 \sin \tfrac{1}{2}x}$$

are the Dirichlet kernels (Equation (10.1.7)). The sequence $\{s_n(t)\}$ converges (for a certain $t$) to a limit $s(t)$ if and only if

$$\lim_{n\to\infty} \frac{1}{\pi} \int_0^{\pi} g(t, x) D_n(x)\, dx = 0$$

where $g(t, x) = f(t + x) + f(t - x) - 2s(t)$ (Corollary 10.1.10), and for this it is necessary and sufficient that

$$\lim_{n\to\infty} \int_0^{\delta} \frac{\sin (n + \tfrac{1}{2})x}{x} g(t, x)\, dx = 0$$

for some $\delta \in (0, \pi)$ (Lemma 10.2.1). A sufficient condition for $\{s_n(t)\}$ to converge to $s(t)$ is that $g(t, x)/x$ should be integrable on $(0, \delta)$ (Dini's test, Proposition 10.2.3.). For instance, if $f$ is differentiable at $t$, then $\{s_n(t)\}$ converges to $f(t)$ (Corollary 10.2.4).

Another convergence test is Jordan's test (Theorem 10.2.7), which states that $\{s_n(t)\}$ converges to $\{f(t + 0) + f(t - 0)\}/2$ for all $t$ in an open interval $(a, b)$ in which $f$ is of bounded variation, and $\{s_n(t)\}$ remains uniformly bounded on each closed subinterval of $(a, b)$. In particular, if $f$ is of locally bounded variation, then $\{s_n(t)\}$ converges boundedly to $\{f(t + 0) + f(t - 0)\}/2$ everywhere (Corollary 10.2.10).

If $f$ is any integrable function on $[0, 2\pi)$ and $g$ is of locally bounded variation, then

$$\int_0^{2\pi} fg\, dx = \tfrac{1}{2}a_0 \int_0^{2\pi} g\, dx + \sum_{n=1}^{\infty} \int_0^{2\pi} g(x)\{a_n \cos nx + b_n \sin nx\}\, dx$$

(Proposition 10.2.11). In particular, the Fourier series of $f$ may be integrated term by term over any interval (whether the Fourier series converges or not) (Corollary 10.2.12).

The Fourier series of $f$ is said to be summable at $t$ by the method of arithmetic means, or $(C, 1)$-summable, with sum $s(t)$ if

$$\lim_{n\to\infty} \sigma_n(t) = \lim_{n\to\infty} \frac{1}{n}(s_0 + \cdots + s_{n-1}) = s(t),$$

where $\sigma_n(t)$ denotes the $n$th arithmetic mean of the sequence $\{s_k(t)\}$ of partial sums (Definition 10.3.1). If $\{s_k(t)\}$ converges to $s(t)$, then so does $\{\sigma_n(t)\}$, but not conversely (Proposition 10.3.2). The $n$th arithmetic mean is given by the formula

$$\sigma_n(t) = \frac{1}{\pi} \int_0^{\pi} F_n(x)\{f(t + x) + f(t - x)\}\, dx$$

(Proposition 10.3.7), where $F_n$ is Fejer's kernel (Equation (10.3.5)),

$$F_n(x) = \frac{1}{n} \sum_{k=0}^{n-1} D_k(x) = \frac{1 - \cos nx}{4n \sin \tfrac{1}{2}x}.$$

The sequence $\{\sigma_n(t)\}$ converges to $s(t)$ if and only if

$$\lim_{n\to\infty}\int_0^{\pi} g(t, x)F_n(x)\,dx = 0$$

where again $g(t, x) = f(t + x) + f(t - x) - 2s(t)$ (Corollary 10.3.8). By Fejer's theorem (Theorem 10.3.9), $\{\sigma_n(t)\}$ converges to $\{f(t + 0) + f(t - 0)\}/2$ whenever $f(t + 0)$ and $f(t - 0)$ exist, and if $f$ is continuous at each point of a closed bounded interval $[a, b]$, then $\{\sigma_n\}$ converges uniformly to $f$ on $[a, b]$ (Corollary 10.3.10). A consequence is the Weierstrass approximation theorem (Corollary 10.3.12) which says that a continuous function on a closed bounded interval can be approximated on that interval by polynomials. In general, $\{\sigma_n(t)\}$ converges to $f(t)$ for a.a. $t$ (Theorem 10.3.13 and Proposition 10.3.14).

Let $L^2(0, 2\pi)$, or simply $L^2$, denote the space of square integrable functions on $[0, 2\pi)$. A sequence $\{\varphi_n\}$ in $L^2$ is said to be an orthonormal system if

$$\int_0^{2\pi}\varphi_n\varphi_m\,dx = \begin{cases}1 & \text{if } n = m\\ 0 & \text{if } n \neq m\end{cases}$$

(Definition 10.4.3). It is said to be complete if, for each $f \in L^2$,

$$s_n = \sum_{k=1}^{n} c_k\varphi_k \qquad \left(c_k = \int_0^{2\pi} f\varphi_k\,dx\right)$$

tends to $f$ in $L^2$ (Definition 10.4.8). For this each of the following are necessary and sufficient (Proposition 10.4.9):

(1) For each $f \in L^2$ and $\varepsilon > 0$, there is a finite sum

$$g = \sum_{k=1}^{n} d_k\varphi_k$$

with $\|f - g\| \leq \varepsilon$.

(2) If $f \in L^2$ and $\int_0^{2\pi} f\varphi_k\,dx = 0$ for all $k$, then $f = 0$ a.e.

For instance, the trigonometric system

$$\varphi_1 = \frac{1}{\sqrt{2\pi}}\chi_{[0,2\pi)}, \quad \varphi_{2k} = \frac{1}{\sqrt{\pi}}\cos kx, \quad \varphi_{2k+1} = \frac{1}{\sqrt{\pi}}\sin kx, \qquad k \geq 1,$$

is a complete orthonormal system (Theorem 10.4.10). For a complete orthonormal system $\{\varphi_k\}$, the sequence $\{s_n\}$,

$$s_n = \sum_{k=1}^{n} c_k\varphi_k \qquad \left(c_k = \int_0^{2\pi} f\varphi_k\,dx\right),$$

converges in $L^2$ to $f$ and

$$\int_0^{2\pi} f^2\,dx = \sum_{k=1}^{\infty} c_k^{\,2}$$

(Proposition 10.4.6). A consequence is Parseval's theorem (Corollary 10.4.12): if $f$ and $g$ belong to $L^2$, then

$$\frac{1}{\pi}\int_0^{2\pi} f^2\,dx = \tfrac{1}{2}a_0^2 + \sum_{n=1}^{\infty}(a_n^2 + b_n^2)$$

$$\frac{1}{\pi}\int_0^{2\pi} fg\,dx = \tfrac{1}{2}a_0a_0' + \sum_{n=1}^{\infty}(a_na_n' + b_nb_n')$$

where $\{a_n, b_n\}$ and $\{a_n', b_n'\}$ are the Fourier coefficients of $f$ and $g$, respectively.

# Bibliographical Comments and Remarks

# COMMENTS ON THE REFERENCES

CHAPTERS 1 AND 2 The theory of integration goes back at least as far as Archimedes [16, in particular, pp. 343–345], who integrated special functions using, essentially, monotone convergent sequences of piecewise linear functions or step functions. When, in the seventeenth century, Newton, Leibnitz, and others created the discipline of calculus, they often conceived this as a heuristic method to derive results similar to, and including, those of Archimedes. Thus, apologies like "this result can also be derived rigorously, using the methods of Archimedes" appear in their writings. But, as confidence in the new calculus grew, the ideal of a rigorous proof à la Archimedes was by and by forgotten. All functions worth dealing with were more or less tacitly assumed to be given by "analytical expressions" —at the worst an everywhere-convergent power series would do for an analytical expression—or at least to be so given in each interval of a finite subdivision of the real line. Under such conditions, of course, elementary calculus gives a complete answer to the problem of integration.

The first severe jolt to the complacency created by this state of affairs came in the beginning of the nineteenth century when Fourier announced that *any* continuous function, "even if it depends on no regular law whatever," could be represented by a trigonometric series. Since then, the serious integration theory has been intimately related to the theory of trigonometric series. Evidently, one would need an integration theory that enables one at least to integrate all continuous periodic functions over finite intervals in order to analyze trigonometric series meaningfully. The approximation method of Archimedes was dug up and applied by Cauchy and, especially, by Riemann [52, pp. 239–241]. The resulting integration theory is today part of many calculus courses that beside this theory contain nothing but the most elementary and manipulative pre-Fourier material. With due respect to tradition and to the genius of Riemann, it seems to be about time that Lebesgue's theory replace Riemann's in this connection. The first two chapters of this book were written with a view to proving the feasibility of such a replacement.

Soon after the posthumous publication of Riemann's integration theory in 1867, its limitations became apparent. Between then and 1902 when Lebesgue's thesis [38] appeared, there was a period during which research in this field was chiefly aimed at investigating the properties of sets of real numbers. (However, the concept of a semicontinuous function was invented in 1899 by Baire [2]. Some of this will be described in the note to Chapter 3.) Lebesgue's main achievement and the cornerstone of his lectures [39] was the theorem called "Lebesgue's dominated convergence theorem" (Theorem 2.3.3). The other two famous theorems, "Fatou's lemma" and "Beppo Levi's theorem" [23, 43], were both published in 1906. The usefulness of the dominated convergence theorem is easily seen when compared with the best result that can be obtained within the framework of Riemann integration theory (and this result, as shown in Exercise 1.2.5, was actually found by Arzela [1] and Osgood [49] in the time between the two dates given above); in Theorem 2.3.3, one has of course to postulate Riemann integrability for all the functions $f_n$ and for $g$. But worse than that, one has to postulate the Riemann integrability of the limiting function $f$ as well! Since a limiting process is often used to define a function, it is clear how inconvenient the Arzela-Osgood version of Theorem 2.3.3 is for "practical" purposes.

In 1918, Daniell [14] published the set of axioms for abstract integration theory that we reproduce in Section 2.5. His main idea was the importance of the continuity property (4). In the special case when the class of elementary functions is the class of continuous functions, each of which vanishes outside some bounded interval, substantially the same method was used in 1911 by Young [77]. In that case, Property (4) followed from a well-known theorem of Dini [18, pp. 110–112] asserting the uniform convergence of a monotone sequence of continuous functions on a closed bounded interval, which is assumed only to converge pointwise to a continuous function (see Exercise 2.5.2). The use of the class of step functions as elementary functions was advocated by F. Riesz [56, 57], also prior to the appearance of Daniell's work. Thus, by 1920, the material of Chapters 1 and 2 of this book was already available in mathematical journals. Of course the job of polishing it and working it into an easily accessible textbook form has gone on ever since. Our most important sources of inspiration have been a series of papers of M. Stone [69] and the books of Riesz-Nagy [61] and Bourbaki [5, 6].

The usefulness of a definition of integrable functions that avoids mentioning null sets was realized by Mikusinski, who uses the Mikusinski lemma in [45] as the definition of integrable functions.

In the historical note of Bourbaki [6] the interested reader will find a more extensive account of the history of integration than we have been able to give here. Finally, we would like to draw attention to the "eyewitness account" of F. Riesz [60], written in 1949.

CHAPTER 3 Four years before Lebesgue's announcement of his integration theory, E. Borel [4] had defined the concept of a measurable set of real numbers and proved its essential properties (Proposition 3.3.3). To be sure, not every "Lebesgue measurable" set is "Borel measurable;" actually, the converse is true. Moreover, a set $A$ is Lebesgue measurable if and only if there exist two Borel measurable sets $B$ and $C$ with the same measure such that $B \subset A \subset C$. Borel developed his measure theory in order to deal with certain problems in the theory of a complex variable. This direction of interest may explain why Lebesgue, and not Borel, discovered integration theory.

Borel's forerunners had the same inclination. Of those, the most important was G. Cantor, the founder of set theory. Cantor proved in [8] that every open set of real numbers is a countable union of disjoint open intervals (see Lemma 3.3.6). Thus, he could—and did—measure open and closed sets; in particular he showed that the famous set bearing his name (Example 1.4.3) has measure zero. However, his main interest was in problems that are of no concern for integration theory, but are otherwise of deep and fundamental interest, namely, those that deal with the determination of cardinal numbers of sets. Foremost among these was the problem of whether the cardinal number of $R$ is exactly the second smallest infinite cardinal number (the "continuum hypothesis") or not. Cantor ruined his mental health (Schoenflies [63]) on futile attempts to solve this formidably difficult problem, the counterpart of which in axiomatic set theory has only recently been satisfactorily answered by P. J. Cohen [13].

The nature of Cohen's answer is as follows. Mathematics can be considered as the set of all theorems that can be derived from a certain axiom system in set theory, referred to as [ZF] (from Zermelo-Fraenkel). So far, nobody has been able to derive both a certain statement and its negation from [ZF] (like showing that $0 = 1$), but neither does there exist a proof that this could impossibly happen, or in other words, a proof of the consistency of [ZF]. However, if one assumes that [ZF] is consistent, then one can prove that the system consisting of [ZF] plus the continuum hypothesis is also consistent; this was done by Gödel in 1938 [29]. We use the expression "the continuum hypothesis is consistent relative to [ZF]" for this.

Cohen has now proved also that the negation of the continuum hypothesis is consistent relative to [ZF]. Thus the continuum hypothesis is quite independent of what most mathematicians consider a sufficient basis for the greater part of mathematics. Cohen also proved that the axiom of choice, which is used in constructing the nonmeasurable set in Example 1.4.4, has the same kind of independence relative to [ZF]. Very recently, R. Solovay [66] has proved, using Cohen's ideas, that the statement "all sets of real numbers are (Lebesgue) measurable" is consistent relative to a slightly larger axiom system ([ZF] + "there exist an inaccessible cardinal"). Beside showing the relative nature of the existence of nonmeasurable sets, this vastly generalizes Theorem 3.2.5, since most constructions that do not explicitly use the axiom of choice, or some such device, will automatically keep within the indicated axiom system and hence produce only measurable functions.

After Lebesgue's creation of integration theory, measure theory has been treated both as an auxiliary subject to integration theory—this is done here—and as a more independent subject. The books of Carathéodory [9] and Halmos [31] are the chief treatises using this mode of exposition, whereas in Chapter 3 we have used many ideas from the already-cited work of M. Stone [69].

In this connection it is interesting to note that Egoroff's theorem (Theorem 3.3.8) and Lusin's theorem (Exercise 3.6.26), which were published in [22] and [44], respectively, can also be proved without the use of measure theory, and can then serve as a basis for the definition of measurable functions and measurable sets. This idea was Borell's and has been developed by Hahn in [30]. Also Bourbaki [5] uses it in his treatment.

The Steinhaus theorem (Theorem 3.3.9) was published in [67]. Kestelman [37] observed that it could be employed in the discussion of the Cauchy functional equation. We have presented Kestelman's ideas in part G of exercise section 3.6. Also, our proof of the Steinhaus theorem is due to Kestelman [37].

The definition and investigation of Baire classes of functions (part C of Section 3.6) by Baire [2] in 1899 belongs to the pre-Lebesgue period of real analysis.

Vitali's theorem (part H of Section 3.6) is in [73]; it is usually proved in connection with the differentiation theorem for monotone functions (see the comments on Chapters 6 and 7).

CHAPTER 4 Stone's papers have also influenced our presentation of the material in Sections 4.1 and 4.2 of Chapter 4, where the main result is Fubini's theorem on multiple integrals, published by Fubini [27] in 1907. This theorem is one of the best proofs of the utter superiority of the Lebesgue integral, because a Riemann integrable function $f(x, y)$ of two real variables will generally not possess a repeated integral at all. Of course, if all one-dimensional integrals that make up the repeated integral exist in the sense of Riemann, then the repeated integral will equal the two-dimensional one, but it seems impossible to prove this in any essentially simpler way than by appealing to Fubini's theorem in the Lebesgue theory. The corollary of Fubini's theorem that we have called Tonelli's theorem was discovered independently by Tonelli [71] and Hobson [33] in 1909.

Jessen [35] has shown that a theory of integration can also be defined for functions of an infinite number of variables. Fubini's theorem and Tonelli's theorem remain valid for this theory. For a discussion of Jesson's results in the framework of the Daniell integral, we refer the reader to Stone [69].

CHAPTER 5 The fundamental ideas on $L^2$ and $L^p$ spaces were developed and published as notes in "Comptes Rendus" during the first half of the year 1907, by Fischer [25], F. Riesz [53], and Frechet [26] (see the beginning of the historical paper of F. Riesz [60]). From the beginning there already was a strong tendency to try to get away from the underlying integration theory and to base the treatment of these topics on general inequalities in the norms. Beurling's and Clarkson's inequalities are good examples of how far one can get in this direction (see Exercises 5.7.19 and 5.7.20). Clarkson's inequality was published in [12] and Beurling's by Hanner [32], who also gives an interesting application of the two inequalities.

The Schwarz inequality is an extension to integrals of the corresponding inequality for sums known as Cauchy's inequality. Cauchy's inequality was published by Cauchy [10] and Schwarz published his inequality in [64], although it had already been stated earlier by Buniakowsky [7].

Minkowski's inequality was proved by Minkowski [46] for finite sums and extended to integrals by F. Riesz. Hölder [34] proved the Hölder inequality for infinite series; the extension to integrals was made by F. Riesz.

The characterization of continuous linear functionals (Theorem 5.3.6) was discovered independently by F. Riesz [53] and Frechet [26]. The Riesz-Fischer theorem appears in Fischer [25] and F. Riesz [53].

The equations giving the Fourier transformation in $L_c^2$ are from Plancherel [50]. The statement in Exercise 5.7.27, which we refer to as Sobolev's lemma, is a very simple, special case of the results of Sobolev [65] that are of great importance in the application of Fourier theory to partial differential equations.

CHAPTERS 6 AND 7 In these two chapters we treat what one might call the finer differentiation theory for functions of one real variable. All important results here are the work of Lebesgue himself; as a matter of fact, they are essentially contained in his treatise of the year 1904 [39]. In 1931, F. Riesz [58] found the "elementary" proof of the almost-everywhere differentiability of a monotone function that we have reproduced here. Another proof uses Vitali's covering theorem [73], outlined in the exercises to Chapter 3 (see part H of Section 3.6).

Fubini's differentiation theorem was published by Fubini [28]. The example in Section 7.1 of a continuous monotone function with an almost-everywhere vanishing derivative is that of F. Riesz [61]. In this connection we should mention that there are examples of continuous functions which do not have a derivative at any point. The first such example is from the work of Weierstrass (published by Du Bois-Reymond [20]). A very simple example was constructed by van der Waerden [72] and is reproduced on the first pages of Riesz-Nagy [61].

The idea (outlined in Section 6.7) to use the differentiation theory to develop the theory of Lebesgue integration is due to Riesz [59].

We have been mainly interested in giving a concrete background to the more abstract developments in Chapter 9. As an example of further results in the fine theory of functions of one real variable, we mention a theorem of Banach [3] which states that a continuous function that maps null sets into null sets will be absolutely continuous even if it is only known a priori to be locally of bounded variation instead of monotone nondecreasing (see Theorem 7.4.2). Another series of results, namely, the density theorem and the theorems on derivates of general functions, are outlined in the exercises. The density theorem is in Lebesgue's lectures [39] and the theorems on derivates are the end product of a series of papers by Denjoy [15], Grace Chrisholm Young [75, 76], and Saks [62].

CHAPTERS 8 AND 9 In 1894, Stieltjes [68] announced the definition of what we here call the Riemann-Stieltjes integral (Proposition 8.2.9) and proved the integrability of continuous functions over bounded intervals. He used this as a tool in his memoir on continued fractions, but his notions were not immediately taken up and combined with Lebesgue's discoveries when these appeared in print. The breakthrough came in 1909 with Riesz' [54] announcement of his representation theorem (Theorem 8.5.3). Lebesgue [42] immediately came forth with a definition of the Lebesgue-Stieltjes integral. By 1913, with the memoir of Radon [51], the subject matter as we have presented it was essentially discovered. Only the abstract theory remained to be clarified, since Radon's proofs worked only in $R^n$. This was done by Nikodym [48] in 1930. Our proof of the Radon-Nikodym theorem for Lebesgue-Stieltjes integrals (Section 9.2) is outlined in Riesz-Nagy [61]. The idea to use $L^2$ theory for the proof of the abstract Radon-Nikodym theorem (Section 9.3) is that of von Neumann [47].

The class of Baire functions (Definition 8.2.4) was introduced in the earlier-cited thesis of Baire [2].

CHAPTER 10 Fourier coefficients and Fourier series are named after the physicist Fourier who, in 1807, stated that any single-valued function $f$ on an interval $(-c, c)$ can be represented by a Fourier series

$$f(x) = \tfrac{1}{2}a_0 + \sum_{n=1}^{\infty} \left( a_n \cos \frac{n\pi x}{c} + b_n \sin \frac{n\pi x}{c} \right)$$

where

$$a_n = \frac{1}{c} \int_{-c}^{c} f(x) \cos \frac{n\pi x}{c}\, dx, \qquad b_n = \frac{1}{c} \int_{-c}^{c} f(x) \sin \frac{n\pi x}{c}\, dx,$$

although trigonometric series had already been studied before by d'Alembert, Euler, and Bernoulli. However, Fourier (naturally) has never been able to prove his theorem logically. The first to find some conditions on the function $f$ that would ensure the convergence of its Fourier series to $f$ was Dirichlet [19]. His condition required that the function $f$ should be continuous and should have only a finite number of maxima and minima. All hope of proving Fourier's theorem for continuous functions was removed in 1876 when du Bois-Reymond [21] constructed a continuous function whose Fourier series did not represent the function at a given point. (See, for instance, Titchmarsh [70, pp. 416–418], or Zygmund [78, pp. 298ff.].

After the discovery of du Bois-Reymond, more general tests for the convergence of a Fourier series than the one found by Dirichlet were given by Dini [20] and Jordan [26]. The real advance, however, came with the discovery of Lebesgue integration. Dini's and Jordan's tests were generalized by Lebesgue [40] and received the form in which we have presented them. A fundamental tool in their proof is the Riemann-Lebesgue theorem which was proved by Riemann [52, pp. 253–255] for Riemann integrable functions and by Lebesgue [41, p. 61] for Lebesgue integrable functions.

Fejer [24] discovered that the summation of a Fourier series of a function $f$ by arithmetic means yields the value $f(x)$ at every point at which $f$ is continuous. He thus obtained a simple proof of the Weierstrass approximation theorem (which was discovered by Weierstrass [74] in 1885).

The Fejer-Lebesgue theorem (Theorem 10.4.13) is proved by Lebesgue in [40]. Also, Proposition 10.3.14 is due to Lebesgue.

Parseval, in 1799, was the first to write down formulas as in Corollary 10.4.12 and so his name is generally associated with such formulas.

The results of the exercises in part B of Section 10.5 on trigonometric series with decreasing coefficients are known as Chaundy-Jolliffe theorems [11].

For a more thorough treatment of the theory of Fourier series we refer the reader to Zygmund [78]. (For instance, the uniqueness of Fourier series mentioned in Section 10.1 is proved on pp. 325ff. of the cited reference.)

## *REFERENCES*


[1] Arzelà, C., "Sulla integrazione per series," *Rend. Accad. Nazl. Lincei* (*Rome*) *1* (1885), 532–537, 566–569.

[2] Baire, R., "Sur les fonctions des variables réelles," *Ann. Mat. Pura Appl.* (*3*) *3* (1899), 1–122.

[3] Banach, S., "Sur les lignes rectifiables et les surfaces dont l'aire est finie," *Fund. Math. 7* (1925), 225–236.

[4] Borel, E., *Leçons sur la Théorie des Fonctions.* Paris: Gauthier-Villars, 1898.

[5] Bourbaki, N., *Intégration*, Chaps. I–IV, *Actualités Sci. Indust. 1175.* Paris: Gauthier-Villars, 1952.

[6] Bourbaki, N., *Intégration*, Chap. V, *Actualités Sci. Indust. 1244.* Paris: Gauthier-Villars, 1956.

[7] Buniakowsky, V., "Sur quelques inégalités concernant les intégrales ordinaires et les intégrales aux différences finies," *Memoires de l'Acad. St-Pétersbourg* (*7*) *1* (1859), N.9.

[8] Cantor, G., "Über unendliche, lineare Punktmannigfaltigkeiten," *Math. Ann. 20* (1882), 113–121.

[9] Carathéodory, C., *Vorlesungen über reelle Funktionen.* Leipzig and Berlin: Teubner, 1918.

[10] Cauchy, A. L., *Cours d'Analyse de l'École Royale Polytechnique*, I^re^ partie. *Analyse algébrique.* Paris: 1821. (Œuvres complètes, II^e^ série, II.)

[11] Chaundy T. W., and A. E. Jolliffe, "The uniform convergence of a certain class of trigonometrical series," *Proc. London Math. Soc.* (*2*) *15* (1916), 214–216.

[12] Clarkson, J. A., "Uniformly convex spaces," *Trans. Amer. Math. Soc. 40* (1936), 396–414.

[13] Cohen, P. J., "The independence of the continuum hypothesis," *Proc. Natl. Acad. Sci. U.S. 50* (1963), 1143–1148; *51* (1964), 105–110.

[14] Daniell, P. J., "A general form of integral," *Ann. of Math.* (*2*) *19* (1919), 279–294.

[15] Denjoy, A., "Mémoire sur les nombres dérivés des fonctions continues," *Journal de Math.* (*7*) *1* (1915), 105–240.

[16] Dini, U., "Sopra la serie di Fourier," Pisa, 1872.

[18] Dini, U., "Fondamenti per la teorica delle funzioni di variabili reali," Pisa, 1878.

[19] Dirichlet, L., "Sur la convergence des séries trigonométriques qui servent à représenter une fonction arbitraire entre des limites données. *J. reine und angew. Math. 4* (1829), 157–169.

[20] du Bois-Reymond, P., "Versuch einer Classification der willkürlichen Functionen reeller Argumente," *Journal für Math. 79* (1875), 21–31.

[21] du Bois-Reymond, P., "Untersuchungen über die Convergenz und Divergenz der Fourierschen Darstellungsformeln.," *Abh. Akad. München 12* (1876), 1–103.

[22] Egoroff, D. Th., "Sur les suites des fonctions mesurables," *Compt. Rend. Acad. Sci. Paris 152* (1911), 244–246.

[23] Fatou, P., "Séries trigonométriques et séries de Taylor," *Acta Math. 30* (1906), 335–400.
[24] Fejer, L., "Untersuchungen über Fouriersche Reihen," *Math. Ann. 58* (1904) 51–69.
[25] Fischer, E., "Sur la convergence en moyenne," *Compt. Rend. Acad. Sci. Paris 144* (1907), 1022–1024, 1148–1150.
[26] Fréchet, M., "Sur les ensembles de fonctions et les opérations linéaires," *Compt. Rend. Acad. Sci. Paris 144* (1907), 1414–1416.
[27] Fubini, G., "Sugli integrali multipli," *Rend. Accad. Nazl. Lincei (Rome) 16* (1907), 608–614.
[28] Fubini, G., "Sulla derivazione per serie," *Rend. Accad. Nazl. Lincei (Rome) 24* (1915), 204–206.
[29] Gödel K., "The consistency of the continuum hypothesis," *Annals of Mathematics Studies, no. 3*, Princeton University Press, Princeton, N.J., 1940.
[30] Hahn, H., "Über eine Verallgemeinerung der Riemannschen Integraldefinition," *Monatsh. Math. Phys. 26* (1915), 3–18.
[31] Halmos, P. R., *Measure Theory*. Princeton, N.J.: D. Van Nostrand Company, Inc., 1950.
[32] Hanner, O., "On the uniform convexity of $L^p$ and $l^p$," *Ark. Math. 3* (1958), 239–244.
[33] Hobson, E. W., "On some fundamental properties of Lebesgue integrals in a two-dimensional domain," *Proc. London Math. Soc. (2) 8* (1910), 22–39.
[34] Hölder, O., "Über einen Mittelwertsatz," *Göttinger Nachrichten* (1889), 38–47.
[35] Jessen, B., "The theory of integration in a space of an infinite number of dimensions, *Acta Math. 63* (1934), 249–323.
[36] Jordan, C., "Sur la série de Fourier," *Compt. Rend. Acad. Sci. Paris 92* (1881), 228–230.
[37] Kestelman, H., "On the functional equation $f(x + y) = f(x) + f(y)$," *Fund. Math. 34* (1947), 144–147.
[38] Lebesgue, H., "Intégrale, longueur, aire," *Ann. Mat. Pura Appl. (3)* 7 (1902), 231–259.
[39] Lebesgue, H., *Leçons sur l'Intégration et la Recherche des Fonctions Primitives*. Paris: Gauthier-Villars, 1904.
[40] Lebesgue, H., "Recherche sur la convergence des séries de Fourier," *Math. Ann. 61* (1905), 251–280.
[41] Lebesgue, H., *Leçons sur les Séries Trigonométriques*. Paris, 1906.
[42] Lebesgue, H., "Sur l'intégrale de Stieltjes et sur les opérations linéaires," *Compt. Rend. Acad. Sci. Paris 150* (1910), 86–88.
[43] Levi, B., "Sopra l'integrazione delle serie," *Rend. Ist. Lombardo Sci. Lettere (2) 39* (1906), 775–780.
[44] Lusin, N., "Sur les propriétés des fonctions mesurables," *Compt. Rend. Acad. Sci. Paris 154* (1912), 1688–1690.
[45] Mikusiński, J., "Una introduccion de la integral sin la nocion de medida," *Cursos y seminarios de matemática, Fasciculo 13, Universidad de Buenos Aires*, 1963.
[46] Minkowski, H., *Geometrie der Zahlen I*. Leipzig: 1896.
[47] v. Neumann, J., "On rings of operators II," *Ann. of Math. 41* (1940), 94–161.
[48] Nikodym, O., "Sur une généralisation des intégrales de M. Radon," *Fund. Math. 15* (1930), 131–179.
[49] Osgood, W. F., "Non-uniform convergence and the integration of series term by term," *Amer. J. Math. 19* (1897), 155–190.
[50] Plancherel, M., "Contribution à l'étude de la représentation d'une fonction arbitraire par des intégrales définies," *Rend. Circ. Math. Palermo 30* (1910), 289–335.
[51] Radon, J., "Theorie und Anwendungen der absolut additiven Mengenfunktionen," *S.-B. Akad. Wiss. Wien 122* (1913), 1295–1438.
[52] Riemann, B., *Gesammelte mathematische Werke*, 2d ed. Leipzig: Teubner, 1892. Reprinted by Dover Publications, New York, 1953.

[53] Riesz, F., "Sur les systèmes orthogonaux des fonctions," *Compt. Rend. Acad. Sci. Paris 144* (1907), 615–619, 734–736.
[54] Riesz, F., "Sur les opérations fonctionelles linéaires," *Compt. Rend. Acad. Sci. Paris 149* (1909), 974–977.
[55] Riesz, F., "Untersuchungen über Système integrierbarer Funktionen," *Math. Ann. 69* (1910), 447–449.
[56] Riesz, F., "Sur quelques points de la théorie des fonctions sommables," *Compt. Rend. Acad. Sci. Paris 154* (1912), 641–643.
[57] Riesz. F., "Sur l'intégrale de Lebesgue," *Acta Math. 42* (1920), 191–205.
[58] Riesz, F., "A monoton függvények differenciál-hatógáról," *Mat. Lapok 38* (1931), 125–131.
[59] Riesz, F., "Sur l'intégrale de Lebesgue comme l'opération inverse de la dérivation," *Ann. Pisa 215* (1936), 191–212.
[60] Riesz, F., "L'évolution de la notion d'intégrale depuis Lebesgue," *Ann. Inst. Fourier (Grenoble) 1* (1949), 29–42.
[61] Riesz, F., and Sz.-Nagy, B., *Functional Analysis*, translated by L. F. Boron. New York: Frederick Ungar, 1955.
[62] Saks, S., "Sur les nombres dérivés des fonctions," *Fund. Math. 5* (1924), 98–104.
[63] Schoenflies, A., "Die Krisis in Cantor's mathematischem Schaffen," *Acta Math. 50* (1920), 1–23.
[64] Schwarz, H. A., "Über ein die Flächen kleinsten Flächeninhalts betreffendes Problem der Variationsrechnung," *Acta soc. sci. Fenn. 15* (1885), 315–362. [= Gesammelte Werke I, 224–269.]
[65] Sobolev, S. L., "Sur un théorème de l'analyse fonctionelle," *Mat. Sb.* (*4*) 46 (1938), 471–496.
[66] Solovay, R., "The measure problem," *Amer. Math. Soc. Notices 12* (1965), 217.
[67] Steinhaus, H., "Sur les distances des points des ensembles de mésure positive," *Fund. Math. 1* (1920), 93–104.
[68] Stieltjes, T. J., "Recherches sur les fractions continues," *Ann. Fac. Sci. Univ. Toulouse 8* (1894), 1–122.
[69] Stone, M. H., "Notes on integration I–IV," *Proc. Natl. Acad. Sci. U.S. 34* (1948), 336–342, 447–455, 483–490; *35* (1949), 50–54.
[70] Titchmarsh, E. C., *The Theory of Functions*, 2d ed. London: Oxford University Press, 1932.
[71] Tonelli, L., Sull'integrazione per parti," *Rend. Accad. Nazl. Lincei* (*Rome*) *18* (1909), 246–253.
[72] van der Waerden, B. L., "Ein einfaches Beispiel einer nichtdifferenzierbaren stetigen Funktion," *Math. Zeitschr. 32* (1930), 474–475.
[73] Vitali, G., "Sui gruppi di punti e sulle funzioni di variabili reali," *Atti Accad. Sci. Torino 43* (1907), 75–92.
[74] Weierstrass, K., *Mathematische Werke*, Band 3, Abhandlung II, pp. 1–37 (especially p. 5).
[75] Young, G. C., "A note on derivates and differential coefficients," *Acta Math. 37* (1916), 141–154.
[76] Young, G. C., "On the derivates of a function," *Proc. London Math. Soc.* (*2*) *15* (1916), 360–384.
[77] Young, W. H., "On a new method in the theory of integration," *Proc. London Math. Soc.* (*2*) *9* (1911), 15–50.
[78] Zygmund, A., *Trigonometric Series*, Vols. I and II. London: Cambridge University Press, 1959.

# REMARKS ON THE LITERATURE

To fix the position of our textbook on integration theory relative to other available treatises on the same subject, we shall here call attention to the differences between these books and ours. For instance, our book is not designed to be the main text in a graduate course on measure theory or analysis; on the contrary, it is designed for lectures to undergraduates that should prepare the student for such graduate courses.

We have already mentioned the books by Halmos and Riesz-Nagy in the Bibliographical Comments. Both these books are on a level well above the present book. While they are formally self-contained, it will be difficult for an undergraduate beginner to learn integration theory from them. Halmos' book has become the definitive text for the above-mentioned graduate courses on measure theory; its nomenclature has become normative because of its widespread influence. The book by Riesz-Nagy is mainly devoted to functional analysis. The part on integration theory covers about one third of the book and is concrete and lucid, but quite condensed.

We will now comment on four of the newer books that, in our opinion, lie nearest to being considered as alternative texts for collateral reading. The first one of these is by McShane and Botts. Its declared level is for "mature senior or beginning graduate student." The first half of the book treats convergence and continuity both in a very general topological setting and in the special case of real-valued functions, and furthermore elementary differentiation theory. (The finer theory, corresponding to our Chapter 6, comes later and is made dependent on the integration theory.) Otherwise, the results and their generality are much the same as in our book. The approach is integration first, measure afterwards, which we have used, but the authors use a two-step procedure of extension by sequences, defining the integral first for the class of semicontinuous functions before proceeding to the most general class of integrable functions.

The next book is the one by Williamson. This is one that comes closest to ours with respect to prerequisites. It is designed to be read by "any student who knows a little about real variable theory and elementary calculus." However, its smaller volume makes it also more condensed in style. Williamson treats measures of sets first and integrals of functions afterwards, and the set-oriented approach is again apparent when he uses Vitali's covering theorem instead of the rising sun lemma in proving the differentiation theorems, and also in his proof of the Radon-Nikodym theorem (certain parts of this proof are disguised as our Exercise 9.5.4). For these contrasts, as well as for its other qualities, Williamson's book should be a very suitable collateral reading to our book.

The third book is Royden's *Real Analysis*. It has grown out of a course in the theory of functions of a real variable given by the author at Stanford University to first-year graduate students in mathematics and statistics. This book is very clear and lucid both in style and in general typographical design. Although it is intended for readers of a scholastic level distinctly above the one foreseen for readers of our book, it should not be too difficult for collateral reading and could be very stimulating as such. The middle third of the book, which is called "Abstract Spaces" and treats general topology and functional analysis, has no counterpart here, nor has the last chapter called "Mappings of Measure Spaces"; but the other nine (out of fourteen) chapters are covered in subject matter by the contents of our book. Royden also introduces measure first, but he then defines the integral for those functions that we call "integrable generalized step functions." With these he can define the general integral in a way very analogous to the construction of the Riemann integral. Royden's proofs are short and direct. This makes the subject look easy and is in its turn a very powerful way of actually making it easy.

The newest book on which we are able to comment is *Introduction to the Theory of Integration* by Hildebrandt. If Royden's book could be said to be advanced in the abstract direction relative to ours, then Hildebrandt's book should be called advanced in the concrete direction. This is exactly the intention of the author, namely, to be "reactionary relative to the present style of graduate mathematical instruction, which veers strongly toward the abstract and sometimes overlooks the concrete basic ideas." The Lebesgue integral is introduced in the seventh chapter (there are eleven chapters in the book) in the standard measure-first way. In the ninth chapter other approaches are treated, including Daniell's. But the distinctive feature of this book is its thorough treatment of the classical theory of Riemann and Riemann-Stieltjes integration in one and several variables. For this reason it has been received with mixed feelings. There are those who welcome it because it deals with concrete entities which are used in trying to present the classical ideas under a modern viewpoint. (See the review by S. Marcus in *Mathematical Reviews 27*, p. 4900.) However, this approach also makes the treatment distinctly more complicated than necessary. It "represents the history, and not the future of integration theory." (See the review by E. Hewitt in *Bull. Amer. Math. Soc. 70* (1964), pp. 490–491.)

There are, of course, many more books on integration theory and related topics available, each with its own distinctive features. A partial list is given below. It includes three of the older works by Carathéodory, Lebesgue, and Saks (of which the former has been reprinted), which we find especially challenging to read.

## *LITERATURE*

Burkill, J. C., *The Lebesgue Integral.* London: Cambridge University Press, 1961.
Carathéodory, C., *Algebraic Theory of Measure and Integration.* New York: Chelsea Publishing Company, 1963.

Graves, L. M., *The Theory of Functions of Real Variables, 2d ed.* New York: McGraw-Hill, Inc., 1956.
Halmos, P., *Measure Theory.* Princeton, N.J.: D. Van Nostrand Company, Inc., 1950.
Hewitt, E., and K. A. Ross, *Abstract Harmonic Analysis.* New York: Academic Press, Inc., 1963.
Hildebrandt, T. H., *Introduction to the Theory of Integration.* New York: Academic Press, Inc., 1963.
Kestelman, H., *Modern Theories of Integration, 2d ed.* New York: Dover Publications, Inc., 1960.
Kolmogorov, A. N., and S. V. Fomin, *Measure, Lebesgue Integrals, and Hilbert Space.* New York: Academic Press, Inc., 1961.
Lebesgue, H., *Leçons sur l'Intégration, 2d ed.* Paris: Gauthier-Villars, 1928.
Loomis, L. H., *An Introduction to Abstract Harmonic Analysis.* Princeton, N.J.: D. Van Nostrand Company, Inc., 1953.
McShane, E. J., *Integration.* Princeton, N.J.: Princeton University Press, 1944.
McShane, E. J., and T. A. Botts, *Real Analysis.* Princeton, N.J.: D. Van Nostrand Company, Inc., 1959.
Munroe, M. E., *Introduction to Measure and Integration.* Reading, Mass.: Addison-Wesley, 1953.
Nachbin, L., *The Haar Integral.* Princeton, N.J.: D. Van Nostrand Company, Inc., 1965.
Natanson, I. P., *Theory of Functions of a Real Variable*, vol. I. New York: Frederick Ungar Publishing Co., 1961.
Riesz, F., and B. Sz.-Nagy, *Functional Analysis.* New York: Frederick Ungar Publishing Co., 1955.
Royden, J. L., *Real Analysis.* New York: The Macmillan Company, 1963.
Saks, S., *Theory of the Integral.* Warszawa-Lwow, 1937.
Williamson, J. H., *Lebesgue Integration.* New York: Holt, Rinehart and Winston, Inc., 1962.
Zaanen, A. C., *An Introduction to the Theory of Integration.* Amsterdam: North-Holland Publishing Company, 1958.
Zaanen, A. C., *Linear Analysis.* Amsterdam: North-Holland Publishing Company, 1953.

# Indexes

# THEOREMS REFERRED TO BY NAME

This is a list of the principal page reference for some important statements that are commonly referred to by name in the text.

# SYMBOLS

This is a list of the first occurrence of a new symbol, or of an old symbol with a new or extended meaning. The page references in italics are to page numbers in the summaries in the more important cases.

| page | |
|---|---|
| 3 | $R, +\infty, -\infty$ |
| 4 | $[a, b], (a, b), [a, b), (a, b], \varnothing, \cup E_n, \cap E_n, \{a_n\}, \lim_{n\to\infty} a_n$ |
| 5 | $\sum a_n, \sum_n a_n, \sum_{n=1}^{\infty} a_n$ |
| 12, *46* | $(a_0, \cdots, a_n; c_1, \cdots, c_n)$ |
| 13, *46* | $L, \varphi \wedge \psi, \varphi \vee \psi, \chi_I$ |
| 14, *46* | $\int \varphi\, dx, \varphi(x+0), \varphi(x-0)$ |
| 15 | $f^+, f^-, [f]$ |
| 16 | mid $(a, b, c)$ |
| 35, *47* | a.e., a.a. $x$ |
| 39 | $I - J, I \Delta J, \varphi_h, \check{\varphi}, {}_k\varphi$ |
| 52 | $\int_a^b f\, dx$ |
| 55, *101* | $\int f\, dx$ |
| 62, *101* | $L^1$ |
| 70 | $\liminf a_n, \limsup a_n$ |
| 78, *103* | $\int \varphi\, d\mu$ |

# SUBJECT INDEX

Italic numbers refer to pages in one of the summaries.

T



U



V



W

302547924-